Jesus
and the
Eucharist

Jesus and the Eucharist

New Edition

Tad Guzie

Gracewing

First published 1974
This Revised Edition 1995

Gracewing
Fowler Wright Books
2 Southern Ave, Leominster
Herefordshire HR6 0QF

Gracewing books are distributed

In New Zealand by
Catholic Supplies Ltd
80 Adelaide Road
Wellington
New Zealand

In Australia by
Charles Paine Pty Ltd
8 Ferris Street
North Parramatta
NSW 2151 Australia

In USA by
Morehouse Publishing
PO Box 1321
Harrisburg
PA 17105 USA

In Canada by
Meakin and Associates
Unit 17, 81 Aurega Drive
Nepean, Ontario
KZE 7Y5, Canada

The publishers would like to thank the Duke of Sutherland and the Trustees of the National Gallery of Scotland for permission to reproduce Poussin's painting of the Eucharist from his Seven sacraments series (second version).

© Tad Guzie 1974 & 1995
© Introduction, Edward Yarnold 1995

Typesetting by the Paulist Press
Additional typesetting by Reesprint, Radley, Oxon, OX14 3AJ

Printed by Cromwell Press, Broughton Gifford, Wiltshire, SN12 8PH

ISBN 0 85244 297 1

Contents

Introduction to the Second Edition

THIS NEW EDITION of Dr Guzie's study of the Eucharist is much to be welcomed. He possesses the rare knack of making the results of scholarly research available to the general reader in a lucid, elegant and attractive manner. It is an honour and a pleasure to be invited to write this introduction.

The strength of his work lies in its combination of many elements synthesised to form an exposition which is fresh and unified. The basic intuition is that we misunderstand the Eucharist if we try to explain it in terms of empirical fact without reference to meaning. Sacraments are symbols, which affect us only in so far as they are interiorised; they are not signs *and* causes of grace, but cause grace by being recognised as signs. Accordingly the transformation of the bread and wine into Christ's body and blood is not an empirical or physical change. The change lies in what they are *for us*. Their deepest and truest reality now is that they have become symbols of the body and blood; their meaning has changed. This was the insight of twentieth-century theologians who wished to speak of transignification instead of transubstantiation. The latter term had been adopted by the Council of Trent in an attempt to express the human meaning of the sacrament in terms of objective fact; by contrast, to speak of transignification is to keep the discussion at the true level of meaning and symbol. This understanding of the sacrament in terms of symbols does not involve the denial of the Real Presence; a symbol is no less a reality than a physical fact, and a change in symbolic meaning is no less real than a physical change.

As Guzie recognises, some symbols are what Mary Douglas calls 'natural', carrying a meaning that is valid for every culture; water, which everyone needs for life, and light, which everyone needs for sight, are examples. In modern western society, however, even these symbols have lost much of their force; when we only get water from the tap and can have unlimited light at the flick of a switch, familiarity breeds contempt. Where families rarely sit down together to dine, people no longer experience at first hand the symbolism of the shared meal.

Other symbols gain their meaning from their context. Bread and wine are examples of this second class of symbol, for there are cultures in which rice is the staple food and grapes are unknown. This does not entitle us, however, to substitute rice and tea for bread and wine, as Christianity is a historical religion, which gains its significance from its living contact with particular events in the past. There is a limit to the freedom we enjoy to modernise our sacramental rites.

The contextual nature of symbols makes it likely that some of the symbolism contained in Christian sacraments will be found also in other religions. Other religions believe in a God who rose again after a passion; other religions too celebrate rites which include participation in a sacred meal in which holy bread is consumed. This does not provide an argument against the truth of Christianity. That Christians should share the symbols of other faiths is in accordance with God the Son's sharing in human nature and confining himself to the social conditions of a particular society.

Another distinction which needs to be drawn is that between the material things used in a sacrament and the action which is performed with them. Sacraments are rites which are celebrated, not simply objects which are administered. The real presence of Christ is more properly located within the action of the Eucharist than in the bread and the wine themselves; consequently adoration of the reserved Blessed Sacrament should be regarded as an extension of the action of the Mass. Transubstantiation is not the only possible explanation of the transformation which the bread and wine undergo; the Council of Trent was content to say that 'the marvellous and unique change of the whole substance of the bread into the body' was 'most aptly' described as transubstantiation.[1] Guzie believes Luther was right to see that belief in the real presence does not depend upon acceptance of the theory of transubstantiation, but goes further than the German by questioning whether 'substance' is an appropriate category at all. 'Substance', he explains, is a term referring to empirical fact, whereas 'a sacrament is a relational being—one whose intelligibility... lies in its relationship to man'.

Originally Christians did not concentrate on the consecrated bread and wine as transformed objects. The Eucharist was a celebration of thanksgiving (this is the meaning of the word 'Eucharist') for God's gifts of creation and redemption. The change

---

1   Council of Trent, Decree on the Eucharist, canon 2 (*Decrees of the Ecumenical Councils*, ed. N. Tanner, Sheed and Ward, London, and Georgetown University Press, Washington DC, 1990, p. 697).

which takes place in the bread and wine is for the sake of a change in the communicants; as St Augustine saw, we are to become what we have received. Dr Guzie identifies two decisive moments in the shift of attention from the action to the objects. The first occurred at the end of the second century when St Irenaeus regarded the bread and wine as objects which were 'offered' to God, thus changing the focus of the Eucharist from the celebration of a thanksgiving to the offering of bread and wine as the firstfruits of creation. The second moment took place in the ninth century when Paschasius Radbertus directed attention to the bread and wine 'out there' on the altar.

Perhaps both of these changes occurred even earlier. St Clement of Rome nearly a century before Irenaeus compared the action of the Jewish High Priest offering sacrifice to the bishop offering the Eucharistic gifts (1 Clement 41, 44), while St Cyril of Jerusalem, four and a half centuries before Radbertus, focused attention on the consecrated bread, maintaining that to drop a crumb would be to lose something 'more valuable than gold and precious stones' (*Mystagogic Catecheses* 5.21). I would also place more weight on the sacrificial overtones of the words of institution themselves: the blood is the blood of the covenant, recalling the blood of the slaughtered animals which Moses sprinkled on the tablets of the commandments (Ex 24.8); it is shed as in a sacrifice for the remission of sins.

Indeed, one interpretation of the word 'memorial' (*anamnesis*), which, according to Luke and Paul, Jesus used at the Last Supper, gives it a virtually sacrificial meaning. According to this interpretation the word implies the calling of something to the attention not of the worshippers but of God: we 'remind' God of Jesus' saving passion. The word thus has a connotation close to 'sacrifice'; though Guzie could justifiably reply that it is the 'doing this' which constitutes the memorial, rather than the sacred objects themselves.

Dr Guzie believes that one result of the 'objectification' of the Eucharist has been the convention of discussing the real presence and eucharistic sacrifice as though they were two distinct subjects. A good illustration of this tendency is provided by the Council of Trent, which promulgated its decree on the Eucharist, including the definition of transubstantiation, twelve years before its decree on the sacrifice of the Mass.

While it is true that the Christ who is present in the Eucharist is the risen Lord, Guzie insists that the sacrament can be understood only in the light of the cross. Following the fourth Gospel, he sees the resurrection to be not so much an event coming *after* the cross (as did St Luke, who tells how the disciples on the Emmaus road learnt that it was 'necessary that the Christ should suffer these things and enter into his glory') as an event already implied in the cross itself. The passion is already the hour of the Son's glorification (Jn 17.1). In the words of Leo the Great, 'the Lord's passion is prolonged until the end of time'. As St Paul saw, and as we repeat in an Acclamation after the words of consecration, when we celebrate the Mass we proclaim the Lord's *death* (1 Cor 11.26). The eucharistic Bread and Wine are, in Guzie's graphic expression, 'our way of sinking our teeth into the mystery of the cross'.

Various recent studies add further light to Guzie's understanding of the Eucharist. Social anthropologists like Roger Grainger and David Martin[1] have investigated the way in which ritual actions contribute to the establishment and preservation of social structures. The revised liturgy of the Catholic Church places first communion as the culmination of the process of Christian initiation. Liturgical scholars like Geoffrey Cuming have attempted to

1   See, for example, R. Grainger, *The Language of the Rite* (Darton, Longman and Todd, London, 1974); D. Martin, *The Breaking of the Image* (Blackwell, Oxford, 1980).

trace the process by which the *epiclesis* (the invocation of the Holy
Spirit) and the narrative of the Last Supper came to be incorporated
into the Jewish meal-blessings.[1]

It is interesting to see how various ecumenical agreements
published after Guzie's book have confirmed his conclusions. This
is especially evident in the *Final Report* of the Anglican–Roman
Catholic International Commission. This document insists like
Guzie on the dynamic character of the Eucharist. 'The real presence
of his body and blood can... only be understood within the context
of the redemptive *activity* [my italics] whereby he gives himself,
and in himself reconciliation, peace and life, to his own' (Eucharist,
n.6). 'The whole eucharistic action is a continuous *movement* [my
italics] in which Christ offers himself in his sacramental body and
blood to his people and in which they receive him in faith and
thanksgiving' (Eucharist Elucidation, n.8). Adoration of Christ in
the reserved sacrament is not just devotion paid to him in the
tabernacle or the monstrance, but is an 'extension' of the movement
of worship expressed in the Mass (ibid. n.8). 'The bread and wine
become the sacramental body and blood of Christ in order that the
Christian community may *become* more truly what it already is, the
body of Christ' (ibid. n.6). 'In the eucharistic prayer the Church
continues to make a perpetual memorial of Christ's death, and his
members, united with God and one another, give thanks for all his
mercies, entreat the benefits of his passion on behalf of the whole
Church, participate in these benefits and enter into the movement
of his self-offering' (Eucharist, n.5).

The ARCIC report stresses the ecclesial dimension of the Eucharist more emphatically than Guzie. The worshipper in receiving
Christ's eucharistic Body is incorporated into his Body, which is
the Church; holy communion is the source of ecclesial communion.

1   G.J. Cuming, 'The Shape of the Anaphora', *Studia Patristica* 20 (1989), pp.
333–345.

In the words of Henri de Lubac, 'the Eucharist makes the Church'. 'By the eucharist all the baptized are brought into communion with the source of *koinonia* [communion or fellowship]' (*Final Report*, Introduction, n.6).

Many of these insights are also to be found in the Faith and Order document *Baptism, Eucharist and Ministry*, which has the additional merit of working out more thoroughly the implications of the communitarian dimension of the Eucharist. 'The eucharistic celebration demands reconciliation and sharing among all those regarded as brothers and sisters in the one family of God and is a constant challenge in the search for appropriate relationships in social, economic and political life.' The Eucharist is the 'Meal of the Kingdom', 'precious food for missionaries, bread and wine for pilgrims on their apostolic journey'. It is 'directly related to Christ's own testimony as a servant, in whose servanthood Christians themselves participate' (Eucharist, nn.20–26).

Let me conclude with a word of warning. Roman Catholic readers may be surprised to find Guzie, as we have seen, in his concern to focus attention on the action rather than the objects, questioning the appropriateness of the terms 'substance' and 'transubstantiation'. Another way to meet his concerns would be to take 'substance' at its deepest level to include a thing's significance for human beings. Then perhaps both he and the reader would find themselves in agreement with the ARCIC report in its final analysis of the transformation which take place in the Eucharist: 'Before the eucharistic prayer, to the question: "What is that?", the believer answers: "It is bread." After the eucharistic prayer, to the same question he answers: "It is truly the body of Christ, the Bread of Life" ' (Eucharist Elucidation, n.6).

Edward Yarnold, SJ

Preface

The real Jesus took real bread and wine and identified himself with it.

This is one very simple way of stating how it all began. More has to be said about the setting in which this action took place, the religious meaning of what Jesus did, how his followers understood it. But the fact remains that we start with a remarkably simple ritual gesture done by a man who was facing death. And just as the man's death was to affect the way millions of people would live, so his gesture at that last meal shaped the way they would worship. Millions and millions of people. There lies the problem. When untold numbers of people, spread over twenty centuries and coming from cultural backgrounds numbering many times twenty, repeat a ritual action which originated outside their own time and culture, it would be amazing if the simplicity of the first gesture were to remain untouched. For that matter it would be amazing if the real Jesus remained untouched.

The theology of the sacraments has usually been handled quite separately from christology, the question of Jesus. But it has been my experience that the kind of questions asked today by college students, religious educators and interested adults makes it important to link these two areas of theology very closely. People's questions have to do with the meaning of Jesus and all the symbols we use to interpret his meaning, both in our worship and in our religious language generally. In our search for the meaning of christian ideas, we have become quite used to the concept that the Old Testament is the dictionary used by the writers of the New; and so we look back at the religious ideas and practices of judaism for the roots of christian ideas. But analytical psychology and other modern sciences of man have made it clear that we must look much further than this, particularly when we are dealing with ritual. Ritual symbols emerge from man's consciousness, at the very dawn of human history, as his most fundamental way of getting hold of the world he lives in. The most basic symbols we use, both in our interpretations of Jesus and in the sacraments that celebrate his mystery, originate entirely outside the Bible.

I have therefore paid much attention to basic questions regarding man's religious imagination. How do our minds meet reality, and how do we ask the God-question at different stages of our development? To what kind of question are rituals and sacraments an answer? How does our religious understanding develop, both historically and in our personal lives? Answers to these questions shed much light on changing interpretations of the eucharist and changing attitudes toward the person of Jesus over the course of two millennia.

Many of the books mentioned in the notes were selected because they are non-technical works of sound scholarship which the reader may find useful for further pursuit of an idea. Biblical quotations throughout the book are taken from *The Jerusalem Bible*.

Marquette University
Pentecost, 1973

1

Flights into Magic

JESUS' LAST SUPPER with his friends was an event, a fact. But important facts are always interpreted. The ritual action that took place at that meal has been interpreted with a variety of concepts and images. It is eucharist, thanksgiving, it is the new passover meal, a representation of the sacrifice of Calvary, a sacrificial meal, communion with God. So for Jesus, who has been understood in an equal variety of ways. He was a man who died, and for those who did not believe in him it all stopped there. His death was a fact, and the fact had no special meaning. But those who believed in him, who underwent the experiences we call easter and pentecost, interpreted his death and his whole life right back to his birth. The first christians saw Jesus as the second Adam, the new Moses, the true high priest, the word become flesh, the cosmic Christ in whom all of creation would be restored. All these images were ways of spelling out the meaning of who Jesus is for us.

Once we get used to interpretations of an event, it is not at all easy to remember that the event and the interpretation are not the same thing. The one cannot simply by identified with the other. Interpretation begins as an effort to unfold the meaning of an event. But as the process of interpretation continues, it is not always controlled. Like a stone wrapped in a snowball and sent rolling down a snow-covered bank, the event can get so wrapped in interpretations, one layer added to another, that there is sometimes little relationship between the last layer and the first fact lying somewhere inside.

The real Jesus took real bread and wine and identified himself with it.

This event, sent rolling down the bank of christian history, has undergone more interpretations than any other incident in Jesus' life. By no means have the interpretations always conflicted. New passover, sacrificial meal, communion with the body of Christ: these ideas all originally complemented one another, each in its own way illuminating some facet of the Lord's supper and its meaning for us. But gradually interpretation was laid upon interpretation. And eventually interpretation came to conflict with interpretation, particularly at the time of the reformation, when understanding of the eucharist became one of the chief issues dividing christians. When one is dealing with, let us say, the tenth or eleventh layers of interpretation (which is roughly the state of things by the time the eucharistic question is formulated in concepts like "real presence" and "transubstantiation"), it is not always an easy matter to see how the interpretations relate to the original event.

It is not just theologians who engage in the business of interpretation. Popular piety has always had a hand in it, and a strong case can be made for saying that popular interpretation has had a more potent influence on the development of christian thought than have theologians. Popular piety embodies a living faith, a lived understanding of faith—and indeed the earliest interpretations of Jesus were not devised by trained theologians. Theologians come along and lay out that lived understanding in disciplined statements, which then feed back into popular piety, and the dialectic begins anew. This is basically how we get the phenomenon of interpretation laid upon interpretation.

In the realm of *ritual*, history indicates that theologians seem to have exercised much less control over the interpretative process than elsewhere. Perhaps this is because theologians have usually been more interested in manipulating ideas, frequently very abstract ones, than in dealing with the maze of concrete behavioral and artistic expressions of faith which we find in rituals like the ritual of the mass. However this may be, the development of christian ritual has been strongly influenced by popular understanding of Jesus and his mystery. Theologians have on the whole intervened only when popular developments have gotten completely out of hand.

The result of all this is that religious rituals tend to deteriorate, to lose their original sense and take on superstitious and magical meanings. Jesus' simple gesture with bread and wine was repeated with equal simplicity when the first christians "met in their homes for the breaking of bread" (Acts 2:46). Incredibly enough, medieval christians were repeating basically the same ritual when they paid priests to hold the host up longer after the consecration, in the belief that so long as the host was elevated, sins were being forgiven and souls released from purgatory. Examples of ritual's tendency to decay into magic are not lacking today. It would be difficult to find so gross an understanding of the eucharist as the one just mentioned, but there is still a good touch of superstition wrapped up in many people's view of that ritual.

Popular piety has also affected the way Jesus himself has been interpreted. Some interpretations of him do not relate to anything like a real person who was "tempted in every way that we are" (Heb 4:15). The trouble here seems to come from the wrong kind of insistence on the classical formula "Jesus Christ is truly God." This is only a half-truth, and half-truths are not really true. One who wants to be faithful to christian orthodoxy cannot insist on the first half of this dogma of Chalcedon without affirming and equally emphasizing the second half. "The same Jesus Christ is truly man." If anything, the bishops of Chalcedon were more concerned with Jesus' manhood, because the immediate occasion for this council was Eutyches' denial of Christ's full humanity. Taken in its historical context, that dogma is telling us that whatever we say about Jesus' divinity cannot *conflict* with the humanity of the carpenter's son. We know his divinity only *in* his humanity; and whatever we say about him as God can be truthfully said only when we start with a real person who lived our human condition and died in it. The dogma formulates, in a particular historical and philosophical setting, the core of christian belief that had already been clearly stated in the less philosophical language and imagery used by the New Testament writers. Jesus is God's final and decisive word to man (Heb 1:2), the unique mediator between God and mankind, himself a man (1 Tim 2:5). The dogma talks about Jesus' relationship to us and to God. It does *not* talk about Jesus' self-awareness, his growth as a human personality, or his own personal experience of the human condition.[1]

But popular understanding of the dogma has applied it to Jesus' personal psychology. There are few christians who (along with the church fathers themselves) have not fallen into the trap of thinking of Jesus as one who played out a script written by the Father—a script which, thanks to his divinity, he knew and understood well in advance, including how it would all end. We see a haloed Jesus with his friends gathered around him at table, a Jesus who is already virtually risen, in total control of history, including his own. He has a rough three days ahead of him. But again, thanks to his divinity, he already has all the answers. There is one sacrament he has not yet "instituted" (traditional language often reinforces the know-it-all Jesus), and so for history's sake he goes on to institute it.

This language sounds flippant, but I do not think it is a complete caricature of the popular view of Jesus at the last supper. It is a view that one can easily enough come away with from the scriptural accounts of the event, which read an easter understanding of Jesus back into his historical life. It is also a view that has been fostered by artists. One need only think of Da Vinci's or Dali's paintings of the last supper, which likewise embody an easter understanding of the event. Or there is the print I saw some years ago, where a haloed Christ is distributing round white wafers to kneeling apostles, who (good catholics that they are) receive the host on their tongues.

The latter example is historically ludicrous, but it should make us aware of the fact that our faith imagery does not necessarily correspond to the original event. There is nothing wrong in itself with faith-interpretation so long as it is understood precisely *as interpretation*. If we allow the interpretation to become totally identified with the event, we are bound to end up with a view that places both Jesus and the last supper outside the human condition, outside life and the experience of death. Interpretation, even the most creative and edifying kind of faith-interpretation, must never be allowed to cloud over the fact that Jesus was a person who experienced the human condition *as we experience it*.[2] The story of the agony in the garden implies that acceptance of death was, to say the least, a real struggle for him. In the Letter to the Hebrews, we read that Jesus submitted so humbly that his prayer to be rescued from death *was heard* (Heb 5:7). The gospel writers indicate that he prayed as any genuinely pious man would pray in the face of death: he prayed that the bitter chalice would *pass him by* (Mt 26:39).

The point is that his victory over death, and the answer to his prayer to be rescued from death, came in a way unforeseen by him (as answers to prayer usually come to us as well). This point is often muddled by popular understanding, which implies that the only reason why Jesus did not in fact use his divine powers to come down from the cross was that the moment was not yet ripe, and he *knew* just how he would be vindicated. In short, though he believed in God's absolute faithfulness to him, Jesus could not have known the outcome of his struggle with death unless he were exempted from the human condition. Whatever he did at the last supper, he did with an awareness of his impending death; and his awareness included all the human uncertainties regarding death. To the extent that interpretation lets us forget this point, we are bound to misunderstand the connection between the eucharist and the death of a man. There is a kind of liturgical triumphalism which emphasizes the risen Christ at the cost of the real Jesus who experienced death as we do, and which therefore pulls both the Lord and his supper outside the human condition.

In all of this one can see a tendency toward magic. Magic involves an attitude which does not take finite reality seriously. Magic deals with supra-human means of escaping from or overcoming the human condition; it does not deal *with* the human condition. Christian faith refuses magic. It does so in its insistence that we are to find and understand the transcendent, the world of God, in the man Jesus who remains finite even as the first-born from among the dead. This is what is meant by saying that Jesus Christ is truly God *and* truly man. But religious interpretation can easily degenerate into a magical attitude, and christian interpretation is no exception. This is the phenomenon we have been looking at. Just as the original meaning of the last supper has often deteriorated into a magical meaning, so has the real Jesus sometimes been all but obscured by a magical Jesus, a Jesus who in the last analysis stands outside humanity. In both cases interpretation, which is initially meant to unfold the meaning of real events and persons, has carried believers in the direction of an escape *from* the human condition rather than a confrontation *with* it.

Why should religious interpretation lead to the unreal, the magical, the superstitious? To answer this question, we have to take a closer look at how the process of religious interpretation works, and specifically how it has worked in the history of christianity. This process has to be understood if we are to distinguish layers of interpretation and come to understand the tradition we have inherited. The following pages will trace the way the magical Jesus and the magical eucharist, both still very much with us, have come about. This is a rather negative way of getting at how the process of religious interpretation works; but unreal interpretations of the person in whom we believe should be brought to light and set aside before we go any further.

***

Christianity has been most reluctant in recent centuries to expose itself to comparison with other religions. This is certainly true of preaching and catechetics, even today. Few people have heard anything in the course of their religious instruction about the similarities between christian doctrines and the teachings of other world religions. Christians believe in a transcendent reality who is also immanent in human hearts, a reality who is supreme beauty and love, mercy and compassion. They believe that the way to him is repentance, self-denial, prayer, love of one's neighbor and even of one's enemies. They believe that only the love of God will bring happiness, and they understand ultimate happiness as knowledge of God and union with him. But most christians are unaware (or sometimes unwilling to accept) that the very *same* beliefs I have just mentioned are found in world religions such as judaism, islam, hinduism, buddhism, taoism.[3]

Prior to the modern age, faith in God and the teachings of the church were very much at the center of man's interpretation of reality. As it saw that world falling apart, the christian church felt an almost compulsive need to defend itself and its traditions against the onslaught of what we now call secularization—a man-oriented rather than God-oriented interpretation of reality and human experience. This resulted in an uncritical emphasis on christianity's uniqueness. Its points of contact with non-christian forms of religious interpretation were largely unknown or ignored. The expert in comparative religions who demonstrated these points of contact was, if not heretical, at least highly suspect and certainly very threatening.

This has not always been the case. We should recall that it took a generation or two for christianity to separate itself decisively from judaism. Paul's insistence that gentile converts not be held to the practices of the old law would have influenced this eventual separation. But opposition to the followers of Jesus developed only gradually, and it is not until the decade of the eighties that we find an organized effort to force the christian jews out of the synagogues. In the meantime, they saw no difficulty in attending the jewish services they had always attended.

Was Jesus himself aware that he was founding a new religion? Scholars have argued whether Jesus was conscious of being the messiah. One must not of course put too much emphasis on a term. In Jesus' day "messiah" was a particularly troublesome term because in its popular sense it suggested a political savior, and Jesus certainly did not see himself in this role. In any case, we define our identities according to the many roles we play, and no single word is ever going to express anyone's total self-definition. This is one reason why the gospels use so many different titles to unfold the meaning of Jesus.

Apart from the question of terms and of what titles Jesus himself would have used to describe his role, there are few current scholars who would not agree that Jesus saw himself as a decisive person—decisive for the kingdom of God and therefore decisive for judaism. Otherwise too many things in the gospels would simply make no sense, even if we allow for the great amount of post-resurrection understanding which the gospels read back into Jesus' historical life. His attacks against the Torah and his deliberate violations of the sabbath laws make sense only if Jesus possessed a mature awareness of his own authority. The same holds true for the events at the end of his life. Jesus went up to Jerusalem fully aware that death awaited him there. His acceptance of death is indicated in the prayer of Gethsemane; and the *nature* of this acceptance, the terms in which

he saw his impending death, is spelled out in the ritual gesture with
bread and wine at the last supper. That gesture would make no sense
unless he consciously attached a messianic significance to his death, a
significance having to do with the whole idea of the kingdom he had
been preaching. Bread and wine, as we shall see later, already had a
messianic meaning in the desert communities.

But for all this, I believe it would be severely anachronistic to say
that Jesus thought of himself as the "founder of a new religion,"
with all that this phrase connotes to modern man. The judaism of
Jesus' day was made up of many schools and sects; there is no reason
to think that either Jesus or his first followers saw themselves as anything but faithful jews trying to penetrate the true meaning of God's
revelation as it was embodied in the history of the hebrew people.

As the gospel spread to the greco-roman world at large, that
world found christian teachings to be rather odd—but for quite different reasons from those which led to jewish rejection of the new
message. The jews had trouble with a few essential points like faith
in a man who was obviously dead, and a man who had taught his
followers to play it so free and easy with the observances of the law.
The gentile world had quite other problems, because belief in Christ
looked so little like their own religions. A century after Jesus' time
we find a writer like Justin Martyr (a greek philosopher who became
a christian and founded a school in Rome) pointing out that christian ideas about Jesus are not really so different as his readers may
think. When christians talk about Jesus Christ who was crucified
and died and rose again, "we propose nothing different from what
you believe regarding those whom you consider sons of Jupiter." Justin goes on to show how, for christians, Jesus is the son of God in a
unique way; but first he is interested in striking similarities.

If we assert that the Word of God was born of God in a special way, different from ordinary births, this should be no extraordinary thing to you,
who say that Mercury is the angelic Word of God. And if anyone objects

that Jesus was crucified [i.e. arguing that gods are not subject to death], in this too he is on a par with those reputed sons of Jupiter of yours who suffered [Aesculapius, Bacchus, Hercules, etc.]. When we affirm that he was born of a virgin, understand this in connection with what you say about Perseus. And when we say that he cured the lame, the paralytic and those born blind, we seem to be talking about deeds very similar to those which Aesculapius is supposed to have done.[4]

Not many pastors would be prepared to try out a comparison like that on their sunday congregations. There is more to be said of course; someone like Irenaeus, writing shortly after Justin, does a detailed analysis of the vast differences between christian teaching and the cosmic myths. Still, in our preaching and catechetics today, we have not yet come to terms with the important historical *fact* that ideas like divine sonship, a god who dies and rises, miracles as proof of divine power, and virgin birth were well known long before christianity came along. Such ideas, as the study of history and culture and psychology shows, belong to a whole category of ancient ideas and symbols which express man's eternal hopes. It was only natural that if such ideas *are* radical symbols, rooted in the mind of man, they would have been applied to Jesus and used to express faith in Jesus as the one who fulfills man's hopes.[5]

Like the hero-gods of antiquity who conquered the powers of evil and who are frequently shown conquering dragons, Jesus is seen as one who vanquishes the powers of death and darkness. All of the church fathers' imagery regarding Christ's victory over Satan is very much in line with ancient mythology. Both Christ and Orpheus (to choose only one of the many god-men of antiquity) were men who became mediators of the divine, a role which both religions symbolize in the image of a good shepherd. The notion of a cosmic man— one who stands at the beginning of life, or who represents the final goal of life and creation—is found under different names and personifications in China, India, ancient Persia. Paul is by no means using an original image when he develops the parallels and contrasts between Adam and Christ, the first and last cosmic men.

Many god-heroes undergo death and rebirth, or achieve the reward of immortality through their sufferings. Justin chose examples only from greco-roman religion. The same process of death and rebirth is emphasized in ancient rituals of initiation which identify the worshiper with the life of the god. John is not being original when he interprets the christian initiation of baptism as a "rebirth" (Jn 3). Nor is Paul when he interprets it, even more vividly, as a ritual in which we "go into the tomb with Christ and join him in death so that we might live a new life" (Rom 6:4). In the ancient world and in primitive cultures today, initiation rituals often take place at various stages in one's life, defining the passage from one stage to the next. This idea too is built into man's psyche, and it is articulated in any religion that provides special rites at the time of birth, marriage or death. In moving the sacrament of confirmation from the middle years of grade school to a time when young people are more capable of personal commitment to an adult faith, recent catholic practice is only affirming our radical need for appropriate "rites of passage." The same need and symbolism is at work in the passover rite, commemorating the hebrews' passage from Egypt to the promised land, from slavery to freedom, death to life. Jesus himself, as the first christians saw it, "passed over" from this world to the father (Jn 13:1).

But the first christians also emphasized that this latter event was a once-and-for-all event. Christianity is an historical and future-oriented religion, not a cyclical one. It looks back to the death and resurrection of Jesus as an event which is decisive for all time, making it possible for us to look forward to final union with a transcendent God. The christian is not to identify himself with the cycle of nature, personified in the stories of Orpheus and other god-heroes of antiquity—an eternally repeated cycle of birth, growth, death, rebirth. So for the first christians any ritual had to be a commemoration of Jesus' death and resurrection with the explicit purpose of expressing their future hope. But once the persecutions were over and christianity entered the mainstream of hellenistic culture, the church began incorporating ideas from the cyclical religions. A liturgical year was gradually built up, cyclically recalling the events of Jesus' life and ministry, beginning with his birth. Today we take all this for granted. But to appreciate the significance of this evolution and the potential impact of bringing back the old in order to interpret the new, we need only recall that the apostle Paul never even thought it worthwhile to talk about any of the events in Jesus' life and ministry except his death and resurrection.

Later on we shall look more closely at the development of symbolism in christian ritual, its values and its aberrations. The point I want to emphasize here is one that is much too easily overlooked, and we overlook it constantly in our effort to defend the uniqueness of christianity. Christian teaching insists that *Jesus* is unique; nowhere does it say that the *process of interpreting him* is unique. In the same way, although christianity is not a cyclical religion, it has nonetheless brought in many symbolic elements from such religions. There is nothing intrinsically wrong with this. The problem arises— and it is a problem we cannot even recognize unless we watch for the profound similarities between christianity and other religions—when the process of interpretation comes to obscure what *is* distinctive about christianity, namely the person of Jesus. This has happened many times in the course of christian history, and it began happening even before the first century was over.

Trouble was inevitable because the tools of interpretation which the biblical writers along with the ancients used were tools which could be indiscriminately applied to any type of reality. Imagination and storytelling were the basic tools, and they could be applied to transcendental ideas and historical realities, to creations and projections of the mind as well as to events in the world of history. Ideas and events: the two categories are not alike. But the mythological imagination handles them both, without distinguishing between them.

Myths, which are simply stories embodying some truth about the world, explain mysterious ultimates like the origin of the universe, or of good and evil. Today we get our models or images for interpreting the universe from the empirical sciences, from technology, from sophisticated psychological and sociological theories. For the ancients, the meaning of the universe was spelled out in stories about the gods. The world of Olympus, the doings of the gods *before time began*, made up a world of archetypal models which provided an explanation for the things that happen in *this* world, which imitates what goes on or went on in the heavenly primordial world. These ancient myths are by no means arbitrary; they very accurately project man's most basic experiences of reality and human relationships. The writer of Genesis shows no interest in what happened in the heavenly world before time began, but he uses the same kind of archetypal myth in his stories about the origin of the universe, the entry of sin into the world, and the breakdown of the relationship between God and man.

Myths are therefore also used to interpret events that happen *in history*—and this not just in the ancient world. Stories are told about great men and events precisely in order to concretize their greatness, to give flesh and blood to what otherwise might remain bare bones in the popular mind. George Washington and the events of World War II have been just as susceptible to this kind of mythologizing as Abraham, the exodus, or Jesus. Such stories are selective in their details; they do not recount the whole event. They heighten a man's greatness; and if his weaknesses appear in the story, they are there to show how he overcame the weakness (like George Washington and the cherry tree). Myths also involve composite figures and events. The french and russian revolutions were both long processes, with important events spread over a period of years. But myth centers many of the accomplishments of these revolutions around single events like the storming of the bastille in Paris or the winter palace in Leningrad—events which were not in themselves all that significant from a military point of view.

The gospels are filled with this type of myth. The sermon on the mount is a composite of Jesus' teaching, just as the accounts of his cures and miracles often conflate many events into a single story. The story of pentecost is another good example. Peter gets up and gives a rousing speech which cuts the people to the heart, and we are told that three thousand were baptized that day. It is quite unlikely that twelve men could accomplish that feat without a firehose. What the story does is to fuse into one day events and experiences which undoubtedly took place over a longer period of time in those exciting days after easter. Such stories are not untrue *unless* we try to make them something other than what they are: stories meant to stress the importance and meaning of a significant person or event.

This may all seem obvious to the reader who has had experience with literature, but it has not always been so obvious. Much of the modern conflict between science and religion stems from a misreading of biblical myths. People who would not dream of reading Shakespeare without a good historical dictionary are still unaware that the creation stories in Genesis have nothing to do with astronomy or evolution. There is a kind of defensiveness deep inside the religious mind that makes us want to read every story about Jesus as though it had appeared on the front page of a newspaper. Even after we have been informed that the biblical writers did not know that kind of reporting, and that the gospels belong more to the editorial page than to the front page, we are still afraid to recognize myths for what they are. We are afraid we are going to lose something.

The real loss comes when we look at the gospel stories as containing simply facts about Jesus and his life; for in this case, we are liable to miss the real fact, namely that the writer is trying to say something about the *meaning* of Jesus. If we take these stories as straightforward pieces of reporting and then go on to ask what the report means, the meaning we come up with is not necessarily going to square with the meaning intended by the writer. This happens of course in much preaching, and it is not a moral evil; such interpretation has fostered much faith. But sooner or later we have to recognize the fact that the scriptures are the normative writings of our faith not because of what we *think* they say, but because of what those writers *intended* to say. The modern age, with its critical methods in so many areas of knowledge, has taken us beyond the point where christianity can remain credible to an educated adult who is consistently given uncritical or merely pious explanations of scripture.

This explanation of mythical thinking has perhaps been unnecessarily long, especially since the importance of myth has been so emphasized by the scholarship of the last few decades, inside and outside the field of theology. But we are not at all finished with the job of clarifying the relationship of myth and imagination to our traditional dogmas. On the one hand, recognizing myth as a way of thinking, as a thoroughly symbolic way of talking about real things, constitutes a threat to much traditional theology and popular understanding of the faith. It has not been easy for catholic theology to abandon Adam as a single first man from whom the entire race got its biological origin; and it is interesting that theologians changed their minds on this point not because of the accumulation of archeological and *scientific* evidence to the contrary, but mainly because comparative *literary* study made the mythical genre of the Adam stories so evident. On the other hand, there is the tendency (stemming to some extent from Bultmann's program of demythologizing the gospel, and often involving much misunderstanding of Bultmann) which wants to do away with the historical events surrounding Jesus as decisive events in the history of man's relation with God. This tension is inevitable. It is not all that easy, even for biblical scholars, to sort out the interpretation of a biblical event from the event itself. As the last century of biblical scholarship has so forcefully taught us, we cannot write a biography of Jesus. And this brings us to the problem with mythical thinking as a tool of interpretation.

What is finite experience and what is not? What belongs to the world of meaning and what is historical fact? What belongs to the transcendent world and what has really taken place in our own? The mythical imagination does not distinguish. It interprets an event in the very act of reporting it, because it does not know how to report events *apart from* their meaning. It draws no line between event and interpretation and thus leaves an ambiguity. Who is the real Jesus and who is the mythologized Christ? Who is the real Jesus, and where is the dividing line between him and a Christ who might be interpreted beyond recognition? To the extent that mythical thinking operates in the gospels as a method of interpreting Jesus, these questions are not answered. For once the process of mythical interpretation goes into full operation, it can run on as it will; there is no built-in control over the process. Myth *can* give us the genuine meaning of an event or person. It can just as easily move us outside the world of history and finite experience into a world of pure meaning unrelated to real life, and ultimately into a world of magic.

Take for example the stories about Jesus' miracles. Such stories were common currency in the religious literature of the day. We saw the parallels which Justin Martyr drew between Jesus' cures and those of a greco-roman god; indeed, most of the hero-gods of ancient times were endowed with superhuman powers. We know too that the gospel stories are based on stories from the Old Testament: like the story of Elijah raising the widow's son to life (1 Kg 17:17-24), or that of Elisha reviving a dead child, or multiplying loaves so that people would have enough to eat (2 Kg 4:29-37, 42-44). People experienced Jesus as a healer, as one who presented the same prophetic credentials as Elijah or Elisha. His healing power very naturally came to be described in stories, myths, just like those told about Elijah or Elisha. If we come away from these stories with the impression of magical or superhuman medical powers, it is because we do not know how to distinguish a medical report from a myth. The gospel myths talk about Jesus' very *real* ability to heal in the same way that other great men have been healers. But what is real healing? The gospel writers knew that such stories were talking about the carpenter's son whose ultimate act of healing was to proclaim the forgiveness of sin (Mt 9:1-8; Mk 2:1-12; Lk 5:17-26). By subordinating the stories about physical cures to the healing which is forgiveness, the gospel writers place a control on the mythology of miracles. They introduce into a traditional form of storytelling a new element which is absent from the old stories about wonders worked by famous men or hero-gods.

It took the christian communities scattered around the mediterranean world a good century to filter out authentic interpretations of their faith from the unreal interpretations that were circulating at the same time. Today we know of gospels according to Matthew, Mark, Luke and John; second-century christians also knew of gospels according to the hebrews, the egyptians, Philip, Matthias, Peter and Thomas. We know of a single book called "Acts," the Acts of the Apostles; early christians were exposed to the Acts of John, of Paul, Peter, Andrew, Thomas and Philip. Some of these writings (the "apocrypha," writings which were not finally accepted as normative expressions of christian faith) are downright silly. The *Gospel of Thomas*, for instance, talks about the child Jesus making sparrows out of clay and turning them into living sparrows that fly. Another little boy who observes this wonder, and who runs to Joseph with the complaint that Jesus did it on a sabbath day, is struck dead in his tracks for his complaint. Jesus is not always such a vicious little brat in these writings, but most of the other stories about his childhood are equally absurd.

Some of the apocryphal writings are a great deal more sophisticated. The *Acts of John* describes a Jesus who isn't human at all. The writer, who gives himself the name of John the apostle, is called by a mature Jesus who is bald but full-bearded; his brother, who is with him at the same time, receives his call from one whom James perceives to be a child. The whole story is filled with different and conflicting physical perceptions of Jesus. The climax comes at the crucifixion when John runs away from Calvary and hides in a cave. Jesus appears to John there and tells him that it is all an act for the crowd's sake; he is only apparently being crucified. He then goes on to explain to John the symbolism of what is (not really) happening on Calvary. The cross, he says, is "sometimes called my word for your sakes, sometimes mind, sometimes Jesus, sometimes Christ, sometimes door, sometimes a way." The list goes on with a dozen other predicates attached to the cross: bread, seed, resurrection, Son, Father, Spirit, life, truth, faith, grace.

We know next to nothing about the century-long process whereby the rather small collection of writings now called the New Testament were sifted out from a vast body of texts, all claiming to be authentic expressions of christian faith. What we do know is that the sifting took place in the face of a strong tendency to do away with the real Jesus. All of these writings, both the accepted and the rejected ones, were interested in the meaning of Jesus, and all of them used myth. But *what* Jesus, and where *is* his meaning to be found? Many writings (I have given only a few extreme examples) attempted to explain his meaning by endowing him with incredible powers, or by presenting one who wasn't a man at all but God playing at being a man.

This latter approach really simplifies the whole thing. God is ultimate meaning. And if Jesus is plain and simply God, your problem of meaning is solved without having to mess about with the finite, and the fact of a man who died.

The same question keeps recurring. Nicaea and Chalcedon had to deal with attempts at philosophical expression which were not yet sufficiently nuanced, and which were unacceptable precisely because they diminished the reality of Jesus. The two councils thus made their contribution toward a christological "logic," a set of guidelines for speaking about Jesus within a particular philosophical frame of reference. But fed back into the popular religious imagination, no-

tions like "Christ and the Father are of the same substance" or
"Christ is truly God and truly man" easily become mythological.
They acquire grossly inaccurate imaginative meanings. The progres-
sion of thought from the New Testament to the christological councils is an evolution from mythical thinking to logical thinking and
the beginnings of philosophical expression. But the *logical* stage,
once it is reached, cannot be *mythologized*. Mythical interpretation is
as valid as the gospels themselves, but not when it is applied to the
kind of logical definition which the conciliar fathers were searching
for. What many christians take away from the doctrines of these
councils bears very little resemblance to what the doctrines originally
meant.

We are probably dealing here with a natural human tendency, for
it is not at all easy to sustain the judeo-christian religious insight.
The world surrounding the hebrews explained the universe, both
human and divine, by appealing to a primordial world which is mir-
rored by the events of our finite world. Hebrew religious experience,
on the other hand, insisted that God was to be found within history,
within man's concrete experience. Christian faith came, asserting that
God is to be found in the finite Jesus. But there is resistance to this
type of faith. We all possess an innate desire for the human condition to be other than it is, and this desire seems easily to translate
into a desire for the magical. The problem is further complicated by
the fact that our most basic tool of religious interpretation—the
mythical imagination—does not guarantee a hold on finite experience as the locus of *christian* faith.

***

All of this deeply affects the understanding of christian ritual. We
have been looking at types of religious imagination which seek to interpret Jesus' meaning for faith by endowing him with superhuman
powers and dispensing him in some way from full human experience

of the finite. The same type of religious imagination has gone to
work in the realm of ritual. James Joyce gives a classic expression of
it in *A Portrait of the Artist as a Young Man*. Stephen, the young
hero of the story, at one stage goes into a big religious fervor. His
elaborate pious practices are noticed by his teachers, and one day the
jesuit director calls him in and asks him if he has ever considered a
vocation to the priesthood.

To receive that call, Stephen, said the priest, is the greatest honor that the
Almighty God can bestow upon a man. No king or emperor on this earth
has the power of the priest of God. No angel or archangel in heaven, no
saint, not even the Blessed Virgin herself, has the power of a priest of God:
the power of the keys, the power to bind and loose from sin, the power of
exorcism, the power to cast out from the creatures of God the evil spirits
that have power over them; the power, the authority, to make the great
God of Heaven come down upon the altar and take the form of bread and
wine. What an awful power, Stephen!

Stephen, we are told, "listened in reverent silence to the priest's appeal and through the words he heard even more distinctly a voice
bidding him approach, offering him secret knowledge and secret
power."[6] The boy has not misunderstood. Implicit in the director's
words is a whole theology, familiar enough to catholics, which interprets the priestly ministry primarily in terms of power. Today, half
a century after Joyce wrote, theology and catechetics emphasize the
priesthood as ministry, as service to the christian community. But the
concept of the "power to forgive" and the "power to consecrate" is
usually still brought in somewhere as a key factor defining the
priesthood.

The difficulty here is the same one we have been noting all along.
Does such interpretation take the finite seriously? Most people will
admit that it is stretching things a bit far to say that a man has the
power to tell God what to do. Even if we exclude this exaggeration,
what does it mean to say (as we often do) that a man has "power"

over finite elements like bread and wine? Is such interpretation necessary to explain the phenomenon of the eucharist? Is it even useful? If the eucharist is to be a genuine memorial of the moment when the real Jesus took real bread and wine and identified himself with it, to what extent do the bread and wine have to become something other than what they are?

Christian orthodoxy demands that whatever statements we make about Jesus' divinity must not be allowed to obscure his humanity. Exactly the same principle comes into play in the case of the sacraments. Whatever else a sacramental ritual is, it is a human action, a human experience, a human expression which originates from man. This by no means precludes a connection with the numinous, with the presence of God in the world of man. Still, christian faith remains a faith that finds a transcendent God in finite experience; and history shows clearly enough that christianity obscures its own most basic insight when it starts reaching into the world of magical understanding. If we are to interpret the ritual of the eucharist accurately, we need a sacramental language that will take seriously the humanness of the action and the finiteness of the people and objects involved in it.

2

Two Questions About Reality

Mᴏsᴛ ᴏꜰ ᴏᴜʀ sacramental language is distinctly sacred language. It begins with God or the sacraments given by God, and it ends with man. One of the first things a child learns from his catechism is that "God gave us the sacraments." Baptism makes us members of Christ's body; in the eucharist the Lord feeds his people; in the sacrament of penance the sinner is reconciled with God through the church; and so on. One first learns what the sacraments are for, what they do, what God does through them. Perhaps this is the only starting point that can be taken in a catechetical situation. But this approach can backfire after one has been exposed to it over a long period of years. It can give the impression that the sacraments finally belong more to God than to ourselves. Our ordinary religious language "divinizes" the sacraments without taking account of their origin from within man's experience.

Anyone who possesses an adult faith has gone through some kind of process of questioning the system with which he grew up: a church, a way to God, a way to live, and an organized set of rituals for every occasion. Frequently, though, the questioning process can get nowhere because one is left with nothing but a sacred language which makes sense only within the very system which is being questioned. This gives us the curious phenomenon of people who become upset or even throw the whole thing overboard when they discover that ideas like virgin birth or the resurrection of a god-man existed long before Jesus, or that the sacraments are all rooted in primitive pagan rituals. I call the phenomenon curious, because the very thing that anchors christian theology and ritual to humanity and the experience of mankind should be anything but an argument against faith. This is what I mean by saying that much of our religious language eventually backfires. Sacred language easily becomes meaningless language, and preaching or catechetics which possesses nothing more than sacred language is destined to provoke unnecessary crises of faith.

This touches on one of the most important insights of Vatican II, which realized that the church could no longer see itself simply from within or attempt to define itself as if from inside an enclosed shell. The church is not the center of everything; it points *to* the center. It is a body of people who are conscious that in Jesus something decisive has happened to the world. The church aims at being in the world as a light on the mountain top, yeast in the dough, a seed planted in the earth. These are images not of what the church actually is, but of what it strives to be, with all of the imperfection and failure it shares with the rest of mankind. And if we talk about ourselves as the body of Christ, the people of God, or whatever, none of this sacred language means anything except *in relation to* the world. The church cannot understand its own efforts to be a living embodiment of Jesus' love and freedom and peace except in relation to the world's own best efforts toward freedom and unity and peace. The church tries explicitly to become what the world implicitly is looking for. A good many sections of the documents of Vatican II struggle with this relationship between the church and the world, showing new respect for the world and for man's efforts toward humanization of the world.[1]

Just as the church loses its true identity if it is cut off from the world, so the sacramental signs with which we worship lose their human meaning if they are defined strictly from within the sacramental system. Ideas like "God feeds his people in the eucharist" or "Christ is present in the eucharist" have a meaning, but the meaning can easily be lost. The things we say about light bulbs or dishwashers rarely become unreal; good light bulbs and dishwashers have to do with the correct functioning of cold empirical realities like filaments, timers and mechanisms. Our sacred language, on the other hand, which reaches beyond the realm of the empirical, does not contain built-in controls which demand realism in what we say. Sacred language can snowball, expressing not only man's search for God but also his desire for some magical power to come along and subdue the nastiness of the finite. Sacred language often wants burnt-out light bulbs and broken-down dishwashers to work. In its search for the transcendent it can break loose from the empirical. This is why the church has at times defined itself as something which it is not. It is also why the eucharistic bread and wine have sometimes become something which they are not. "Christ is present in the eucharist" can make sense. But it will make sense only if we can locate expressions like this in a world which also speaks of light bulbs and dishwashers.

There are basically two ways we go about interpreting finite reality, two questions we ask about our experience of the finite. By "finite reality" I simply mean the things we run into, the events and people and happenings and objects that impinge upon us. Implicitly or explicitly, we react to these things and experiences in two ways. Implicitly or explicitly, we ask two sorts of questions of the things that happen around us and to us. The questions can be schematized this way:

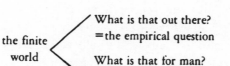

the finite
world

What is that out there?
=the empirical question

What is that for man?
=the human question

The first question is the factual question. That is a truck thundering down upon me at a speed of some fifty miles an hour, and unless I get out of the way I am going to be hurt. It makes no difference whether it is a Mack truck or a GMC truck, and my dog will react the same way I do. The second question is irrelevant at this point; the truck in this situation has no *human* meaning. With my human intelligence I could calculate the weight and acceleration of the truck, the relative harm its velocity could do, and the relative merits of one make of truck over another. I can always ask those questions and give an erudite human answer. But I have not yet asked *man's* question. Despite my ability to measure the speed and velocity of the truck, both I and my dog are going to react to the event in exactly the same way, by getting out of the road.

The first question, the first level of perceiving events, has to do with the interpretation of signals. Smoke signals fire, wet streets indicate rain, and a rapidly moving truck signals destruction for anything that gets in its way. I know this from my experience, and Fido knows it from his. The fact that I can abstract from my experience and formulate rules about cause and effect does not change the nature of the experience, where I react without having to reason. Trucks that move and light bulbs that burn and dishwashers that work affect a great deal of our behavior and occupy much of our mental time. This is nothing demeaning. But at this level of perception one has not yet asked the question of *human* meaning.

At the second level of questioning, where man deals with man, it can matter whether one's truck is a GMC or a Mack. If I own a car that doesn't start on extremely cold mornings, I share an empirical fact with many of my neighbors. But if my car happens to be a Continental or a Cadillac, the fact that it won't start is a fact I might not be too interested in sharing with my neighbors. Certainly it would make no difference to Fido, who would make little distinction between one running engine and another. Like myself, Fido appreciates that the sun gives heat and light; but for me, the sun is also warmth and brightness. It symbolizes something, it says something more than its physical self. This of course does not change the physical self of the sun or the Cadillac. What they say to man (the second question) is all tied up with what they are (the first question). It is because the sun gives light and heat that it can *mean* warmth and brightness; and the Cadillac is a status symbol precisely because of the physical properties and equipment it is endowed with.

This is not simply a matter of the "objective" and the "subjective," though the latter is a rather commonly accepted distinction. It usually implies that whenever we talk about light bulbs or dishwashers or the sun rising in the morning, we are talking about the objective order; on the other hand, whenever we say anything about human values or symbols or religion, we are dealing with the subjective. Wherever this distinction operates, we usually find an enshrinement of the empirical question, the first question; the second question becomes subordinate to the first because it is "not objective." When people say "That's *only* a symbol," they are implying that the second question does not bring us as closely in touch with reality as the first, and thus that the symbolic and the real are somehow opposed. This whole attitude (which revolves implicitly around the objective-subjective distinction) has taken its toll in theology, especially sacramental theology, because it has made us mistrust the category of the symbolic. This is why many christians are deeply disturbed when they hear the eucharistic presence frankly described as a symbolic presence; for whatever else "symbolic" may mean to them, it certainly means "not real."

Part of the confusion can be straightened out simply by noting that both the first and the second questions are at once objective and subjective. The empirical question is objective inasmuch as it asks for hard facts, a description of what that is out there, or what actually happened out there. But the question also has its subjective aspect because it involves our mental perception of what that is out there. An animal reacts to a sunrise or to a rapidly moving truck according to patterns of cause and effect he has learned from his experience; man behaves according to much the same patterns, and of course he can go on to formulate laws of cause and effect based on his experience. But in either case, at the empirical level of behavior or questioning, we are dealing with perception and therefore with one form of subjectivity.

As for the second level of questioning, the human question, no one would deny its subjective aspect. But that second question is also an *objective* question because the answer we give to it does not leave us locked up in pure subjectivity. If the sun symbolizes warmth and brightness in the human sense of those terms, it does so because it gives heat and light; and the human meaning of the sun is *objectively* different from the human meaning of a grey and cloudy day. This is true not just for myself but for millions of people. Of course, we all have symbols that are personal to ourselves alone. "What is that for man?" can often mean "What is that for me alone?" Only I can know the human meaning of, let us say, a book given to me by a close friend on a special occasion in my life. But the fact that this is a *personal* meaning does not make it any less *objective*. My answer to the human question here is rooted in the empirical fact that a friend gave me a gift.

The two questions are therefore two different ways of getting at reality. They are complementary ways of sinking one's teeth into reality, and insofar as they are both ways of *interpreting* reality, they both have their subjective and objective aspects. Susanne Langer uses an excellent image to express this interlocking: the factual and the symbolic make up the *warp and woof of the fabric of meaning.*[2] The interweaving is of course complex. The color green elicits a simple response at the empirical level when it appears in a traffic light; exactly the same color has human and symbolic meanings when it appears in a painting or a poem.

The difficulty is that the fabric can and does break down. This is seen in the tendency to view the empirical question as the only question which really puts us in touch with "objective reality." The technological society and the age of space exploration have come about as a result of a perfectly valid interest in the first question. But this development, as we hear and read constantly these days, has raised fantastic human problems because we have systematically neglected the human question. When a society finds its most significant values in how much a person earns or how fast one can get from one place to another, the second question is swallowed up in the first, and progress *becomes* human meaning.

Opting for material values as the most important human values is of course not a new phenomenon. People of every era have been drawn in this direction, whether wealth lay within their reach or not. Fairy tales about princes and beautiful ladies and happy endings in splendid palaces were undoubtedly first told in peasant cottages, not in the royal banquet hall. The problem for us is that technical progress and the wealth it promises have been the *main* preoccupation of the era. Construction of freeways and rapid movement from one town to another in ever larger automobiles and airplanes seem to be good things—until one starts trying to pin down the exact human "good" of speed and mobility. A higher standard of living is sought by everyone, but no one is quite sure just what "higher" means. What it means in most cases is quite simple: the empirical question tends simply to *become* the human question.

The human worth of simple everyday activities is a problem for the man or woman of the late twentieth century. Hard work, parenthood, and civic life once had definite values which were simplistically but clearly enough symbolized in the american dream of prosperity, the flag, motherhood and apple pie. Twentieth-century americans have had these values drummed into them, and advertising constantly evokes them; but one wonders to what extent they are factual twentieth-century realities.

Most men never see the goods they produce, but stand by a traveling belt and turn a million identical passing screws or close a million identical passing wrappers in a succession of hours, days, years. This sort of activity is too poor, too empty, for even the most ingenious mind to invest it with symbolic content. Work is no longer a sphere of ritual; and so the nearest and surest source of mental satisfaction has dried up.[3]

Mrs. Langer wrote these words shortly before World War II, when the american dream still said much more to people than it says now, and long before the counterculture of the late 1960's brought the tyranny of technology and its implicit values to national attention. If anything, the human problem has become more severe. The white-collar workers and computer technologists of our decade are still further removed from the product that is made and sold. Still fewer people know the carpenter and plumber who helped build the dwelling they live in.

Work has become monotonous to the point where the fatigue factor interferes with productivity. The success of Muzak in offices and factories stems from the idea that productivity might be increased if the monotony of work is relieved by music. But what kind of music? Artistic, creative music? No, such music would attract attention to itself. What is needed is functional music—music chosen, as one writer puts it, on the principle that "boring work is made less boring by boring music."[4] In a cultural atmosphere where human progress is implicitly identified with technical progress, it is only natural that an art form like music should be banalized and put at the service of productivity. In just the same way, the highest forms of human expression can be reduced to depersonalized technique. The famous Masters and Johnson study, *Human Sexual Response*, gives a detailed account of changes in body chemistry during coitus. Couples are hooked up to a barrage of instruments and data is collected. Whatever merits the study has on its own, it is symptomatic of the wider cultural tendency to reduce what can be the most intimate of human experiences to an impersonal physiological encounter, in which how well you perform is more important than whom you are with or what the action is saying.

We are not yet fully aware of the extent to which we have enshrined the empirical level of looking at things. A man who raises value questions when he is at home with his wife and family might not be in a position to do much about such questions at work, if indeed the questions even occur to him there. Some years ago, a large american corporation which owned a banana plantation in Central America decided that a particular shipload of bananas, if put on the market, would upset the market and jeopardize the company's investments. The bananas were dumped into the sea. The banana pickers, who had been paid well above the average wage of other laborers in their country, protested violently. When told about this protest some time later, an american businessman was perplexed. "But why should they get so excited? They were generously paid for their work."

It is not difficult to find other examples of cases where we reduce human meaning to economic and technological progress. The movement for women's liberation, for instance, asks questions about the value of woman, her image as mother and sex partner, her freedom, her role in society. These are valid second-level questions, and extremely pressing ones. But it is interesting that some of the heroines of the movement are women who have decided that real freedom is to be found in successfully entering that world where technical progress is seen as human progress. There is no reason to insist that a woman must find her personhood in being a mother and a baker of apple pies. Religious women have known this for many long centuries, and most married women have undoubtedly been much more than their husbands ever thought they were. The problem in our day seems to be whether the male world, so dedicated to the empirical question and to economic and technological manipulation of "what that is out there," is going to impose its definition of priorities on women's quest for freedom and womanhood.

It is hard for us to project ourselves back into an age when the empirical question was not the first nor the more important question for people. There was a time when the world out there, the world of nature, was a very integral part of man's own awareness of himself. Take the moon. Most readers will remember the time before one could ask the question "What can we use the moon for?" The song "Shine on, harvest moon, for me and my gal" is out of date for more than musical reasons; it evokes a symbolic attitude toward the moon which becomes quite difficult to sustain once the moon becomes just another body to be explored. But even so relatively recent a song still contains echoes of the way man *first* perceived the moon. It was intimately related to his own life. It was a mysterious orb which affected the rhythm of nature, fertility, the powers of life, love itself. It was a god or goddess in its own right, so powerful was its influence.

The same thing applied to simple realities like earth and water. Today few people are close enough to the land to know it as Mother Earth. But that is how the land was first perceived. It was not a neutral substance but a power, one which could be called "mother" because it possessed all the mysterious forces and influences of a mother. It is no accident that the ancient creation story found in the Book of Genesis spoke of man's being formed out of the clay of the earth (Gen 2:7). The connection here is really untranslatable; *adam* (man) is made from *adamah* (earth), so that in this story man is by definition "earth-being." The process of emerging from the womb and becoming physically and psychically independent of the womb is a lengthy process for any person. In just the same way, it took a long time before man could even *define* himself apart from the earth, which symbolized all that a mother is.

As for water, this commodity has been so bottled up and brought under man's control that it takes a disaster like drought or a flood to reawaken in us what primitive man felt so deeply. For him, water was a life-bearing force so basic to human existence that it symbolized life, it "spoke" life, the origin of life, the womb itself. In Genesis, the creation of life begins with God's mastery over the watery abyss (Gen 1:2). But water is also a death-dealing force, and so it appears as God's agent of destruction in the days of Noah. Because it speaks both life and death, ancient man perceived water as a mediator between the two. This idea is embodied in the story of the hebrews' passage through the waters of the Red Sea, a passage from death to life.

Christian baptism of course makes use of all this symbolism, and the new roman rite for baptism sharpens and highlights the ancient ideas. The difficulty for us is that when baptism is explained, we are not usually satisfied until we *translate* the water symbolism into some other language. The person baptized "becomes a member of the community of faith" and he is "made to share the fruits of Christ's redemptive work." Such statements are true, but they are also colorless. Compare most any recent sermon on baptism with this explanation given by Cyril of Jerusalem in the fourth century:

After the anointing you were conducted by the hand to the holy pool of sacred baptism, just as Christ was conveyed from the cross to the sepulchre close at hand. Each person was asked if he believed in the name of the Father and of the Son and of the Holy Spirit. You made the confession that brings salvation, and submerged yourselves three times in the water and emerged: by this symbolic gesture you were secretly re-enacting the burial of Christ three days in the tomb. . . . In one and the same action you died and were born; the water of salvation became both tomb and mother for you. What Solomon said of others is apposite to you. On that occasion he said: "There is a time to be born, and a time to die." But the opposite is true in your case—there is a time to die and a time to be born. A single moment achieves both ends, and your begetting was simultaneous with your death.[5]

"The water became both *tomb and mother* for you." When the church fathers explained baptism, they appealed not to abstractions but to radical experiences of what water is *for man*, what water *means* to man in his innermost psyche. The basic symbolism was expanded through the notion of "figures" and their "fulfillment." Christian baptism is "prefigured" by the great flood, by the crossing of the Red Sea, by the healing of Naaman the Syrian who was cured of leprosy when he washed in the Jordan. All these figures were "fulfilled" in the death and resurrection of Jesus, which we symbolically re-enact in the ritual of baptism. But the language of figure and fulfillment makes human sense only because man first saw water as a radical symbol of life and death. It is to this experience, this perception, that early christian catechesis appealed. Of course, the baptismal rite itself was much richer in those days: one was actually immersed in the water, indeed three times (the basic baptismal action was expanded to express faith in the trinity and Christ's three days in the tomb). But if later christian practice reduced baptism to the act of pouring a few drops of water over the forehead, it was because the archetypal meaning of water became virtually forgotten.

Depth psychology reminds us that archetypal symbols like earth and water still operate in our unconscious and manifest themselves, for instance, in our dreams. But the old symbols have little hold on our everyday *conscious* behavior. In this sense, we are different people from those to whom Cyril of Jerusalem explained the "heavenly mystery of baptism." How did we get where we are, where it is so difficult to recover the basic meanings man once saw in the world around him? The answer to this question has to do with the evolution of thought, particularly as it took place in the western world.

The evolution is a fascinating one, and the strange science of alchemy holds an important place in it. Alchemy seems to have originated in the mediterranean world during the first centuries of the christian era. Alchemists wanted to make gold from base materials like lead—a venture which sounds to us like a hopelessly naive attempt at some sort of magic. But much more is going on here than meets the eye. The alchemical process consisted of various stages, beginning with base matter (represented by the color black), then quicksilver (white), then sulphur (red), and finally gold. Why this process, and why was it expected to work? Because this is the way *man* works. In our own interior world, we begin with the soul in its original condition, a condition of darkness and guilt (black). We go through initial transformation (white) and the purification that comes through passion, suffering, conflict (red). And we are finally destined for salvation, perfection, wholeness, all that comes from a union of the preceding opposites (gold). The alchemical principle was *Solve et coagula:* "Analyse all the elements in yourself, dissolve all that is inferior in you, even though you may break in doing so; then, with the strength acquired from the preceding operation, congeal."[6]

The gold for which many alchemists searched was therefore not ordinary gold. For many, the symbolism took over the material reality of the symbol. "You will never make Oneness out of Otherness until you yourself have become Oneness." What the alchemists did was to project man's *interior* process of psychic growth onto the *exterior* world of inanimate matter. They assumed that the question "What is that out there, and how do I manipulate it?" could be answered by working according to the model of interior growth which mankind had laboriously learned over the ages. In short, they thought empirical questions could be answered with principles coming from second-level questions. And why shouldn't this work? If *man* has to go through various transformations in order to become what he should be—whole, free, gold—why shouldn't the same rules apply to matter?

The projection didn't work, of course. As the centuries passed, it became clear that the material world did not operate according to quite the same rules as those of the psychic world. And if man had learned something about his own inner development, he had not yet learned the empirical "laws" that govern the workings of the material universe. Those laws were gradually uncovered as experimental scientific methods were developed, tested, re-tested. The process was long and slow. But by the seventeenth century, discoveries of the laws of nature began coming rapidly, one on the heels of another.

A curious shift then took place, as western man became more and more intrigued with his discoveries and excited with their possibilities. He began to construct systems in which the new and successful *empirical* theories became the model for *every* kind of understanding, including the understanding of God. Leibniz (+1716) was able to describe God as the perfect geometrician, the perfect orderer of the universe. "It can be said that God as architect satisfies God as lawgiver in everything, and that sins must therefore carry their punishment with them *by the order of nature*, and even *by virtue of the mechanical structure of things*."[7] Empirical understanding was thus becoming the model for understanding religious ideas. In this atmosphere miracles, which once meant signs of God's presence among men, came to have a scientific meaning which would have been quite inconceivable to the biblical authors who wrote about miracles. In this late scientific age, miracles came to mean interruptions in nature, divine exceptions to empirical laws. Voltaire (+1778) was perfectly logical in rejecting miracles on these grounds. In his treatise *Of Miracles,* he argued very soundly that God either foresaw the necessity for a exception to his immutable laws, or he did not foresee it. If he foresaw it, he must have made the necessary regulations of the law in the beginning; if he did not foresee it, he is no longer God.

Here were the thought models inherited by the nineteenth and twentieth centuries. The drive to manipulate matter led to the discovery of empirical principles, which then became the primary model for interpreting practically everything else. In our century, psychology and the sciences of human behavior have had to shake themselves free of faulty presuppositions coming from physical science—or rather, from a use of the methods of physical science where those methods do not apply. Theology is no exception here. Much damage has been done, and much atheism generated, by conceiving of God as a super-orderer who operates according to the same rules as does the physical universe. This God is worlds removed from the God who is love, the Father of Jesus Christ, who in entirely too recent times had to bend to the inexorable Executor of the laws of the universe.

We look on alchemy as a foolish endeavor. How silly to think that material phenomena can be explained by models drawn from inner experience or from second-level questioning! But the flip-side of the coin is no different. Is it any less foolish to think that man's interior human growth can be fully explained by the laws of matter? Behavioral psychology has not yet really come to terms with this question, and the theories of a behaviorist like B. F. Skinner have to be subjected to the same basic methodological question that we ask of the alchemists. If the alchemists went astray in projecting the model of psychic evolution onto matter, to what extent can the laws of matter provide a model for understanding inner psychic growth?

***

These pages have attacked a good many elements in the concept of technological progress. I must admit that there is a strange and perhaps hypocritical element in the attack. The words on this page are the product of ink and paper mills, a typewriter and a printing press, not to mention basics like electricity and light bulbs. Plato, Jesus, and Johann Sebastian Bach would have been astounded at such "basics." Our problem is that all these things are useful, so useful that they become valuable, so valuable that they start controlling values, and controlling them to such an extent that manipulation of material reality becomes the *really* real. Every thinking person knows this is not so. But we do not always think, because our very freedom to *ask* the human question is jeopardized by preoccupation with the empirical question.

Perhaps this is why Saint-Exupéry's fable, *The Little Prince*, has become a modern classic. The whole story makes a plea for imagination, for fantasy. It keeps driving away at the point that "what is essential is invisible to the eye." In making this point the story insists, from the first page to the last, that contemporary man must rediscover our second question, the question he seems most reluctant to ask. At one point the narrator and the little prince, walking through the desert, come upon a well. Both are thirsty, and the narrator draws up a bucket of water for them to drink. The narrator sees this as a simple event, something to be interpreted in a straightforward factual sort of way, until the little prince forces him to ask the human question.

"I am thirsty for this water," said the little prince. "Give me some of it to drink . . ."

And I understood what he had been looking for.

I raised the bucket to his lips. He drank, his eyes closed. It was as sweet as some special festival treat. This water was indeed a different thing from ordinary nourishment. Its sweetness was born of the walk under the stars, the song of the pulley, the effort of my arms. It was good for the heart, like a present. When I was a little boy, the lights of the Christmas tree, the music of the Midnight Mass, the tenderness of smiling faces, used to make up, so, the radiance of the gifts I received.

"The men where you live," said the little prince, "raise five thousand roses in the same garden—and they do not find in it what they are looking for."

"And yet what they are looking for could be found in one single rose, or in a little water."

"Yes, that is true," I said.

And the little prince added:

"But the eyes are blind. One must look with the heart . . ."[8]

Those last words and a good many of the earlier ones can easily be turned into sentimental slogans. The human question can be turned into a purely emotional question, and "seeing with the heart" can be reduced to a matter of warm feelings and good vibes. According to innumerable books and movies and popular songs, seeing with the heart means turning on to another person—and turning off to most of the rest of reality. Search for human value and for what is invisible to the eye can become a form of escapism as immature and limited as its opposite extreme of preoccupation with the empirical, the merely visible.

The Little Prince rises above sentimentality by asking not how we are to *feel* about reality but how we are to *see* it. Saint-Exupéry is concerned above all with *perception*. A single rose or a little water can contain the really real only if one's fabric of meaning is a whole fabric. What is most humanly real about them can be grasped only if one's perceptions are whole, and yet there is no question of turning the rose or the water into something they are not.

The passage just quoted makes essentially the same point as the conclusion of John's gospel. "Happy are those who have not seen and yet have believed" (Jn 20:29). The point here is that the believer is the one who *really* sees. John of course is talking about faith, and there are a great many things that need to be said about the perception of reality which we call "faith." But basically, faith is one form of second-level perception, a form of seeing things that answers to the question "What is that for man?" And so a faith-view of reality and human experience presupposes that one knows how to perceive reality in the manner of the little prince.

If the human or symbolic question is the woof of the fabric of meaning, the empirical or factual question is its warp. And if the fabric breaks down with neglect of the human question, it will also be undone if it loses its warp. The single rose and the little bit of water can always be made into something other than what they are. In the last chapter we saw examples of what happens, both to Jesus and to christian worship, when the factual question is not asked along with the symbolic question. Alchemy, too, failed because it could not adequately distinguish the two questions. So we have to face the fact that the old symbols have often exercised unrealistic controls over people's lives.

Our religious symbolism today—where it is not entirely lost—is much less ornate than that of an earlier age, when every conceivable area of life had a religious value attached to it, a religious symbol to interpret it, and a ritual or prayer to control it. If esteem for the empirical has led many people to reject religion, it has also made religion look into its symbolism and purify it. But anyone who has made religion a part of his or her life will admit that there are people whose lives are still deeply affected by symbols which have gotten out of hand. One need only think of the symbolism connected with sin and its forgiveness, God and the devil, confession and repentance, heaven and hell. While such symbols provide a genuine means of understanding and coping with evil and guilt, there is no doubt that for many people christian symbolism has also fostered guilt.

Preoccupation with technical progress, then, is not the only thing that jeopardizes our freedom of mind. Religious symbols, meant to interpret human life and free the human spirit, have also been known to enslave it. Our challenge is to hold the factual and symbolic questions together, keep the fabric of meaning from unraveling, and enable christians to interpret their experience in a way that will produce something whole.

3

The Last Supper
and the Eucharist

THE TWO questions about reality have to be asked about the christian eucharist. If this is to be done with any accuracy, and if our assertions about the eucharist are to remain anchored to reality and to the real Jesus, we should begin by looking at the last supper. Asked of a past event, the two questions take on an historical character. The empirical or factual question has to do with what actually happened; the symbolic question deals with the human and religious meaning of what happened.

the last supper
{
What did Jesus and his disciples do?

What was the meaning of what they did?
}

The second question has to be handled in various stages: What did the action mean to the people there present? What did it mean to the New Testament writers? What did it mean to a later era? Distinguishing these stages is important if we are to sort out different layers of interpretation, or check later interpretations against the earliest ones.

The first question is rather easily handled, at least so far as the basics are concerned. What Jesus and his friends did was to have a meal together, a meal which had ritual connotations. In our day political organizations, sections of industry, societies for the promotion of ecology, or bowling teams will get together for dinner at a Holiday Inn to commemorate or celebrate a particular occasion, or to provide the proper human setting for a business meeting. The situation was not that much different in Jesus' day. We tend to look upon the jewish religion of his time as a huge institutional church, unified in its religious views and goals and ultimately united against Jesus of Nazareth and his disciples. But the large institutional churches of our day had no real parallel in Jesus' time; his contemporaries experienced the same sort of division and sectarianism that we do today. The gospels allude to this when they bring up the conflict of opinion between the pharisees and the sadducees over the question of the resurrection of the dead. But even apart from doctrinal disagreements, there were within the jewish congregations of that time small informal groups of friends who gathered because of a particular religious interest. These groups, among which Jesus' group would have been numbered, had meals together, even weekly, when they would meet for fellowship and conversation as well as to take care of their business.

Every jewish meal is a ritual meal, and the suppers held by these small societies of friends would have been no different, except that the ritual customs were probably observed with somewhat more formality than at an ordinary family meal. No dish was eaten without a prayer of thanksgiving or blessing, a *berakah*, which the host or the leader of the group said over each kind of food as it was served. Near the beginning of the meal, for example, the host took bread and broke it, saying "Blessed are you, Lord our God, eternal king, for bringing forth bread from the earth." He then gave a piece of the bread to everyone at the table. The main course followed with similar blessings for each dish. If wine was served, each person would bless his own cup every time he refilled it, saying "Blessed are you, Lord our God, eternal king, for making the fruit of the vine." At the end of the meal, especially on more solemn occasions, came a longer prayer of thanksgiving.

Leader: Let us give thanks.
All assembled: Blessed be the name of the Lord from this time forth and forever.
Leader: Let us bless our God of whose bounty we have partaken.
All assembled: Blessed be our God of whose bounty we have partaken and through whose goodness we live.
Leader: Blessed are you, Lord our God, king of the universe. You feed the whole world with your goodness, with grace, with loving kindness and tender mercy. You give food to all flesh, for your loving kindness endures forever. Through your great goodness food has never failed us. May it not fail us forever and ever, for your great name's sake; for you nourish and sustain all beings, and do good to all, and you provide food for all your creatures. Blessed are you Lord, for giving food to all.

We thank you, Lord our God, for giving as a heritage to our fathers a desirable, good and ample land, and for bringing us forth from the land of Egypt and delivering us from the house of bondage. We thank you for your covenant which you have sealed in our flesh, your Torah which you have taught us, your statutes which you have made known to us, the life and grace and loving kindness which you have bestowed upon us. . . .

Have mercy, Lord our God, on Israel your people, on Jerusalem your city, on Zion the abiding place of your glory, on the kingdom of the house of David your anointed, and on the great and holy house that was called by your name. Our God, our Father, feed us, nourish us, sustain, support, and relieve us. And speedily, Lord our God, grant us relief from all our troubles. . . .

May we receive a blessing from the Lord, and righteousness from the

God of our salvation. And may we find grace and good understanding in the sight of God and man.[1]

Christian eucharistic prayers have their own complex history, but it is not difficult to see their origins in a prayer like this one. The idea behind the earlier, shorter blessings has been brought back into the roman liturgy in the prayers recited at the preparation of the gifts. On a more solemn occasion the long concluding prayer of thanksgiving, known simply as "the blessing," was recited over a special cup of wine, which was then passed around to everyone at table when the prayer was finished. This is undoubtedly the ritual custom Paul refers to when he talks about "the cup of blessing which we bless" (1 Cor 10:16).

Here, very briefly and stripped of details, are the ritual customs that were associated with family meals or fellowship meals in Jesus' time. Variations were made depending on the occasion or the particular religious emphasis of the group. The passover meal itself, seen against this background, is simply an annual meal with special foods and blessings. But whatever the variations, the basic ritual character of the jewish meal comes into play: prayers of blessing recited over each kind of food, and a concluding prayer of thanksgiving often recited over a cup of wine.

This is the starting point for answering our second question, regarding what Jesus and his friends understood by what they did at the last supper. Even apart from any association with the passover feast, their meal already had a symbolic value; it was already a ritual meal. Whatever we mean by saying that Jesus "instituted the eucharist," it cannot mean that he instituted a new ritual. Every christian is familiar with the New Testament accounts of the last supper and Jesus' command to "do this in memory of me." But we get the whole thing backwards if we understand this command as meaning that we are to remember Jesus by doing something new and unusual. We are of course affected by our culture; for us it *is* unusual to break bread or share a cup with accompanying prayers anywhere but in church. But whatever the command to "do this" may have meant, it was not a command to break bread or share the cup.

Gregory Dix handles this point very effectively in his classic work *The Shape of the Liturgy*. To break bread and give thanks, in just the way Jesus did, was an obligation for every devout jew. Jesus was neither instituting a new ritual nor telling his friends to continue an existing ritual: it would be pointless to command something that would go on in any case. The real meaning therefore falls on the last half of the command. Do this *in memory of me*. That is, whenever you do this in the future, whenever you gather for a meal and do what we have so often done together, you will be remembering *me* in what you do. What Jesus did, then, was to attach a new meaning to the most ordinary ritual in jewish life—indeed, to the only ritual or corporate act he could be sure his disciples would do together regularly in any case.[2]

It is difficult to determine historically what sort of meal the last supper was. Was it the passover meal itself? Was it an ordinary fellowship meal of the sort I have been describing (which of course would have had a special significance because of Jesus' impending arrest)? Scholars argue the point. Mark, Matthew and Luke present it as a passover meal. But in that case Jesus and his friends anticipated the official celebration; John makes this point, noting that when the jews brought Jesus to Pilate they had not yet eaten the passover (Jn 18:28). John's own treatment of the last supper is consistent with this remark, for he does not call it a passover meal.

There have been many attempts to reconcile this conflict between John and the synoptic authors. The answers have ranged from the simplistic (Christ is God, and he could celebrate the passover whenever he liked) to the scholarly. An attempt has been made, for instance, to show that two different liturgical calendars were followed by the jews of that time. According to this hypothesis Jesus and his disciples, in celebrating the passover early, were following an older calendar which was just as acceptable as the "official" calendar to which John refers. This is Annie Jaubert's thesis, and she argues it on the grounds that we must not compromise "the historical character of the very clear statement of the synoptics."[3] But there is no reason to assume that the primary intent of these writers in this instance is historical rather than theological. One of the earliest faith-understandings of Jesus is that he is the new passover; Paul mentions this in one of the earliest New Testament writings (1 Cor 5:7). The theme of Christ "our passover who has been sacrificed" would easily have become associated with the event of the last supper because of its proximity to the hebrew passover and of course to Jesus' own sacrificial death. Thus the idea that the last supper was a passover meal could be a *theological interpretation* on the part of the synoptic writers rather than an *historical statement*. Or to put it in terms of our two questions, this would not be the first time the gospel writers were answering the symbolic question rather than the purely factual one.

In any case, that last meal with Jesus could not have been completely tied up with the passover meal in the religious consciousness of the disciples. If this were so, it would be hard to see how they would have followed the command to "do this in memory of me" more than once a year. The thought of celebrating the passover any oftener than that simply could not have occurred to any good jew. Yet we know from various remarks and stories in the New Testament that the first christians met regularly for the breaking of the bread. The symbolism of the jewish ritual meal—*any* ritual meal—therefore underlies whatever other symbolism may have been in play at the last supper. Jesus gave a new meaning not just to the passover meal but to any meal for which his friends would gather in the future.

But why bread and wine? Why should these two elements have been singled out from among the many other dishes that would have been served at that important meal?

Here again Jesus was not an innovator. During the past few decades, especially since the discovery of the famous Dead Sea scrolls, we have learned much about the religious practices of various monastic communities that existed in the wilderness of Palestine before and during Jesus' time. The documents we now possess are a sharp reminder that there were many more ideas abroad in the judaism of that era than one might gather from a casual reading of the gospels, which concentrate heavily on the judaism of the pharisees. Qumran is probably the best known of these desert communities, but there were others as well. John the Baptist undoubtedly came from one of them, and scholars debate whether Jesus himself might have had some personal contact with the wilderness groups, particularly during his earlier years. In any case, there is little doubt that their main ideas and religious practices would have been known to Jesus and his followers.

One important practice of the Qumran sect was a ritual meal presided over by a priest who, at the beginning of the meal, pronounced a blessing over the first-fruits of bread and wine. These meals looked forward to a messianic banquet when the two messiahs would be present: a priest-messiah, a descendant of Aaron; and a king-messiah, the messiah of Israel. There were even rules laid down for how that ideal banquet was to be celebrated in the age to come.

When they gather for the community table, or to drink wine, and arrange the community table and mix the wine to drink, let no man stretch out his hand over the first-fruits of bread and wine before the priest [the priest-messiah]. For it is he who shall bless the first-fruits of bread and wine, and shall first stretch out his hand over the bread. And afterwards, the messiah of Israel [the king-messiah] shall stretch out his hands over the bread. And afterwards, all the congregation of the community shall bless, each according to his rank. And they shall proceed according to this rite at every meal where at least ten persons are assembled.[4]

This was the liturgy of the age to come, the messianic liturgy, and it was anticipated at the daily supper held in every community where at least ten members were present. The note of anticipation is significant. The gospels sound the same note when they report the last supper—as in Mark, where Jesus tells his disciples that he "will never again drink of the fruit of the vine until the day when I drink it new in the kingdom of God" (Mk 14:25). The first christians clearly understood their eucharistic meals in connection with the ideal age to come. This is echoed in Paul's insistence that "every time you eat this bread and drink this cup, you proclaim the death of the Lord *until he comes*" (1 Cor 11:26).

Such eucharistic themes become all the more intelligible against the background of the Qumran supper ritual. As I emphasized earlier, the last supper makes no sense apart from Jesus' own awareness that he was indeed the messiah (however any of his contemporaries may have understood that idea)—his awareness that his impending death was to have a profound and central religious significance for the coming reign of God which he had been preaching. It seems that at the last supper the disciples had not yet caught on to what Jesus himself understood by messiahship. But if they knew anything of the Qumran practice, Jesus' action at the meal would at least have been recognizable to them as an action with messianic implications. They would have had no trouble understanding that their last meal with the master had become a ritual meal with a new religious significance. Their problem was how to understand that in this man Jesus the messianic age had really come, and this understanding broke in on them only with the easter experience.

Whatever influence the Qumran practice may have had on the actual form of the last supper, it seems to have influenced some of the earliest christian communities. In a document called *The Didache* or *The Teaching of the Apostles*—which may be as old as a number of the New Testament writings—we find these instructions for blessing bread and wine at the beginning of the meal:

Give thanks in this way. First, over the cup: "We give thanks to you, our Father, for the holy vine of your son David, which you have made known to us through Jesus your son. To you be glory forever." Then over the broken bread: "We give thanks to you, our Father, for the life and knowledge you have made known to us through Jesus your son. To you be glory forever. As this broken bread was once scattered grain on the hillsides and was gathered together and made one, so let your church be gathered together from the ends of the earth into your kingdom. For yours is the glory and the power through Jesus Christ forever and ever."⁵

This text echoes the Qumran practice and dovetails with Mark's and Matthew's accounts of the last supper, which suggest that Jesus blessed the *bread and wine together* at the *beginning* of the meal (Mk 14:22; Mt 26:26). Paul and Luke, on the other hand, speak of his blessing the *bread at the beginning* and the *cup at the end* of the meal (Lk 22:20; 1 Cor 11:25). This latter, as we saw earlier, was the common jewish custom.

When we lay the six texts side by side—the Qumran *Rule*, the *Didache*, and the last supper narratives in Mark, Matthew, Luke and Paul—we are reminded of several points. First, the accounts of the last supper found in the New Testament are influenced by the actual eucharistic practices of the particular christian communities in which they were written. Just as there were variations in jewish rituals for meals, so there were differences in the way the first christians celebrated their eucharists. Secondly, whatever connection the first christians made between the last supper and the passover meal, a far more basic factor at work in their minds was the religious significance of a corporate meal. And in the context of such a meal, the elements of bread and wine already had a special significance, indeed a messianic one, long before the last supper.

It should be mentioned that there are many counts on which Jesus' teachings disagree sharply with that of the wilderness sectarians. The daily life of these monks was filled with one prescribed washing after another (someone has remarked that it seems they never got out of the bathtub). They had a detailed code of laws with strict penalties for violations, even accidental failures: man was definitely made for the sabbath. And they were strong on secret teachings, knowledge revealed only to initiates who had proved themselves worthy. We know from the gospels how flatly Jesus was opposed to such doctrines and practices. In fact, one scholar very successfully defends the thesis that if Jesus had fallen into the hands of a group like the Qumran community, he would have been condemned to death just as he was in Jerusalem.[6] So in no sense could Qumran or any other desert monastery have been the spiritual home of christianity.

What the wilderness documents show us is simply that the same religious symbolism can have any number of homes. Indeed, if Jesus and the first christians had not drawn on religious ideas that were in the air at the time, the christian message would have had a hard time implanting itself anywhere. The mind has no place to put brand new symbols woven out of whole cloth; our minds are fabrics into which threads are woven one next to another. New meanings, new religious insights can be worked into the fabric, but only if there is a fabric there and a thread to which the insights can be tied.

This seems obvious, and maybe that is why it is so easily forgotten. Christians have too often thought of christianity, its doctrines and its rituals, as a whole cloth which appeared almost out of nowhere. "Conservatives" are then shaken upon discovering that their religion is not at all original when it comes to the forms and concepts and symbols that have been used to express faith in Jesus. But the same mentality of the whole-cloth affects many a "liberal" as well. One cannot expect to communicate new forms of worship, new religious language, new ways of talking about God or praising him, unless the existing fabric has been prepared to receive new threads. New wine cannot be put into old wine sacks; the gospel does call for radical conversion. But this does not do away with the problem of communication, and even radical conversion needs a context wherein the radicalness of God's call can be understood.

This whole problem is not just a modern one. Curious things happened to the christian theology of worship when, as time passed, the jewish origins of the eucharist were forgotten and the eucharistic meal broke off from its historical roots. More of that later.

One final point on the wilderness sect. The Qumran community was extremely clerical and sectarian. It was organized around a group of priests who would have nothing to do with the temple in Jerusalem because they looked upon the temple priesthood of their day as illegitimate. It was also a strictly male community, and no women ever assisted at those meals which anticipated the messianic banquet. But we know of at least one other sect of jewish ascetics, the "therapeutae" or "healers," which included women as well as men. The members of the community all lived in separate houses, seeking solitude for prayer and contemplation; but both men and women met together for common worship on the sabbath. We also know that women shared in the christian eucharist from the earliest times—not a common religious phenomenon in that male and patriarchal world where not even a court of law would accept a woman's testimony. Jesus' own friendship with women, as we read of it in the gospels, was rather unusual, given the cultural and religious atmosphere of the time. Perhaps the first christians' acceptance of women as full participants at its central act of worship owed something not just to Jesus' emphasis on the universality of the Good News, but also to ideas fed into the culture by one or another of those desert communities.

As the various forms of christian life and religious practice developed in the church, christianity came to be the only agency which resisted the greco-roman cultural doctrine of woman's subservience to man. The view of virginity as a "higher" form of christian life has come in for much criticism in recent years—and rightly so, insofar as it implies that virginity is *in itself* a more perfect way of life than marriage. At the same time, we should not forget that the practice of virginity by religious congregations of women was, until very recently, one of the only cultural influences forcing western man to distinguish between woman and sex-object, and above all between woman and mother.

One might ask why the whole thing never developed further, why women could not eventually have presided over the eucharistic meal and thus performed the same roles of leadership as men. There was of course a whole cultural dynamic working against this. The early christians could say with Paul that there is no longer any distinction between male and female in Christ. No distinction in spiritual benefits, that is. Neither Paul nor Jesus himself (none of the Twelve were women) did away with the social and cultural distinctions of the time. The passage of time might have overcome this problem. Deaconesses were very important people in the early church, and the role of these women might well have expanded and evolved further. But such development was short-circuited as the president of the eucharist came to be seen as a "priest," as one who performed a ministry modeled on the idea of Christ as "priest" who did once and for all what the priests in the temple used to do. Chapter 6 will show how the transition from eucharistic celebrant to "priest" depends on the gradual introduction of the symbolism of cultic sacrifice into the eucharistic ritual.

This is not to say that the eucharistic ministry is not a specific ministry—indeed, a ministry so tied up with the essential life of the church that a ritual of ordination came to be required. The christian community needs and wants a covenanted sign, traditionally called "holy orders," a sign which says that the word proclaimed in sermon and sacrament will be the word of God and not simply the word of the minister. But this ministry does not have to be designated by the term "priesthood," which is only a way of interpreting what the minister of the eucharist does. "Priest" is originally an image borrowed from pre-christian cults and applied to Jesus in order to describe his work and mission. When the author of the Letter to the Hebrews makes this application, he knows he is using an interpretative symbol, because he is well aware that sociologically Jesus was not a member of the priestly class (Heb 7:13). What the writer of Hebrews does is to evoke a whole set of symbols and cultic actions, well known to his readers, and use them to interpret the meaning of the salvation accomplished in the layman Jesus. Eventually all this imagery came to be applied to the minister of the eucharist, with some very negative effects. Probably the biggest problem over the centuries has been the view that the ordained minister is "another Christ" in a way that the baptized christian is not. This is simply false, if it means that a man's role gives him an intrinsic value not shared by one who does not perform that role.

Applying to the ordained minister the title of "priest," a title originally given to Jesus alone, has also complicated the role of women in the church. There are enough social and cultural complications (protestant communities which reject "priesthood" as a useful description of the ministry of word and sacrament also have problems with the ordination of women). We need no theological complications! If the eucharistic minister is understood according to the prechristian cultic model of priesthood, and if moreover the image of "Christ the priest" is rigorously applied to the eucharistic ministry, it will be all but impossible to get people to accept a woman in this position.

The problem here is therefore not a theological problem. The "priesthood" of Jesus has to do with the event of the cross, not with his being a male. His humanity has to do with his being human, not with his being a male. The problem is cultural; and christianity, given its historical origins, is bound to have strong resistance against a female priesthood. But the resistance has nothing to do with the theology of "priesthood," any more than male resistance to the equality of women has anything to do, today, with the intrinsic nature of "woman."

* * *

At the last supper Jesus was building on symbols which already had a long and complex history, a history which began at that mysterious moment in time when thought was born and when man

began to cash in his ordinary everyday experience and convert it into
the stuff of symbolism. His mental images were, as they always are,
the means of expressing the most essential human meanings. His
most basic symbols were, and are, those which have the most to do
with life and death and the critical dividing line between them.
"Archetypal" symbols, we often call them. These are the symbols
that first and most easily emerge in response to the second question,
the human question. From time immemorial, the act of sharing food
with another has connoted fellowship, life shared, exultation at being
alive. From time immemorial, the image of blood has connoted a
"matter of life and death." The shedding of blood radically signifies
loss of vitality; so the use of blood in the rituals of primitive man
signified his search for life and the preservation of life. When Jesus
associated his body and blood, his life and death, with the elements
of a communal meal, he evoked symbols which reach back into the
origins of man's consciousness.

We can watch the development of these archetypal symbols in the
religious history of Israel. The precise meaning of any religious symbol comes from a people's interpretation of their experience, including their experience of the divine. Historically, these experiences are
embodied in rituals long before anyone theologized about them. People *did* symbolic things long before they talked about the meaning of
their symbols.

The ancient hebrews inherited pastoral rituals from the tribes surrounding them, and when they offered their best lambs or burnt the
first-fruits of their fields as a sacrifice to God they were doing nothing new. But after the escape from Egypt, the old rituals acquired a
new significance. Chapter 12 of the Book of Exodus, which describes
the passover ritual, shows us what happens as further religious experience adds new meanings to existing rites. That chapter deals in detail with the sacrificing of the lamb, the sprinkling of its blood on
the doorposts, the preparation of the unleavened bread, and how the
lamb and bread are to be eaten. We now have a complex combina-

tion of the primitive rituals involving the offering to God of the best of the crops and flocks. The new meaning of it all is defined in the light of the people's experience.

When your children ask you "What does this rite of yours mean?" you shall reply: "This is the passover sacrifice of the Lord, who passed over the houses of the israelites in Egypt; when he struck down the egyptians, he spared our houses." (Ex 12:26-27)

The basic ritual symbols have not changed, but their meaning has been newly defined.

Further experiences add further meanings. Later on, after Moses had received the law on Mount Sinai and the people agreed to do everything the Lord told them, Moses sacrificed a bull. Half of the blood he sprinkled on a stone altar, the other half on the people, thus signifying the covenant between Yahweh and his chosen people. "This is the blood of the covenant which the Lord has made with you in accordance with all these words of his" (Ex 24:8). After that, the people shared a meal together (Ex 24:11).

All of this symbolism comes into play at the last supper. It is pointless to ask how much of it Jesus or his disciples would have been able to articulate in logical language. The symbols evoked by Jesus already had a rich history, and they spoke for themselves. The past experience of the hebrew people, together with the rituals in which those experiences had been incorporated, told them that it is Yahweh who gives life and saves from death, it is Yahweh who gives them their identity as a people, uniting himself with them in a covenant of life. All these abstract words are much more vividly and humanly expressed in the rituals of the sacrificial lamb, the blood of the lamb, the outpouring of blood, the unleavened bread, the sharing of a meal. No matter what sort of meal the last supper was, Jesus' words about his body and blood—about himself and his death and the bread and wine his friends would share in the future—evoked symbols of events which were the common heritage of the jewish people. Perhaps the disciples right then began to grasp more than we usually give them credit for. In any case, it was all a very concrete and definite and, above all, natural way for Jesus to express the meaning of his impending death, a death which he knew lay at the heart of Yahweh's promise of life and a kingdom for his people.

The symbolism of the last supper was spelled out as the early christians reflected on who Jesus was for them. It was spelled out in subtle ways like Mark's formula, "This is *my* blood of the covenant which is to be poured out" (Mk 14:24). This is simply clumsy grammar (in greek as in english) until it is seen in relation to Moses' formula at Sinai, "This is *the* blood of the covenant" (Ex 24:8). There is also the symbolism of the messianic banquet evoked by Jesus' saying, "I will never again drink of the fruit of the vine until the day when I drink it new in the kingdom of God" (Mk 14:25). The idea of a future banquet was emphasized not only in the Qumran ritual meals, but in the thanksgivings of any jewish meal. This was the future time which christians saw as present in Jesus, the time when

the Lord of hosts will provide for all peoples a feast of rich food and choice wines, juicy, rich food and pure choice wines. On this mountain he will destroy the veil that veils all peoples, the web that is woven over all nations; he will destroy death forever. (Is 25:6-7)

Much of this is foreign to the modern mind, because we have so little experience of the richness or depth of symbolism that can be given to a simple meal shared together. It is ironic that we who possess the eucharist, an action which we can call "the summit toward which the activity of the church is directed and the fountain from which all her power flows,"[7] should have lost the *sensitivity toward meals* which alone gives this statement of Vatican II its human foundation. The meaning of the eucharist is not easy to communicate to people whose family meals lack all ritual—meals which, except perhaps for Thanksgiving or weddings or birthdays, amount mostly to eating and running. Religious educators have found that if they can talk people into making one meal a week a real family meal, a ritual meal with a blessing and a sharing of thanks and a cup of wine passed around the table, catechesis on the eucharist becomes easy sailing.

Pastors and religious educators often express a need for new symbols, new images, new ways of getting across the meaning of Jesus and the gospel. There is no question that many of our traditional religious symbols no longer communicate. But it is hard to see how anyone can come up with a more natural symbol than that of breaking bread and sharing a cup together. Our problem is not one of devising new symbols but of working with the radical symbols we already possess. This means, of course, restoring to the christian eucharist some atmosphere of a fellowship meal, whether it be solemnly or simply done. The basic symbolism of the original event is not recaptured when only one member of the community drinks from the cup, or when one needs to make a natural act of faith to the effect that a tasteless little white wafer is in fact a piece of bread.

Some would plead that beer and pretzels or coke and potato chips should replace bread and wine in a truly contemporary eucharist. Much more realistically, oriental christians will ask why bread made from wheat and wine made from grapes should have to be imported into a country where the ordinary "bread and wine" is made from other fruits of the earth. The only religious question at stake here seems to be this: christians should be sure that the choice of food and drink *says everything that Jesus meant.*[8] Once we formulate the question this way, it becomes clear that christianity is after all a historical religion; if we always have to check our doctrinal formulations against the original experience reported in the New Testament, in just the same way our choice of symbolic elements cannot become arbitrary. Once again, it is not a question of new symbols or new symbolic elements. We need to establish the relationship of the few symbols that are still alive for us to a heritage which is much richer than we have often suspected.

Even more basically, our problem is to refurbish the radical symbols that have all but disappeared, not because the *symbols* are defective but because our ability to *think symbolically,* to let the symbols of our religious heritage speak to us, has been clouded over by ways of thinking that leave little room for questions of human and religious value.

4

The Bread and Wine

AROUND THE YEAR 830 A.D. a man by the name of Radbert, who was the abbot of the monastery of Corbie near Amiens in northern France, wrote a treatise for his monks entitled *The Lord's Body and Blood.* The ideas contained in his treatise need not concern us here. In fact Radbert was not much of a theologian; one of his monks, named Ratramnus, did a much better job on the same question a decade or so later. What is interesting is the way the question was posed. Radbert's treatise is the first historical document we possess which approaches the eucharist by focusing directly on the elements of bread and wine. Centuries earlier, men like Augustine and Ambrose and Chrysostom talked about what christians were doing when they gave thanks to God with bread and wine as Jesus did at the last supper. But "with" is the important word here. What the church fathers said about the bread and wine was said in the context of the eucharistic *action.* For Radbert, the starting point was no longer the action but the *elements* out there on the altar table.

Radbert himself was not responsible for shifting the question. By his time the eucharist was no longer an action in which all the faithful participated, and this was bound to affect understanding of the sacrament. Nor was Radbert writing for a religiously sophisticated group of men; many of his monks seem to have been warlords who got into trouble with the emperor and were exiled to the monastery. In any case, we find here a reversion to a primitive religious mentality. Primitive religions all have *sacra*, sacred objects or images which symbolize life and death and for this reason gradually acquire in the people's consciousness a power actually to give life and deal out death.[1] For the people of ancient Crete the bull was such an object, for the canaanites it was the serpent. The hebrews were forbidden to worship a golden calf. But while hebrew religion rejected *sacra* from the animal world, an object like the ark of the covenant at times served the same function in the people's consciousness: it brought them victory when it went before their armies, but when the philistines got hold of the ark it brought them only disease. Christians have attributed this sort of power to crosses and other blessed objects.

As for the eucharistic bread and wine, Paul once blamed the corinthians for engaging in the eucharistic *action* unworthily and for not recognizing the meaning of what they were doing (1 Cor 11). But none of the earliest christian writers described the eucharistic elements as sacred *objects*. It would have been difficult to do so, given the origins of the eucharist in the blessings and ritual actions of an ordinary jewish meal. But by Radbert's time those origins had long since been forgotten. It is possible that the monks of Corbie, whose religious consciousness was much more primitive than that of the early christians, regarded the eucharistic elements primarily as *sacra*, possibly substituting for the sacred objects of some primitive teutonic religion. In any case, Radbert's treatise reflects how the whole manner of regarding the eucharist had shifted from ritual action to sacred object. The shift was perhaps inevitable. A strong case can be made for saying that man, who has never succeeded in running away from archetypal symbols, wants and needs *sacra*. And christian man, once he forgets the ritual origins of the eucharist, will inevitably fasten on the bread and wine as his sacred objects.

By Radbert's time there were already historical factors contributing to the shift. Eucharistic practice had been in decline for several centuries. Few people were receiving communion, and the eucharistic action was becoming the province of the clergy alone. The result was that a cult of looking replaced a cult of doing. The cult of Christ's real presence in the eucharistic elements substituted for the action which at one time had engaged the whole christian community. The practical piety of the faithful once again set the pace for the theologians, and the theology of the eucharist was now destined to split in two. For centuries to come theologians would, like Radbert, start with the bread and wine and develop a theology of the real presence. They would then discuss, as a separate and distinct question, how the sacrifice of the mass is related to the sacrifice of Calvary. The Council of Trent echoed the whole medieval tradition when, some seven hundred years after Radbert, it wrote two such treatises on the eucharist, the second eleven years after the first (1551 and 1562).

We are the inheritors of this tradition, and Radbert's approach has for the most part been ours. Liturgical renewal has made us focus our attention once again on the eucharistic action. But the eucharistic elements remain a preoccupation. Indeed, for a good many christians, understanding of the eucharist begins and ends with the question of the real presence. That question might not be the best question to ask; many centuries went by before anyone explicitly formulated it. But since this is the approach we have inherited, let us take the eucharistic elements and see what happens when we ask our two questions about them.

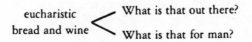

eucharistic bread and wine
What is that out there?
What is that for man?

There is only one answer we can possibly give to the first question, the empirical question. That is bread and wine out there. The only real presence at this level is the physical presence of bread and wine. Some form of magic is needed to sustain any change in the bread and wine at this level, because the physical bread and wine would somehow have to be combined with the physical Jesus. One might insist that Christ is present in his "glorified" body. But at this level of understanding, real presence can only mean physical presence, and the glorified body can be no less physical than the bread and wine. It is simply a body we can't see, and magic or a miracle is still needed to put it together with the eucharistic elements. This physical understanding of the real presence has not been an uncommon one. Historically, as the eucharistic elements gradually became sacred objects, what was known as the *mystery* of the eucharist became a physical *miracle*. As early as the sixth century, we begin to get those fantastic miracle stories which the middle ages thrived on, stories about blood coming out of hosts or the baby Jesus appearing on the paten.

The problem here is not a simple one. Chapter 2 talked about the second question, the symbolic question, as the distinctively human question and the one that brings man into contact with reality even more profoundly than the first. Man has never stopped asking the second question, least of all medieval man who gloried in symbolism. The difficulty is that as attention shifted away from the eucharistic action toward the eucharistic elements "out there," the empirical question entered the scene and became confused with the symbolic or human question. In every culture *sacra* originate as symbols of life and death; they originate as an answer to the second question. But the objects remain what they are at the first level of questioning: they remain serpents or bulls or a cross or bread and wine. The trouble starts only when one begins to assume that a symbolic reality can be dealt with and understood at the same level as an empirical reality.

Today, people tend to look upon symbolic realities as "merely" symbols, "only" symbols. Our particular temptation is to give greater value to the empirical question, and to apply that question to more realities than it is capable of handling. This gives us our own set of problems so far as understanding of the sacraments is concerned. Medieval man was not preoccupied with technology, but he had an analogous problem when it came to discerning the relationship between empirical and symbolic realities. He did not have a set of mental categories that would enable him to distinguish clearly between objects as empirical and those same objects as symbolic. The problem was further complicated by a serious lack of historical knowledge. The medievals were unable to get at the historical origins of existing symbols and rituals, and thus reflect on the process by which ordinary objects and actions *become* symbolic.

In the eleventh century, a man by the name of Berengar reacted against the physical understanding of the eucharist that was then prevalent. His teachings touched off a controversy that became rather ugly on both sides. In 1059 a roman council made Berengar take an oath which illustrates the extent to which the symbolic had been forgotten as a valid category for interpreting reality. He had to swear that "the bread and wine on the altar after the consecration are *not only* a sacramental symbol but the *true* body and blood of Christ, which the priest handles and breaks and which the faithful bite with their teeth." The word *sensualiter* occurs in the last clause, further emphasizing how "true" presence had become identified with *sensory* presence. The only way this council seemed able to preserve orthodox understanding and protect the realism of the eucharistic presence was simply to affirm a physical presence. Thus, the categories which man needs for understanding the sacred had become absorbed into the objects representing the sacred.

During the twelfth century, the concept of "substance" began to come into prominence as a means of explaining the real presence. The development of this concept involves the whole history of medieval scholasticism and its rediscovery of Aristotle's thought. Theologians began asking what happens to the substance of the bread and wine, and all agreed that a change takes place. Explanation of *how* it takes place varied according to one's understanding of "substance" and its metaphysical characteristics. Some held that the substance of bread and wine remains together *with* the body and blood of Christ (the theory of "consubstantiation"). Others taught that the original substances are annihilated and *replaced by* the body and blood (the "annihilation" or "succession" theory). But the explanation which became most prominent was that the substances of bread and wine are changed into the Lord's body and blood, with only the species or accidents of the original substances remaining ("transubstantiation"). The Council of Trent came out in favor of the last explanation, without however going into any discussion of the metaphysics of substance.

What were Trent's options, given the intellectual milieu of the day? Schillebeeckx maintains that the fathers of Trent were not in a position to safeguard the traditional doctrine of the real presence without affirming the particular theory known as transubstantiation.[2] Historically, however, the situation is a great deal more complex. Owing to his very nuanced metaphysics of substance, a theologian like Thomas Aquinas was able to argue for transubstantiation as the only viable explanation of the real presence. But metaphysics was not the real ground on which the discussion took place in the two centuries preceding the Council of Trent.

In 1215 the Fourth Lateran Council had stated in its profession of faith that the eucharistic bread and wine are "transubstantiated." This was *prior to* the major intellectual developments of the scholastic era, and it did not stop theologians from discussing a variety of theories as they went about working out the category of "substance" itself. But eventually, particularly after the thirteenth century, Lateran IV's profession of faith came to be seen as having the force of dogma. Both Scotus and Ockham preferred *con*substantiation on metaphysical grounds; but since the philosophical arguments were not overwhelming on the side of either theory, they had no trouble accepting *trans*ubstantiation, the theory which they understood to be the church's official position. Historically, the connection between the doctrine of the real presence and transubstantiation as the only orthodox explanation of that doctrine came about by ecclesiastical *fiat* and not because of inner philosophical necessity. This is the conclusion of James F. McCue, whose careful analysis of the relevant medieval texts is quite coercive.[3]

At the conclusion of his study, McCue makes some observations which should be kept in mind by any religious educator who has to deal with the theory of transubstantiation. Contrary to the impression common among catholics, Luther had no intention of denying the real presence. But Luther (along with many catholic theologians of the time) held that there was no necessary connection between the traditional doctrine of the real presence and the theory of transubstantiation; and he questioned the church's right to demand adherence to one theory among many. The irony is that in the centuries prior to Trent, the ecclesiastical position to which Luther was objecting had never been formally taken.

Like Topsy, it just growed. The anti-Albigensian confession of faith of Lateran IV was not interpreted as a dogmatic exclusion of all theories of the real presence other than transubstantiation until eighty-five years after that council. Thus what Luther was objecting to would seem to have come about through inadvertance and misunderstanding. Fourteenth and fifteenth century theologians considered themselves bound by a decree which they misinterpreted. This misunderstanding is understandable enough and one could perhaps find other instances similar to this; but the question inevitably arises: is Roman Catholicism to consider itself bound by this series of events? Are theologians of the 14th and 15th centuries and the council of the 16th to be taken as the crooked lines with which God has written straight, or is the Roman Catholic self-understanding and its understanding of the nature and function of dogma such that it can reopen this question in a more basic way than thus far it has done?[4]

Dogmas are expressions of how the church has understood its

faith, and they must be taken seriously. But if we are to take dogmas seriously, we can never read them outside the particular historical contexts in which they were formulated. Nor has any dogma ever carried with it a divine guarantee that it is the *best possible* expression of a point of faith. This is certainly true of transubstantiation, whose status as the official teaching of Trent does not make it the most useful or most adequate teaching for our age. Transubstantiation is an answer to a specific question: how is Christ present in the elements of bread and wine? The problem is whether this is the best question to ask in the first place. To what extent are we to go along with Radbert and the whole medieval tradition which treats the eucharist as an *object*? And, to get behind the various theories of *trans*ubstantiation and *con*substantiation, to what extent is *substance itself* a useful category for understanding the eucharist?

The category of substance originates as an answer to the question "What is that out there?" It is a category basically meant to explain the nature of things like rocks, plants, animals, men and angels. But a sacrament is not that kind of being. A sacrament is a *relational* being—one whose intelligibility, precisely as a being, lies in its relationship to man. This is another way of saying that sacraments exist because man asks the second question, the symbolic question; there would simply be no sacraments if he only asked the empirical question. Now medieval theology lacked the categories needed to deal with the symbolic, with relational beings. It "objectified" such beings and handled them with concepts that belong to and originate from the empirical level of questioning. In explaining the real presence by way of the category of substance, therefore, medieval theology was using analogy. It was understanding a second-question reality by means of a first-question category.

The practical result of all this is an ambiguity built into the theory of transubstantiation itself, or into any other theory that uses the notion of substance to explain the eucharist. The "change" in the bread and wine can be understood as a change at the second level of looking at reality: as a very *real* change, but not one that has to do with the physical order. Our experience of physical change thus provides an analogy for understanding changes that are not physical. The trouble is, we do not usually use the word "change" in this way. When we use it of *exterior objects,* we normally mean some sort of *physical* change: the weather changes, chemical substances change, traffic lights change. It is quite impossible to do away with the ambiguity contained in the statement that "the bread and wine are changed," simply because people naturally understand in a physical way words which originate and are constantly used in empirical contexts. Catechists, beware!

In recent years theologians have brought into play concepts like "transignification" which strive to emphasize that the change is not a physical one.[5] I have heard teachers say that contemporary theology is simply attempting to "translate" transubstantiation and make it meaningful for our age. This is incorrect. It is transubstantiation which is the translation, because the theory uses first-question categories to explain second-question realities. Current theology is returning to categories belonging to the second level of questioning, where the eucharist in fact originated. For behind the entire question of the real presence lies the fact that what began at the last supper as an action came to be treated as an object. The real problem we have to deal with is the objectification of the eucharist and the focusing of attention on the elements out there on the altar.

This problem shows up not only in the language of "change" but in the concepts we have inherited for talking about the "efficacy" of the sacrament. Medieval theology wanted, quite rightly, to show how the grace of any sacrament comes to the faithful through the redemptive work of Jesus and not through human merit. As part of this effort, the objective aspect or "givenness" of the sacraments was distinguished from the human quality of the sacramental celebration. God's offer of grace and salvation, which is expressed and communicated in sacramental signs, was not to be confused with the personal disposition of the minister or of the faithful. God's initiative, in other words, had to be distinguished from man's response to that initiative. This is where the famous expression *ex opere operato* comes into play. The formula came into common use by the second half of the twelfth century, and it was used to handle various questions. It was associated with the question of the minister's morals: as an *opus operatum*, a sacrament has its effect even if the minister of the sacrament is sinful. The same phrase was later brought into discussion of the acts of the recipient. After considering various expressions, the Council of Trent finally opted for this formula in order to affirm what it thought the reformers were denying, namely, that the faith of the recipient is not the only basis for the efficacy of the sacraments.

Any good theologian knew that *ex opere operato* in no sense implies an automatic effect apart from the acts of the believer. The difficulty is that the medieval analysis of the sacraments treats those acts as the acts of one who is no more than a "recipient" of something given. Once the sacraments were objectified, the ritual activity of all the participants was no longer seen as integral to their meaning; and the interior activity of the faithful was largely reduced to a matter of "right intention" or "proper disposition." Any adult catholic will recognize those expressions, which do have a positive meaning, but an extremely minimal one. For this development finally led to a totally negative concept of the recipient's acts. As Scotus saw it, the sacraments are efficacious so long as the recipient "places no obstacle" in the way of their effect.

In this theological climate, with its passive view of man's response to God's initiative, the doctrine of the *opus operatum* came to suggest exactly the *opposite* meaning from that which it was originally intended to express. It fell open to the interpretation that grace is automatically given by the correct performance of a sacramental ritual. Luther quite correctly reacted against the mechanistic implications of this formula. He saw the idea of "placing no obstacle" in the way of an otherwise efficacious sacrament as a denial of the efficacy of faith.

But Luther's condemnation of a formula that had become traditional was too strong for the fathers of Trent, who finally chose to canonize the formula against his denial of it. It is unfortunate that they did not take a hint from Aquinas, who used the formula *ex opere operato* in his earliest work but dropped it entirely in his last writings.[6]

Once again we find ourselves dealing with the problem of how the eucharistic question ought to be formulated. It is one thing to show, as medieval theology did, that the sacraments are spiritually efficacious because of God and not because of man. It is quite another thing to turn an action into a thing, and to reduce the faithful engaged in an act of worship to simple "recipients" of a sacrament correctly performed. When this happens, thoroughly legitimate ritual gestures are bound to acquire superstitious and magical overtones. The problem of magic will remain, I suspect, so long as christians think of themselves as "receiving" the sacraments rather than doing them, celebrating their own identity as christians.

This is more than a matter of sound catechetics and preaching. The smallest gesture communicates volumes. One need only think of the eucharistic words of institution. They are an account of the last supper, addressed to people who are engaged in doing what Jesus said we should do. But as the people became recipients, the words came to be addressed, by the priest bent low over the bread and cup, to the objects to be received. I am reminded of one priest who, shortly after Vatican II, was annoyed at having to celebrate mass facing the people. He had no theological objections to turning the altar around; but at the words of institution he was "distracted from consecrating" by all those people whom he could now see out of the corner of his eye. The theology embodied in ritual and gesture is indeed more powerful than the theology written up in books.

* * *

Radbert and Trent and the whole subsequent history of eucharistic theology tell us that if we are to answer the question about what the bread and wine are, we have to return to a far more basic way of asking what the eucharist *is*. We have to start not with the objects of bread and wine, nor with the efficacious sacrament and its recipients, but with the action that "proclaims the death of the Lord until he comes," the action that has its roots within the context of an ordinary jewish meal. Our questions then become:

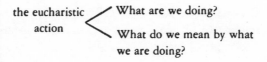

the eucharistic action
- What are we doing?
- What do we mean by what we are doing?

The answer to the first question is as simple as it was at the last supper: we are eating and drinking together. As for the second question, the meaning of what we are doing has been *objectively fixed* by the last supper and the death of Jesus. No one who believes in Jesus and who gathers with others to break bread in memory of him can "do this" without of necessity doing it "in memory of me." The essential point of the medieval *ex opere operato* remains: the meaning of the bread and wine are fixed by Jesus and his death, not by my personal faith in him. My faith does not create his presence. His identification of himself with the bread and wine is something given, it is a fact.

But if I am to understand that objective fact, if I am to see any human meaning in what I am doing when I gather with fellow christians to share the bread and the cup, I cannot presuppose my faith in Jesus and then lay it aside as I go about articulating my understanding of what the bread and wine are. The "real presence" is not and never was a substance. That presence makes no human sense, it has no meaning, it has no relation to the human spirit, it is in short unintelligible apart from faith (a second-level perception of reality) in the real Jesus who himself saw (a second-level perception of reality) that the bread and cup would keep telling his followers who he was for them.

This raises another point about our mental models. Some symbols are *like sentences*. They are made up of elements that have independent meanings like words which, apart from any sentence in which they are used, have defined denotations and connotations. Discursive speech—from sophisticated scientific or philosophical language to the everyday language we use to impart information to other people—involves this kind of symbolism. Other symbols are *like a painting or a dance*. There are handbooks of artistic rules governing the balance of color and light and shade used by a painter, or the rhythmic movements of a dancer. But the colors and strokes Da Vinci used to paint the Mona Lisa's mouth have no meaning apart from their relationship to the rest of the painting; that famous smile loses its enchantment if we try to abstract it from the rest of the picture. Nor does any single motion of a ballet dancer make sense apart from the movements that precede and follow.[7]

Sacraments belong to the second type of symbolism. They interweave gestures and objects and words in a complex relationship, so complex that the units which make them up do not have the kind of independent meaning that can be set down in a dictionary. Rituals and sacraments are not discourses. They originate as expressive actions, and it is the action that always remains basic: going into the water or pouring water, laying on hands, anointing with oil, eating and drinking. Indeed, such actions as breaking bread and sharing a cup say what a thousand sentences could not say. But such actions are symbolic in many contexts; so words enter to fix the context and interpret the precise meaning of the action.

The christians of Corinth knew they were meeting for a fellowship meal; eating and drinking together has a radical symbolic meaning in any culture or religion. But Paul had to remind them that because they were meeting precisely as *christians*, their action had a definite religious meaning, one which they were overlooking (1 Cor 11:17-34). He reproached them for behaving rudely toward one another, embarrassing the poor, getting drunk. They were to realize that whenever they met for this ritual meal, they were "proclaiming the death of the Lord," whether they liked it or not. This is why the christian tradition came to attach *words* to the eucharistic *action:* so that the meaning of the action would not slip away and become vague and indeterminate. Eventually christians would come to think of the "consecration" of the mass and "communion" as two separate and even quite unrelated moments. Originally, the whole thing was much simpler: the eucharistic prayer "worded" what the action of eating and drinking together was saying. So for the other christian sacraments. The words and prayers all have to do with relating the particular *action* to the death and resurrection of Jesus. It is in this sense that Christ is the "primary sacrament" whose redemptive work is celebrated in the actions and named in the words of any of our acts of worship.

Medieval theology took account of essential actions and words when it spoke of the "matter" and "form" of the sacraments. But it also treated the sacraments like sentences. It tried to filter out their basic units and analyze the separate meaning of each unit. It is true that the grace of the sacrament, the faith of the recipient, the morality of the minister, and the quality of the celebration are not the same thing. Nor are the bread and wine, some of which can remain after the eating and drinking are finished, quite the same thing as the water that is poured in baptism or the laying on of hands in confirmation and orders. The Mona Lisa's mouth is not the same thing as her eyes or the placement of her hands. There are always basic questions we can ask about faith, or the bread and wine, or the words we say or sing at mass—just as there are basic techniques that enter into the creation of a painting or a poem. But no artist will get very far simply by knowing the elements that make up his art. In just the same way, theology gets into trouble when it forgets that the units of a sacramental action are capable of just so much separate analysis. The lesson of history is that the eucharist loses its bearings and even its relationship to the last supper when its elements—the action, the bread and wine, the faith of the worshipers—are handled like words in a dictionary.

The following chapters will try to pick up the bread and wine out there and put them back into the picture together with faith and people and priests and the death of Jesus.

5

The Cross
and the Eucharist

WHEN YOU AND I are in the process of doing something symbolic, we do not accompany our action with a coldly rational reflection on what we are doing. A lover who gives his beloved a bouquet of roses does not, in the act of presenting the flowers, say either to himself or her, "Empirically, my dear, these roses are but one species of plant life among many others which I might have chosen; but because of the analogy at the symbolic level between their beauty and your own, I trust you will understand that my gift of these flowers says something important about what I think of you." To lay out in rational terms what lies behind a symbolic action often sounds ridiculous, simply because the symbolism is infinitely richer than the logical expression of it. There are surely few christians who, while engaged in eucharistic worship, have consciously said to themselves, "Empirically that is obviously bread and wine, but for me it means Christ's body and blood." When we look at the way human awareness really works, it becomes clear that we do not spontaneously know something "out there" as roses or bread and wine, and then *add* an interpretation to our knowledge.

Our *use* of symbols is far more fundamental, therefore, than our *reflection* on the symbols we use. We make and use symbols in a spontaneous way long before we do a logical and reasoned analysis of what our symbols say. And when we finally get around to the analysis, we discover that our symbolic actions still say much more than the analytic language we use to express what symbols are saying. No essay on the nature of love is quite the same thing as that bouquet of roses. This is important. On exactly the same grounds, no dogma on the nature of Christ says exactly what the breaking of the bread says.

Symbols originate as man's means of getting hold of his existence, his *present* existence. When the ancients told stories about the gods and their doings on Olympus before the world began, they were not talking about the past for its own sake. Those stories were explanations of the world of the storyteller's own experience. They explained why there *is* good and evil, why nature *is* fertile, why men and women *now* relate to each other in the way they do. Nor were those stories about the gods and the origins of the world simply told on quiet evenings around the fire. Because they had to do with man's *present* existence, they were solemnly acted out in religious rituals. Christians do the same thing, except that the stories are about Jesus and his forebears (and, unfortunately, the biblical stories are told and re-enacted in a much duller fashion than the ancients would have done).

Still, even though we use symbols because of what they say about our present existence, *ritual* symbols have a unique place in our consciousness. Words and sentences are symbols; rituals are symbols writ large, involving actions and objects, gestures and stories and songs, not just words and sentences. Because of their richness, rituals create a unique intersection between present, past and future. On thanksgiving day, for instance, americans re-enact a ritual meal. Any family which is conscious of the meaning of this feast is giving thanks for blessings in their own lives, not just blessings of the historical past. No story is told as part of the ritual, and yet the past is there. Perhaps the past is *articulated* only by a picture of the pilgrims in the morning newspaper, or among the table decorations, or when one needs to explain the origins of the feast to children. But the past is *evoked* in the consciousness of every american by the very celebration of the feast. The *future* is also there, even when it is not articulated. Thanksgiving, celebrated in homes across the nation at the same time, is saying something about the nation's desire for a future, and about the individual family's hope for the future.

The christian eucharist, seen against this background, is like any other symbolic action. It is not *merely* a symbol but *fully* a symbol. What is unique about the eucharist is not its symbolic status, but rather the reality which this symbolic action reaches and touches and proclaims.

I can sit around a table with my family (I am duly ordained; we talked about that earlier) and celebrate a christian eucharist. I can sit around the same table, with the same people, and pass a cup of wine in memory of my dead grandfather. Assuming that the cup had always been a family ritual at sunday dinner, and assuming that my grandfather was the old-time patriarchal sort of grandfather who might have said "Whenever you pass the cup at future meals you will do it in memory of me," this action would be symbolically identical to the eucharistic action. What is different about the eucharist is the meaning of the action and the reality it reaches. God raised Jesus from the dead and gave him the name that is above every other name. My grandfather has not been given that name, nor does our passing the cup in his memory proclaim the death of one who is named Lord. To say that the eucharist does just this is not to change its symbolic nature; it remains a symbol, our human means of getting hold of our present existence. At the last supper Jesus expressed the meaning of his own existence through a rite which he knew his followers would repeat. The actions done with bread and wine would henceforth be a way for his followers to say that *their* existence and search for the kingdom of God was bound up with himself.

There were other ways to "say" this. The early christians also told stories about Jesus—not just to report what he did for people in the past, but especially to show what is happening now in the midst of the faithful. We have no reason to suppose that the storytellers, the evangelists, were not borrowing from memories of the kind of things Jesus did for people. But their final product was not meant to be a simple report about the past. In *telling stories* about Jesus, the gospel writers were engaged in basically the same type of *symbolic* (and very real) action as we are when we celebrate the eucharist today. Both we and they are saying, in different symbolic forms, what God does for us through Jesus: he heals, he gives life. What the evangelists say through *stories* about what Jesus did for people, we also say through the ritual *action* with bread and wine. Both the stories and the rituals are in their own way interpretations of Jesus; they are different ways of saying who he is for us.

But because story and ritual are also *similar* ways of saying who Jesus is for us, it is not surprising that they would eventually be joined. The rite of the Lord's supper soon came to include lessons from the scriptures and stories about Jesus, in addition to the eucharistic meal itself. The readings and stories were so many different ways of wording what the action with bread and wine was saying in a non-verbal way. Many centuries later, theology would talk about the "presence of the Lord in word and sacrament." This is another way of expressing the similarity between what the gospels are doing when they talk about Jesus, and what christians are doing when they break bread and share the cup. Both are ways of proclaiming that Jesus is Lord and that for us he means life.

"God gave us the sacraments." It is by no means incorrect to say that in our rituals God shares his presence with us. But this presupposes an equally important point which is illustrated by the connection between *story* and *ritual* as complementary interpretations of the meaning of Jesus. If God communicates with us in our rituals or in the words of the Bible, it is because in our rituals and in the written book handed down to us, man is saying something to himself about God. Communication is a symbolic thing, and God does not reveal himself to us apart from the symbols of our own making.

The author of the fourth gospel knew this, and he gave considerable attention to the connection between story and ritual. Modern textual criticism indicates that the final editor of this gospel drew upon various sources and materials. We are certainly not dealing with a single author who sits down and writes about Jesus with a single personal interpretation in mind, the product of one man's mind. Yet despite all the questions one can raise regarding the author's sources, this gospel as it stands gives us a remarkably unified perspective which is most significant for any christian theology of worship. The stories talk about how Jesus gives living *water*, how he brings new *wine*, how he is the living *bread*. We have to be careful not to read medieval sacramental theology back into this symbolism; but the fact remains that many of the stories John tells about Jesus make their point by calling upon ritual symbols to explain the meaning of Jesus. How is Jesus to be understood? What is his meaning for the christian? This is the second-level question which John, like the other evangelists, is attempting to answer. And in order to give his particular interpretation of Jesus, John draws on symbols from the realm of worship known to his readers. In so doing, he gives an important lead to answering important christian questions:

What is the relationship between our eucharist and the cross of Jesus? What does it mean to say that the mass re-enacts Calvary?

John's storytelling technique is different from that of Matthew, Mark and Luke. All the evangelists are of course writing after the resurrection, and their stories about Jesus' miracles and cures have in mind the power of the risen Lord and the faith experience of their own christian communities. But Matthew and Mark and Luke make no effort to explain that this *is* the standpoint from which they are writing. They tell their stories in the first person, relating the event as an eyewitness would. The synoptics occasionally remark that the disciples did not understand what Jesus was doing. But these three writers never step outside the role of narrator, the first-person point of view, in order to tell the reader what the disciples *should* have understood.

John, on the other hand, introduces the third-person point of view in telling his story.[1] He is both a narrator and a commentator. He tells his story as an eyewitness would, but at the same time he will separate himself from the story in order to comment on it. He reports, for instance, that the disciples did not understand the cleansing of the temple or the entry into Jerusalem; he then tells the reader how they *did* understand these incidents after Jesus was raised from the dead (Jn 2:22, 12:16). In the same vein, John keeps interweaving into his stories references to a future event: Jesus' crucifixion, his "hour," the time when his "glory" will be seen. John is quite explicit about not wanting his readers to interpret any of the incidents in his stories apart from Jesus' death and glorification. This means that his readers are to watch for double meanings, because two kinds of understanding are at work throughout his narrative. There is the limited or simply incorrect understanding on the part of the characters in the story. But the reader knows more than those who participated in the events of the story, and John insists that his readers bring their easter faith into play when they read what he has to say. This is the only way the story will be *correctly* understood.

The two kinds of understanding are laid out in a variety of ways. John likes the terms "flesh" and "spirit." *Flesh* sums up the old order, the old law given through Moses, all that is ineffective or no longer effective, now that Jesus has appeared in history. *Spirit* designates what Jesus brings: the new, the effective, the really real. The levels of flesh and spirit also involve two levels of perception, corresponding to many aspects of my "two questions about reality":

namely, seeing the surface of things or seeing merely what is apparent (flesh), as opposed to seeing things the way they really are, seeing the real meaning of things (spirit).

This sounds all very theoretical. It is, compared with the concrete
way John makes his point. His whole story unfolds as a dialogue between these two levels of meaning. The dialectic is summed up in the
story of Thomas the apostle at the conclusion of the gospel (Jn
20:24-29). Thomas is determined to operate at the level of flesh: he
will not believe until he sees and touches the Lord's wounds. Jesus
rebukes him by telling him that this level of perception just isn't
enough, nor is it ultimately important. It is the people who believe
without having to "see" in the manner Thomas insisted on—these
are the people who really "see," who really understand the meaning
of Jesus and his resurrection.

Thomas is typical of all the characters in this gospel. They all ask
questions and understand Jesus at the level of flesh; Jesus answers
questions and talks consistently at the level of spirit. In the incident
of the cleansing of the temple, the jews talk about a sanctuary it took
forty-six years to build; Jesus is talking about the sanctuary of his
body. Jesus tells Nicodemus about rebirth through water and the
spirit; Nicodemus asks how a grown man can go back into the womb
and be reborn. Jesus talks to the samaritan woman about living
water that will satisfy thirst once and for all; the woman thinks how
nice it would be not to have to come back every day to her well of
running water. The crowds are excited over Jesus because they think
he is going to provide all the bread they want to eat; Jesus tells them
they missed the point, and after he explains about his being living
bread and giving his flesh to eat, many left him because they could
not understand at the level of spirit. The jews, after excommuni-
cating the man born blind, insist they are not blind; Jesus tells them
that at the level of perception which really counts, they are indeed
blind.

In short, the supporting characters in John's cast consistently operate at the level of the apparent; they fail to get beyond the first level of questioning. Jesus on the other hand deals only with meaning, faith-meaning, the meaning of events in the light of the resurrection. In John's story there is a near-perfect non-communication between Jesus and the supporting cast. But John's reader is supposed to understand what Jesus means; the reader who possesses the easter faith is equipped to understand the second-level realities Jesus is talking about.

Warned to watch for two levels of understanding, let us see how John works this out as he goes about telling his story. After an introductory chapter which presents the theme and brings the disciples onto the scene, the first part of the gospel (chapters 2 through 12, the "Book of Signs") presents stories about Jesus' works, with lengthy discourses interwoven among the stories, explaining and developing what is going on in the narratives. Laying out the development of John's narrative, with detailed references to chapter and verse, would be long and tedious reading; the gospel is not short, John is repetitious, and many themes are woven together. I shall rely on the reader's general familiarity with the text and use a schematic outline to summarize some of John's main symbolism. The symbols which come into play in worship, and which John uses to interpret the meaning of Jesus, are capitalized.[2]

FLESH, the old, the ineffective. Surface understanding.	SPIRIT, the new, what Jesus brings and is. Real understanding.
At the wedding at Cana, they ran out of wine. There were water jars standing there, WATER used for the ritual purifications customary among the jews.	Jesus transforms the ritual water into WINE. The old gives way to the new, and the transformation is associated with "my hour," the hour when Jesus would shed his BLOOD.
Jesus drove the money changers and SACRIFICIAL ANIMALS out of	Jesus replaces the sacrificial animals and the temple itself. The sanctuary

the TEMPLE. The jews saw the temple as a sanctuary which surely could not be rebuilt in three days.

of which he speaks is the SANCTU-ARY OF HIS BODY. The "body of Christ" replaces temple worship.

Nicodemus cannot understand how a grown man can go back into his mother's womb and be born again.

The rebirth Jesus means is not a physical return to the womb but re-birth through WATER AND THE SPIRIT.

The samaritan woman draws her WATER out of Jacob's well, run-ning water for which one needs a bucket. (The story is built around a play on words: in greek, the same word means "running" water and "living" water.)

Jesus promises LIVING WATER which will turn into a spring inside the believer, welling up into eternal life. The water of Jacob's well, like the water of purification at Cana, is ineffective.

The paralytic at the pool has lain there for thirty-eight years. The WATER of Bethesda is ineffective.

Like the centurion's son, the para-lytic is cured at the WORD of Jesus, who replaces the angel that moved the waters at Bethesda. Any-one who hears his word passes from death to life. The Lazarus story later illustrates how even the graves give up their dead at the sound of Jesus' voice.

The jews wanted to make Jesus king because they thought he would give them all the bread they wanted to eat, just as Moses had given them BREAD in the desert.

It was not Moses who gave them the manna but God; besides, those who ate the bread in the desert are dead. Jesus is the LIVING BREAD given by God. The bread that he gives is himself, his FLESH and BLOOD, for the life of the world.

The jews do not understand how he can give his flesh to eat and his blood to drink.

It is the spirit that gives life, and Jesus' words cannot be understood at the carnal, material level.

The liturgy of the feast of tabernacles included prayers for rain, libations of water, and evoked the theme of life-giving WATER for the nation.

In the context of this feast, Jesus says that anyone who is thirsty should come to *him* and drink. He will provide fountains of LIVING WATER which (as in the Nicodemus story) is associated with the SPIRIT to be given to the faithful.

[Christian baptismal symbolism includes both WATER and LIGHT. The liturgy of the easter vigil makes this connection, but the ordinary baptismal ceremony does not give much stress to the idea of light. In the early church much emphasis was laid on baptism as illumination. John develops this theme:]

The feast of tabernacles also evoked the coming "day of the Lord," ritually symbolized by LIGHT and an illumination of one of the temple courts.

At this feast Jesus proclaims that it is *he* who is the LIGHT of the world. This idea is further spelled out in the story of the man born blind, who receives that LIGHT by washing with WATER at Jesus' command.

In the story of the samaritan woman, Jesus says that the time has come when people will worship no longer on Mount Gerizim or in Jerusalem; they are to worship in spirit and truth. What is this worship? Spirit and truth, as John develops these ideas, refer to the level of perception and understanding which becomes available through faith in Jesus. "Reality" would probably be a more helpful translation of John's term than "truth." In our modern terminology, "truth" tends to refer to abstractions or propositions *about* reality. John uses the word in a much more concrete sense: truth is the new reality which Jesus brings and which the christian grasps through faith.

Worship begins back in the dim moments of archaic time, when men did such things as sprinkle blood on tentposts to ward off demons that could harm their flocks. This ancient ritual was given a new meaning with the hebrews' liberation from Egypt. The ritual of slaying a sacrificial lamb was incorporated into the passover rite; but the blood was no longer sprinkled on doorways, because the ritual was no longer conceived mainly as a protection against the dark forces of nature. The rite now focused on God rather than on demons. It spoke of the Lord as a saving God, a liberator, one who gives his people good things, the best of things, freedom itself.

The passover was not the only ritual which, transformed from a fertility rite, came to express a higher stage of religious consciousness. Just as christianity a millennium later took over pagan feasts like that of the sun-god on December 25th, so the israelites transformed existing feasts in the light of their own religious experience. The festival of pentecost or "weeks" began as a fertility rite performed at the time of the wheat harvest in late spring; it was later associated with Israel's history, particularly the covenant with Noah. Of great importance in the hebrews' early history was the feast of tabernacles. This feast began as a fertility rite connected with the fruit harvest in fall; it came to be associated with the hebrews' own history and the gift of their land, and thus became a time for renewal of the covenant with Yahweh. John's gospel stresses the association of this feast with the coming "day" of the Lord. As time passed, the different feasts acquired additional meanings, so that there were many rituals, including daily rituals of purification, which filled the lives of the people of Israel with reminders of God's gifts to them.[3]

This is the situation John is dealing with, and what his stories are saying is that in Jesus a new and further stage of worship has been reached. For in Jesus God has reached *us* in a new and decisive way. God is spirit, and his spirit is manifested to anyone who accepts Jesus and who, like the man born blind, sees reality in a new and effective way. To worship the Father in spirit and reality (the two terms are for all practical purposes interchangeable) is to worship God through Jesus. The old rituals, the purification rites, the animal sacrifices, the temple itself, are no longer effective. They no longer "work" because they do not designate the new stage of religious awareness that has arrived in Jesus, who transforms all that went before.

The theme of transformation is superbly expressed by Ephraim of Syria, a fourth-century church father, whose commentary on the wedding at Cana uses John's own symbolism to say what these last paragraphs of mine have been saying so prosaically:

The jugs were used for the purification rituals of the jews. Our Lord poured his doctrine into them, to show that he had come according to the way of the law and the prophets, but with the intention of changing everything through his teaching, like water changed into wine. The steward said, "Everyone serves the finest wine first, then the inferior wine." In this way the Lord showed that the old covenant was already a storehouse of provisions, for "the law was given through Moses." But then "grace and truth came through Jesus."

The earthly bridegroom invited the heavenly bridegroom, and the Lord came, ready for the banquet. The guests seated at table invited him who brings the world into his kingdom, and he brought them a marvelous wedding gift. In his richness he did not scorn their poverty. They didn't have enough wine, even ordinary wine, for their guests. And if he had not poured out for them a few of his riches, they would have left the table thirsty and sad. In return for their invitation, he invited them to *his* banquet. . . . Without saying a word, he changed the water into wine. His divine silence awakened his glad heralds, and the steward announced this happy news to the guests; for wine naturally gladdens the heart. Jesus' command made all this happen in an instant, and the bouquet of this wine surpassed the fragrance of any other wine. And so people started asking who was the author of it. . . .

Jesus did not bring with him any strange new creature. He transformed the things that were already there, in order to show he was the master of them. And at the end of time, these same creatures will all be renewed. The will that changed ordinary water into the finest wine with a simple, swift command has the power to give every creature, at the end of time, an inexpressible savor. . . . He started his career by giving to the mouth the taste of his wine, so that he could then attract the ear and lead it to the delights of his savorous teaching.[4]

Ephraim's allegory on the Cana story, which expands the symbolism contained within the story itself, stresses the idea that the event of Jesus is not a break with the past but a further development of it. The old law was good, the wine first served at the feast was good; but Jesus brought the finest wine. (The steward expresses the world of appearances and conventions: one should serve the best wine first. John's story says that in the interior world, the world of religious experience, the best comes after lower stages have been experienced.) John himself, as subsequent stories in his gospel indicate, is much more emphatic than Ephraim about the ineffectiveness of the old, now that the new has appeared. But the essential point remains. Because of Jesus, the old worship is transformed—just as, in fact, Israel's own religious experience had transformed and given new meaning to the ancient fertility rites.

Note that the signs used in worship have not changed. When we were discussing Jesus' action at the last supper, we noted that the bread and wine already had a religious significance, even a messianic significance. The new meaning which Jesus gave to these elements of the meal did not abolish the old meaning but advanced it, concretized it. The fourth gospel works with this same idea and expands it. Christians use the old symbols, but the *meaning* of the symbols has changed because the *reality* they touch is new. Jesus *is* everything the symbols of hebrew worship had been saying. And when christians worship with symbols like light and water, bread and wine, they are saying precisely that Jesus is this "everything" God has promised to man. This last sentence is an abstraction; it becomes concrete and real to you and me *in* the ritual actions we perform with light and water and bread and wine.

* * *

What is the meaning of the "transformation" worked by Jesus? What is this new stage of religious consciousness that has arrived in him?

This question has to do with the most basic meaning of christian faith as *christian*. John sums up his answer in the words addressed by Jesus to the greeks who asked to "see" him. "Unless a grain of wheat falls into the earth and dies, it remains a single grain of wheat; but if it dies, it brings a good harvest" (Jn 12:24). The *Living Bible*'s paraphrase and expansion of this image is excellent: "I must fall and die like a kernel of wheat that falls into the furrows of the earth. Unless I die I will be alone—a single seed. But my death will produce many new wheat kernels—a plentiful harvest of new lives." The paradox of christian faith, the well-known stumbling block and piece of foolishness, is that life and true union with God is to be found in the death of a man and union with his death.

Christians have heard words like these so often that a certain numbness sets in. We have not been raised as jews or buddhists, and we do not really know any other way to God than the christian way. We accept Jesus; but we do not necessarily go on to ask what makes the phenomenon of a man who died a unique page in the history of religious experience. Some of our own conceptions work against us, particularly the whole notion that the main idea of the christian religion is *life after death*.

That idea is not at all original to christianity. Indeed, christian faith is much less explicit than many other religions about what life after death will be like. Various non-christian beliefs about the reincarnation of souls, for instance, are much more *definite* about the next life than the simple christian image of a new heaven and a new earth where every tear will be wiped away (Rev 21:1-4). And if one is going to believe in the immortality of the human spirit, the theories about absorption into a world-soul are probably more satisfying from a purely rational viewpoint than the overwhelming notion of a personal existence in a new creation.

The mystery cults of the greco-roman world guaranteed life after death, and the greeks of Corinth who converted to christianity had no trouble accepting initiation into "eternal life" through baptism.

They could easily accept Christ as a cosmic symbol. Paul had to remind them that as *christians* their new and eternal life made no sense apart from the cross; the actual death of the man Jesus transformed the symbols of the initiation rites known to the corinthians. The problem is by no means absent today. In the past few decades, we have rightly corrected a false understanding of the resurrection (it "proves Christ's divinity"), but often with a new form of triumphalism that skirts around the cross. "Look, everybody, Christ is alive!" —and his *way* to glory is soft-pedaled in favor of the result, which is much too facilely proclaimed on banners in our churches. If Jesus is victorious *over* death, it is first of all because he is victorious *in* his death.[5]

Christians sometimes conceive of Jesus' life as a kind of horizontal line that starts with his birth and runs through his ministry, then is interrupted or becomes a dotted line for three days between Good Friday and Easter Sunday, after which the solid line is resumed and the cosmic Christ picks up where the historical Jesus left off. This conception is exemplified by the kind of questions sometimes asked about the resurrection. One reads that the risen body of Jesus is a unique body that passes through closed doors or suddenly appears out of nowhere; from this, theologians have gone on to speculate on the qualities of glorified flesh and of the heavenly life that awaits us. This is the mentality of the horizontal line interrupted and resumed, because the question implicitly being asked here is how Jesus' new bodily life (or our future bodily life) compares with the bodily life we now experience. It is probably human enough to ask such questions now and again. The trouble is that such speculations have made their way into a good many catechisms and conveyed to christians a basically *materialistic* notion of the resurrection. The resurrection stories in the gospels are stories of the first christians' experience of the risen Lord; they are not empirical speculations on life after death.

The horizontal line will not do. Our usual physical way of thinking does not work when it is applied to the resurrection. Life as we know it and *Jesus'* life as *he* knew it came to a crashing end on the cross, and that is where the line ends. If Jesus "draws all people to himself," he does so not because he picked up the line of life after a three-day parenthesis, but because the cross at the end of the line becomes a point from which flow out into history the rays of a totally *new* sort of life. There are many things to be debated about the nature and intent of the resurrection narratives, but one would have a difficult time maintaining that these stories are concerned with the material details of Jesus' risen life. It is risky exegesis to try to show that the resurrection narratives do more than "enflesh" the basic kerygma preached by Paul: Jesus is established Lord, raised up and given the name that is above all names, precisely because he accepted *death* (Phil 2:6-11; cf. Rom 1:4). The trouble with the whole horizontal-line view of Jesus is that in such a perspective the cross itself tends to be put into parentheses, as just one more event which is part of the whole package labeled "Christ." We miss the point entirely unless we ask our questions with the understanding that the cross *is* the package.

The fourth gospel is quite explicit (more so than the synoptics) about seeing Jesus' miracles and cures, the doings of his historical life, as possessing a meaning only in relation to the cross. Each of these stories, as they appear in John, evokes the cross, the "hour" of Jesus. The healing of the blind man, the feeding of the multitude, and the raising of Lazarus had, as Dodd puts it, no lasting effect in history. These miracles involved the giving of bodily light, bodily food, bodily life. But the sight of the man born blind would have deteriorated as he got older, the multitude would have been hungry again a day later, and Lazarus had to die again. Such considerations show how useless it is to ask empirical questions of the gospel text (What exactly did Jesus do when he multiplied the loaves? How did he pull off that trick?) when the text is talking about something else. The point of John's stories is that Jesus is the *real* light and bread and life. The stories about him are stories about what Jesus does for the christian *now*, not just for a handful of people in past history. The signs recounted in the fourth gospel are true *for us*, true as present and not past realities, only because of the cross which is *the* life-giving event. The fine wine provided by Jesus at Cana would have run out even more quickly than the inferior wine; the wine he gives now never runs out. The money changers undoubtedly returned to the temple, which in any case was finally destroyed by the romans; the sanctuary of Christ's body is the christian's possession forever. All this is a result of the death of Jesus, his hour, the event that alone enables him to provide the finest wine and to be true light, true bread, true life.

A materialistic understanding of the light or bread or life that Jesus gives obviously does not work. Nor does a materialistic understanding of his death and resurrection. Christian faith does not affirm that life is *resumed* after death. It affirms something much more profound, namely that life comes *out of* death. This is the point of the image about the rich harvest that will come only if the grain of wheat falls into the ground and dies. True, the living harvest comes after the death of the grain; but this is so only because it comes *out of* the death of the grain. This does not imply any rejection of the afterlife. Christians have always taken the moment of physical death seriously; Jesus' preaching talks about the need to make something of our lives before God requires our souls of us. The gospel, however, is much less concerned with the final crunch of physical death than it is with giving us an interpretation of life. It is much less concerned with the material facts of Jesus' own death than it is with his *acceptance* of death as the *meaning of his life* and of the kingdom he was preaching.

When, as John reports it, Jesus washed his disciples' feet the night before he died, he was explaining what typified his own ministry and what kind of service should distinguish anyone who followed him. (Another striking piece of johannine symbolism here. The water of baptism, the water without which "you can have nothing in common with me," is in this episode given the meaning of commitment to service.) At the same time Jesus was explaining his death, his final act of service; for his physical death was his last lesson to his disciples. But since his death wrapped up the meaning of his whole life and ministry, it was much more than a lesson in what to do in the face of total rejection. What Jesus' whole ministry says to mankind is that life and the essential activities of living—being with other people, relating to them, loving and serving them—are tied up with dying. The good news is that Jesus offers a new way of interpreting life and its experiences of death.

So it is that the experience christians are called to live on is the experience of Jesus. That is, ever since the first disciples had their experience of the risen Lord, christians have been using Jesus' experience as a key for interpreting life. Now when christian faith, looking at the Christ-event, issues the invitation to die in order to be alive, it is not saying we should simply make the best of death, whether as physical death or as daily self-sacrifice. This is hardly the "folly" of the cross. Everyday human wisdom tells us we have to make the best of a bad job. What christian faith is saying is that death to self is the precise means through which we experience being alive. We are invited to die to ourselves precisely so that life can be experienced as life. This is the principle that allows our personal faith to be founded not just on hearsay *about* the resurrection, but on concrete experience *of* the kind of life which "resurrected" life is.

John, along with the other New Testament writers, saw this as a new page in the history of religious experience. The event of Jesus simply overturned all normal ideas about the meaning of death and the experience of death. This comes across emphatically in the meaning John gives to the cross. "The son of man must be lifted up as Moses lifted up the serpent in the desert" (Jn 3:14). In order to develop his symbolism of the cross, John reaches back to primitive times, to an incident reported in the Book of Numbers, when the hebrews in the wilderness lost their patience.

They spoke against God and against Moses. "Why did you bring us out of Egypt to die in this wilderness? There is neither bread nor water here; we are sick of this unsatisfying food." At this God sent fiery serpents among the people; their bite brought death to many in Israel. The people came and said to Moses, "We have sinned by speaking against Yahweh and against you. Intercede with Yahweh for us to save us from these serpents." Moses interceded for the people, and Yahweh answered him, "Make a fiery serpent and put it on a standard. If anyone is bitten and looks at it, he shall live." So Moses fashioned a bronze serpent which he put on a standard, and if anyone was bitten by a serpent, he looked at the bronze serpent and lived. (Num 21:4-9)

The story throws us back into the era of fertility cults. The cult of the serpent was apparently quite widely practiced in Canaan, and images of serpents were venerated as sacred objects. (Think of the possibilities for the archaic mind. The snake's characteristics symbolize energy and force: its threatening tongue, the sinuous movements of its body, its method of coiling itself around the victim it attacks. It even sheds its skin, and so for the ancients the snake symbolized the restoration of new life, "resurrection" in its cyclical sense.) Whatever the hebrews of Moses' time may have understood back in the wilderness, the writer of Numbers implies that it was Yahweh who healed, not the bronze serpent itself. Many centuries later, the Book of Wisdom would be much more insistent about this, forbidding any magical or superstitious interpretation of the incident: the people were saved not by what they looked at, but by God the universal savior (Ws 16:5-7).

It is this curious story that John evokes in Jesus' words to Nicodemus about the son of man being "lifted up." The same idea is brought back several chapters later when Jesus tells the unbelieving jews, "When you have lifted up the son of man, then you will know that I am He" (Jn 8:28). John's intention is clear; he wants his reader to identify the power of Yahweh (He Who Is, the divine name revealed to Moses) with the cross of Jesus. The image is fully clarified when, at the end of John's Book of Signs, Jesus explains that "when I am lifted up from the earth, I shall draw all men to myself" (Jn 12:32). These words, John adds, describe the kind of *death* Jesus was going to die.

There is no ascension story in John. For him, Jesus' only journey to the Father is the crucifixion. Jesus' return to the Father *is* the cross, which is at once his humiliation and his exaltation. For John, the process of man's salvation is a "coming down" and a "going up."[7] The process is carried out in Jesus, the word made flesh, who suffers rejection and indignity at the hands of men. But the lowest step in his "coming down," his crucifixion, is also his "going up," his being "lifted up," his exaltation, his return to the Father. The cross is thus an event in two worlds. In the temporal and historical order, Jesus laid down his life for his friends; in the transempirical order, Jesus' self-oblation is accepted by the Father and becomes an event of divine and eternal value. That is, it becomes an event of ultimate *human* value. For anyone who believes in the cross, no distinction need be made anymore between divine and human values. In Jesus, God's world and our own are decisively joined. It is this junction that constitutes a new chapter in the religious experience of mankind. To speak of Jesus as the "god-man" is a very inadequate way of putting this, because it hyphenates what someone like John presents as a union. Much of our inherited religious language implies a kind of opposition between the human and the divine in Jesus; insofar as we create such an opposition in our minds, or attempt to juggle and combine divinity and humanity as separate components, we are doing a poor job of understanding the core of our christian faith.

What the writer of the fourth gospel has done, therefore, is to take a piece of ancient symbolism, the lifting up of a sacred object, and use it to convey the meaning of the death of Jesus. We move once again from fertility cult, through the hebrew realization that it is not objects but Yahweh who saves, to the christian experience that the salvation promised by Yahweh is to be recognized finally in the person of Jesus and in his death. This new stage of religious understanding is reinforced by John's presentation of the crucifixion scene itself. A soldier pierces the side of Jesus, and from his side flow blood and water (Jn 19:31-37). The author emphasizes this detail, arguing against those who were saying that Jesus did not really die, that he was a god who played at being a man, dropping the curtain on the last act and returning to his divine state at the moment of apparent "death." (Recall the episode from the apocryphal *Acts of John* mentioned in chapter 1, where the real Jesus explains the meaning of the cross to the apostle John while the sham Jesus is finishing the show on the cross.)

But there is much more than John's insistence on the actuality of Jesus' death, given the symbolism developed earlier in the gospel. From the physical fact of Jesus' death, the author moves us again to the meaning of that death. In chapter 6, Jesus had spoken of his flesh as real food, his blood as real drink. With his account of Jesus' death, John now makes it clear how Jesus' personal sacrifice—the giving of his body and the outpouring of his blood—could be identified with the eucharistic signs. In the same way, in chapter 7, Jesus had spoken of satisfying the thirst of all who would come to him. John there made one of his third-person editorial remarks, speaking of the "fountain of living water" that was to pour from Jesus' breast, water associated with his glorification and the spirit that was to be given (Jn 7:38-39). With the cross, that water is now given, and along with it the spirit that gives life. In typical johannine fashion, the words referring to the moment of Jesus' death carry a double meaning—a physical meaning and a theological one, very much like the play on words between "running" water and "living" water in the conversation with the samaritan woman. The greek of John 19:30 at the empirical level means simply "he gave up the spirit," he expired, he died. At the symbolic level, the level of human and divine meaning, the same words mean "he gave the Spirit."

John's picture of the crucifixion therefore suggests the following equation:

$$\begin{array}{ccccccccc} \text{Jesus'} \\ \text{death} \end{array} = \begin{array}{c} \text{his glori-} \\ \text{fication} \end{array} = \begin{array}{c} \text{the gift} \\ \text{of living} \\ \text{water} \end{array} = \begin{array}{c} \text{the gift} \\ \text{of his} \\ \text{flesh and} \\ \text{blood} \end{array} = \begin{array}{c} \text{the outpour-} \\ \text{ing of the} \\ \text{Spirit} \end{array}$$

What are we to make of this plethora of symbolism, where Jesus' exaltation (indeed his resurrection) and ascension and even the gift of the Spirit seem to be all wrapped up with the event of the cross itself? We are not used to putting such weight on the single event of the crucifixion. We tend to think not with John's mind but with the mind of *Luke*, because it is Luke's symbolism that has been incorporated into the liturgical cycle. The first chapters of the Acts of the Apostles (the second part of Luke's work) contain the familiar ascension and pentecost stories: forty days after the resurrection a "cloud takes Jesus from their sight," and ten days later the tongues of fire came to rest on the heads of the disciples. This is Luke's way of telling about the easter experiences of the first disciples and the birth of the church that resulted from this experience. Luke gives dates, a local habitation and a name, to what went on among the first disciples of Jesus. He is the only New Testament writer to "historicize" the easter experience in quite this detailed way. It was only natural, as christianity gradually became interested in structuring the time of the year according to the events of Jesus' life, that the liturgy should pick up Luke's symbolism. It provided a handy ready-made scheme for an "easter season."

A number of points should be kept in mind here. The original christian "feast" was the Lord's day, *dies dominica*, sunday, the weekly celebration of the death and resurrection of Jesus. It took several centuries for series of special feasts and liturgical seasons to develop. That development took place because of man's radical need to give meaning to the passage of time. But there is a danger to be avoided here. If Luke's way of historicizing the experiences of the early church is combined with a materialistic view of Jesus' life after death (the horizontal-line mentality I described earlier), one is liable to fragment the easter experience in an artificial way. Easter Sunday, Ascension Thursday, and Pentecost Sunday are not *historical dates* in the modern sense of the term, like the Fourth of July. The experiences of death, life, and the entry of the Spirit of God into our lives are a composite experience which is played out differently in the history of each of our different individual lives. Luke's scheme structures the experience of the early church. The liturgy picks up that scheme to remind us of the process that should be going on in our lives and to identify our worship—which celebrates what should be going on in our lives—with the total process of death and resurrection.

John himself eventually goes on to tell of the easter event. But he does it quite differently from Luke-Acts. The gift of the Spirit, for example, is given by Jesus himself on the evening of the resurrection. "Receive the Holy Spirit; for those whose sins you forgive, they are forgiven" (Jn 20:22-23). In his resurrection stories John, like the other evangelists, is dealing with the disciples' own experience of the risen Lord, and the effect of that experience on their lives. The stories talk about *their* experience of *him*, not *his own* experience of the new creation. (This should again warn us not to read the resurrection stories as stories about life after death.)

The story of the cross, on the other hand, as John tells it, is the story of Jesus' own experience; and John does not want the story of easter and its sequel—the story of *our* experience—to break loose from the cross. *Prior to* any accounts of the disciples' reaction to and realization of Jesus' glorification and union with the Father, John insists on the cross as the event which contains that glorification and everything which would flow from it, including the outpouring of the Spirit. Good Friday, as John presents it, is Jesus' feast day, the day of his exaltation. Easter and pentecost are *our* feasts, engaging every man's response, in the history of his own life, to the death of the man Jesus.

* * *

I have been trying to come at John's theme of the cross from many directions, in order to emphasize that christian faith—and any sacramental celebration of it—is rooted in the death of a man and what we make of that death. At our eucharists today, we are tempted to amend Paul's words to read "Whenever we eat this bread and drink this cup we proclaim the death *and resurrection* of the Lord," or some addition to that effect. The addition (which Paul, that great apostle of the resurrection, thought it unnecessary to make) shows our tendency to create a tension between Good Friday and Easter Sunday. Perhaps the life-after-death syndrome comes into play here. The fact is that in proclaiming the death of the Lord we are also proclaiming his exaltation, because the kind of life we call "resurrection" comes only out of death. That is the point which is so hard to appreciate. There is something in us that makes us want to restrict the meaning of the cross to physical death; and this makes the resurrection simply an *after*life.

What kind of life comes out of physical death? Obviously we have no idea, and no one has returned from the grave to describe it to us —not even Jesus. But if death means suffering and conflict and the kind of death to self we have to go through in order to grow as human beings, then we have (or should have) some experience of what life out of death is. The trouble is, we can never define that life in advance. Every such experience is unique and provides us with new answers. And it is within such experiences that we discover the meaning of the resurrection and touch upon "resurrected life."

As John sees it, the orders of flesh and spirit are united in the event of the cross, and the tension between them is overcome. That is, *Jesus* overcame the tension. *We* still experience it. This is evident in the way we *see* things: we have not yet integrated the apparent and the real, the empirical world and the world of values, first- and second-level questioning. (As I mentioned earlier, we also project our perceptions of tension between the divine world and the human world onto our understanding of the humanity and divinity of Jesus. The problem here is in our heads, not in the reality of Jesus.) The tension is evident in the way we *do* things: the struggle between flesh and spirit, the law of our members and the law of the spirit of life in Christ, goes on constantly in our behavior. Jesus' being "lifted up" is God's pledge that integration, wholeness, is possible. And so the christian is called to identify with the process that was carried out in Jesus on behalf of mankind.

Identification with the process begins in baptism. As Paul puts it (Rom 6:4), when we went into the water, we went into the tomb with Christ Jesus and joined him in death. (Our practice of pouring water at baptism "speaks" far less eloquently than the original ritual.) Paul does *not* add that emergence from the water symbolizes resurrection to a new life. The church fathers later expanded Paul's baptismal symbolism. For Paul himself, it was sufficient that baptism be conceived as identification with the *death* of Christ. For him, identification with the resurrection comes *gradually*, as the christian lives out the death to sin symbolized in the baptismal rite. This connection between the cross, baptism, and christian living is beautifully expressed by Leo the Great, a fifth-century church father, who sees the sign of the cross at the center of the christian life:

The process of suffering, dying, and rising again with Christ begins with the mystery of rebirth itself, when death to sin is life for one who is born anew. . . . Those whom the font had taken into its womb as old creatures, the baptismal waters now bring into the world as new beings. But we must still carry out in our behavior what was celebrated in the sacrament. Those who are born of the Holy Spirit cannot control what remains of this world in their bodies unless they take up their cross. . . . The christian, then, must take his stand on Calvary where Christ has brought him. He should direct all his steps to the place where he knows his salvation is to be found. For the Lord's passion is prolonged until the end of time. Just as it is he who is honored and loved in his saints, he who is fed and clothed in the poor, so it is he who suffers in all those who undergo hardship for justice' sake.[8]

A later age would discuss the efficacy of the sacraments in one context and the principles of christian morality in another. In so doing, it forgot the theological profundity of imagery like that used by Leo and Paul.

Now how are we to express the connection between the *eucharist* and the cross? Put in its simplest terms, the eucharist celebrates the cross. But so does baptism, and so do all our sacramental rituals. Many kinds of language have been used to express the uniqueness of the eucharist as the central act of christian worship: the mass is a "sacrifice," it is an action that "renews" or "re-enacts" the saving act of Calvary. Some of this language has proved extremely detrimental, to the point of dividing the christian church at the time of the reformation. In order to get behind these different statements and lay a groundwork for evaluating them, I would propose a frame of reference suggested by the mind of John:

If the cross is a true sign of life and a true junction of flesh and spirit, then what the eucharist says is true and real. The cross *is* what it signifies: Jesus' death *is* his glorification. The eucharistic bread and wine *are* what they signify: they *are* the body and blood of Christ. The same way of speaking, the same level of perceiving and understanding, is involved in both cases. The statement about the bread and wine is not true on the physical plane, any more than Jesus is physical light for the blind, physical bread for the hungry, or physical life for the dead. In their physical selves the bread and wine are *not* the body and blood of Christ, any more than the cross in its physical self is anything more than the death of a man. But the death of Jesus is *more* than its physical self; the bread and wine say more than their mere physical selves. For we are talking about the humanly real, not merely what is empirically real.

At that second level of perception, christian faith sees that the event of the cross brought about a union between God and man. The Father accepted Jesus' total gift of himself, and this we believe constituted a definitive relationship between God and man. This is the "efficacy" of the cross. Celebrating the eucharist brings about a union between God and ourselves, but only in proportion to our response: the Father accepts *our* self-gift insofar as we give it. This is the "efficacy" of the eucharist.

The cross is, for Jesus, a sacrament of union with God. The eucharist is, for us, the sacrament of a union which has not been fully accomplished. Jesus' historical life ended in union with the Father. Our historical lives are meant to end in the same union. But as we work out our historical lives, we are to serve and heal, unify and reconcile as Jesus did. Our eucharist is a covenanted sign that union with God is possible, that the spirit of God is at work in us as in Jesus, and that our own efforts at healing and reconciliation will not be in vain.

On the cross, one man died to "gather together in unity the scattered children of God" (Jn 11:52). In the eucharist, there is bread broken, a cup of wine shared. Bread made one, harvested from scattered grains on the hillside, bread which tells of a body given for the life of the world. Wine made from grapes taken off the branches of the vine, he the vine, we the branches. Anyone who proclaims Jesus' death by eating the bread and sharing the cup commits himself to the work of unity, to the work of making a body.

The thing which becomes a symbol retains its original form and its original content. It does not become, so to speak, an empty shell into which another content is poured; in itself, through its own existence, it makes another reality transparent which cannot appear in any other form.[9]

Those words of a modern jewish writer bear re-reading, particularly when we are tempted to make of the finite something other than what it is. Think of the cross. Then think of the eucharist which celebrates the cross. They are two "things," an event and a ritual action which have become symbolic and therefore divinely and humanly *real* to us, without becoming anything more than what they are: the death of a man, a piece of bread, a cup of wine. The death of that man, without becoming anything other than what it empirically is, says life. And the bread and wine, without becoming empty shells into which another content needs to be poured, are our way of sinking our teeth into the mystery of the cross.

Symbol Upon Symbol

A la recherche du temps perdu. A few pages of nostalgia for old and not-so-old catholics.

The time was when the big hurdle for the budding altar boy to overcome, before he could graduate to service at the altar, was memorization of the latin prayers. *Et cum spiritu tuo* and the like were of course easy. But for some reason the answer to the *Orate fratres* was a tough one; the end of the *Suscipiat* was a real tongue-twister for a ten-year-old: *ad utilitatem quoque nostram totiusque ecclesiae suae sanctae.* Still, the priest would wait for you to finish that one; and in any case, you started reciting it while he was still saying the rest of the *Orate fratres.* The prayers at the foot of the altar were much more of a challenge, where you had to dialogue the verses of Psalm 42 with the priest. In those days you judged the quality of celebrants on how much time they'd give you to squeeze in the *Quia tu es Deus fortitudo mea*'s and *Spera in Deo quoniam adhuc*'s. Some would never wait for you; they'd even cut you off in the middle of the *Confiteor*. You were really a seasoned server when you could get all the prayers in without skipping anything, no matter how fast the priest went or how loud the music was (a high mass complicated things). This gave you even more status than being able to carry the missal from the epistle side to the gospel side without looking as though the thing was too heavy for you, and without tripping on your cassock as you genuflected at the bottom step. (The good priests were the ones who gave you a nice clear hand-signal to let you know they had finished the epistle.)

But in any case you got plenty of practice with the *Confiteor* because you recited it twice at every mass—at the beginning and again before communion. For the most part, anyway. Before you started the *Confiteor* at communion you had to look out into the congregation (that was a big moment which could be carried off with varying degrees of ostentation) to see if anyone was actually coming to communion. Rarely were there any communions at funerals or weddings, and sometimes not at the sunday noon mass. The early risers catching a late mass had eaten breakfast, and the late risers had undoubtedly eaten or drunk something after midnight (besides, just laughing at a dirty joke at that party the night before was enough to keep you from communion). It was at the late mass, too, that many more people left before the end of the mass (you fulfilled your obligation by staying for the priest's communion). But you had to get out before the priest turned around, came down the altar steps and began the prayers for the conversion of Russia. Maybe staying for these prayers, once you were caught, had something to do not so much with poor Russia but with the fact that the prayers after mass were, after all, the only prayers recited by the congregation.

During the 1950's liturgists and theologians were talking about the possibility of changes in the mass. Momentum was given to these discussions by the revision of the holy week ceremonies which began to take place in the mid-fifties. The new order for these services (simpler ceremonies, restoration of the easter vigil) made it clear that the Roman Missal, whose regulations had been left quite untouched since 1570, was not sacrosanct. At a liturgical conference at Assisi in 1956, many bishops recommended use of the vernacular at mass; at least one urged that the eucharistic fast be reduced to three hours for morning masses, as had already been done for certain evening masses. The communion fast was in fact changed by Pius XII in April 1957: three hours for solid foods, one hour for liquids, and water no longer broke the fast. But the thought of any vernacular at mass was a hard pill for many to swallow. One of John XXIII's first official acts was to issue an encyclical reaffirming the importance of latin and insisting on its use in seminary lectures. Latin was a universal language, many argued, and use of the vernacular at mass would lead to nationalism and isolationism; it would prevent the spread of catholic worship and of the universal message of Christ.[1]

Then Pope John called his council, but few people thought much would come of it. Cardinal Tardini, the Vatican secretary of state, summed up the attitude of many when he said, "It will not last long; we shall already be agreed on many things by the time the council opens."[2] He also added that there would be no discussion on reform of the liturgical calendar. In 1960, not long after Tardini's statement and fully two years before the first session of the council, Rome issued a substantial reform of the calendar. The complex rankings of feasts (the old doubles of the first or second class, double majors, semidoubles, and all that) were simplified, many vigils and octaves and complicated commemorations were dropped, and "high" and "low" mass gave way to more flexible norms for "sung" and "simple" masses. Such reforms were a great relief for many priests, organists and choirmasters who had never managed to figure out the old system anyway. What the faithful in the pews noticed was that the *Confiteor* before communion had been dropped. Maybe Tardini and others thought this would take care of liturgical reform, and the council wouldn't have to bother with it.

The bishops of course thought otherwise. Their first decree, issued late in 1963, was the *Constitution on the Sacred Liturgy*, a broad plan for liturgical reform which was to be implemented in the years to come.

Dialogue masses (in latin) and various other forms of congregational participation had already begun to spread more widely in the early 1960's. A really up-to-date congregation knew how to sing not only the latin responses but even a few chant masses. The only official liturgical change between 1960 and 1964 came when, in 1962, Pope John inserted Saint Joseph's name into the list of saints in the canon of the mass. Archbishop Grimshaw of Birmingham felt that this bold move was "more than one had dared to hope for." (It was later noted, in a source I no longer recall, that this happened shortly after Cardinal Ottaviani had told the council that no matter what liturgical changes the fathers were to make, the venerable roman canon, unchanged for well over a thousand years, must surely remain untouched. The manner of Pope John's response—if that is what it was—was not out of character.)

In April 1964, catholics had to start changing their communion habits, answering *amen* to the priest's words, *corpus Christi*. One actually had to *say* something before sticking out one's tongue to receive the host (many people, until they got the new procedure down pat, would get nervous and snap at the host). But by the end of the year the priest was saying "The body of Christ," and one could answer "aay-men" instead of "ah-men." For on the first sunday of advent 1964, several weeks after Lyndon Johnson defeated Barry Goldwater in a landslide election, american catholics went to church and faced their first official half-english half-latin mass.

There was much shuffling of papers as the congregation read prayers and responses in english, while the priest shifted back to latin for the orations, the canon, and all prayers recited by himself alone. No one had to learn english responses to Psalm 42, which was dropped from the prayers at the foot of the altar, along with the last gospel and the prayers after mass. One could set the papers aside at the epistle and gospel (unless there was a poor reader) and at the Our Father (unless some ambitious liturgist was trying to get you to sing it). It would be at least another six or seven years before the average parish had to cope with the greeting of peace. But in any case, for all the distraction, you could at least come to church and receive communion, even at an early mass, with a good breakfast under your belt. In November 1964, Pope Paul had reduced the eucharistic fast to one hour.

There was much left to be desired here. Everyone sensed that the mixture of languages was a compromise, an interim measure—and a clumsy one at that. Even more basic was the difficulty a great many people experienced in shifting from mass as private devotion to mass as communal expression. Why couldn't everyone "follow the mass" in their own private way, using their missals as they always had? In 1964, "some of the traditionalists among the clergy are beginning to wonder just how far 'togetherness' and 'participation' can lead us. It appears that some of the scholars will not be content until the laity are breathing down our necks at Mass and getting underfoot at the Lavabo."[3]

Altars were being turned around by this time. For some this meant embarrassment or self-consciousness at finding oneself "staring directly into the eyes of the priest."[4] Nor did many priests find it easy actually to *look* at people when greeting them "The Lord be with you." The ingrained habits of years had to be broken. A still more difficult re-programing of rubrical automatisms was called for in May of 1967, when a roman instruction eliminated numerous genuflections, altar-kissings, signs of the cross over the offerings, and the need to keep thumbs and forefingers joined after the consecration. The same month brought permission, at long last, for the latin canon to be recited aloud, and for vernacular translations of the canon to be prepared. (The avant-garde meanwhile, not content with

the roman canon, were actually asking for new eucharistic prayers.)
Saturday evening masses were officially approved, along with the
practice of receiving communion standing. (What will become of our
marble altar rail?) Experimental weekday lectionaries had been in
use for awhile in many places, and the daily mass-goer no longer had
to listen to the parable of the wise and foolish virgins three times a
week.

The forms and formulas of the old Roman Missal were no longer
sacred. But using anything other than official translations and approved formulas still seemed quite daring in the late sixties. Celebrations done in a style which has now become normal and accepted,
even in parish churches, were in those days known as "underground"
liturgies. Helicon Press in 1968 brought out a little volume called
The Underground Mass Book, containing such shocking things as alternative eucharistic prayers, guitar hymns, and readings on social or
human concerns excerpted from contemporary writers. Meanwhile,
back at the parish church, ordinary sunday mass-goers were coping
with what seemed to be ever-changing translations of texts and new
hymns (What ever happened to our beautiful choir?), commentators
who were forever telling them to stand or sit or kneel, and pastors
who were reluctantly introducing the latest liturgical orders from the
bishop without very often explaining *why*.

In the spring of 1969 the new lectionary was completed, with its
three-year cycle of readings for sundays (it seemed priests would really have to learn to preach on scripture). At the same time the new
Order of Mass was published, giving a framework which would not
need substantial alteration in the near future. Plenty of room was left
for the addition of alternate prayers; and the rubrics frequently call
attention to the need for flexibility, adaptation and imagination.

Like a similar commission some four centuries earlier, the many
scholars who collaborated on these new liturgical books could hope
that their efforts would be "well accepted and approved by all sober,
peaceable, and truly conscientious sons of the church"; but of course

they could not expect "that men of factious, peevish, and perverse spirits should be satisfied with anything that can be done in this kind by any other than themselves" (from the preface to the anglican *Book of Common Prayer*, 1552). Since 1970, there has been some factiousness in parishes which have not yet learned that different styles of liturgy are needed for different people, and that not all the sunday masses need be alike. Then there are the perverse spirits who have been agitating for communion in the hand. And as for peevishness, it is evident to all that not even the best liturgical texts in the world can turn a bad celebrant into a good one, or a poorly planned and poorly executed liturgy into an exciting religious experience.

***

There are two sorts of symbolism connected with the eucharist. The first I would call *primary symbolism*. This includes the action of eating and drinking and whatever words and gestures articulate the *basic* meaning of the ritual meal. Then there is *secondary symbolism*, the symbolism built up around the inner primary core and intended to enhance it. Most of the elements in the ritual of the mass, taken by themselves, are secondary symbols. The primary meaning of the eucharist is given in the action of eating and drinking, and in whatever symbols are used to "word" the action, to say that in this particular action we are "proclaiming the death of the Lord until he comes." The christian tradition has at some point normally used a verbal formula in order to make the meaning of the action as explicit as possible. But the eucharistic ritual in fact contains many kinds of "language"—prayers, readings, processions, gestures, music, color, dress, the arrangement and design of the church building itself—all meant to point to and lead the participant into the primary core.

Taken singly, most of the ritual actions and symbols mentioned in my survey of liturgical reforms are arbitrary and not essential to the eucharist. But the *composite* is by no means arbitrary. Most of the liturgical changes over the last decade or so have had to do with eliminating secondary symbolism which detracted from the primary, and replacing it with ritual activity which would once again focus in on the core. Most of the symbolism of the old roman rite was calculated to call attention to the *objects* of bread and wine; the new rite stresses the *action* of a faith community which is celebrating its redemption. The latter is a much more difficult thing to handle than the former. When the ritual is built around the idea of action, and there is in fact little or no engagement on the part of the participants, the only result is dullness and wordiness. People who prefer to be spectators at a rite and priests who do not really want their parishioners engaged in the ritual would probably be better off with the old tridentine mass. It at least guaranteed, in the unfolding of the rite, a central object which one could focus on. I could contemplate and receive the body of Christ without having to come to terms—at least in church—with the body of Christ which is my neighbor next to me in the pew.

The importance of secondary symbolism and its influence on the primary is well summed up in the complete shift in attitude toward the tabernacle (the body of Christ "out there") which took place over a period of just ten years. Back in 1957 it was decreed that mass should be celebrated on the altar where the eucharist is reserved; a church having only one altar should have the tabernacle on that altar. In 1964 it was decreed that the eucharist *could* be reserved on the main altar *or* on a truly prominent side altar; masses could be celebrated facing the people *even with* a tabernacle on the altar. By 1967 the full circle was turned: the tabernacle should *not* be on the eucharistic altar; in fact, it should ideally be placed not even in the sanctuary but in a chapel distinct from the central part of the church.[5]

Along with this development came the gradual disappearance of crosses standing on the altar. When altars were first turned around, it was felt that there must be a crucifix on the altar. Some church-goods stores even came out with crucifixes which had a corpus on either side of the cross, one facing the priest and the other facing the people. Historically, as Dix notes, the placing of anything whatsoever on the altar except the bread and cup for the eucharist was "entirely contrary to normal christian feeling" until around the ninth century. This included not just tabernacles and altar crosses but even candle-sticks, which were originally placed around or beside the altar but not upon it.[6]

Thus what we have seen over the last decade is a correction, by primary symbolism, of the secondary visual and even architectural dimension of eucharistic symbolism. The eucharist as object, a conception which became ritually supreme during the second millennium of christian history, had at last to bow to the eucharist as action.

The problem of benediction and the "cult of the real presence" obviously arises here. The catholic tradition will have to keep re-evaluating its practice in this area, just as it has gradually (and even rapidly) changed other secondary symbolism in line with a restored eucharistic theology. It would be foolish to condemn a ritual like benediction out of hand. Such condemnation would ignore the reality of history and the christian people's search for self-understanding in different eras and cultures. The practice of reserving the eucharist goes back to the earliest times, when the faithful would take eucharistic bread home with them to make their communion on mornings when there was no liturgy. The bread was also taken to those who were absent from the sunday liturgy. There is no historical or theological reason why the eucharist, when reserved in churches, should not be reserved in a setting of dignity and beauty. Trouble arises only when an elaborate cult gets built around the reserved sacrament, and that cult comes to detract from or virtually replace the eucharistic action.

Historically even such aberrations had their positive side. The protestant reformers rightly wanted to do away with the superstition and idolatry which had grown up around the sacrament of the altar. But as the history of the reformation churches unfolded, most of them all but lost the eucharist; the Lord's supper came to be celebrated only a few times a year. The eucharistic *action* was, in different ways, virtually lost to protestants and catholics alike. For all its distortions, the cult of the blessed sacrament did keep the eucharist alive as a primary christian sacrament, and one must be careful not to judge a ceremony like benediction too harshly. As for the future, I would only point out that a ritual like benediction involves secondary symbolism; if it is to be retained, it cannot be allowed to lose its roots in the primary meaning of the eucharist. This is not an easy thing to manage ritually and symbolically, as history has shown. And this may explain why benediction has entirely disappeared from the religious practice of many catholics who have learned to experience the eucharist as action. I suspect that the practical piety of the faithful will solve the problem of the cult of the real presence, just as that piety originally created the problem. The job of catechists and preachers is to help the faithful form their piety along the lines of a critically sound eucharistic theology.

The distinction between primary and secondary symbolism is extremely important for interpreting the eucharistic language we have inherited. Take the terms "real presence" and "consecration." These ideas will mean one thing when we are talking about sharing the bread and cup in memory of the Lord. The meaning will change, however, if it comes out of secondary symbolism, particularly the kind of secondary symbolism which led to the development of the object-mentality.

It is hard for us today to think of the "real presence" as anything but an objectified physical presence, because use of the expression and the meaning of "real" in that context has been so tied up historically with the eucharist as object. In recent years theologians have been emphasizing that Christ's eucharistic presence is a *personal* presence, a type of presence which is humanly much more "real" than mere physical presence. I can be physically present in a room with you without being personally present to you; indeed, I can be personally present to someone I love even when I am physically absent.[7]

Once we return to primary symbolism, the idea of the eucharistic "presence of Christ" basically becomes a way of symbolizing the connection between our action and the Lord whose victory it celebrates. Luke's story of the disciples at Emmaus is a good example of what the "real presence" means, prior to and apart from objectification of the eucharistic elements: the risen Lord is in the midst of his people, and he is recognized in the breaking of the bread (Lk 24:13-35). If this presence is what we call a mysterious presence, it is no less mysterious and no more objectifiable than the personal presence of you or me to someone we love. People can even *make* love without being present to each other. At the level of primary symbolism, the kind of presence of which the eucharist speaks cannot be laid out on a table, any more than you or I can nail down and take hold of what makes another personally present to us, least of all in intimacies like the act of love. We can say a great deal about what personal presence is *not*, but we can never objectify everything it *is*.

The notion of consecration is closely related to that of presence. One might ask the classic question, "What happens at the moment of consecration during mass?" Put this way, the question draws us back into the object-mentality, because what the question really means is, "What happens to the bread and wine when the words of institution are pronounced?" At the empirical level *nothing* happens to the bread and wine, as any chemical analysis would demonstrate. (Such an analysis was attempted, with no result, back in the nineteenth century; even so recently as the late 1950's there was a debate over the viability of interpreting the eucharistic "change" as a change in the arrangement of molecules, electrons, etc.[8]) The *sense* of the question about "consecration" has nothing to do with a magical moment involving an empirical transformation of elements. What then does the idea of consecration mean in connection with the eucharist?

Once again the gospel of John is helpful because it provides a primary core meaning for the idea, a meaning directly associated with the event of the cross. John uses two traditional liturgical terms to describe the work and mission of Jesus. Early in the gospel Jesus tells his disciples that his food is to do his Father's will and to "complete" his work (Jn 4:34); the works his Father has given him to "complete" testify that the Father has sent him (5:36). In the priestly prayer, which is uttered from the viewpoint of the crucifixion already having taken place, this work is declared as finally "completed" (17:4). The theme of completion is evoked once again in John's picture of the crucifixion. In Matthew and Mark, Jesus utters a "loud cry" before he dies (Mt 27:50, Mk 15:37). Luke makes that cry a prayer: "Father, into your hands I commend my spirit" (Lk 24:46, quoting Ps 31:5). John makes it a theological statement: "It is completed" (Jn 19:30). The expression gets its meaning from the themes mentioned earlier in the gospel.

But what is interesting is that the greek word used here *(telein)* also has a liturgical meaning. The word is quite extensively used in greek literature to refer to the performance and "completion" of a sacred rite; a "completed" person was one who was now consecrated to a god and initiated into his mysteries. It is not unlikely that the evangelist had this connotation in mind when he placed the word on Jesus' lips. For in the priestly prayer of Jesus, John uses a second liturgical term to describe Jesus' self-oblation: "For their sake I *consecrate* myself so that they too may be consecrated in truth" (17:19). What John is suggesting, therefore, is that Jesus' death is the completion of a sacred rite.[9] This symbolism goes hand in hand with what we saw in the last chapter. Just as Jesus' death changes the meaning of religious symbols like bread and light and water, so his death gives a new meaning to the ancient idea of ritual consecration and sacrifice.

If we follow John's lead and prescind from later historical and theological developments, the meaning of "consecration" becomes quite simple. The "moment of consecration" is the death of Jesus; what our eucharistic action does is to celebrate *that* moment. There is no need for any further moments of consecration except the ones that take place in our own hearts. The words of institution, along with other words used in the eucharistic ritual, articulate the meaning of our action. They affirm the connection between this action, this moment, and the moment of the cross. The narrative of the last supper acquired liturgical importance precisely because it *states* a meaning which was actually *given* in the event of the cross.

Even so, the institution narrative acquired its importance only gradually. There are very good historical indications that the account of the last supper did not become a regular part of christian eucharistic prayers until sometime during the second century. The earliest christians probably "worded" their eucharist with a series of thanksgivings modeled on the jewish thanksgiving prayers used at ritual meals. (See the prayer quoted at the beginning of chapter 3.) Specific reference to the last supper developed later, as christianity separated more and more from judaism and as the need developed to state the specifically christian meaning of the eucharistic meal.[10]

Paul gives an account of the last supper in 1 Corinthians 11. This was probably not a liturgical text, not a text used in the eucharistic action itself, but a piece of *catechism* to be learned and kept in mind during worship because it interprets what christians are doing when they gather for their ritual meal. If the christians at Corinth were actually *using* a narrative like this one in their gatherings, why should Paul have to remind them of it in such detail? They could forget their catechism, but it is most unlikely that Paul would have had to repeat a text which they heard every time they met for the breaking of the bread.[11] The first christians did what Jesus *did* at the last supper; they were not immediately concerned with what he *said*, even though they knew from their catechism what he said. Paul had to remind the corinthians of what he had taught them because they were forgetting the indissoluble connection between their meal and the death of Jesus, a connection Jesus had affirmed at the last supper.

The first christians, in short, did not think in terms of *words* of consecration. For them the eucharist was an *action* of consecration, because what the action bespoke was the consecration that took place on the cross. As for ritual words, the thanksgivings of the jewish ritual meal—repeated and further embellished with christian ideas—would initially have been quite sufficient, particularly in an era when the sharing of the bread and cup had not yet been separated from a larger meal.

In this connection I would again emphasize a point made in chapter 1, namely that a good many of the early christians knew little about the life of Jesus beyond the basic facts of his death and resurrection. Throughout the letters of Paul, which are our earliest christian documents and which antedate the written gospels, there is no concern with the historical ministry of Jesus. Candidates for baptism received instruction not on the historical life of Jesus but on the points that we find stressed throughout Paul's letters: Jesus' lordship, his redeeming death, the kind of conduct expected of a christian. But once the written gospels were formed, and particularly after they came into general circulation during the first half of the second century, a new trend began developing which would have great importance for christian worship. Dix emphasizes a point which is too easily forgotten by modern christians who have grown up with the gospels. We must not forget "the immense difference which the circulation of written gospels must have made to the way in which christians regarded the historical origin of their faith, and to the store they set by detailed allusions to it."[12]

As interest in the historical life of Jesus developed, accounts of the last supper would have become a more and more natural way of wording the eucharist. But the process did not stop with the mere addition of an institution narrative to a series of thanksgivings modeled on jewish practice. The church was also losing contact with its jewish origins, and this would necessarily affect its understanding of the eucharistic action. Following the jewish model, christians could recite a series of thanksgivings for the works of God and for the work of redemption wrought in the person of Jesus; and such prayer would have been seen as quite sufficient for expressing the new meaning of an old ritual, a ritual now done "in memory of me." But by the third century, this was no longer an adequate way of wording the eucharist. Looking at the texts of this era, we find that once the historical reference to the last supper had been introduced or elaborated, the eucharistic prayer came to acquire a new focus or center.[13] The focus was now the institution narrative and the material built around it, including invocation of the Holy Spirit to transform the bread and wine.

There is of course no reason why christian prayer should not have its own history, its own evolution; there is nothing sacrosanct about the forms of jewish prayer. But once again, if the origin of the eucharist and therefore its *primary* symbolism is tied up with a ritual meal and the relationship of that meal to the death of Jesus, then the *secondary* symbolism which is built into the surrounding rite must not be allowed to lose sight of these origins. The words of institution are by no means opposed to primary symbolism; on the contrary, they affirm it. But as the account of the last supper and the invocations surrounding it gradually became the *center* of the eucharistic prayer, *displacing* the original idea of thanksgiving (which was eventually confined largely to what we call the "preface"), there also developed a type of secondary symbolism which would become more and more troublesome.

Chapter 4 discussed the object-mentality which was the end result of this development. We should now see something of how this occurred. This is not the place for a history of the liturgy, which would have to pick up with the gradual separation of the eucharist as such from the agape or fellowship meal, and go on to detail the evolution of ceremonies through the centuries. I want to highlight only those developments which throw light on the eucharistic language and theological concepts we have inherited.

***

John's gospel evokes sacrificial imagery along with the many other ritual symbols to which the author sees a new meaning given by the death of Jesus. The Letter to the Hebrews, a late New Testament writing, picks up the same theme and develops it at length: the old animal sacrifices, which in any case were only provisionally effective, are now no longer effective at all, because the ultimate sacrifice, the decisive reconciliation between God and man, has taken place in Christ Jesus. The imagery of sacrifice, which originated in ancient rituals dealing with the death of a victim or the destruction of an offering, thus came to take its place alongside other symbols interpreting the death of Jesus—such as John's "lifting up," or his image of the seed dying in the ground in order to bring forth life in abundance. As I shall emphasize in the next chapters, the concept of sacrifice has no fixed meaning; it means different things at different stages of religious consciousness. But the concept evokes an action in which men and women have been engaged since the dawn of mankind, whatever they may have understood by the action. So it is that the language of "sacrifice" was destined to become a powerful tool for conveying the meaning of what Jesus did, what *his* "death and destruction" meant.

Since the eucharist celebrates the cross, it was only natural that imagery applied to the cross should eventually be applied to the eucharist. This happens very early, even before the end of the first century. The *Didache* calls the eucharist a sacrifice, and the *First Epistle of Clement* associates the eucharist with the cultic ideas of priesthood and sacrifice that had been applied to Jesus himself by the author of Hebrews.[14] Clement also insists on the old cultic distinction between priesthood and laity (this is the first extant document which uses the word "layman"). Ideas stemming from the wilderness sects may also have been operative here, at least in some churches, from the earliest days of christianity. Qumran's ritual meals of bread and wine were presided over by one called a "priest," and those meals substituted for the temple sacrifices conducted by priests whom the desert sects considered illegitimate.

Given the religious ideas that were in the air at the time, the application of old cultic and sacrificial imagery to the eucharist would have been a natural enough development, not in itself unfaithful to the meaning of the cross or the intention of Jesus. The distinction of roles in any sort of community is a sociological reality. The gospels make it clear enough that Jesus was opposed to *caste distinctions* based on roles (see Mt 23:1-12 for a strong statement of this). But it is equally clear that his followers would and did perform different functions within the community. It is one thing for different people to perform different functions within society; it is another thing (though unfortunately a very human thing) for a group to "sacralize" a person because of the role he or she plays. It is one thing to attach the very ancient idea of sacrifice to the eucharist as a means of interpreting this central act of christian worship. It is quite another thing to bring back the ritual forms and caste distinctions associated with the immolation of a sacrificial victim, and impose these forms on an action which is not in itself a sacrificial rite.

The last supper was not a sacrifice; it was a ritual meal at which Jesus declared the meaning of his impending death. His followers continued to gather for such a meal, and they would borrow from the language of sacrifice in order to interpret the meaning of that meal and its relationship to the cross. They would start running into trouble when the old sacrificial cultic activity began to reshape the ritual. At this point secondary symbolism—that is, the actions and procedures surrounding the concept of animal sacrifice—began running counter to the origin and intent of the eucharist.

Two very important theological developments greatly affected the evolution of ritual symbolism: the church's reaction to gnosticism, and the orthodox reaction to arianism. Chapter 1 talked about the gnostic tendency and its appearance in the earliest days of christianity. This tendency, the first heresy and the heresy that has never really ceased to threaten the christian message, wants to do away with the humanness of Jesus, his finiteness, and make him a god appearing in human form but not really subject to the finite human condition. Gnosticism disdained the world of flesh and matter; so the only body the son of God could have without contaminating himself was an apparent body.

In order to defend the doctrine of the incarnation, orthodoxy had to defend material creation itself. In the area of worship, this led to an increasing emphasis on the material elements of bread and wine, and the objects and exterior actions of the ritual.[15] Ancient sacrificial rites and the rites of the mystery cults provided a ready-made set of cultic ideas for carrying out this emphasis. Thus, at the end of the second century, Irenaeus would speak of the bread and wine as *offerings*.[16] A simple idea like this had far-reaching consequences. Formerly the bread and wine had simply been brought to the table; now they were not only brought but "offered to God." The preparation of the bread and cup became the "offertory." The act of worship which had been known mainly as the eucharist, the "thanksgiving," came more and more to be called the "offering" or the "sacrifice." Presiding celebrants became known as "priests." And the eucharistic table, which had never been important as an object, came to be seen as an "altar" because on it the victim was offered. Christians were once opposed to tables of stone, which suggested pagan sacrifices; by the middle ages, so thoroughly had sacrificial symbolism taken over that stone altars (or at least an altar stone) were formally required.

There were positive sides to this development. For example, along with the idea of the bread and wine as an offering made to God came the practice of bringing gifts to the altar. The symbolism here could be very rich, and it is retained in the blessing prayers of the new roman rite. The bread and wine, along with whatever other gifts are brought forward, are "the fruit of the earth and the work of human hands." Thus is the whole of creation, including our lives and our labor, offered to God the creator and goal of creation. But this aspect of sacrificial symbolism presupposes the engagement of the faithful in the eucharistic action. This activity was destined to diminish as a result of a second theological development, namely the orthodox reaction to arianism.

Arianism put Christ the Word in a platonic netherworld between God and man. Orthodoxy insisted that if Christ is to be the savior of mankind and the reconciliation between God and man, he must be thought of as one in substance with the Father. A century later emphasis would have to be put on his being equally one in substance with mankind. But in the meantime, throughout the fourth and fifth centuries, there was an increasing awe for the divinity of Christ and fear at approaching the holy table where his most sacred mysteries were celebrated. The language of fear and awe became common in sermons. Church architecture, ceremonial and liturgical prayers all emphasized Christ's distance from man (a curious reversal of the central meaning of the incarnation), and communion gradually ceased to be understood as an integral part of christian worship. The anti-arian development came during the centuries after christianity had become a legal religion, an event which brought about much adaptation to and influence from the culture at large. The church's liturgical symbolism may well have been influenced by the rites of the mystery religions, which stressed the secret and the awesome. There are strong overtones of this influence in the baptismal and eucharistic instructions of this era.[17]

The combined reactions to gnosticism and arianism cannot of course be isolated from the many other social and cultural factors which influenced christianity and its self-understanding during these five centuries. But the combination is significant. First came emphasis on the material elements of worship, and a much too facile accommodation of old cultic symbolism to the primary symbolism of eucharist, thanksgiving. But the elements were, so to speak, still in the hands of the faithful, who still had a place in the "offering of the sacrifice." Then came an emphasis on the sacredness of the act, which finally moved the objects and the activity surrounding them away from the faithful.

Eucharistic *theology*, as we read it in the church fathers, still had its roots in the biblical tradition and was often extremely rich. But the eucharistic *liturgy* and the liturgical practice (or non-practice) of the faithful was moving in another direction. The objectification of the bread and wine was not formalized until after the patristic era; as I mentioned in chapter 4, Radbert's ninth-century treatise is the first extant document which makes the eucharistic question a question about the bread and wine "out there" on the altar table. But the liturgical symbolism of the fourth and fifth centuries already contained a focus on objects, with an overlay of old cultic symbolism, which would later divide eucharistic theology in two: a theology of the real presence, and a theology of sacrifice which abstracted from the participation of anyone but that of the celebrant. Hearing bishops like Ambrose and Chrysostom complain about the large number of people who communicated only once or twice a year or never, one can guess that the eucharist had already become an object "out there" for a great many of the faithful long before theology adopted the same position.

But there is one extremely important factor in the patristic way of seeing material reality which continued to protect the eucharistic theology of this era. People were not yet in a position to distinguish the empirical question from the symbolic question. It was assumed that anything real was symbolic, that any object out there was a symbol of something hidden, something *more* real, something still to come. Since no distinction was made between the empirically "real" and the symbolically "real," we have to be careful how we interpret the "realistic" language of the church fathers.

In fourth- and fifth-century writers like Cyril of Jerusalem, Ambrose, Chrysostom and Theodore, there are a good many expressions referring to a change or transformation in the eucharistic elements, to something happening at the words of institution. Their language was most vivid, and that vividness extended to every detail of the rite.

Theodore of Mopsuestia, for example, wanted his flock to see the death and resurrection of Jesus played out in the eucharistic ritual. When the bread and wine are brought out, we are to imagine that Christ is being led out to his passion. Placing the offerings on the altar completes the representation of the passion, and "from now on we should consider that Christ has already undergone the passion and is now placed on the altar as if in a tomb." All of this takes place in silence because "when our Lord died, the disciples also withdrew for a while in a house in great recollection and fear." With such dispositions we watch what is being done because "at this moment Christ our Lord is to rise from the dead, proclaiming to all a share in his sublime blessings." At the invocation of the Holy Spirit, by whom Christ was once raised from the dead, the dead body of Jesus becomes his risen body. The bread is finally broken and given out in communion "just as our Lord shared himself out in his appearances, appearing to different people at different times, and finally to a great gathering. In this way everyone was able to come to him."[18]

We would hardly be inclined to carry secondary ritual symbolism quite this far (liturgical reform has done away with similar medieval interpretations of the roman rite). But we must also appreciate what Theodore is trying to do. He sees the connection between the eucharist and the cross, and he affirms it much more simply in other places. But he also exploits secondary sacrificial symbolism in order to relate the present to the past. Still more important for him is the future: the earthly liturgy, which re-enacts the past in the present, is also a symbol of the heavenly liturgy and the future existence that awaits the christian people. Eating the bread which is the Lord, "with great delight and joy and in strong hopes, we are led in this way to the greatness which through the resurrection we hope to experience with him in the world to come."[19]

Theodore therefore works his symbolism at three levels: the present action is related both to the past and to the future. All three levels are evoked in the following statement, a typical interpretation of primary meaning through secondary cultic symbolism:

In every place and at every time we continue to perform the commemoration of this same sacrifice; for as often as we eat this bread and drink this chalice, we proclaim our Lord's death until he comes. Every time, then, there is performed the liturgy of this awesome sacrifice, which is the clear image of the heavenly realities, we should imagine that we are in heaven. Faith enables us to picture in our minds the heavenly realities, as we remind ourselves that the same Christ who is in heaven, who died for us, rose again and ascended to heaven, is now being immolated under these symbols. So when faith enables our eyes to contemplate the commemoration that takes place now, we are brought again to see his death, resurrection and ascension, which have already taken place for our sake.[20]

Within the patristic context, this is a superb statement of the meaning of the eucharist. What distracts us today is the expanded imagery of sacrifice, for we no longer practice cultic sacrifices; at best we simply know of them historically, and at worst we associate them with some sort of magic. Kaesemann makes a significant point in asserting that if we have any concern for the clarity of the gospel and its intelligibility to the present generation, theological responsibility compels us to abandon the kind of sacrificial interpretation which began developing with the Letter to the Hebrews.[21]

But this should also warn us how to interpret patristic statements about what "happens" to the bread and wine at the words of institution. We have inherited the language of "change" in this connection, a language which does not mean to us what it meant to the church fathers. They do *not* shift from the symbolic to the empirical level (as we are inclined to do) when they make statements about the bread and wine "becoming" the body and blood. Their language of change and moment of change is radically symbolic, and indeed associated with *secondary* eucharistic symbolism. Such language does not appear historically—and I would maintain *could* not appear—until the cultic ideas of oblation and sacrifice had expanded into a dramatic rite surrounding the breaking of the bread.

Moreover, even after the language of change came into use, it was never isolated from the ceremony and applied to the bread and wine alone. What is said of the *participants* goes hand in hand with what is said of the *elements*. Leo the Great once used the easter passover theme to stress this connection. If our food and drink is the Lord himself, the important thing is that sharing this food "makes *us* 'pass over' into what we receive, so that everywhere we carry him with whom we are dead, buried and raised to life."[22] John Chrysostom is even more vivid. Through the food the Lord has given us, we become "members of his flesh and of his bones," we are "mixed into" that flesh, and he has "kneaded his body with ours."[23] This rather carnal symbolism might not appeal to the modern mind. But the point is that such symbolism must be taken right along with the fathers' language about change in the elements of bread and wine.

So long as secondary symbolism had not cut loose from the primary and become independent of it, such symbolism could reinforce the primary. The imagery of Leo and Chrysostom, for example, builds on the original pauline image of the body of Christ. When Paul warns the corinthians that they are eating and drinking their own condemnation because they have failed to "discern the body," he has several notions of "body" in mind. He is referring not just to the eucharist and the risen Lord, but above all to the *ecclesial* body of Christ which figures so prominently in Paul's writings. Much as Theodore sees the "sacrifice" of Christ in three dimensions—past, present and future—so the fathers see the "body of Christ" at the same three levels: the body of Jesus dead and raised up, the body of the church (head and members) as it is now, and the body of the

church as it is destined to become. All three bodies are signified by
and celebrated in the eucharistic action, which thus intersects
present, past and future.

Augustine explained it this way in one of his easter sermons: The
bread and wine which you see on the altar, sanctified through the
word of God, are the body and blood of Christ. If you receive wor-
thily, "you are what you have received." You are to "become bread,
that is, the body of Christ" because "in that bread you are taught
how you ought to value unity." The bread was made from many
grains ground together, mixed with water, baked with fire: you were
ground by your lenten penance, baptized with water, anointed with
the fire of the Holy Spirit. This "being what you have received" is
what Paul meant when he said that as the bread is one, so we
though many are one body. The eucharistic sacrifice is therefore "a
sign of what we are," because Christ "wished us also to be his sacrifice." This is why after the eucharistic prayer, after the "sanctifica-
tion of the sacrifice" is completed, we say the Lord's Prayer and
embrace one another with a sign of peace. Our hearts are to be with
our brothers, just as our lips have touched them. We then eat the
body of Christ. But is the body of Christ eaten? No, it is not consumed. The church of Christ, the members of Christ who are now
cleansed, will one day be crowned. So what is signified in the body
that is eaten will last eternally, even though it seems to pass.[24]

Augustine thus expands the original pauline "body of Christ" by
adding further liturgical symbols. He also brings in the idea of sacrifice, and he makes statements about the elements of bread and wine.
The primary pauline meaning, though expanded through secondary
symbolism, remains the same and is in fact reinforced. Augustine
cannot speak of the eucharistic body without speaking of the body
which is the church; the one does not make sense without the other.
Both together explicate the meaning of the historical body and blood
given for the forgiveness of sins: we are to seek unity, become one
just as the bread is one, in order one day to join our head where he
has gone.

Unfortunately the richness of this theology was not to be sustained. Secondary symbolism was also sacralizing the liturgical action itself, and the gradual removal of the faithful from any active part in the ceremony would eventually take its toll. During the last half of the first millennium, the meaning of "body" changed.[25] For as the faithful no longer saw themselves as an essential part of the eucharistic body, the *ecclesial* meaning of body was lost and an essential link was broken.

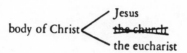

Theology would now have to find some other way to link the bread and wine with the historical body of Jesus or with a heavenly body. Heavily physical notions of real presence and sacrifice were the way found, and perhaps the only possible way.

As for the church, it was no longer seen as the fathers saw it: a eucharistic community, a faith community which receives and expresses its identity in the breaking of the bread. The church would now become primarily a legal body, a "perfect society" like the state, and juridical concepts would take over from the theological concepts that were lost. That is a very important point omitted in the nostalgic sketch at the beginning of this chapter. For along with the liturgical reform of the past decade has come more and more resistance to legalism in the church, and to any conception which would define the church mainly as a juridical body. Such resistance is eucharistically well founded.

7

From Magic to Mystery

IN OUR GROWTH as persons, our personal past history feeds into and shapes what we are now, what we have become. We might reject what we have done in the past, undergo a change of heart, follow a new course; but we never throw off our past. This is a truism, but it always bears repeating because it has profound consequences for us. If some important stage of personality development whereby a child learns how to relate to others is shortcircuited in infancy or adolescence, this will naturally affect how the person behaves as an adult. Everyone has short circuits of some kind, and the constant challenge for an adult is to understand what he has become, know what his resources are and what they are not, and how to rally the resources he possesses to meet his own and others' needs. The forgiveness of sin gets its religious importance from the fact that our past includes sinfulness which affects our present resources. The forgiveness of sin does not negate the past; it says that whatever the past may have been, this does not matter now. Go in peace, knowing that you are accepted by God not just despite your past but *with* your past.

The gospel message is a promise of a new future, a future that has broken in upon us in the person of Jesus. But a tension regarding the value of the past runs through all the New Testament writings: the "fulfillment" accomplished in Jesus involves continuity as well as discontinuity with what went before. The same tension occurs in our own experience of religious conversion, and it is what makes conversion difficult to live out. Conversion involves a change of heart, a determination to take a new direction. But that direction is taken from where one stands now, with everything his past has made him—happily and unhappily.

Our religious past tells us much about the present and about the stages we go through in interpreting the meaning of God, religion, and all the concepts tied up with religion. The development of religious practice and understanding from primitive times to our own is of course a complex story. For the purposes of this chapter, the story can be schematized into three stages:

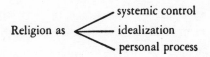

Each stage is exemplified both by the history of mankind's religious development, and by our individual personal development.

Religion as systemic control. The consciousness of primitive man was completely tied up with what goes on in the world of nature.[1] God, man and nature were all indistinct, undifferentiated in man's perception of reality. There was one single energy or animating principle pervading everything, a "soul-substance" forming a bond between man and animals and the crops. Animals and plants constitute man's food supply, and primitive man's religious concerns revolved around his search for food. His rituals were means of renewing and keeping "charged" the productivity and fertility of nature, and thus of enabling the community to preserve its life and to control the unpredictable.

Animals and plants shared the same sacred energy as man, and this made nature both helpful and dangerous. Men chose animals to be their guardian spirits because of the animal's particular characteristics (the eagle, the fox, the serpent, the bear). But this created problems because animals also provide food for man. Killing any animal whose soul-substance was tied up with the individual or the tribe called for an appropriate ritual. If animals were eaten, this had to be done with respect and reverence and due apology. Certain animals, especially those who were guardian spirits for the whole community, were too sacred to be eaten at all; and yet the inherent vitality or soul-substance of the guardian spirit had to be imbibed. This was often accomplished by a ritual sacrifice once each year. It is the giving of life rather than the taking of life that is important here. The outpouring of an animal's blood established a bond between man and what he saw as the supernatural order, between man and the mysterious uncontrollable world that provided him with food.

A more settled agricultural society gradually came to replace the tribes who lived by hunting alone (a development not unlike that of the famous american wild west, when the cowboys and cattlemen had to come to terms with the farmers who were putting up fences and roping off the land to protect their crops). With the dawn of agriculture, the meaning of religion did not change; man, God and nature were still quite undifferentiated. The food supply had to be maintained, and yet the soul-substance inherent in the crops made them dangerous unless they were approached with due solemnity and apology. The first-fruits of the earth had to be offered to the deity if they were to be eaten with impunity, and the life-giving energy contained in the newly reaped grain had to be ritually transmitted back to the earth, so that the guardian spirit would not take revenge and withdraw from the processes of growth.

We thus find primitive religion dealing with three basic elements: ritual *impulsion* of soul-substance into nature, so that animal and vegetative processes could remain charged with energy; ritual *expulsion* of any demonic forces which might interfere with these processes; and *control of taboos,* so that animals and crops could be eaten without injury either to the eater or to the productive forces of nature itself.

Systemic control reached an extreme in the practice of human sacrifice. The aztecs of Central America required a perpetual round of human sacrifices to enable the sun to continue its daily course across the heavens and thus ensure the fertility of the crops. The extraction of hearts from human victims who represented the gods kept the gods alive ("the god is dead, long live the god"). In this way the powers of nature were kept alive and enabled to perform their functions. African tribes, too, made human sacrifices in order to guarantee the fertility of the land; the ritual pouring of human blood into the ground invested the earth with vitality. Head-hunting and ritual cannibalism are related forms of systemic control. Soul-substance resides especially in the head, and the head-hunters' villages needed this vital energy in order to guarantee fertility. As for cannibalism, its purpose was to imbibe the soul-substance of the deceased in order to gain possession of his vital energy. Moreover, imbibing the vitality of the person whom one has killed forms a sacred bond which prevents the ghost of the dead man from doing any injury.

It is easy for modern man to write off such practices as gross and extreme, or at least hopelessly naive. This is to forget that at least some of these practices or variations on them are inevitable so long as God, nature and man remain undifferentiated in man's consciousness. A two- or three-year-old child's concept of God is not distinguishable from his concept of mother or father or whatever other people supply him with what he needs, reward him when he has done the right thing, and punish him when he has done something wrong.

As a child grows older, he is taught to pray. His first prayers are bound to deal with such things as asking for a bike for his birthday. For all of us, prayer begins as a means of systemic control. If I get my bike, I have said the right prayer or performed the right ritual; if I don't get it, something was lacking in my prayer. As I grow older, I realize that the correct performance of a ritual does not guarantee control over the system. But this realization comes only as I grow up. (And the old practices die hard: deep down I still feel that the right prayer will help my team win the championship game.) Morality does not come into play until much later. Prayer, worship, God and mother and dad are initially all wrapped up with reward for saying and doing the right thing, rejection or punishment for saying or doing what this mysterious pack of authorities defines as wrong. At this stage I don't yet understand "right and wrong." All I know is what brings me satisfaction and what does not. The fact that my big sister is going to have an expensive wedding next month, or that my little brother has fewer toys than I do—this does not yet matter to me and my birthday bike. These are negative forces that can be repulsed if only I perform the right ritual. The right prayer, the right words, the right behavior is bound to bring me what I want.

A child needs to go through the stage of magic, of not stepping on the cracks in the sidewalk, just as mankind had to work its way through attempts at ritual control of the fields and flocks. The difficulty is that adult man has shown himself quite capable of reverting to this stage where religion is basically systemic control. When this happens, faith in God is indistinguishable from faith in any of the systems that surround us. We all know about the american dream and the whole conception of America as the land of opportunity. "Anyone who does a good day's work will succeed." Straightforward magic is involved here, and it is little different from the primitive notion that the correct performance of a ritual will guarantee fertility and productivity.

When christians revert to this stage of religious awareness, the church is little different from any other system or institution. It has its own internal structure and method of government, but basically it reinforces the status quo and lets the devotee know that the systems do work and will continue to work. A "religious person" will here be defined largely as one who goes to church on sunday. But even for the so-called non-religious person, such things as a church wedding or the baptism of one's children will be most important. The church and what it says about God is indistinguishable *from* God, and indeed from the other processes of nature and society. So to ignore the most basic and socially accepted rituals of the church is to invite trouble. There may be no faith-commitment, no follow-up for the baby who was baptized or for the couple who exchanged their consent before a christian community instead of a justice of the peace. But to ignore such rituals would be to violate basic systems and thus to invite some unknown punishment.

Punishment is a very important concept at this stage of religious understanding, because the deity is here seen mainly as one who rewards and punishes. Salvation itself comes from Jesus' having won approval by paying the required pound of flesh to a wrathful God. Working out our own salvation means keeping the commandments and doing all the things that guarantee divine approval. Heaven and hell, ultimate approval or ultimate rejection, are strong preoccupations at this stage. Resurrection from the dead has no relation to the christian idea of life *out of* death; at this stage it will mean the ultimate *reward* of life *after* death. As for suffering, this is a punishment sent by God, a punishment which would not have come had there not been some violation of the system. This attitude is exemplified by Job's friends who argued that his sufferings were at the very least a punishment for sins he had committed unwittingly or out of weakness. It is exemplified by one of the characters in the film "The Emigrants" who understood the death of his only child as a punishment for his having been too attached to the child.

Thus, while God might be quite fully personified at this stage and not *consciously* identified with the powers of nature, he nevertheless remains quite undifferentiated from other systems. He is conceived as one who works according to the patterns of cause and effect observed in the natural world—like Leibniz's great Orderer who sees to it that sins carry their punishment with them "by the order of nature" or "by virtue of the mechanical structure of things." Orsy has given a good example of a similar conception, once common in catholic moral theology, which saw God operating according to rigid systems of reward and punishment more typical of primitive societies than of a modern civilized state. A young delinquent might be guilty of a serious crime, even murder, and yet no civilized state inflicts the death sentence on minors. Modern jurisprudence recognizes the fact that it takes time to become an adult who can be held fully responsible before the law. Yet classical moral theology was able to hold that once a child reaches the so-called age of reason, somewhere around seven years, he is capable of making a radical and fully responsible break with God. "To push this reasoning to its logical limits, such moral theology believes in a God who is willing to let the child, the work of his hands, be destroyed forever whenever this child, with full deliberation and knowledge, commits a mortal sin. No legal system with a grain of humanity would authorize or permit such sanction under any circumstance."[2]

Reversion to this early stage of religious consciousness is of course very common, and no culture or christian denomination is exempt from the phenomenon. Such reversion is even very tempting. We like recipes, definite precepts and rituals which will unfailingly produce a desired effect. This tendency is deeply imbedded in us, it provides a simple and clear explanation for everything, and it will remain with us so long as people are people. Christians, however, are not to indulge in the tendency. Jesus' scathing attack on the formalism and ritualism of the pharisees implies that once a higher stage of religious consciousness is reached, certain kinds of reversion are totally destructive. There is really no place here for a theology of the

Spirit or for "discernment of the Spirit" as a fundamental principle of the interior life. Religion as systemic control does not know what to do with that wind which "blows wherever it pleases; you cannot tell where it comes from or where it is going" (Jn 3:8). Christian tendencies to regress to the level of the systemic are probably one reason why the theology of the Spirit has remained relatively undeveloped in the christian tradition.

Religion as idealization. As human consciousness develops, man becomes more aware of his own interiority, of the life-energy and capacities within himself, energy which he is now able to distinguish more clearly from the forces surrounding him. This brings a change in religious understanding, one which is well exemplified by the "mystery cults" of the greco-roman world. Nature and the processes of nature still had to be conserved and promoted, but now the emphasis shifted to man himself. It is man who is to experience the full fertilizing powers of the Earth Mother, both in this life and in the hereafter. Immortality, the ultimate form of vitality, here emerges as a primary religious preoccupation.

The mystery cults were all based on the death and resurrection of a god-hero (a Dionysus or Orpheus or Osiris) who successfully struggled with the forces of evil and passed through the doors of death into immortal life. The experiences of these divine heroes were ritually re-enacted, and those who took part in the rites were assured of immortality in union with the deity. We possess few details about the way these rituals evolved historically or how they were carried out, but the main outlines are clear. As E. O. James summarizes it, they were "essentially *sacramental dramas* in the sense that they offered to all classes the promise of a blessed hereafter, and aimed at producing inner and mystical experiences calculated to quicken the religious life of the initiates through *outward and visible portrayals of the passion and triumph of a divine hero.*"[3]

The mystery cults thus "humanized" the ancient search for abundant life; nature's cycle of birth, death and rebirth was personalized and idealized in the person of the god-hero. There is an awareness here that the individual must move toward personal autonomy if he is to have any kind of self-determination and freedom. The possibility of such autonomy arises once man begins to realize that his own inner energies are not identified with the energies of the outside world, even though the energies remain related. This awareness opens the way to conception of a more personal deity. But the mystery cults do not reach full interiority. The emphasis is on contemplation of the ideal, not on personal engagement in the process that leads to the ideal. The sacred drama is contemplated from the outside, even with a great deal of emotion; but it is not yet lived from the inside.

This stage of religious development is as important for us personally as it was for mankind historically. We have to go through a process of identifying with heroes and contemplating ideals before we can appropriate ideals and make them our own. This of course is a basic human truth. There is no way our inner strengths and resources can be tested by the fire of experience unless we have first recognized, through idealization, *which* strengths and resources make the battle worthwhile. One of the very important functions of religion, therefore, is to present an ideal with which one can identify. (I should point out that throughout this chapter, whenever I talk about individual experience of the three stages, I am choosing my examples from christian and sometimes specifically catholic experience. The same principles apply outside christianity, but the symbolic forms will be different.)

At this stage one's concept of God changes, and the change is a very refreshing one from the God of systemic control, God the Enforcer. At this stage, as the contemporary christian experiences it, God is Love, and Jesus is the perfect lover of God and man. The "mythologized Christ" is very important here, that is, all of the comforting and inspiring imagery created around the risen Jesus: he is the new Adam, the new man, the new creation, the ideal toward which the entire cosmos is moving. I suspect it was no accident that the thought of Teilhard de Chardin, which developed this type of imagery and made it acceptable to contemporary man, appealed so strongly to catholics at a time when they were beginning to raise questions about formalism in the church. For many, Teilhard provided an exciting and even scientifically interesting means of working a transition from the stage of systemic control to idealization (and beyond; Teilhard by no means stops short with idealization).

At this level of experience worship is or can be a strongly emotional experience (some styles of worship are too incessantly dull to be able to exploit this stage of religious development). It is especially in the liturgy that the sacred drama is contemplated, a drama that is enhanced by all the colors and sights and sounds of the ritual action. The sacraments are no longer basically rites that must be performed to keep the systems working and to ward off possible evils. Now the sacraments become identification with Christ the hero, involvement in ideal love, the great "yes," an affirmation of commitment to the gospel way of life. *Commitment* is a very prominent idea at this stage, and it is enforced by the strong feelings that regularly accompany worship here. (But dark shadows loom up from time to time, suggesting that commitment *to* the gospel might not be quite the same thing as engagement *in* the gospel. Am I really committed if I don't always *feel* my commitment? How am I going to say yes, and what is my yes going to mean, if ever these positive, reinforcing feelings go away?)

This is a very necessary stage of religious development, and we all repeat it from time to time. We can easily recall the times in our lives when idealization and all the religious attitudes that go with it have been primary forces in our lives. We can also confirm from personal experience that a return to this stage is an entirely different thing from reverting to the first stage. The trouble is, this stage is so *comfortable* that we are reluctant to move on. A good many christians want the church to remain right here, and their wishes are granted by a great deal of preaching. Tell me about the love of Christ, and give me a reassuring message to help me through the coming week; but for heaven's sake don't make me shake hands with the fellow next to me whom I don't even know. Sermons are supposed to be about God, not about politics or social welfare. I have been redeemed by the cross, and I am committed to Christ who promises me immortality. This is what I want to hear, and a preacher has no business telling me how I ought to get involved in social movements. The church is the place I go to find God and hear about God's love for me, not about other people's problems.

That caricature is rather strong, but not untypical; for at this stage, religion is still very much an individual matter between me and God. Morality is no longer mainly obedience to the commandments for the sake of an eternal reward; sin is now seen as an offense against a loving God, and one tries to live up to the ideal that is contemplated. But there are other people out there, and they have not yet seriously entered my whole conception of religion. They have not yet become an integral part of my pursuit of a relationship with God. I will love my neighbor in order to *show* my love for God, but at this stage my neighbor is not part of my notion of a union with God. He has his union, I have mine.

The difficulty of moving beyond the stage of idealization is exemplified by people's reactions to the gospel stories about Jesus. Christians are terribly threatened by the fact (and it is a fact, not a theological theory) that the life of Jesus as it is narrated in the gospels follows the same pattern as countless other ancient stories about hero-gods: a miraculous but humble birth, a rapid rise to prominence, a triumphant struggle with the forces of evil, a betrayal and death and final vindication through some sort of immortality. As I tried to emphasize in chapter 1, what is unique about christianity is Jesus, not the way his story is told. This is precisely the point that cannot be grasped unless one goes beyond the stage of idealization and tries to find out what the stories are saying about human experience. The stories about Jesus are hero-stories recounting a sacred drama. The problem is whether the drama is going to be merely looked at or also lived. Many people are deeply moved by the story of Jonathan Livingston Seagull; but being able to *recognize* the marvels of taking flight and becoming free does not mean that one has thereby *done* it.

What is very easily forgotten at the stage of idealization is that when we are all wrapped up with looking at the ideal, we are also compromising with it. Or at least, compromise is all that is left for us if we never move beyond the stage of idealization. "Compromise" is the only concept we have for interpreting our failures to live up to an ideal we observe in our heroes, in *someone else*. But at the next stage, the ideal has to become a personal interior reality, not a beautiful something-outside-me but rather something which is beautiful because it has taken a unique shape *within me*. And the trick is that the ideal I manage to realize within me never looks at all like what I once thought it would look like. If one moves beyond idealization, there will be no need to compromise with an abstraction. There will only be the need to realize that one has much further to fly.

Religion as personal process. This is the stage where death and resurrection become an interior part of our personal histories, not just a process carried through on our behalf by someone else. The transition to this stage brings with it a new attitude toward suffering and conflict and the unexpected—or rather, it is in this stage that one painfully *acquires* a new attitude toward such experiences. This is illustrated by the story of Job, who refuses to accept his friends' arguments that suffering is a punishment from God or a mere call to repentance. Job emerges from his trial with no easy answers to the problem of suffering; in fact he has fewer answers than ever before. But he is now aware that the experience of suffering has deepened him and even changed the meaning of trust in God for him. The same point is stressed by the prophet Ezekiel, who moves far beyond the view that the nation's exile in Babylon is a punishment for sin;

he sees the nation's sufferings as an occasion for conversion, interior growth and a new self-understanding. At this stage of development, suffering is no longer a thing to be tolerated and, so far as possible, held at arm's length. Suffering now has to be dealt with, appropriated in an interior way and understood as a necessary part of becoming a person. One will therefore no longer be content with contemplating the fact that God is love. Now the *meaning* of a loving God has to be coped with, in the face of all the conflict that arises when we begin taking other people seriously as *other*.

Formerly, religion was largely a matter of my personal relationship with God; now other people become an integral part of my personal religion. Love of God and love of neighbor used to be fairly separate questions; now, terrifyingly, the one is all wrapped up with the other. The whole God-question comes up for grabs and one is forced to rethink the whole thing: Who is God? Where is he? Who is Jesus? At this stage death to self starts to become more than a notion. The process begins to take place, really and often painfully, as we come to terms with other persons as truly other. Grace and the risen life therefore acquire a new meaning, for it is at this stage that one begins to understand experientially and not just notionally the sense of life coming *out of* death.

There is strong resistance to entering this stage and living in it. The transition from systemic control to idealization is reasonably natural, and certainly comforting. But a firm line, difficult to cross, divides idealization from personal process, because now the sacred drama has to be lived and not just looked at. Peter wanted to pitch tents and prolong the experience of the transfiguration. "Rabbi, it is wonderful for us to be here." The disciples were already perplexed at Jesus' remark about his having to suffer and die; and after the transfiguration they began to discuss what "rising from the dead" could possibly mean (Mk 9:2-10). Like them and like Jesus himself, we have to find out, by dropping below the line and entering the personal process of death and resurrection.

systemic control

idealization

---

personal process

Above the line, the transfiguration and the comfort of the mythologized Christ is sufficient. Below the line, the experience of the man
Jesus becomes a pressing question. Why were all those inspiring
hero-stories told about him in the first place? Why was he given the
name that is above all names?

Above the line, one will be content to explain the divinity of
Christ by appealing to his pre-existence as the second person of the
blessed trinity. Below the line, this explanation of why Jesus is
proclaimed Lord becomes distant and unreal—as unreal as any other
explanation of things which appeals to a world we do *not* experience.

Above the line, the concepts of grace and resurrection are quite
reassuring in themselves; they are also generally indistinguishable
from the blessed immortality guaranteed by the mystery cults. At this
level one will normally be content with the explanation that such
things are "mysteries which we must accept on faith." Below the
line, any concept unrelated to concrete human experience loses its
content, and one will begin to question seriously any religious idea
that sounds suspiciously unreal or unrelated to the finite human condition.

Above the line, it is enough to know that Jesus died to save us
from our sins, and to be identified securely with that death through
baptism and occasional renewal of one's commitment. Below the
line, one has to work out the process of rising to new life by accepting responsibility for oneself as Jesus did.

Above the line, the "will of God" is something out there, something I can find by turning my gaze in the right direction. Below the
line, the will of God is a process, something which I discover only by

coming to terms with myself, who I am and what I have become, what my resources are and what they are not.

The institutional church is made up of people who live at every stage of religious development, and of people like you and me who are frightened at the thought of dropping below the line and living there. Institutions therefore do not drop below the line; people do. But if the gospel has been preached only as systemic control or at best idealization (often enough because people want it that way), religion will very often be abandoned as one moves into adulthood. The process of *human* development goes on as people (not all, but many) become socially and ethically concerned and engaged in "meeting the other." But religion is often abandoned in the process because it is no longer a viable interpretation of human experience; it has nothing to do with the process of becoming a person. The sacred drama, once so meaningful, slips away into another world; or rather, it never gets brought from that other world into *this* world. Jesus is in heaven with his glorified body and the heavenly liturgy goes on, but what is that to me? I am sorry, but all your talk and promises of immortality will not do anymore.

The feelings and emotions associated with the stage of idealization recede as one enters the stage of personal process, and the old images and symbols are no longer the comfort they used to be. With this stage's emphasis on interiorization, public worship will be abandoned unless it is seen as a social action, an action which expresses a communal quest for meaning and a communal coping with the process of suffering and growth. In short, at this stage the "body of Christ" becomes more than a sacred object to be contemplated. If it does not, and if preaching and liturgical practice have not restored the ecclesial meaning of the eucharistic body, this sacrament will be as irrelevant as the rest of religion. It will be just one more of those beautiful incense-clouded symbols which a mature adult looks back on with fond memories of the time when idealization worked.

Above the line, faith in Jesus is basically faith in an outsider. Below the line, one comes to know the Jesus in whom one believes.

Faith is now fully an assent to the presence of God in one's own *personal history,* and this assent is quite indistinguishable from hope. The faith and the hope is this: that to engage in the process that went on in Jesus is to know God and find union with God. At this stage one begins to understand the death-exaltation symbolism of John, and some of those wild statements of Paul which sound beautiful but make little sense at the stage of idealization: "The Spirit of God has made his home in you," and "if the Spirit of him who raised Jesus from the dead is living in you, then he who raised Jesus from the dead will give life to your own mortal bodies through his Spirit living in you" (Rom 8:9-11). Resurrected life is no longer some vague immortality or life after death, but the wholeness of life that comes *out of* death in any form. It is an integration of flesh and spirit, a type of life which we touch upon and discover in single experiences of death to self.

Christian ritual, particularly the eucharist, will be saying something quite new at this level—the only level where the idea of expectation and future hope makes fully human sense. Celebrating the eucharist once expressed commitment to an ideal; now it expresses a search for integration, the hope that such integration is personally possible, that my own history will lead to wholeness. Once the eucharist celebrated the drama of Jesus, not yet my own drama. Now it celebrates something of my own and proclaims a death I have begun to understand.

Christian worship celebrates the process that mystics like Saint John Eudes saw as necessary if we are to make any sense of that phrase we use so glibly: the "mysteries" of Christ's life.

Since your duty is to continue and fulfill in yourselves the life, virtues and actions of Jesus Christ on earth, so must you also prolong and fulfill, in yourself, the states and mysteries of Jesus, and frequently implore Jesus himself to consummate and accomplish them in you and in his whole church.

You cannot too often realize and reflect on the truth that the mysteries of the life of Christ have not yet reached their full perfection and complete-ness. Although they are perfect and complete in Christ's own person, they are not yet completed in you who are his members. . . . It is the plan of the son of God that his whole church should participate in and actually be, as it were, the continuation and extension of the mystery of his incarnation, birth, childhood, hidden life, public life of teaching and of labor, his pas-sion and his death, by the graces he desires to impart to you, and by the ef-fects he wishes to accomplish in you through these same mysteries. By this means, he desires to fulfill his mysteries in you.[4]

But such language, like all religious language however inspiring, can only lead us to the line where religion becomes personal process. The "mystery of Christ" can never be anything more than a beautiful and elaborate puzzle until the process is engaged in.

8

Sacrifice

THE IDEA OF SACRIFICE has been floating in and out of these pages, and it has not yet been dealt with adequately. It is a troublesome idea which complicated the history of the eucharistic ritual and eventually led to divisions in the western church. And yet we continue to speak of the "eucharistic sacrifice," of "altars" and "priests" and all the trappings of ancient sacrificial cults. What does the idea mean?

A few years back, catholic journals and newspapers and letters to the editor were putting the question this way: Is the mass a meal or is it a sacrifice? Much of the debate was prompted by the fact that the catholic tradition of recent centuries did not really possess a theology of the *eucharist*. There was, as I have noted in several contexts, a theology of the real presence and a theology of the sacrifice of the mass. But as the liturgical changes of the 1960's were introduced, it became painfully evident that the two theologies were inadequate for interpreting the developments that were taking place.

Protestant theology was in no better shape to deal with the idea of eucharist as sacrifice. Protestant positions on this idea had been formulated in reaction to medieval abuses, and the concept had virtually dropped out of their theological vocabulary. Ecumenism and the need to re-evaluate positions taken four centuries ago have made both sides deal with theological inadequacies and blind spots in their interpretations of the idea of sacrifice.[1]

In one sense the meal-sacrifice debate can be resolved quite simply. The concept of *meal* answers the question "What are we doing?" The eucharist is and always was a ritual meal; it was intended to be, but not always was in fact, a meal in which all the faithful share. The concept of *sacrifice* answers the question "What do we mean by what we are doing?" This meal proclaims the saving death of the Lord, the sacrificial act which reconciled man and God. So there is no need for any conflict between the two concepts.

But this solution is somewhat too neat. Chapter 6 pointed out some of the serious problems that developed as sacrificial symbolism was gradually worked into the eucharistic ritual, which was not in its origins a rite of blood sacrifice. It is all very well to say that the sacrifice of the mass is in every way the same as the sacrifice of Calvary, except that it is unbloody. This same idea brought with it (inevitably?) a whole package of secondary symbolism which eventually squeezed the laity out of the ritual action and quite thoroughly changed the shape of the eucharist. We are now in a position to remove the accretions of secondary cultic elements which are not natural to the eucharistic action. Much of this has in fact been done.

Hindsight tells us much about how christian worship and its symbolic forms *ought* to have developed. But if Jesus is new, and if in the breaking of the bread we are celebrating a new thing, we are also tied up with the old. The religious forms and symbols of the pre-christian era are part of our collective history. Our psyche continues to supply us with the past and with our most human roots, and there is simply no way for us to expect the future or reach for it apart from symbols we have inherited from our collective past. This is why it is and has been possible for christianity to make use of past religious *forms* without necessarily reverting to past religious *consciousness*.

A good example of this is the development of the liturgical year. For perhaps a century after the death of Jesus, sunday was the only christian feast. This was the Day of the Lord when the faithful met for worship, strongly aware that in breaking bread in memory of the risen Lord they were looking forward to that final Day when the new creation would be realized. During the first century there does not even seem to have been a feast of easter, that is, a time of the year which commemorated the historical event of Jesus' death and resurrection. The liturgical cycle was based on the week, not on the year. Four centuries later the picture looked quite different. Sunday retained its importance, of course; but there was now a fully developed cycle of feasts and seasons commemorating the events recounted in the New Testament. By the fifth century, in other words, the historical *past* had acquired an importance which it did not have for earlier christians.

Scholars have evaluated this development in different ways. There are dangers inherent here, some of which I have already mentioned. If one's only model for interpreting the easter event is the historical sequence known as Good Friday—Easter Sunday—Ascension Thursday, the resurrection of Jesus can easily come to mean simply life after death: he picked up with a glorified body where he left off with an ordinary body. The liturgical scheme, if it is treated as straightforward history, will also have little relationship to our own personal histories—to our own experiences of death, resurrected life and the coming of the Spirit into our lives.

Further problems arise if the idea of commemorating the *past* leads to a loss of the *future* dimension of the liturgy. The eucharistic action proclaims the death of the Lord "until he comes." It is a sacrament of union and reconciliation accomplished in Jesus, but not yet accomplished *in us*. If this orientation toward the future, this theme of expectation and hope is forgotten, christian worship simply becomes a matter of present and past. When this happens, the liturgical cycle draws us into an eternal repetition of events which, however meaningful and comforting they may be, really lead us nowhere. At christmas we think of how nice it is that there was at least one peaceful, peace-bringing event in history. We think of how nice it would be if there were more of the spirit of this beautiful season in the world, this season of good cheer and twenty-four-hour ceasefires. At easter we are reassured that Christ came out of the tomb, that spring is coming, that the lilies still bloom. Period. In this perspective the past reassures us and makes the present tolerable. As for the future, there will always be another christmas, another easter, an endless cycle to comfort us and give meaning to the passage of time, while we go on living pretty much as we always have.

This attitude toward christian worship, where it exists, is of course a complete reversion to primitive cyclical religion, where religious experience was completely undifferentiated from the cycle of nature, and where the cyclical re-enactment of sacred dramas made the "terror of history" tolerable. Primitive man found himself powerless against any kind of flood or famine or natural disaster, the misfortune of war or the injustice built into the rigid codes of ancient society. The regularity of sacred feasts and seasons enabled him to put up with these terrifying irregularities.[2] But *tolerating* suffering and conflict is not the same as *appropriating* suffering and conflict as a necessary part of the "personal process," the process of human and religious growth. Where interiority is lacking, the liturgical cycle commemorating the life, death and resurrection of Jesus is nothing more than idealization. It is a comforting story that enables one to hold the question of personal engagement in this process—the personal "terror of history"—at arm's length.

I keep repeating phrases like "when this happens" or "where this attitude exists." This does happen of course in the case of people for whom religion is mainly a sociological thing. It happens with those for whom religion and worship consecrate the status quo, the search for the good life, people who are disturbed by anything which upsets the present order of things or by anyone who challenges that order. Many church-goers are quite content with the present and the past. The liturgical cycle recreates the inspiring life of Jesus, and the mass re-enacts the beautiful saving act of Calvary. As for the future, it will surely be a magnification of the present, a divine reinforcement of the same cycle that enables assistant vice-presidents to become first vice-presidents and eventually presidents.

But anyone reading these pages already knows the many uses to which religion can be put. For all the distortion that is possible here, it is much too simplistic to say (as not a few scholars have said) that the idea of an annual liturgical cycle is merely a christian takeover of pagan feasts of sun-gods and nature-gods, for the sake of accommodation to the mentality of the age. Something far more basic is going on here. For one thing, christians live between the past and the future, between the coming of Jesus and the coming of Jesus. The symbolism of worship tries to express this—not always successfully, because any symbols which attempt to create an intersection between past, present and future are eminently subject to distortion in one direction or another. One need only think of the "real presence" where that presence is quite reduced to the *present* with little relation to the past *or* the future.

Despite all the distortions and formalism that always had to be corrected, the hebrews very naturally took over fertility rites and nature feasts, reinterpreting them in accord with their own religious experience. Christianity did the same thing in a different cultural context. What the hebrews did with mesopotamian and canaanite culture, christians did with the greco-roman culture. One liturgical scholar has observed that what is astonishing about the christian liturgical year is not that it developed so slowly, over a period of four or five centuries, but that it developed at all; for every celebration of the eucharist is a celebration of the life, death and resurrection of the Lord.[3] On the contrary, I think it would have been astonishing if christianity had *not* eventually restructured the time of the year and given a new meaning to the passage of time, however superficial that meaning might have become with the further passage of centuries. The psychological needs and religious insights of primitive man are not abolished by a new religious insight, even if the new experience transcends the old.

I have elaborated on the problem of the liturgical cycle at some length because this example shows things we need to watch for in evaluating the symbolism of blood sacrifice. Such symbolism is woven through the whole New Testament interpretation of the death of Jesus, and it was very naturally attached to the eucharist before the end of the first century. Now if problems eventually developed at the altar, what about the cross itself? What does it mean to call *the cross* a sacrifice, and how has this been understood?

There is no need to give a long list of New Testament passages which evoke the ancient world of ritual sacrifices. In addition to John's symbolism which we have looked at, there is Paul's and that of others. We are redeemed, bought back for God by the blood of Christ, paid for in the blood of the Lamb, redeemed in Christ Jesus who was appointed by God to sacrifice his life so as to win reconciliation for us. Here as elsewhere, numbness sets in because we have heard such words so often. But how are they to be understood? What is such imagery saying about the event of Calvary? The interesting thing is that the christian tradition has understood the atoning act of the cross at *all* of the levels of religious consciousness outlined in the last chapter.

Some of the church fathers developed interpretations in line with the negative force of ancient blood rituals, where blood was understood to ward off evil forces. According to this view, the offering made on Calvary satisfied the devil's rights; it was a ransom paid by the god-man to Satan in order to rescue the world from his clutches.

Other interpretations fell in line with the positive aspect of blood rituals, where the outpouring of a victim's blood kept the systems of
nature charged with vitality. In line with this view, Satan had no
rights, and mankind did not need to be "ransomed" from the devil;
it was the rights of God that were vindicated and "satisfied" on Calvary. The first interpretation runs through the theology of the patristic era, and the second is that of Anselm and many medieval scholas-
tics.

Both of these interpretations of the sacrifice of Calvary operate at
the level of systemic control. That is, a blood sacrifice performed by
a representative of the human race is needed in order to expiate
guilt, bring the cosmic system back into balance, and guarantee the
supply of vitality from God to man. The idea of "grace" here has
close affinities to the soul-substance of archaic religion, if one were
to push the "ransom" and "satisfaction" theories to their logical
conclusion. In this view, moreover, the redemption of mankind is
quite exclusively the activity of Jesus; there is a definite passivity on
the part of the christian. The various theories of vicarious substitution, in which Jesus is the god-man paying a debt owed by a guilty
race, opened the way to theological interpretations which would
place a wide gulf between the initiative of Jesus and the christian's
personal response to that initiative. Many aspects of the controversy
over faith versus good works flow from a rather systemic view of the
redemptive act of Christ.

Some of the church fathers resisted this line of interpretation.
Gregory of Nazianzus wrote that there was no satisfaction paid either to Satan *or* to God because there was no question of mankind's
being held captive. Gregory's explanation appeals to a very sophisticated concept of the divinity as something, someone, who is made
fully manifest in the man Jesus. "The Father accepts the sacrifice,
not because he demanded it or needed it, but because this was part
of the divine plan, since man had to be sanctified by the *humanity of
God*."[4] This line of interpretation was picked up at the beginning of

the scholastic era by Abelard, who saw the death of Jesus as the supreme manifestation of the love of God, not a ransom paid to Satan or a satisfaction of the divine anger. Thomas Aquinas followed the same line of thought.

With these thinkers we get beyond the more primitive idea of sacrifice. No vicarious substitution or ritual expiation for sin is needed in this latter view of the cross of Jesus. But note that such an interpretation does not in itself solve the problem of making the transition from idealization to personal process. The saving work of Jesus can still be simply contemplated as an ideal act of love for God, an act which saves us who remain quite passive and unengaged. Or on the other hand, the action of Jesus can be reflected on, interiorized, and become an act in which we ourselves become involved.

***

What then are we to make of the whole notion of sacrifice, with all its connotations of ancient blood rituals and all the varied interpretations to which the concept has led? Earlier I mentioned Kaesemann's suggestion that fidelity to the gospel message in our time might mean doing away with sacrificial interpretation in an age when people have no experience of the cult of sacrifice. This would certainly apply to secondary symbolism and the material trappings and social castes of the ancient cults: priests as sacred people, the laity as not-so-sacred people; altars and churches as divine places, streetcorners and homes as non-divine and secular places. But the basic symbolism of sacrifice has been written into christian self-understanding much too thoroughly to be written off by twentieth-century criticism, despite whatever distortions might have come out of this symbolism. Whatever one does with the *ritual accouterments* of sacrifice, the *conception* of sacrifice has to be dealt with. If sacrifice can mean, as it does mean in everyday parlance, everything from giving up candy for lent to doing something truly noteworthy for someone else, then we are inevitably going to *symbolize* this archetypal concept in our worship. The concept is not going to be detached very easily from the death of Jesus or from the eucharist simply because we are removed from the old order of blood sacrifices. The idea of sacrifice—the giving of life to promote and conserve life—remains in us in radical psychic forms.

James makes the interesting observation that where sacrificial symbolism ceases to operate "the associated religious order tends to disintegrate." At the time of the reformation, protestantism shifted the emphasis from the eucharist to the atonement, from the altar back to the cross. Eventually the idea of sacrifice disappeared almost totally except as a purely subjective offering of a pure heart. Any external symbolization of this offering, through the symbolism of sacrifice, came to be seen as unfaithful to reformation principles. James concludes that this break-up of the old ritual order was one of the most important causes of the modern collapse of institutional religion.[5] Whether or not one can put this much weight on sacrificial symbolism alone, it is certainly true that the fear of over-externalizing has often stripped protestant worship of all color and human feeling.

The problem lies not in *using* the symbols of sacrifice and altar and priesthood, but in *how* we use them. Understanding of the sacrificial idea will go hand in hand with one's understanding of salvation, resurrection, immortality, and the atoning act of Calvary itself. *All* of these concepts, as I have tried to emphasize, are understood differently at the different stages of religious consciousness—both historically and personally, both by catholics and by protestants.

If one reads the idea of sacrifice in a systemic way, priests will be magical people ordained to control our relationship with God the Enforcer, and endowed with the power to tell even God what to do —like Joyce's priest, who spoke of the power and authority "to make the great God of Heaven come down upon the altar and take the form of bread and wine." The idea of sacrifice changes at the stage of idealization; at that stage, sacrificial symbolism enhances contemplation of the sacred drama. The patristic elaboration of the symbols of sacrifice, discussed in chapter 6, took place under the influence of idealization, and the old roman rite inherited much of this emphasis. Finally, at the stage where religion becomes personal process, the understanding of sacrifice must become truly interior. Protestantism rejected sacrificial symbolism in the very good interests of interiorization; but this led to an unrealistic rejection of externals and of the very positive contributions of the stage of idealization. And if catholicism has sometimes reverted to the magical understanding and ritual formalism of the systemic stage, protestantism has also frequently returned to non-ritual aspects of that stage, where God is one who rigorously rewards and punishes and rigidly predestines. (*All* christians share reversions to stages of religious consciousness where none of us should be. The only way for us, the western church, to cut through our scandalous divisions is to admit where we have been, recognize that where we have been is human enough, and move on again to the death-resurrection process in which we are all supposed to be engaged.)

A thoroughly christian and interiorized notion of sacrifice is possible. As Augustine develops it in the *City of God,* sacrifice becomes a concept which expresses the whole meaning of christian interiority and its relation to worship. Augustine is aware that sacrifice has always been associated with the worship of God. But as we have learned from the prophets, God is not benefited by sacrifice. Ritual offerings are symbolic of what goes on in man's heart, symbolic of the true sacrifice he makes of *himself* as he "dies to the world in order to live for God." True sacrifices are the works of mercy done for ourselves or our neighbor, the same works of mercy in which we find our own peace and happiness. Our bodies themselves are a sacrifice, as Paul suggests when he tells us to worship God by "offering your living bodies as a holy sacrifice pleasing to God" (Rom 12:1). The symbol of *sacrifice* thus links up with the symbol of *body*. Since the true sacrifice of works of mercy is our means of finding happiness and belonging to God, "it follows that the whole of that redeemed city, that is, the congregation or communion of saints, is offered as a universal sacrifice to God through the High Priest who, taking the form of a servant, offered himself in his passion for us that we might be the body of so glorious a head."

It is therefore we ourselves who constitute the whole sacrifice, all of us with the different gifts and graces we bring to the love and service of our neighbor.

Such is the sacrifice of christians: "We, the many, are one body in Christ." This is the sacrifice, as the faithful understand, which the church continues to celebrate in the sacrament of the altar, in which it is clear to the church that she herself is offered in the very offering she makes to God.[6]

The key to Augustine's interiorization of sacrifice, and the link between the altar and the cross, is the ecclesial body living for God. It is this ecclesial, social reality which gives reality to the sacrificial symbolism applied to the eucharist. With this ecclesial understanding of the body of Christ, Augustine is able to exploit the old cultic symbols:

Christ Jesus is both the priest who offers and the oblation that is offered. And it was his will that as a sacrament of this reality there should be the daily sacrifice of the church, which, being the body of him, her head, learns to offer itself through him. This is the true sacrifice of which the ancient sacrifices of the saints were but many and manifold symbols.[7]

Another age would see in this passage an interpretation of the eucharist, plain and simply. But here as above, the "sacrament" and "daily sacrifice" refer not just to the rite but even more importantly to the church, the living sacrifice without which the eucharist is *unintelligible* as sacrifice.

Sacrament, body of Christ, sacrifice—in Augustine's hands these ideas and images are all ways of spelling out the meaning of the church and the kind of personal process its members are called to engage in. I mentioned earlier how the notion of "body of Christ" was evacuated when its ecclesial meaning was forgotten. The same thing applies to "sacrifice."

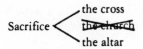

$$\text{Sacrifice} \begin{cases} \text{the cross} \\ \text{the church} \\ \text{the altar} \end{cases}$$

With the living sacrifice missing, one is left with an exterior cult which at best represents the sacrificial drama of Calvary (idealization) and at worst magically reproduces it (systemic control).

But the notion of "church" is no different from the other religious ideas discussed in this book. Until religion becomes a personal process, the church will be understood as merely a system or an ideal. In giving a title to this book, I was tempted to write *Jesus, the Church, the Eucharist.* But I felt this would have been misleading, because the word "church" as we normally use it does not yet make most of us think of a living sacrifice, a personal process writ large. Maybe it will be difficult ever to grasp the magnitude of such an idea. It is quite enough to deal with the personal process writ small. This involves keeping hold of the core of our faith, and seeing to it personally and in our own small communities that our rites and symbols express the core rather than pull us away from it: God is not first to be found out there, in temples on Twelfth Street or Pleasantview Avenue, but in the temple of our hearts. What was once outside is now within, so that finding God and worshiping him is completely tied up with finding ourselves.

Notes

Chapter 1: Flights into magic

1. See P. Schoonenberg, *The Christ* (New York: Herder, 1971), pp. 50-188.

2. Here and elsewhere in this chapter, I am borrowing some of the materials I used in my article, "The Scandal of the Cross," *The Way* 13 (1973) 33-40.

3. This is Lonergan's summary of F. Heiler's analysis of common characteristics in these world religions. See B. Lonergan, *Method in Theology* (New York: Herder, 1972), p. 109.

4. Justin, *First Apology*, chaps. 21-22.

5. For an excellent introduction to this fascinating area of knowledge, see C. G. Jung (ed.), *Man and his Symbols* (London: Aldus, 1964; New York: Dell Laurel edition). Part 1 on approaching the unconscious and Part 2 on ancient myth and modern man are especially useful. A well-organized collection of interesting ancient texts can be found in J. Henderson and M. Oakes, *The Wisdom of the Serpent: The Myths of Death, Rebirth and Resurrection* (New York: Collier, 1971). Joseph Campbell's *The Hero with a Thousand Faces* (Princeton/Bollingen, 1949) is a classic.

6. Penguin edition, pp. 158-159.

Chapter 2: Two questions about reality

1. This idea is effectively developed by Jan Groot, "The Church as Sacrament of the

World," in *The Sacraments in General*, vol. 31 of the *Concilium* series (New York: Paulist, 1968), pp. 51-66.

2. S. Langer, *Philosophy in a New Key* (3d ed.; Harvard, 1957), chap. 10. My treatment of the "two questions about reality" relies heavily on the philosophy of sign and symbol developed by Mrs. Langer. Chaps. 2-6 are particularly useful for sacramental theology.

3. *Ibid.*, p. 291.

4. A. Haden-Guest, "The Ubiquitous Sound of Muzak," in *Insight*, sunday magazine of the *Milwaukee Journal* (March 4, 1973), p. 27.

5. Cyril, *Baptismal Homilies*, 2; trans. E. Yarnold, *The Awe-Inspiring Rites of Initiation* (London: St. Paul Publications, 1971), p. 76.

6. J. Cirlot, *A Dictionary of Symbols* (New York: Philosophical Library, 1962), p. xxviii, p. 8.

7. Leibniz, *Discourse on Metaphysics*, 89. Italics mine.

8. St-Exupéry, *The Little Prince* (New York: Harcourt Brace, 1943), pp. 96-97 (Harbrace paperbound).

Chapter 3:   The last supper and the eucharist

1. Translation abridged and modernized from *The Authorized Daily Prayer Book*, ed. Hertz (New York: Bloch, 1948), pp. 965 ff.

2. Dom Gregory Dix, *The Shape of the Liturgy* (London: Dacre Press, 1945), chap. 4. Research done since 1945 enables us to nuance a number of Dix's points, but his whole treatment of the last supper remains one of the most insightful ones I know of; the entire book shows unusual sensitivity to the many facets of christian liturgical history. For a more recent (and very detailed) explanation of the jewish liturgy, the blessing prayers, the development of the eucharistic prayer, and eucharistic developments during the middle ages and the reformation, see Louis Bouyer, *Eucharist* (Notre Dame, 1968).

3. A. Jaubert, *The Date of the Last Supper* (New York: Alba House, 1965), p. 96.

4. A. Dupont-Sommer, *The Essene Writings from Qumran* (New York: World, 1962), pp. 108-109.

5. *Didache*, 9.

6. E. Stauffer, *Jesus and the Wilderness Community at Qumran* (Philadelphia: Fortress, 1964).

7. *Constitution on the Sacred Liturgy*, par. 10.

8. See J.-J. von Allmen, *The Lord's Supper* (Ecumenical Studies in Worship, no. 19; London: Lutterworth, 1969), pp. 42-43. This book is one of the best and most readable works on eucharistic theology which has appeared in the past decade. The author's treatment of various ecumenical questions (intercommunion, priesthood, pluralism of understanding) is particularly outstanding.

Chapter 4:   The bread and wine

1. On the origin of *sacra* and sacraments, see Langer, *Philosophy in a New Key*, chap. 6.

2. E. Schillebeeckx, *The Eucharist* (New York: Sheed & Ward, 1968), p. 59. Except for

this point, the first chapter of this book is a valuable historical study of what the Council of Trent did and did not say.

3. J. McCue, "The Doctrine of Transubstantiation from Berengar through the Council of Trent," *Harvard Theological Review* 61 (1968) 385-430. The same article is published in *Lutherans and Catholics in Dialogue, III: The Eucharist as Sacrifice* (published jointly by the U.S. Catholic Conference and by the U.S.A. National Committee for Lutheran World Federation).

4. *Ibid.*, pp. 429-430.

5. An excellent survey of this development can be found in J. F. Powers, *Eucharistic Theology* (New York: Herder, 1967), pp. 111-179.

6. Useful historical surveys of the medieval developments can be found in Bouyer, *Eucharist* (see above, chap. 3, note 2); see also E. Schillebeeckx, *Christ the Sacrament* (London: Sheed & Ward, 1963), chap. 3, and appendix to chap. 2.

7. See Langar, *op. cit.*, chap. 4, on the difference between presentational and discursive symbols. For a good appreciation of the many non-verbal aspects of worship, read Marianne Micks, *The Future Present: The Phenomenon of Christian Worship* (New York: Seabury, 1970).

Chapter 5: The cross and the eucharist

1. This difference in "mental and physical standpoint" is developed by D. W. Wead, *The Literary Devices in John's Gospel* (University of Basel, 1970), chap. 1.

2. I am much indebted to C. H. Dodd, *The Interpretation of the Fourth Gospel* (1st ed. 1953; Cambridge paperback, 1968). Dodd's analysis of johannine sources in the first part of his book is now out-dated, but his treatment of the argument and internal structure of the gospel (pp. 289-453) remains one of the most insightful studies available. See also O. Cullmann, *Early Christian Worship* (London: SCM, 1953); though Cullmann has been criticized for pushing johannine "sacramental" symbolism too hard, his study nonetheless calls attention to symbolic elements that cannot be overlooked in the gospel as it stands.

3. A very readable study of the development of worship in ancient Israel, with many interesting suggestions for contemporary worship, is that of Walter Harrelson, *From Fertility Cult to Worship* (New York: Doubleday, 1970).

4. Translated from the french edition of Ephraim's *Commentary on the Diatessaron*, in *Sources chrétiennes*, vol. 121, pp. 110-112.

5. In the following paragraphs I am borrowing from my article, "The Challenge of Christian Faith," in *The Way* 11 (July, 1971) 192-201.

6. Dodd, *op. cit.*, p. 439.

7. *Ibid.*, pp. 434-435.

8. Leo the Great, *Sermon* 70, 4-5.

9. G. Scholem, *Major Trends in Jewish Mysticism* (New York: Schocken, 1951), p. 27.

Chapter 6: Symbol upon symbol

1. John H. McGoey in *Homiletic and Pastoral Review* 61 (1960-61) 541-547.

2. Quoted in *HPR* 60 (1959-60) 353.

3. Fr. Ginder in *Our Sunday Visitor*, February 2, 1964.

4. *Ibid.*

5. *Acta apostolicae sedis* 49 (1957) 425-426; Instruction *Inter oecumenici* (Sept 26, 1964) n. 95; Instruction on the Worship of the Eucharistic Mystery (May 25, 1967) nn. 53-55.

6. Dix, *Shape of the Liturgy*, p. 412, 419.

7. This theme was developed especially by dutch theologians during the 1960's and is closely linked with the debate over "transignification." See Powers' survey and summary (reference above, chap. 4, note 5).

8. C. Vollert summarizes this curious debate in *Theological Studies* 22 (1961) 391-425.

9. Dodd, *Interpretation of the Fourth Gospel*, p. 437. It is remarkable that Raymond Brown's commentary on John's gospel in the Anchor Bible series makes no allusion to the liturgical meaning of *telein* in greek literature.

10. Dix finds two strata discernible in the development of eucharistic prayers, *op. cit.*, pp. 214-237.

11. Austin Farrer, "The Eucharist in 1 Corinthians," in *Eucharistic Theology Then and Now* (London, 1968).

12. Dix, *op. cit.*, p. 232.

13. *Ibid.*, p. 234.

14. *Didache*, 14; *1 Clement*, 36, 40-44.

15. See J. Jungmann's excellent summary of this development, "The Defense against Gnosticism," *The Early Liturgy to the Time of Gregory the Great* (Notre Dame Press, 1959), chap. 10.

16. Irenaeus of Lyons, *Adv. Haer.* 4.17.5.

17. See E. Yarnold, *The Awe-Inspiring Rites of Initiation* (London: St. Paul Publications, 1971), pp. 50-62.

18. Theodore, *Baptismal Homilies*, 4.25-26, 28-29; 5.11-12, 17-18 (Yarnold, pp. 227 ff.).

19. *Ibid.*, 5.18 (Yarnold, p. 249).

20. *Ibid.*, 4.20 (Yarnold, p. 224).

21. E. Kaesemann, *Jesus Means Freedom* (Philadelphia: Fortress, 1970), p. 114.

22. Leo, *Sermon* 63.7.

23. Chrysostom, *Homilies on John*, 46.

24. Augustine, *Sermon* 227. Augustine has traditionally been considered a "symbolist" in contrast to "realists" like Ambrose. This distinction, which comes out of the eucharistic disputes of the 9th and 11th centuries, does not seem to me to stand up under examination of the texts. Augustine does not carry his secondary symbolism as far as some of the other fathers do, and so his symbolism sounds less "physical." The question here is one of *degrees* of secondary symbolism, not of difference in symbolic mentality.

25. H. de Lubac, *Corpus Mysticum* (Paris: Aubier, 1949).

Chapter 7: From magic to mystery

1. For an excellent survey of the development of sacrificial ritual and the concept of sacri-

fice, see E. O. James, *The Origins of Sacrifice* (London, 1933; reissued by Kennikat Press, 1971). J. G. Frazer, *The Golden Bough*, contains a goldmine of historical data (Macmillan, 1922; abridged paperback edition, 1963). I am indebted to one of my students, Dennis Blaser, for some of the summaries I have used in this chapter.

2. L. Orsy, "Communal Penance: Some Preliminary Questions on Sin and Sacrament," *Worship* 47 (1973) 341.

3. James, *op. cit.*, p. 138. Italics added. For a provocative study of man's interpretations of death and the question of immortality, see John Dunne, *The City of the Gods: A Study in Myth and Mortality* (New York: Macmillan, 1965).

4. John Eudes, *The Life and the Kingdom of Jesus in Christian Souls* (New York: Kenedy, 1946), p. 251.

Chapter 8: Sacrifice

1. For a fine example of how ecumenical dialogue is carried on at the theological level, see the volume of *Lutherans and Catholics in Dialogue* cited above, chap. 4, note 3.

2. This is the central theme of Mircea Eliade, *Cosmos and History: The Myth of the Eternal Return* (New York: Harper & Row, 1959). The author develops the difference between cyclical religion and judeo-christian faith.

3. Cyrille Vogel, cited by T. Talley, "History and Eschatology in the Primitive Pascha," *Worship* 47 (1973) 212.

4. Gregory Naz., *Orations*, 45.22.

5. James, *op. cit.*, pp. 288-289.

6. *City of God*, 10.6; Image edition (Doubleday, 1958), pp. 193-194.

7. *Ibid.*, 10.20 (p. 196).

Bibliography to the Second Edition

Anglican–Roman Catholic International Commission, *The Final Report*, CTS/SPCK, London, 1982; also in C. Hill and E. Yarnold (edd.), *Anglicans and Roman Catholics: The Search for Unity*, SPCK/CTS, London, 1994, pp. 12–76.

L. Bouyer, *Eucharist: Theology and Spirituality of the Eucharistic Prayer*, University of Notre Dame Press, Notre Dame and London, 1968.

H. Davies, *Bread of Life & Cup of Joy*, Gracewing, Leominster, and Wm B. Eerdmans, Michigan, 1993.

G. Dix, *The Shape of the Liturgy*, 2nd edn, Dacre, London, 1945; new edn, Seabury, New York, 1982.

Faith and Order Commission, *Baptism, Eucharist and Ministry*, Faith and Order Paper No. 111, World Council of Churches, Geneva, 1982.

P. Fink (ed.), *The New Dictionary of Sacramental Worship*, Liturgical Press, Collegeville, 1990, pp. 391–462: 'Eucharist'.

R. Jasper and G. Cuming, *Prayers of the Eucharist: Early and Reformed*, 3rd edn, Pueblo, New York, 1987.

C. Jones, G. Wainwright, E. Yarnold and P. Bradshaw (edd.), *The Study of Liturgy*, SPCK, London, 2nd edn, 1992. Part II.3: 'The Eucharist'.

G. Macy, *The Theologies of the Eucharist in the Early Scholastic Period*, Clarendon Press, Oxford, 1984.

P. McPartlan, *The Eucharist Makes the Church: Henri de Lubac and John Zizioulas in Dialogue*. T. & T. Clark, Edinburgh, 1993.

R. Moloney, *The Eucharist*, G. Chapman, London, 1995.

D.N. Power, *The Sacrifice We Offer: The Tridentine Dogma and its Reinterpretation*, T.T. Clark, Edinburgh, 1987.

J.M. Powers, *Eucharistic Theology*, Burns & Oates, London, 1968

E. Schillebeeckx, *The Eucharist*, Sheed & Ward, London, 1968.

M. Thurian, *The Eucharistic Memorial*, Lutterworth, London, 1961.

Your opinion matters. It matters to us. It matters to your fellow Fodor's travelers, too. And we'd like to hear it. In fact, we need to hear it.

When you share your experiences and opinions, you become an active member of the Fodor's community. That means we'll not only use your feedback to make our books better, but we'll publish your names and comments whenever possible. Throughout our guides, look for "Word of Mouth," excerpts of your unvarnished feedback.

Here's how you can help improve Fodor's for all of us.

Tell us when we're right. We rely on local writers to give you an insider's perspective. But our writers and staff editors—who are the best in the business—depend on you. Your positive feedback is a vote to renew our recommendations for the next edition.

Tell us when we're wrong. We're proud that we update most of our guides every year. But we're not perfect. Things change. Hotels cut services. Museums change hours. Charming cafés lose charm. If our writer didn't quite capture the essence of a place, tell us how you'd do it differently. If any of our descriptions are inaccurate or inadequate, we'll incorporate your changes in the next edition and will correct factual errors at fodors.com immediately.

Tell us what to include. You probably have had fantastic travel experiences that aren't yet in Fodor's. Why not share them with a community of like-minded travelers? Maybe you chanced upon a beach or bistro or B&B that you don't want to keep to yourself. Tell us why we should include it. And share your discoveries and experiences with everyone directly at fodors.com. Your input may lead us to add a new listing or highlight a place we cover with a "Highly Recommended" star or with our highest rating, "Fodor's Choice."

Give us your opinion instantly at our feedback center at www.fodors.com/feedback. You may also e-mail editors@fodors.com with the subject line "Puerto Vallarta Editor." Or send your nominations, comments, and complaints by mail to Puerto Vallarta Editor, Fodor's, 1745 Broadway, New York, NY 10019.

You and travelers like you are the heart of the Fodor's community. Make our community richer by sharing your experiences. Be a Fodor's correspondent.

¡Buen Viaje!

Tim Jarrell, Publisher

CONTENTS

PUERTO VALLARTA IN FOCUS

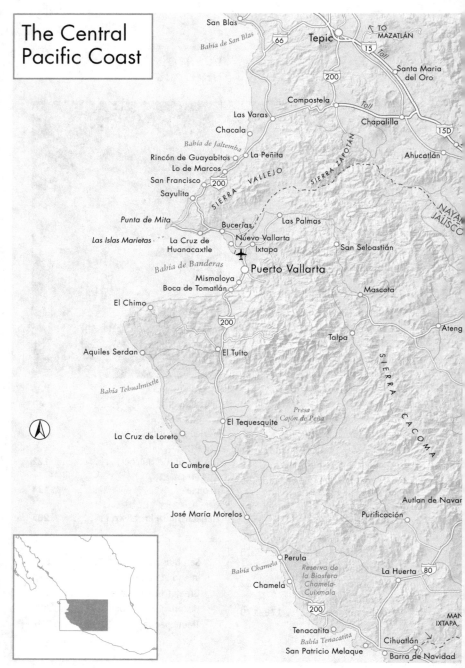

The Central Pacific Coast

San Blas

Bahía de San Blas

Tepic

TO MAZATLÁN

66

15 Toll

Santa Maria del Oro

Compostela

Toll

Las Varas

Chapalilla

Chacala

15D

Bahía de Jaltemba

La Peñita

Ahucatlán

Rincón de Guayabitos

Lo de Marcos

San Francisco

200

SIERRA VALLEJO

SIERRA ZAPOTÁN

Sayulita

NAYAR JALISCO

Punta de Mita

Bucerías

Las Palmas

Las Islas Marietas

La Cruz de Huanacaxtle

Nuevo Vallarta

Ixtapa

San Seloastián

Bahía de Banderas

Puerto Vallarta

Mismaloya

Boca de Tomatlán

Mascota

El Chimo

200

Ateng

Talpa

Aquiles Serdan

El Tuíto

SIERRA CACOMA

Bahía Tehualmixtle

Presa Cajón de Peña

El Tequesquite

La Cruz de Loreto

La Cumbre

Autlan de Navar

José María Morelos

Purificación

Perula

Reserva de la Biosfera Chamela-Cuixmala

La Huerta

80

Bahía Chamela

Chamela

200

MAN IXTAPA,

Tenacatita

Bahía Tenacatita

Cihuatlán

San Patricio Melaque

Barra de Navidad

Fodor's 2008

PUERTO VALLARTA

Where to Stay and Eat
for All Budgets

Must-See Sights
and Local Secrets

Ratings You Can Trust

Fodor's Travel Publications   New York, Toronto, London, Sydney, Auckland
www.fodors.com

FODOR'S PUERTO VALLARTA
Editor: Laura M. Kidder

Editorial Production: Linda K. Schmidt
Editorial Contributors: Jane Onstott
Maps & Illustrations: David Lindroth, cartographer, with additional cartography provided by Henry Columb, Mark Stroud, and Ali Baird, Moon Street Cartography; Bob Blake and Rebecca Baer, *map editors*
Design: Fabrizio LaRocca, *creative director*; Guido Caroti, *art director*; Tina Malaney, Ann McBride, *designers*; Melanie Marin, *senior picture editor*
Cover Photo: (Los Arcos Amphitheater on the Malecon): Karen Huntt/Corbis
Production/Manufacturing: Angela McLean

ISBN 978–1–4000–1856–7

ISSN 1558–8718

SPECIAL SALES
This book is available at special discounts for bulk purchases for sales promotions or premiums. Special editions, including personalized covers, excerpts of existing books, and corporate imprints, can be created in large quantities for special needs. For more information, write to Special Markets/Premium Sales, 1745 Broadway, MD 6-2, New York, New York 10019, or e-mail specialmarkets@randomhouse.com.

AN IMPORTANT TIP & AN INVITATION
Although all prices, opening times, and other details in this book are based on information supplied to us at press time, changes occur all the time in the travel world, and Fodor's cannot accept responsibility for facts that become outdated or for inadvertent errors or omissions. So **always confirm information when it matters,** especially if you're making a detour to visit a specific place. Your experiences—positive and negative—matter to us. If we have missed or misstated something, **please write to us.** We follow up on all suggestions. Contact the Puerto Vallarta editor at editors@fodors.com or c/o Fodor's at 1745 Broadway, New York, NY 10019.

PRINTED IN THE UNITED STATES OF AMERICA
10 9 8 7 6 5 4 3 2 1

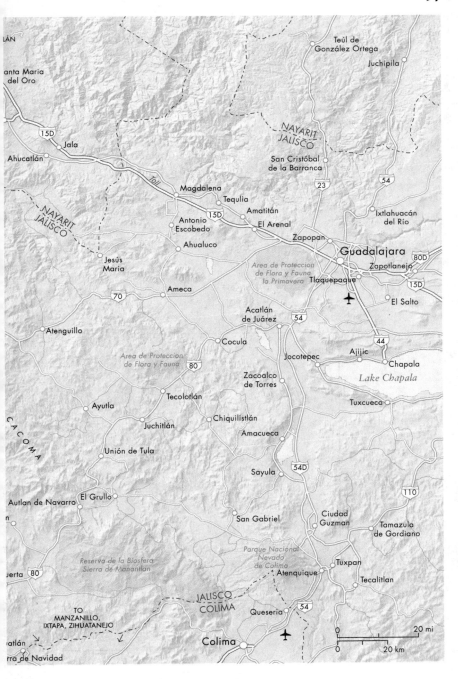

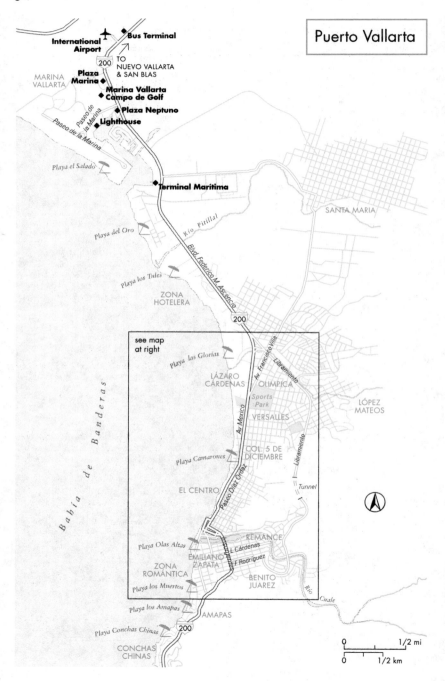

Puerto Vallarta

International Airport

Bus Terminal

TO NUEVO VALLARTA & SAN BLAS

200

MARINA VALLARTA

Plaza Marina

Marina Vallarta
Campo de Golf

Plaza Neptuno

Lighthouse

Paseo de la Marina

Paseo de la Marina

Playa el Salado

Terminal Marítima

Río Pitillal

SANTA MARIA

Playa del Oro

Blvd Federico M Ascencio

Playa los Tules

ZONA HOTELERA

200

see map at right

Playa las Glorias

LÁZARO CÁRDENAS

OLIMPICA

Av Francisco Villa

Libramiento

Sports Park

VERSALLES

Av Mexico

LÓPEZ MATEOS

COL. 5 DE DICIEMBRE

Playa Camarones

Libramiento

EL CENTRO

Paseo Díaz Ordaz

Tunnel

Playa Olas Altas

REMANCE

EMILIANO ZAPATA

L Cárdenas

F Rodriguez

ZONA ROMÁNTICA

BENITO JUAREZ

Playa los Muertos

Bahía de Banderas

Río Cuale

Playa los Amapas

AMAPAS

200

Playa Conchas Chinas

CONCHAS CHINAS

| 0 | | 1/2 mi |
| 0 | | 1/2 km |

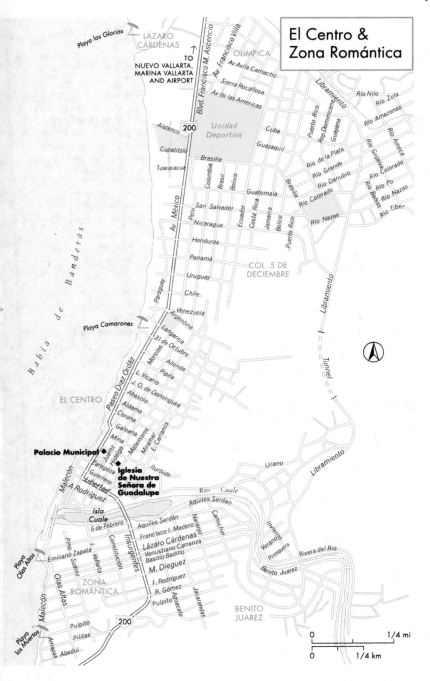

El Centro &
Zona Romántica

Playa las Glorias

LÁZARO CÁRDENAS

TO NUEVO VALLARTA, MARINA VALLARTA AND AIRPORT

Blvd. Francisco M. Ascencio

Av. Francisco M. Villa

OLIMPICA

Av. Avila Camacho

Sierra Rocallosa

Av. de las Américas

Libramiento

Río Nilo

Río Zula

Río Amazonas

Alatenco

200

Unidad Deportiva

Cuba

Guayaquil

Puerto Rico

Rep. Dominicana

Guapana

Guayana

Río Ameca

Río Grijalva

Río Colorado

Río Po

Río Balsas

Río Nazas

Río Tiber

Cupatitzio

Tzararacua

Brasilia

Río de la Plata

Río Grande

Río Danubio

Río Colorado

Colombia

Brasil

Bolivia

Guatemala

Río Colorado

Río Nazas

Av. México

Perú

San Salvador

Ecuador

Costa Rica

Jamaica

Belice

Puerto Rico

Nicaragua

Honduras

Panamá

COL. 5 DE DECIEMBRE

Uruguay

Libramiento

Paraguay

Chile

Venezuela

Argentina

Langarica

Playa Camarones

31 de Octubre

Morelos

Allende

Pipila

L. Vicario

J. O. de Dominguez

Abasolo

Aldama

Corona

Galeana

Mina

Matamoros

Miramar

E. Carranza

Paseo Díaz Ordáz

EL CENTRO

Bahía de Banderas

Juárez

Hidalgo

Iturbide

Palacio Municipal ◆

Zaragoza

Guerrero

Libertad

A. Rodríguez

◆ **Iglesia de Nuestra Señora de Guadalupe**

Río Cuale

Aquiles Serdán

Urano

Libramiento

Tunnel

Malecón

Isla Cuale

5 de Febrero

Aquiles Serdán

Francisco I. Madero

Lázaro Cárdenas

Venustiano Carranza

Basilio Badillo

M. Dieguez

F. Rodríguez

R. Gómez

Pulpito

Naranjo

Camichín

Jacarandas

Invierno

Verano

Primavera

Rivera del Río

Benito Juarez

Pino Suárez

Emiliano Zapata

Constitución

Insurgentes

Vallarta

Playa Olas Altas

Olas Altas

Malecón

ZONA ROMÁNTICA

BENITO JUAREZ

Pulpito

200

Pilitas

Playa los Muertos

Amapas

Abedul

Aguacate

0   1/4 mi

0   1/4 km

ABOUT THIS BOOK

Our Ratings

Sometimes you find terrific travel experiences and sometimes they just find you. But usually the burden is on you to select the right combination of experiences. That's where our ratings come in.

As travelers we've all discovered a place so wonderful that its worthiness is obvious. And sometimes that place is so experiential that superlatives don't do it justice: you just have to be there to know. These sights, properties, and experiences get our highest rating, **Fodor's Choice,** indicated by orange stars throughout this book.

Black stars highlight sights and properties we deem **Highly Recommended,** places that our writers, editors, and readers praise again and again for consistency and excellence.

By default, there's another category: any place we include in this book is by definition worth your time, unless we say otherwise. And we will.

Disagree with any of our choices? Care to nominate a place or suggest that we rate one more highly? Visit our feedback center at www.fodors.com/feedback.

Budget Well

Hotel and restaurant price categories from ¢ to $$$$ are defined in the opening pages of each chapter. For attractions, we always give standard adult admission fees; reductions are usually available for children, students, and senior citizens. Want to pay with plastic? **AE, D, DC, MC, V** following restaurant and hotel listings indicate if American Express, Discover, Diners Club, MasterCard, and Visa are accepted.

Restaurants

Unless we state otherwise, restaurants are open for lunch and dinner daily. We mention dress only when there's a specific requirement and reservations only when they're essential or not accepted—it's always best to book ahead.

Hotels

Hotels have private bath, phone, TV, and air-conditioning and operate on the European Plan (aka EP, meaning without meals), unless we specify that they use the Continental Plan (CP, with a Continental breakfast), Breakfast Plan (BP, with a full breakfast), or Modified American Plan (MAP, with breakfast and dinner) or are all-inclusive (AI, including all meals and most activi-

ties). We always list facilities but not whether you'll be charged an extra fee to use them, so when pricing accommodations, find out what's included.

Many Listings

★	Fodor's Choice
★	Highly recommended
✉	Physical address
✛	Directions
⬧	Mailing address
🕾	Telephone
🖷	Fax
⊕	On the Web
✎	E-mail
🎫	Admission fee
☉	Open/closed times
Ⓜ	Metro stations
🚐	Credit cards

Hotels & Restaurants

🏨	Hotel
🛏	Number of rooms
♨	Facilities
❍	Meal plans
✕	Restaurant
🍴	Reservations
⤹	Smoking
🍸	BYOB
✕🏨	Hotel with restaurant that warrants a visit

Outdoors

🏌	Golf
⛺	Camping

Other

♟	Family-friendly
⇨	See also
✉	Branch address
☞	Take note

Experience
Puerto Vallarta

Looking out over downtown and the Bay of Banderas

WORD OF MOUTH

"I've been to PV several times now and have loved it every time. It doesn't have the perfect water that Cancún does, but it also doesn't have as many drunk college kids."

—Montanacan

"Spend the day under a *palapa* on Playa Los Muertos. Stroll the *malecón* in the evening, eat an ice cream cone, or get a corn on the cob."

—suze

WELCOME TO PUERTO VALLARTA

Huichol Art

TOP REASONS TO GO

★ **Legendary restaurants:** Eat barbecued snapper with your feet in the sand or chateaubriand with a killer ocean view.

★ **Adventure and indulgence:** Ride a horse, mountain bike or go four-wheeling into the mountains, dive into the sea, and relax at an elegant spa—all in one day.

★ **Natural beauty:** Enjoy the physical beauty of Pacific Mexico's prettiest resort town, with cobblestone streets to climb to emerald green hills, and the big, sparkling bay below.

★ **Authentic art:** PV's artists and artisans—from Huichol Indians to expats—produce a huge diversity of exceptional folk treasures and fine art.

★ **Diverse nightlife:** Whether you're old, young, gay, straight, mild, or wild, PV's casual and unpretentious party scene has something to entice you after dark.

1 Old Vallarta. Rising abruptly from the sea are the hilly cobblestoned streets of El Centro (Downtown), lined with white-washed homes and shops. South of the Cuale River, the Zona Romántica (Romantic Zone, or Col. E. Zapata) has PV's highest density of restaurants and shops.

2 North of Downtown. Facing a busy avenue, the Zona Hotelera Norte (Northern Hotel Zone) has malls, businesses, and high-rise hotels. The shopping centers and deluxe hotels of Marina Vallarta are sandwiched between a golf course and the city's main marina.

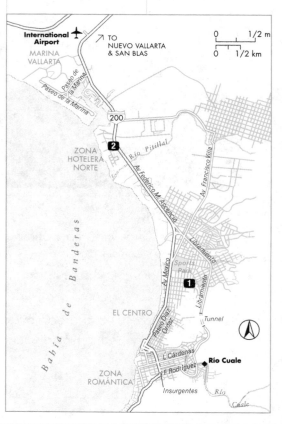

3 Nuevo Vallarta. The southernmost spot in Nayarit State, this planned resort is ideal if you want all-inclusive hotels. It has few restaurants and shops outside the Paradise Plaza mall.

4 The Southern Nayarit Coast. Exclusive Punta de Mita is dominated by the Four Seasons. Sayulita, San Francisco, and La Cruz de Huanacaxtle attract visitors with their small-town charm. Lovely, un-touristy beaches like Playa Chacala complete the picture.

5 South of Puerto Vallarta. To Mismaloya, the hotels of the Zona Hotelera Sur hug the beach or overlook it from cliffside aeries. Between La Cruz de Loreto and the Colima State border, the Costalegre is a mixture of luxury resorts and earthy seaside hamlets.

Dreams Hotel, Puerto Vallarta, Jalisco, Mexico

Playa Chacala
San Francisco 200
Sayulita
Punta de Mita
SIERRA VALLEJO
3
Las Islas Marietas La Cruz de Huanacaxtle Bucerías **4**
NAYARIT / JALISCO
Nuevo Vallarta Ixtapa
Marina Vallarta
Mismaloya **Puerto Vallarta**
Boca de Tomatlán
200
El Tuito

GETTING ORIENTED

The original town, Old Vallarta, sits at the center of 42-km (26-mi) Bahía de Banderas, Mexico's largest bay, in Jalisco State. From here, the Sierra Madre foothills dive into the sea. Mountain-fed rivers nourish tropical deciduous forests as far north as San Blas, in Nayarit State. South of PV the hills recede from the coast and the drier tropical thorn forest predominates south to Barra de Navidad.

Bahía de Banderas

La Cruz de Loreto
El Tequesquite
La Cumbre
5
José María Morelos
200
Bahía Chamela Perula
Reserva de la Biosfera Chamela-Cuixmala
Chamela

0   10 mi
0   10 km

Tenacatita
Bahía Tenacatita San Patricio Melaque

PUERTO VALLARTA'S TOP EXPERIENCES

The Malecón

Nighttime is the right time for strolling PV's famous *malecón*. Bring your camera to photograph the seawalk's whimsical statues at sunset. Sip a cool drink, buy a caramel-topped crêpe from a vendor, or eat at a restaurant across the street. At the end of your eight-block promenade, take in the near-nightly free evening entertainment—be it a brass band or outdoor dance at the town square or a magician or mime at adjoining Los Arcos outdoor amphitheater, overlooking the sea.

Canopy Tours

Zinging through the treetops makes even a timid traveler feel like a superhero. Canopy tours are action-packed rides, where, fastened to a zip line high off the ground, you fly from tree to tree. Blue sky above, ribbons of river below, and in be-

tween: a forest of treetops and a healthy shot of adrenaline. The most highly praised area operators are El Edén and Canopy Tour Los Veranos, both south of PV near Mismaloya.

In, On, Under and Above the Water

Spend a day on the bay. Dive the varied landscape of Las Marietas Islands, angle for giant billfish, or soar above the scene in a colorful parasail. Look for orcas or humpbacks in winter and dolphins year-round. Swim, snorkel, or learn to surf or sail. Perhaps just build a sandcastle with your kids.

What You Want & Where To Get It

This table reflects the atmosphere in high season. In low season, most beaches are uncrowded, activities may decrease, and some shops and restaurants close.

AROUND PV	Peace & Quiet	Luxury Digs	Natural Beauty	Known for Restaurants	Shopping	Lots of Sports	Low on Tourists
Old Vallarta			✔	✔	✔	✔	
Nuevo Vallarta	✔	✔				✔	
Bucerías	✔			✔			✔
Punta de Mita		✔	✔				
Zona Hotelera Sur	✔	✔	✔				
Costalegre	✔	✔	✔				✔
Barra/Melaque	✔		✔				✔
Rincón de Guayabitos			✔				
Zona Hotelera Norte		✔		✔		✔	
Marina Vallarta	✔	✔				✔	

Late Nights, Latino Style

Much of Vallarta is geared to the gringo palate, however, there's plenty of authentic spice for those who crave it. Stray a bit from the tourist scene for a *mojito*—Cuba's version of the mint julep—at La Bodeguita del Medio, on the malecón. Dine on roast pork, black beans, and fried plantains before heading for the dance floor at around 9, when the house band comes to life. Wednesday through Friday, take a taxi to J.B. Dance Club, in the hotel zone, for $2 dance lessons at 9:30. Otherwise hang at La Bodeguita until around 11, when the Mexican and Latino crowds start to arrive at J.B. for a late night of cumbia, salsa, and hot merengue.

Sensational Sunsets

After a day of activity, you deserve some R, R, and R: rest, relaxation, and rewarding views. Sip a fancy cocktail with a live music accompaniment at busy Los Muertos Beach or indulge in dessert from the crow's nest at Bucerías's The Bar Above. For the most dramatic views from high above the sea head to Barcelona Tapas, Vista Guayabitos, Las Carmelitas, or Le Kliff (⇨ chapter 3). All of them serve dinner and drinks.

20 Minutes to a More Elevated You

Get away from the gringo trail 4,000 feet above sea level in the mountain towns west of PV. Admire the elegant simplicity of tiny San Sebastian; in Talpa, visit the diminutive Virgin of Talpa statue, revered throughout Mexico for petitions granted. Buy keepsakes and mountain-grown coffee in small shops around the square. Or fly to Mascota, where you can sample homemade *raicilla*—second cousin of tequila. Hike into tapestry hills and deep green valleys where, on a good day, you can spy Puerto Vallarta and a ribbon of the Pacific far below.

AUTHENTIC IS KEY

"I love Puerto Vallarta dearly and have been there many times, but I mostly just kick around downtown, lay by the hotel pool, go to the supermercado, have drinks at the beach, enjoy the wonderful restaurants, eat ice cream on the Malecon, and hit the fabric stores. Other fun things to do: hang around Playa los Muertos, go shopping and to the galleries, parasailing, cruises, jungle tours, visiting the cathedral. People in PV are incredibly friendly, welcoming, and proud. The town is authentic, which is important to me."

—suze

"DON'T MISS"

1) Every sunset.
2) Eating out at all the great restaurants. Don't stay in the hotel even if it is all-inclusive. There are too many great places to go.
3) A visit up the coast to Punta Mita
4) Bus rides in town
5) Getting to know the local people

—Anne-Marie

PUERTO VALLARTA THEN AND NOW

People and Culture

Despite its population of more than 200,000, Puerto Vallarta feels—and thinks—like a small town. People know their neighbors; school chums run the city and the corner taco stand. Although the majority of *vallartenses* (residents of Puerto Vallarta) are far from wealthy, most are middle class, and securely employed; few of the alms-seekers downtown are locals.

Vallartenses value nice things, but much less so than sharing and socializing with family and friends. In her book *The Magic of Puerto Vallarta,* Venezuelan Marilú Suárez-Murias aptly describes Puerto Vallartans as "free, proud, simple, noble, friendly, kind, and never in a hurry."

Like many others from around the world, Ms. Suárez-Murias visited in the 1980s and opted to stay. Vallarta has one of the largest English-speaking expat communities in Mexico consisting of Americans and Canadians especially. Expats tend to settle in Old Vallarta or the condos and private homes climbing the ocean-facing hills south of town. Small towns like Sayulita, north of PV, are also increasingly popular.

The Hotel Scene

Choosing where to stay may be half of the equation to having a fabulous vacation. Unfortunately, it's not an easy task since Puerto Vallarta has something for every budget and personality, from cliffside condos with stairs winding down to the sea to classy little cottages surrounded by nature trails. *Gran turismo* (beyond 5-star) hotels and resorts are found up and down the coast; think beachside villa with a private plunge pool. Some of those on the prettiest beaches are in Punta de Mita

and the Costalegre, but you'll find them also in the south and north hotel zones, Marina Vallarta, and Nuevo Vallarta. Nuevo Vallarta has mainly all-inclusive hotels. Southern Nayarit State, north of PV, has a sprinking of small hotels, guesthouses, private rentals, and B&Bs, many of them popular with honeymooners, families, and anyone looking for more intimate digs away from large crowds.

The Food Scene

First-time travelers come for the sun and sea, but it's PV's wonderful restaurants that create legions of long-term fans. Only a generation ago, much of the best, locally caught fish was shipped to Guadalajara; Vallartans had to buy it back frozen, or overstock and freeze fresh catches for future meals. Likewise, a variety of vegetables was hard to find. But as the destination has grown in popularity and dozens of excellent chefs have opened restaurants, the culinary outlook has improved exponentially. Now those who know where to look can shop locally for designer greens, baby eggplant, and an increasingly sophisticated range of ingredients.

PV's level of culinary chic is reflected in November's International Gourmet Festival, when dozens of guest chefs bring new recipes and ideas from around the globe.

It's not just foreigners and Cordon Bleu-trained chefs, however, that keep the foodies fat and happy. Seaside family-owned eateries grill fish right off the boat, and tiny city cafés have great eats at bargain prices. And a number of streetside stalls are as hygienic as five-star-hotel restaurants.

The Overall Vibe

Mexico's second-most-visited resort after Cancún, Puerto Vallarta is, without a doubt, "touristy." From the clean streets to

the English-speaking personnel and menus, business owners and tourism officials aim to help you feel at home. But you won't feel like a cipher or, worse, a bothersome intruder. Cancún didn't exist before the 1970s, and employees and business owners are imported from elsewhere. In contrast, the majority of Puerto Vallarta's tour companies, restaurants, and hotels are run by local people—proud of their city and happy to have you. Happy, because tourism is PV's only real industry. And though plenty of twentysomethings party all night at Señor Frogs or Carlos O'Briens, this is not a spring-break destination. A sense of decorum and pride in the city keeps things reasonably restrained.

Thinking Outside the Bay

As numerous as the activities in and around Puerto Vallarta and Banderas Bay are the opportunities beyond its boundaries. Vallarta Adventures and smaller tour operators make things easy with day trips to the mountains, Guadalajara, San Blas, and La Tovara estuaries. While tour companies can design individual, overnight tours, most folks heading north or south of Banderas Bay rent a car (or hop on a bus) and go on their own. But there's plenty to keep you busy in and around Puerto Vallarta, so if your time is limited, establishing a base of operations there is usually the least hassle-free way to explore.

A Brief History

Except for small coastal settlements that subsisted on fishing and a small enterprise importing salt (used to separate silver from stone), the first European and mestizo settlers in the region were miners and mine owners far from the coast, in the mineral-laced Sierra Madre. When mining petered out in the early 20th century, many families moved to the band of rich farmland near the coast around present-day Puerto Vallarta. Tourism along the gorgeous, 42-km (26-mi) Bahía Banderas (Bay of Flags), really took off in the '50s and '60s, when a Mexican newsreel showed off its natural beauty and famous lovers Elizabeth Taylor and Richard Burton brought the paparazzi during the filming of *Night of the Iguana,* in 1963.

GREAT ITINERARIES

Each of these fills one day. Together they touch on some of PV's most quintessential experiences, from shopping to getting outdoors for adventure tours or golfing, or just relaxing at the best beaches and spas.

Romancing the Zone

Head south of downtown to the **Zona Romántica** for a day of excellent shopping and dining. Stop at Isla del Río Cuale for trinkets and T-shirts; have an island breakfast overlooking the stream at the River Cafe or an excellent lunch at Le Bistro, where the romantic, neo-Continental décor and monumental architecture produce a flood of endorphins.

■TIP➔ Most of the stores in the neighborhood will either ship your oversized prizes for you or expertly pack them and recommend reputable shipping companies.

Crossing the pedestrian bridge nearest the bay, drop nonshoppers at **Los Muertos Beach.** They can watch the fishermen on the small pier, lie in the sun, sit in the shade with a good book, or walk south to the rocky coves of **Conchas Chinas Beach,** which is good for snorkeling when the water is calm. Meanwhile, the shoppers head to **Calle Basilio Badillo** and surrounding streets for folk art, housewares, antiques, clothing, and accessories. End the day back at Los Muertos with dinner, drinks, and live music.

■TIP➔ Some of the musicians at beachfront restaurants work for the restaurant, others are freelancers. If a roving musician (or six) ask what you'd like to hear, ask the price of a song.

A Different Resort Scene

If you've got wheels, explore a different sort of beach resort. After breakfast, grab beach togs, sunscreen, and other essentials

for a day at the beach and head north. Those with a sweet tooth might make a pit stop at Pie in the Sky, with excellent pie, chocolate, and other sugar fixes. About an hour north of PV, join Mexican families on the beach at **Rincón de Guayabitos,** on attractive Jaltemba Bay. Play in the mild surf; walk the pretty, long beach; or take a ride in a glass-bottom boat to **El Islote,** an islet with a small restaurant and snorkeling opportunities. Vendors on the sand sell grilled fish and chilled coconuts and watermelon from their brightly colored stands. On the way back south, stop in the small town of **San Francisco,** aka San Pancho, for dinner. You can't go wrong at La Ola Rica, Gallo's Pizzeria, or the slightly more sophisticated Cafe del Mar (brush the sand off your feet for that one). In high season and especially on weekend evenings, one of the three will probably have live music, especially Gallo's.

■TIP➔ Take a water taxi out for a look at El Islote island, where with luck you might spot a whale between December and March.

Head for the Hills

For an unforgettable experience (at least for a few days, until your thigh muscles recover), take a horse-riding expedition (➾ Chapter 7) into Vallarta's verdant tropical forest. Rancho Charro and Rancho Ojo de Agua have full-day excursions; the former offers multiday excursions as well, including tours to the former silver-mining towns of Mascota and San Sebastián. For those who prefer motorized horsepower, Wild Vallarta runs full-day ATV tours to San Sebastián.

■TIP➔ Full-day and overnight trips provide food and refreshments, but if possible bring a day pack with things to make yourself comfortable: bottled water, tissues or

handkerchief, bandana, and plenty of sun-block. Don't pack it so full that it's unpleasantly heavy, however. Wear a hat.

A Day of Golf and Steam

Puerto Vallarta is one of Mexico's best golfing destinations (⇨ Chapter 7). And what better way to top off a day of play than with a steam, soak, and massage? At the southern end of the Costalegre, Tamarindo and Grand Bay Isla Navidad have courses (18 great holes and three 9-hole courses, respectively) and very good spas. Above PV, the Four Seasons has 19 holes of good golfing (the optional 19th on its own little island) and an excellent spa, but the latter is for guests only. In between these extremes are less-exclusive but still great courses. The closest spas to the greens of Marina Vallarta and the excellent Vista Vallarta are those of the Westin Regina and the CasaMagna Marriott. The El Tigre course is associated with the Paradise Village resort, but this moderately priced spa is open also to those who golf at Mayan Palace, just up the road and at Flamingos, at the far northern edge of Nuevo Vallarta.

■ TIP➔ Ask your concierge (or look online) to find out how far ahead you can reserve, and then try for the earliest possible tee time to beat the heat. If the course you choose doesn't have a club pool, you can have lunch and hang at the pool at the resorts suggested above, or get a massage, facial, or other treatment (always reserve ahead).

Downtown Exploration

Puerto Vallarta hasn't much at all in the way of museums, but with a little legwork, you can get a bit of culture. Learn about the area's first inhabitants at the tiny but tidy **Museo Arqueológico** (closed Sunday), with info in English. From the museum, you can head downtown along the newest section of the **malecón,** which now crosses the river. About four blocks north, check out the action in the main plaza and Los Arcos amphitheater. At the **Iglesia de Nuestra Señora de Guadalupe,** you can pay your respects to the patron saint of the city (and the country). Taking a stroll farther north along the malecón is like walking through a sculpture garden: look for the statue of a boy riding a sea horse (it's become PV's trademark), and La Nostalgia, a statue of a seated couple, by noted PV artist Ramiz Barquet. Three figures climb a ladder extending into the air in Sergio Bustamante's In Search of Reason. One of the most elaborate sculptures is by Alejandro Colunga. Rotunda del Mar has more than a dozen fantastic figures—some with strange, alien appendages—seated on chairs and pedestals of varying heights.

WHEN TO GO

The beach resorts are the most crowded and expensive December through Easter, especially the Christmas/New Year's holiday and the weeks before and after Easter. Despite the humidity, upper-class Mexican families book resort hotels during July and August school vacations while the masses rent bungalows in the smaller beach towns and camp out on popular beaches. Mexicans also travel over extended national holiday weekends, called *puentes* (bridges).

Holy days and cultural festivals play a big role in Mexican life. If you plan to travel during a major national event, reserve lodgings and transportation well in advance. November brings the PV Film Festival of the Americas and International Gourmet Festival.

Climate

On the same latitude as the Hawaiian Islands, Puerto Vallarta is tropical, and can be visited any time of year. Mid-June through mid-October is the rainy season; afternoon showers clear the air and temporarily reduce humidity. Rainy season temperatures are often in the 80s and 90s and feel hotter due to high humidity. November through May is the dry season. Summer means bathtub-like ocean temperatures, the best diving and snorkeling conditions, and the most surfable waves. December through March brings the coolest temperatures: daytime temps still reach the 80s but at night drop to the 50s or 60s. May, June, August, and September are the hottest months. The proximity of tall mountains to the coast increases humidity: from Puerto Vallarta north to San Blas there's jungly terrain (officially, tropical deciduous forest). South of PV, the mountains recede from the coast, making that area's thorn-forest ecosystem drier.

Forecasts **U.S. National Weather Service** (⊕ *http://weather.noaa.gov/weather/current/MMPR.html*). **The Weather Channel** (⊕ *www.weather.com*).

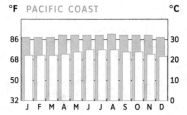

Where to Stay

Massage pavillion at El Tamarindo Golf Resort

WORD OF MOUTH

"In PV I like the Buenaventura, close to town, cheap, great pool, clean. If you are an upscale traveler or need to be out of town, the Velas Vallarta is nice but 15 minutes from the action."

—Montanacana

"We absolutely loved the Presidente Intercontinental. ... It's a great hotel in a ... tranquil place where you can enjoy the sounds of waves."

–twinkee

www.fodors.com/forums

LODGING PLANNER

When to Go

High season is November through April, but if you don't mind afternoon rain showers and a lot of humidity, late June through October is a great time to visit for lower-priced lodgings (up to 40%) and rental cars and smaller crowds.

By August the entire coast and inland forests are green and bursting with blooms. Afternoon rains clean the streets and houses; waterfalls and rivers outside of town spring into action. On the downside, many restaurants and some other businesses close up shop in the hottest months, August and September, and live performances and nightlife slack off. The humidity is most manageable in May, October, and November, and at its worst in September.

⚠ **Overbooking is a common practice. To protect yourself, get a confirmation in writing, via fax or e-mail.**

Parking Blues

Very few downtown Puerto Vallarta hotels have parking, and there are few pay lots. Most of the condos in the Zona Hotelera Sur have parking, but not necessarily one space per apartment. Virtually all of the hotels outside the city center have free parking for guests.

Choosing a Hotel

If you want to walk everywhere, **Old Vallarta** (downtown, which includes El Centro and the Romantic Zone) is the place to be. El Centro's hilly, cobblestone streets provide excellent views and aerobic workouts. South of the Cuale River, the Romantic Zone has more shops, restaurants, and Los Muertos Beach—and no hills. Most hotels here are inexpensive to moderate.

South of town, the **Zona Hotelera Sur** has many condos as well as luxury and a few moderately priced hotels—most with dramatic ocean views. Downtown is a short cab or bus ride away. The beaches and views aren't as appealing in the **Zona Hotelera Norte.** The long stretch of mid-range and higher-end chains is interspersed with malls and mega–grocery stores. Relatively car-free **Marina Vallarta,** with its luxury hotels, is close to golf courses and is a good place for biking and strolling.

Nuevo Vallarta is a planned resort on a long, sandy beach about 12 miles north of downtown PV—about 45 minutes by car or bus when traffic complicates things. This is a good place to stay if you're content to stay put and enjoy your all-inclusive, high-rise hotel. Bucerías and the towns of **southern Nayarit** (north of PV) call to adventurous souls. Several hours south of Vallarta, the **Costalegre** is a place of extremes. High-priced hotels on gorgeous beaches attract celebs and honeymooners, while small towns like Barra de Navidad have modest digs and a more authentically Mexican experience—and nice beaches, too.

Gran Turismo

The government categorizes hotels as *gran turismo* (five-star-plus), of which only about 30 are chosen nationwide each year; five-star to one-star. Note that hotels might lose out on a higher rating only because they lack an amenity like air conditioning (which isn't always needed if there are good breezes).

Lodging Alternatives

APARTMENTS & VILLAS

When shared by two couples, a spacious villa can save you a bundle on lodging and on meals. Villas often come with stereo systems, DVD players, a pool, maid service, and air conditioning. Prices range from $100 to $1,000 per night, with 20% discounts off-season.

At Home Abroad ☎ 212/421-9165 ⊕ www. athomeabroadinc.com. **Cochran Real Estate** ☎ 322/228-0419 in PV, 800/603-2959 in U.S. ⊕ www. buyeragentmexico.com. **Hideaways International** ☎ 603/430-4433, 800/843-4433 in U.S. ⊕ www.hideaways.com. **Pacific Mexico Real Estate** ☎ 329/298-1644 in Bucerías ⊕ www.pacific mexicorealestate.com. **Villas and Apartments Abroad** ☎ 212/213-6435, 800/433-3020 in U.S. ⊕ www.vaanyc.com. **Villas International** ☎ 415/499-9490, 800/221-2260 in U.S. ⊕ www.villasintl.com.

BOUTIQUE HOTELS

México Boutique Hotels (☎ 01800/508-7923 in Mexico, 877/278-8018 in U.S., 866/818-8342 in Canada ⊕ www. mexicoboutiquehotels.com) is a private company that represents 45 intimate and unique properties—most with fewer than 50 rooms—selected for their setting, cuisine, service, and overall allure. Each is inspected annually.

CHAIN HOTELS

Tried-and-true chains may have excellent rates, and can be good last-minute options.

Holiday Inn ☎ 800/465-4329 in U.S. ⊕ www. holiday-inn.com. **Inter-Continental** ☎ 888/424-6835 in U.S. ⊕ www.ichotelsgroup.com. **Marriott** ☎ 888/236-2427 ⊕ www.marroitt.com. **Sheraton** ☎ 800/325-3535 in U.S. ⊕ www.starwood.com/sheraton. **Westin** ☎ 800/937-8461 ⊕ www.starwoodhotels.com.

What it Costs In U.S. Dollars

FOR 2 PEOPLE

$$$$	$$$	$$	$	¢
over $250	$150-$250	$75-$150	$50-$75	under $50

For a standard room, generally excluding taxes and service charges.

Our Ratings

The lodgings we list are the cream of the crop in each price category. Hotels have private baths, phone, TV, and a/c, and don't include meals, unless we specify otherwise.

Meal Plans

EP: European Plan; without meals
CP: Continental Plan; continental breakfast
BP: Breakfast Plan; full breakfast
MAP: Modified American Plan; breakfast and dinner
FAP: Full American Plan; breakfast, lunch, and dinner
AI: All-Inclusive; including all meals, drinks, and most activities

Pricing

We give high-season prices before meals or other amenities. Low-season rates usually drop 30%-40%. We always list the available facilities, but we don't specify whether they cost extra.

Less expensive hotels include tax in the quote. Most higher-priced resorts add 17% tax on top of the quoted rate; some add a 5%-10% service charge. Moderately priced hotels swing both ways. You might be charged extra for paying with a credit card. Tax and/or tips are often included with all-inclusive plans, making a $$$$ property affordable.

■ TIP→ An all-inclusive (AI) might make you reluctant to spend money elsewhere. So you don't miss out on area restaurants and activities, stay at more modest digs for part of your trip, and go AI for a day or two. Many AI hotels have day passes ($50-$75).

PUERTO VALLARTA

$$$$ ⚅ **Barceló La Jolla de Mismaloya.** Guests consistently give this hotel high
☾ marks despite the reduction of the once-pristine beach by Hurricane
Kenna. Each of the huge, brightly decorated suites has a separate living
area and ample terrace with a table and four chairs; some also have
well-equipped kitchens. Most two-bedroom suites have two baths but
no kitchen. The pools are surrounded by spacious patios, so there's
plenty of room to find the perfect spot in the sun, whether you're on
your honeymoon or with the kids. At this writing, the all-inclusive plan
costs about the same as the room alone. ⊠ *Zona Hotelera Sur, Km
11.5, Mismaloya, 48300* ☎ *322/226–0660, 800/227–2356 in U.S. and
Canada* ⊕ *www.lajollademismaloya.com* ⥂ *304 suites* ♿ *In-room:
safe, kitchen (some), dial-up. In-hotel: 5 restaurants, room service,
bars, tennis court, pools, gym, spa, beachfront, diving, water sports,
bicycles, concierge, children's programs (ages 5–11), laundry service,
public Internet, executive floor, parking (no fee), no-smoking rooms,
refrigerator* ⊟ *MC, V* ⊠ *AI, EP.*

$$$$ ⚅ **CasaMagna Marriott.** The CasaMagna is hushed and stately in some
☾ places, lively and casual in others. Here's a classy property that none-
★ theless welcomes children. All of the restaurants—including a sleek
Asian restaurant serving Thai, sushi, and teppanyaki and a large, pleasant sports bar—have kid's menus. Indicate you are traveling with kids
when you book to ensure cookies and milk in your room at bedtime.
The meandering grounds boast a large infinity pool as well as indigenous plant and chile gardens. Rooms have an upbeat, classy decor;
each has a balcony and most have an ocean view. The Marriott chain
requires smoke detectors, sprinklers, thrice-filtered water, and other
beyond-the-pale safety features. The expansive spa has separate facilities for men and women. ⊠ *Paseo de la Marina 5, Marina Vallarta,
48354* ☎ *322/226–0000, 888/236–2427 in U.S. and Canada* ⊕ *www.
casamagnapuertovallarta.com* ⥂ *404 rooms, 29 suites* ♿ *In-room:
safe, DVD, Wi-Fi. In-hotel: 4 restaurants, room service, bars, tennis
courts, pools, gym, spa, beachfront, concierge, children's programs
(ages 4–12), laundry service, public Internet, parking (no fee), minibar*
⊟ *AE, DC, MC, V* ⊠ *EP.*

$$$$ ⚅ **Dreams.** The dramatic view of the gorgeous, rock-edged beach is
☾ just one reason that this all-inclusive is special. Theme nights go a bit
Fodor'sChoice beyond the usual Mexican fiestas: there are salsa dancing classes, reg-
★ gae and circus nights, and for sports night, ball games with hot dogs
and beer, and movies on the beach. Instead of buffet restaurants there
are four à la carte eateries and one with pizza, taco, pasta, and other
stations. All of the charming suites, decorated in aqua and white, have
fab views but only the newer ones have balconies, some with a hot
tub. There are tons of activities for both kids and adults, and no wrist-
bands to clash with your resort-casual clothes. ⊠ *Carretera a Barra
de Navidad (Carretera 200), at Playa Las Estacas Zona Hotelera Sur,
48300* ☎ *322/226–5000, 866/237–3267 in U.S. and Canada* ⊕ *www.
dreamsresorts.com* ⥂ *337 suites* ♿ *In-room: safe, DVD. In-hotel: 5
restaurants, room service, bars, tennis courts, pools, gym, spa, beachfront, water sports, bicycles, concierge, children's programs (ages 4–*

17), laundry service, parking (no fee), no-smoking rooms, refrigerator ⊟*AE, D, DC, MC, V* ⦿I*AI.*

$$$$ ⌖**Fiesta Americana.** The dramatically designed terra-cotta building rises above a deep-blue pool that flows under bridges and beside palm oases; a seven-story palapa (which provides natural air-conditioning) covers the elegant lobby—paved in patterned tile and stone—and a large round bar. The ocean-view rooms have a modern pink and terra-cotta color scheme, beige marble floors, balconies, and tile baths with powerful showers. The beach bustles with activity and equipment rentals. It's about halfway between the Marina Vallarta complex and Downtown PV. ⊠*Blvd. Federico M. Ascencio, Km 2.5, Zona Hotelera Norte, 48300* ☎*322/226–2100, 800/343–7821 in U.S.* ⊕*www.fiestaamericana.com* ⇦*288 rooms, 3 suites* ♿*In-room: safe, dial-up, Wi-Fi. In-hotel: 3 restaurants, room service, spa, bars, pool, gym, beachfront, concierge, children's programs (ages 4–12), laundry service, parking (no fee), no-smoking rooms, minibar* ⊟*AE, DC, MC, V* ⦿I*EP.*

$$$$ ⌖**Hacienda San Angel.** Each room is unique and elegant at this bou-
★   tique hotel in the hills six blocks above the malecón. Public spaces also exude wealth and privilege: 16th- through 19th-century antiques are placed throughout, water pours from fonts into Talavera tile–lined basins, mammoth tables grace open dining areas. The Celestial Room has a wondrous view of Bahía de Banderas and the cathedral's tower from its open-air, thatch-roof living room. You can call or e-mail Canada or the United States for free; enjoy live music with complimentary cocktails in the early evening. ⊠*Calle Miramar 336, at Iturbide, Col. El Cerro, 48300* ☎*322/222–2692, 415/738–8220 in U.S.* ⊕*www.haciendasanangel.com* ⇦*14 rooms* ♿*In-room: safe, DVD, VCR. In-hotel: restaurant, pools, no elevator, concierge, laundry service, public Internet, airport shuttle; no kids under 16* ⊟*AE, MC, V* ⦿I*CP.*

$$$$ ⌖**Majahuitas.** If travelers were animals, Majahuitas's guests would be bears, not butterflies. Eating well and resting are the two top activities. After a 20-minute boat ride you (and, hopefully, your sweetie, as this intimate place doesn't have a singles scene) arrive at a shell-strewn beach where hermit crabs scuttle about seeking larger accommodations. Eight casitas crouch amid jungly plants (and biting bugs; bring repellent) overlooking the tiny cove. Guest rooms are open to the air and have low-wattage lights and tiny, solar-powered fans. It's a romantic place that also happens to be good for families with tots. Older kids, type-A adults, and anyone who doesn't read will be bored. ⊠*Playa Majahuitas, Cabo Corrientes Norte* ☎*322/293–4506, 800/728–9098 in U.S. and Canada* ⊕*www.mexicoboutiquehotels.com/majahuitas* ⇦*8 rooms* ♿*In-room: no a/c, no phone, no TV. In-hotel: restaurant, bar, beachfront, water sports* ⊟*AE, MC, V* ⦿I*FAP* ⊘*Closed Sept.*

$$$$ ⌖**Sol Meliá Puerto Vallarta.** The sprawling Meliá, on the beach and
♨   close to the golf course, is popular with families and hums with activity. An enormous birdcage with several parrots dominates the breezy lobby, which also houses an eclectic collection of Mexican art and memorabilia. The plazas beyond have still more artwork as well as garden areas, fountains, ponds, and such bits of whimsy as a supersize chessboard with plastic pieces as big as a toddler. There's a huge pool,

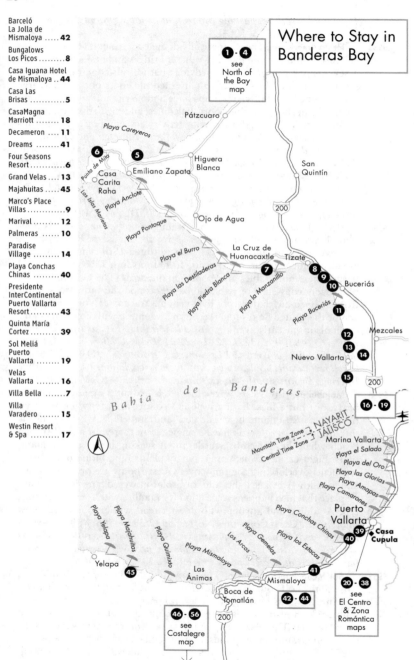

Where to Stay in Banderas Bay

an outdoor theater with nightly shows, and elaborate children's programs and amenities—including a climbing wall and a batting cage. Rooms are havens in subdued blues, creams, and sands. Considering it's an all-inclusive only, prices are extremely reasonable. ⊠*Paseo de la Marina Sur 7, Marina Vallarta, 48300* 🕾*322/226–3000, 800/336–3542 in U.S.* ⊕*www.solmelia.com* ⇱*217 rooms, 4 suites* ⚒*In-room: safe, refrigerator, dial-up. In-hotel: 6 restaurants, bars, tennis courts, pool, gym, beachfront, concierge, children's programs (ages 4 mos.–13 years), laundry service, public Internet, parking (no fee)* ⊟*AE, MC, V* ⏀*AI.*

$$$$ 🖾**Velas Vallarta.** Silky sheets and cozy down comforters, multiple ceiling fans, and large flat-screen TVs are a few of the creature comforts that set Velas apart from the rest. Each large living area has two comfortably wide built-in couches in colorful prints and a round dining table. Huichol cross-stitch and modern Mexican art decorate the walls. Studios and one-, two-, and three-bedroom suites have the same amenities except that the studios don't have balconies with a view of the pool and the beach. Tall palms, pink bougainvillea, and wild ginger with brilliant red plumes surround the three enormous pools. ⊠*Av. Costera s/n, Marina Vallarta, 48354* 🕾*322/221–0091 or 800/835–2778* ⊕*www.velasvallarta.com* ⇱*339 suites* ⚒*In-room: safe, kitchen, dial-up. In-hotel: 2 restaurants, room service, bars, tennis courts, pools, gym, spa, beachfront, concierge, children's programs (ages 6–12), laundry service, public Internet, public Wi-Fi, parking (no fee), no-smoking rooms, minibar (some)* ⊟*AE, MC, V* ⏀*AI.*

$$$$ 🖾**Westin Resort & Spa.** Hot pink! Electric yellow! Color aside, the Westin's buildings evoke ancient temples and are about as mammoth. There's not a bad sightline anywhere—whether you gaze out to the leafy courtyard or down an orange-tile, brightly painted corridor lined with Mexican art. The jarring echoes here are tempered by the rush of an enormous water feature. In the spacious, balconied rooms concrete-and-stone floors massage bare feet, and top-of-the-line mattresses with whisper-soft duvets make for heavenly siestas. Guest quarters above the sixth floor have ocean views; those below face the 600 palm trees surrounding the four beautiful pools. The Westin's Nikki Beach Club is one of Vallarta's hippest night spots, but time-share touts make some guests miserable. ⊠*Paseo de la Marina Sur 205, Marina Vallarta, 48321* 🕾*322/226–1100, 800/228–3000 in U.S. and Canada* ⊕*www.westinvallarta.com* ⇱*266 rooms, 14 suites* ⚒*In-room: safe, Wi-Fi. In-hotel: 2 restaurants, room service, bars, tennis courts, pools, gym, spa, beachfront, concierge, children's programs (ages infant–12), laundry service, executive floor, public Internet, parking (no fee), no-smoking rooms, some pets allowed* ⊟*AE, DC, MC, V* ⏀*BP.*

$$$–$$$$ 🖾**Sheraton Buganvilias.** Juan Carlos Name, a disciple of modern-minimalist Mexican architect Luis Barragán, designed this looming high-rise near the Hotel Zone's south end and within walking distance of downtown. It's reliable, anonymous, and geared toward conventioneers and other groups. Rooms have very snug and comfortable beds with pillow-top mattresses and downy duvets. This is the closest of the Zona Hotelera Norte hotels to downtown PV. ⊠*Blvd. Fran-*

28

PUERTO VALLARTA HOTELS AT A GLANCE

Puerto Vallarta

HOTEL	Worth Noting	Cost	Rooms	Restaurants	On the Beach	Dive Shop	Pools	Spa	Golf Course	Tennis Courts	Health Club/Gym	Children's Program	Location
Ana Liz	Mexican tradesmen, and backpackers	$26	23										Col. E. Zapata
Andale	well-known bar-restaurant	$55–$125	20	2									Col. E. Zapata
Barceló	all suites; lots to do	$277	304	5	yes	yes	4	yes	1	yes		5-11	Mismaloy
Buenaventura	ideal location	$129	231	5	yes		2	yes		yes			Centro
Casa Andrea	homey apartments	$700/week	11				1						Centro
Casa Dulce Vida	spacious apartments	$60–$120	6	1			1						Centro
Casa Iguana	all suites; full kitchens	$139	52	1			1						Mismaloya
CasaMagna Marriott	something for everyone	$269	433	4	yes		1	yes		yes	yes	4-12	Marina Vallarta
Los Cuatro Vientos	Old PV spirit; good restaurant	$59–$69	14	1			1						Centro
Dreams	elaborate theme nights	$600	337	5	yes		3	yes	2	yes			Zona Hotelera Sur
Eloísa	request a free view	$65–$78	74	1			2						Col. E. Zapata
Emperador	viable budget option	$69–$74	69	1	yes		1						Col. E. Zapata
Fiesta Americana	amazing palapa	$297	291	3	yes		1	yes		yes	yes	4-12	Zona Hotelera Norte
Gaviota Vallarta	a block from the beach	$65–$82	84	1			1						Centro
Hacienda San Angel	only $$$$ downtown; elegant	$370	14	1			3						Col. El Cerro
Majahuitas	romantic, isolated casitas	$375	8	1	yes								Cabo Corrientes Norte
El Pescador	modest Mexican favorite	$99	102	1			1						Col. 5 de Diciembre
Playa Conchas Chinas	great beach	$119	22	1	yes		1						Conchas Chinas
Playa Los Arcos	fab location w/rates to match	$95–$112	171	1	yes		1						Col. E. Zapata
Posada de Roger	downtown; varied crowd	$60	47	1			1						Col. E. Zapata
Presidente InterContinental	secluded cove	$204	120	3	yes	yes	1	yes	1	yes	yes	4-12	Mismaloya
Quinta María Cortez	warm staff; lots of soul	$105–$235	10	1	yes		1						Conchas Chinas
Rio	24-hour computer room	$53–$63	47	1			1						Centro
Rosita	north end of Malecón	$99–$150	115	1			1						Col. 5 de Diciembre
Sheraton Buganvilias	large but reliable	$240–$280	600	3	yes		2	yes	2	yes	yes	4-12	Zona Hotelera Norte
Sol Meliá Puerto Vallarta	great for younger kids	$265	221	6	yes		1		2	yes	yes	inf-13	Marina Vallarta

HOTEL	Worth Noting	Cost	Rooms	Restaurants	On the Beach	Dive Shop	Pools	Spa	Golf Course	Tennis Courts	Health Club/Gym	Children's Program	Location
Tropicana	modest beachfront digs	$75–$91	160	1	yes		1						Col. E. Zapata
Velas Vallarta	all suites; lots of comforts	$370	339	2	yes		2	yes		3	yes	6-12	Marina Vallarta
Westin Resort & Spa	great architecture	$269	280	2	yes		3	yes		3	yes	inf-12	Marina Vallarta
Yasmin	budget rooms w/ cable	$45	27										Col. E. Zapata

North of Puerto Vallarta

HOTEL	Worth Noting	Cost	Rooms	Restaurants	On the Beach	Dive Shop	Pools	Spa	Golf Course	Tennis Courts	Health Club/Gym	Children's Program	Location
Bungalows Los Picos	secluded beach	$36	56	1									Bucerías (Playa del Beso)
Casa Las Brisas	excellent eats included	$395–$515	7	1			1						Punta de Mita, Playa Careyeros
Casa Obelisco	romantic and cozy	$225	4	1			1						Fracc. Costa Azul, San Francisco
Costa Azul	lots of sports and activities	$140	27	1	yes		1						Fracc. Costa Azul, San Francisco
Decameron	bargain, all inclusive	$98–137	620	7			4			3			Bucerías
Four Seasons Resort	excellent spa, golf	$545	168	3	yes		1	yes	yes	4	yes	5-12	Punta de Mita
Grand Velas	sleek majesty	$1,080	269	4	yes		4	yes		1	yes	4-12	Nuevo Vallarta
Marco's Place Villas	basic but comfortable	$62	18	1			1						Bucerías
Marival	lots to do	$292	495	6	yes		4	yes		4	yes	4-17	Nuevo Vallarta
Palmeras	bright, cheerful rooms	$55–$85	11	1			1						Bucerías
Paradise Village	great for families	$185	490	4	yes		2	yes	yes	7	yes	4-11	Nuevo Vallarta
Villa Amor	terrific views	$85–$145	32	1									Sayulita
Villa Bella	tranquil	$150–$200	6	1			1						La Cruz de Huanacaxtle
Villas Buena Vida	good swimming beach	$91	45	1			2						Rincón de Guayabitos
Villa Varadero	great Nuevo Vallarta value	$98	58	1	yes		1						Nuevo Vallarta

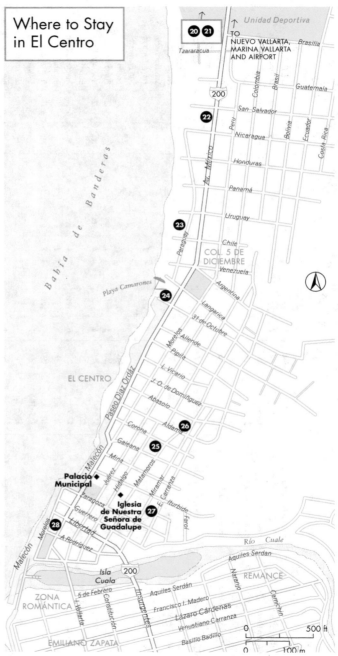

Where to Stay in El Centro

2

TENNIS, ANYONE?

Public tennis courts are few and far between in Vallarta, although most hotels have courts for guests.

Of the public tennis complexes, **Club de Tenis Canto del Sol** (✉ *Hotel Canto del Sol, Local 18, Planta Baja, Zona Comercial Zona Hotelera* ☏ *322/226—0123*) is the largest, with four clay and four asphalt courts; all but two are lighted. Private lessons are $32 per hour, including racquet; court rental is $13 per hour, $20 per hour for

night play. Club hours are 7 AM to 10 PM (7:30–4:30 on Sunday); fees give you access to showers, lockers, and steam room. The **Holiday Inn** (✉ *Blvd. Federico Medina Ascencio, Km. 3.5 Zona Hotelera Norte* ☏ *322/226–1700*) has two asphalt courts rented out at $8 per hour, and $14 per hour at night. Hours are 8:30 AM–7 PM; make arrangements to stay later. A pro gives lessons. Reservations are essential.

cisco *Medina Ascencio 999, Zona Hotelera Norte, 48330* ☏ *322/226– 0404, 800/942–6155 in U.S. and Canada* ⊕ *www.sheratonvallarta. com* ↻ *480 rooms, 120 suites* & *In-room: safe, kitchen, refrigerator, Internet. In-hotel: 3 restaurants, room service, bar, tennis courts, pools, gym, spa, beachfront, concierge, children's programs (ages 4–12), laundry service, executive floor, public Internet, parking (no fee), no-smoking rooms* ☰ *AE, MC, V* ⅏ *EP, CP.*

$$$ 📷 **Presidente InterContinental Puerto Vallarta Resort.** The beautiful aquatone cove the hotel overlooks is the property's best asset. Check-in is handled right in your room, with its white-tile floors and citrus-color fabrics. You'll be asked to choose from among four experiences (Joy of Life, Renewal, Romance, and Peace of Mind) that involve changing the scents, music, stones, flowers, and certain amenities in your room to set the desired tone. Will your choice dictate complimentary red wine or premium tequila? Casablanca lilies or red roses? This marketing gimmick doesn't dramatically enhance the hotel experience, though pillow menus are a nice touch. The long-heralded spa is tiny and has few treatments. ✉ *Carretera a Barra de Navidad, Km 8.6, Mismaloya, 48300* ☏ *322/228–0191* ⊕ *www.acquaesencia.com* ↻ *97 rooms, 23 suites* & *In-room: safe, Wi-Fi (some). In-hotel: 3 restaurants, room service, bars, tennis court, pool, gym, spa, beachfront, diving, concierge, children's programs (ages 4–12), laundry service, public Internet, public Wi-Fi, parking (no fee), no-smoking rooms* ☰ *AE, D, MC, V* ⅏ *EP.*

$$–$$$ 📷 **Quinta María Cortez.** This B&B has soul. Its seven levels ramble up
Fodor's Choice a steep hill at Playa Conchas Chinas, about a 20-minute walk along
★ the sand to the Romantic Zone (or a short hop in a bus or taxi). Most rooms have balconies and kitchenettes; all are furnished with antiques and local art. Other draws are the efficient and welcoming staff, the fortifying breakfast (cooked to order) served on a palapa-covered patio, the nearly private beach below, and the views from the rooftop sundeck. It's popular and has few rooms, so make reservations early. Minimum stays are five nights in winter, and three nights in summer. ✉ *Calle Sagitario 126, Playa Conchas Chinas, 48310* ☏ *322/221–*

CLOSE UP

An Over-the-Top Experience

You don't have to be a rock star to rent one of Vallarta's most beautiful homes, but a similar income or a never-ending trust fund might help.

Just beyond Destiladeras Beach at the north end of Banderas Bay, **Casa Canta Rana** (⊕ *www.casacantarana. com)* provides stunning views of the coast from inside a gated community. Indoor-outdoor living and dining spaces have bay and island views. Decorated with tasteful, seductively subdued furnishings, two of the three bedroom suites share a tall palapa roof; the master suite has an indoor-outdoor shower and private patio. A maid, gardener, and pool boy are included. Additional staff, airport transfer, and other services are provided at additional cost. For the nanny, pilot, or bodyguard on your payroll, there's a separate apartment with bedroom, kitchen, and bath. High season (November 1–April 30) rate is $1,350 per night.

What could be better than a former president's home, the site hand-picked for its almost incomprehensibly beautiful vistas of the sea? President Luis Echevarrí's mansion, **Villa Vista Mágica**, is on a highly forested point between Sayulita and San Francisco, Nayarit. The circular, 10-bedroom property comes with a cook who will prepare three meals a day (Mexican food from a Mexican cook). The waverunners and two Suburbans are also at your disposal. This fabulous place costs a mere $31,250 a week (much more during holidays). To rent this—or a less-pricey property where you'll feel equally special and pampered—contact **Boutique Villas** (866/823–9739 ⊕ *www.boutiquevillas.com*).

Twenty years ago the private heaven of simple fisherfolk and their families, the spearhead-shape point at the northern point of Banderas Bay is today home to the gated, low-density community **Punta Mita** (☎ 888/647–0979 in U.S. and Canada ⊕ *www.puntamita.com.mx*). Here you find the Four Seasons (with Rosewood and St. Regis resorts to open in late 2007), as well as multiple golf courses, beach clubs, spas, and shops. Within the 1,500-acre retreat, the Four Seasons and other brands rent luxury villas whose high-season rates range from $4,000 to $10,000 per night. Floor plans vary but there's consistency in the large outdoor living spaces; air-conditioned common areas and bedrooms with natural-hue, high-quality furnishings; and attentive staff members, including your own full-time chef.

5317, 888/640–8100 *reservations* ⊕ *www.quinta-maria.com* ⤶7 *rooms, 3 villas* ☖ *In-room: no a/c (some), safe, kitchen (some), refrigerator, no TV. In-hotel: pool, beachfront, no elevator, public Internet, no kids under 17* ☰ AE, MC, V ☉BP.

$$ ⊡ **Buenaventura.** The location is ideal: on downtown's northern edge, just a few blocks from the malecón, shops, hotels, and restaurants. The beach has gentle waves, but with brown sand and rocks, it's not the prettiest beach and attracts few bathers. There's a lively pool scene; the adults-only area facing the sea, always crowded, is a big part of the draw. Some rooms are cheerful, with bright striped textiles and framed tropical prints; the drab ones are undergoing renovation at this writing. Ocean-facing balconies are tiny, and if you sit, you can't see a thing.

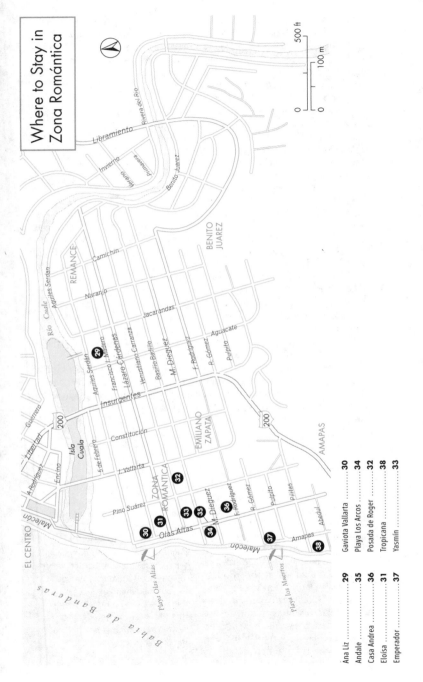

Where to Stay in Zona Romántica

500 ft

100 m

Still, the sum of the whole makes up for the so-so rooms (with hard beds), and the all-inclusive rate is a good deal, especially for families. ⊠*Av. México 1301, El Centro, 48350* ☎*322/226–7000 or 888/859–9439 in U.S. and Canada* ⊕*www.hotelbuenaventura.com.mx* ⊶*216 rooms, 15 suites* ⌂*In-room: dial-up. In hotel: 5 restaurants, room service, bars, pools, spa, beachfront, concierge, laundry service, public Internet* ⊟*AE, MC, V* ⦿*AI, EP.*

$$ **Casa Andrea.** One- and two-bedroom apartments in this spiffy property are truly homey. Each has a different floor plan—some have tiny kitchen-dining areas; others are spacious—but all have ceiling fans and dark-wood beams that contrast with white ceilings and walls. Use the hotel's computers to check your e-mail, or curl up with a book or watch a video in the library. Coffee and pastries are served each morning on the garden patio, where guests (many of them return visitors) sit and chat. The location, a few blocks from Los Arcos and the malecón, is a real plus. With some exceptions, high-season bookings are by the week. Expect some homely but sweet rescued dogs to be wandering about. ⊠*Calle Francisca Rodríguez 174, El Centro, 48380* ☎*322/222–1213* ⊕*www.casa-andrea.com* ⊶*11 apartments* ⌂*In-room: no phone, kitchen, no TV, Wi-Fi. In-hotel: bar, pool, gym, no elevator, laundry facilities, public Internet* ⊟*No credit cards* ⦿*CP.*

$$ **Casa Iguana Hotel de Mismaloya.** Palms and plants edge walkways that line the swimming pool and goldfish ponds. Balconies look down on this garden scene and on the palapa bar-restaurant. Standard suites have full kitchens, shower-only baths, chunky furniture with cast-iron hardware, and tiles with folkloric patterns. Electric orange and yellow plaids brighten spaces that can be dark at certain times of the day. The hotel is on a cobblestone street off the highway; if you don't want to hoof it into PV, take one of the local buses that pass every 15 minutes. The beach is a five-minute walk away; and the village of Mismaloya, with wandering chickens and even burros, is within braying distance. The all-inclusive plan isn't available during high season. ⊠*Av. 5 de Mayo 455, Mismaloya, 48394* ☎*322/228–0186, 877/893–7654 in U.S., 877/224–5057 in Canada* ⊕*www.casaiguanahotel.com* ⊶*49 2-bedroom suites, 3 3-bedroom suites* ⌂*In-room: kitchen, refrigerator. In-hotel: restaurant, room service, bar, pool, laundry facilities, public Wi-Fi, parking (no fee), no-smoking rooms* ⊟*AE, MC, V* ⦿*AI, EP.*

$$ **El Pescador.** Fall asleep to the sound of the waves at this modest yet cheerful hotel that's a favorite among Mexican travelers. Balconies are narrow but provide a view of the pool area and beach. The latter has sand but also fist-size rocks in the tidal zone; the curvy,

---

CAN I DRINK THE WATER?

Most of the fancier hotels have reverse osmosis or other water filtration systems. It's fine for brushing your teeth, but play it safe by drinking bottled water (there might be leaks that let groundwater in). Note that the bottled water in your hotel room may be added to your bill when you leave, even if it appears to be free. It seems that the nicer the hotel, the costlier the water. Buy a few bottles at the corner grocery instead.

medium-size pool is a nice alternative. Bright white and inexpensive, El Pescador is about five blocks north of the malecón (and a sister property, Hotel Rosita). ✉ *Calle Paraguay 1117 at Uruguay, Col. 5 de Diciembre, 48350* ☎ *322/222–1884, 888/242–9587 in Canada, 877/813–6712 in U.S.* 🌐 *www.hotelpescador.com* *102 rooms* *In-room: no a/c (some). In-hotel: restaurant, bar, pool, laundry service, public Internet, public Wi-Fi* *MC, V* *EP.*

MONEY CAN'T BUY HAPPINESS

Not all Los Arcos's guests are budget travelers: some better-heeled guests stay here for the easy-going ambience and the location on the beach near Zona Romántica restaurants, bars, and shops.

$$ **Playa Conchas Chinas.** Studios here have functional kitchenettes, basic cookware, and somewhat thin mattresses on wood-frame beds. Each has a small tiled tub as well as a shower. The real pluses of this plain Jane are the balconies with spectacular beach views and the location above Conchas Chinas Beach, about a 20-minute walk to downtown PV along the beach. The three-bedroom presidential suite has a sound system and large-screen TV. ✉ *Carretera a Barra de Navidad (Carretera 200) Km. 2.5, Conchas Chinas, 48380* ☎ *322/221–5763 or 322/221–5230* 🌐 *www.hotelconchaschinas.com* *21 rooms, 1 suite* *In-room: safe, kitchen, refrigerator, DVD (some). In-hotel: restaurant, bar, pool, beachfront, no elevator, public Wi-Fi, parking (no fee), no elevator* *AE, MC, V* *EP.*

$$ **Playa Los Arcos.** This hotel is attractive because of its location: right on the beach and in the midst of Zona Romántica's restaurants, bars, and shops. Though the price is right, both service and quality have slipped in recent years: Some guests have complained of overbooking, furnishings are tired, and tour groups abound. That said, yellow trumpet vines and lacy palms draped in tiny white lights enliven the pool and the bar-restaurant, which has music nightly and a Mexican fiesta on Saturday evening. If you're willing to cross the street, you can get a better deal at Los Arcos Vallarta, or upgrade slightly to Los Arcos Suites, which has larger rooms with kitchenettes; some have balconies, too. ✉ *Av. Olas Altas 380, Col. E. Zapata, 48380* ☎ *322/222–1583, 800/648–2403 in U.S., 888/729–9590 in Canada, 01800/327–7700 toll-free in Mexico* 🌐 *www.playalosarcos.com* *158 rooms, 13 suites* *In-room: safe (some), kitchen (some). In-hotel: restaurant, bar, pool, beachfront, parking (no fee), no-smoking rooms* *MC, V* *AI, EP.*

$$ **Rosita.** What started as a sleepy 12-room hostelry—one of PV's very first—is now a busy 115-room downtown hotel. It's still a viable budget option, mainly recommended for its location on the north end of the malecón. Rooms are very basic; expect shower-only baths, white-tile floors, and fabrics with floral prints. The cheapest have neither TV nor air-conditioning. Request a room facing the water, as much for the view as for the natural light; rooms facing the street are dark, making them feel cramped. ✉ *Paseo Díaz Ordaz 901, Col. 5 de Diciembre, 48300* ☎ *322/223–2000* 🌐 *www.hotelrosita.com* *115 rooms* *In-*

2

room: *no a/c (some), no TV (some). In-hotel: restaurant, bar, pool, laundry service* ⊟*AE, MC, V* ⊓○⊺*EP.*

$$ ⊡**Tropicana.** This is a well-groomed, bright white hotel at the south end of Playa Los Muertos for a reasonable price. Save $15 a night by booking a standard rather than superior room; except for the size of the TV, they're almost the same. Each has several different areas for sitting or playing cards, but the beds are hard. Suites have no separate living area, but are larger than other rooms and each has a four-burner stove, blender, and fridge. Room views vary, and so do amenities (e.g., some rooms have larger beds than others, some rooms have TV and some don't, and so on). Ask to change rooms if the one you're given doesn't suit you. Also note that many guests have complained about the quality of breakfast, and some people love the staff while others say they aren't wild about the customer relations. ⊠*Calle Amapas 214, Col. E. Zapata, 48380* ☎*322/222–0912* ⇥*148 rooms, 12 suites* ⧖*In room: no TV (some). In-hotel: restaurant, bar, pool, beachfront, parking (no fee)* ⊟*MC, V* ⊓○⊺*BP.*

$–$$ ⊡**Andale.** Deep in the heart of—no, not Texas, but PV's south side— is a little-known hotel above a well-known restaurant-bar. Brick-lined rooms are charming although somewhat stuffy in the hot season. A few lucky rooms and suites have wonderful views of the bay and of the town creeping up the adjoining hills. Down the street from the original Andale are eight luxurious apartments ranging from one-bedroom units with single baths ($150) to three-bedroom units with three baths ($500). All have full kitchens, dining rooms, and great views. There's a swimming pool, a bar, and a lounge area as well. Note that the 15% state tax is included in the rate; only the 2% hotel tax is added to your bill at the end of your stay. ⊠*Calle Olas Altas 425, Col. E. Zapata, 48380* ☎*322/223–2622* ⊕*www.andales.com* ⇥*7 rooms, 2 mini-suites, 2 suites, 8 apartments* ⧖*In-room: no a/c (some), kitchen (some), refrigerator (some). In-hotel: 2 restaurants, room service, bar* ⊟*MC, V* ⊓○⊺*EP.*

$–$$ ⊡**Casa Dulce Vida.** Hidden four blocks off the busy malecón, this '60s-era villa has apartments of various sizes filled with modern Mexican art and comfortable, if well-worn, furniture. All apartments have well-equipped kitchens—again, we're not talking sparkly here (some fridges have rusty faces), but everything works. A few rooms have ocean-view terraces; the largest has three bedrooms, two baths, and a separate dining room. There's a red-tile pool and tropical gardens. In high season the property only accepts weeklong bookings. ⊠*Calle Aldama 295, El Centro, 48300* ☎*322/222–1008* ⊕*www.dulcevida. com* ⇥*6 suites* ⧖*In-room: no a/c (some), no phone (some), safe (some), kitchen, no TV, Wi-Fi (some). In-hotel: pool, no elevator, public Wi-Fi* ⊟*V* ⊓○⊺*EP.*

$–$$ ⊡**Eloísa.** Despite being a block from the beach, this hotel has more of a downtown feel, and sits on pretty Lázaro Cárdenas Park; rooms 211–216 have the best park views. Rooms are generally plain but clean, and there's a great city-and-mountain view from the rooftop, which has a pool and party area. Bungalows have small kitchenettes in one corner; suites have larger kitchens, separate bedrooms, and two quiet

2

CLOSE UP

Buying a Time-Share

■ If you return to PV frequently, a time-share might make sense. Here are some tips for navigating the shark-infested waters:

■ Cruise the Internet before your vacation. Check out resale time-shares in the area, which makes it easier to determine the value of what's offered.

■ Worthwhile time-shares come with the option of trading for a room in another destination. Ask what other resorts are available.

■ Time-share salespeople get great commissions and are very good at their jobs. Be brave, be strong, and only sign on the dotted line if it's what you really want. Remember there are plenty of good vacation deals out there that require no long-term commitment.

■ Buyer's Remorse? If you buy a time-share and get buyers' remorse, be aware that most contracts have a five-day "cooling off period." Ask to see this in writing before you sign the contract; then you can get a full refund if you change your mind.

air-conditioners. Units with great views cost the same as those without, so ask for one *con vista panorámica* (with a panoramic view). ✉*Lázaro Cárdenas 179, Col. E. Zapata, 48380* ☎*322/222–6465 or 322/222–0286* 🌐*www.hoteleloisa.com* *60 rooms, 6 studios, 8 suites* *In-room: no phone, kitchen (some), refrigerator (some). In-hotel: restaurant, bar, pools* ▭*MC, V* *EP.*

$–$$ **Gaviota Vallarta.** Simple rooms in this six-story low-rise have somewhat battered colonial-style furnishings; some have tiny balconies but only a few on the top floors have a partial ocean view. The small figure-8 pool in the middle of the courtyard feels exposed, but still refreshes. The best perks are the location one block from the beach and free parking. Choose air-conditioning or fan, cable TV or no, and a fridge if you like; room costs vary according to these choices. ■ TIP→ **Don't bother with the two-bedroom apartments; they are poorly designed and not worth $150 a night.** ✉*Francisco I. Madero 176, Col. E. Zapata, 48380* ☎*322/222–1500* 🌐*www.hotelgaviota.com* *84 rooms* *In-room: no phone, kitchenette (some), refrigerator (some). In-hotel: restaurant, bar, pool, parking (no fee)* ▭*MC, V* *EP.*

$ **Los Cuatro Vientos.** Gloria Whiting has owned this Old Vallarta original, which opened in 1955, for about 25 years, and some guests have been coming forever. That explains why most of the guests and staff seem like old friends. The restaurant, Chez Elena *(⇨Chapter 3)*, once the toast of the town; the unadorned rooftop bar; and the best room (3-A) have nice views of the bay and of the city's red rooftops. Come to rub shoulders with Europeans and others who appreciate a bargain and a bit of history. Although it's less common today to hear roosters crowing or see donkeys clomp down the street, it's more likely here than elsewhere in PV. Rooms are plain, yet the traditional brick ceilings give a homey feel. ✉*Calle Matamoros 520, El Centro, 48300* ☎*322/222–0161* 🌐*www.cuatrovientos.com* *14 rooms* *In-room: Wi-Fi, no* *a/c, no phone, no TV. In-hotel: restaurant, room service (some), bar, pool, no elevator* ▭*MC, V* ⏏*CP (high season only).*

$ ⌂**Emperador.** Ask for a room on the beach side of the street—those on the other side have no view. In exchange for pressed-wood and faux-bamboo furniture and a tepid-tempered staff, you get an inexpensive lodging overlooking the pier at Playa Los Muertos, and proximity to Old Vallarta. A standard suite for two has a kitchen (with plastic plates, and just the basic, beat-up pots) on a balcony hanging just above the sand. Less than 10 bucks more gets you a junior suite, where the sitting room between the bedroom and outdoor kitchen has two (stiff) couches. The pool and hot tub are down the street. ✉*Calle Amapas 114, Col. E. Zapata, 48380* ☏*322/222–5143 or 322/222–3329* ⊕*www.hotelemperadorpv.com* ⇥*19 rooms, 50 suites* ♿*In-room: kitchen (some). In-hotel: restaurant, bar, beachfront, no elevator (in one tower)* ▭*MC, V* ⏏*EP.*

$ ⌂**Posada de Roger.** If you hang around the pool or the small shared balcony overlooking the street and the bay beyond, it's not hard to get to know the other guests—many of them savvy budget travelers from Europe and Canada. A shared, open-air kitchen on the fourth floor has a great view, too. Rooms are spare and vaultlike—some have scruffy features—and security on the first floor isn't what it should be. But the showers are hot, and the beds comfortable (if you like a very firm mattress). Freddy's Tucan, the indoor-outdoor bar-restaurant (no dinner; $) is popular with locals—mainly for breakfast. The hotel is in a prime part of the Zona Romántica known for its restaurants and shops; Playa los Muertos is a few blocks away. ✉*Calle Basilio Badillo 237, Col. E. Zapata, 48380* ☏*322/222–0836 or 322/222–0639* ⊕*www.hotel-posadaderoger.com* ⇥*47 rooms* ♿*In-hotel: restaurant, bar, pool, no elevator* ▭*AE, MC, V* ⏏*EP.*

$ ⌂**Río.** This budget hotel get points for its location just north of Isla Río Cuale, two blocks from both the beach and the main plaza. It gets even more points for the cheerful, well-air-conditioned little restaurant-bar serving Mexican specials, and for the computer room with many stations, open 24 hours a day. On the downside (way down) are visible plastic tubing in the halls, uninspired, older furnishings in many rooms, and rusted fridges in "suites," which are slightly larger than standard rooms and have sinks and microwaves for $10 more. ✉*Calle Morelos 170, El Centro, 48380* ☏*322/222–0366* ⊕*www.hotelrio.com.mx* ⇥*47 rooms* ♿*In-room: kitchen (some), refrigerator (some). In-hotel: restaurant, bar, pool, public Internet* ▭*MC, V* ⏏*EP.*

¢ ⌂**Ana Liz.** Those who prefer to spend their vacation cash on eating out and shopping might consider this clean, bright, motel-like budget hotel a few blocks south of the Cuale River, behind Cine Bahía. Two floors of rooms face each other across an outdoor corridor and have tiny bathrooms but comfortable beds. Ask for a room away from the noisy street; don't ask to use the lobby phone—it's not allowed. Small TVs (local channels only) are available for about $3 a day; a deposit is required for a towel. Small-time businesspeople and backpacking Europeans stay at this extremely plain place when they come to town; they're likely drawn by the substantial discounts for monthly stays.

⊠*Francisco I. Madero 429, Col. E. Zapata, 48380* ☎*322/222–1757* ✆hotelanaliz@hotmail.com ↻*23 rooms* ⚭*In-room: no a/c (some), no phone. In hotel: no elevator* ▤*No credit cards* †⊙*EP.*

¢ ⊞**Yasmín.** Two-story and L-shaped, this budget baby has no pool, but it's just a block from the beach and joined at the hip to Café de Olla *(⇨Chapter 3)*, the extremely popular Mexican restaurant. Small, ho-hum rooms have low ceilings, firm beds, and open closets but also floor fans and cable TV: not a bad deal for the price. ⊠*Calle Basilio Badillo, Col. E. Zapata, 48380* ☎*322/222–0087* ↻*27 rooms* ⚭*In-room: no phone. In-hotel: no elevator* ▤*No credit cards* †⊙*EP.*

NORTH OF PUERTO VALLARTA

$$$$ ⊞**Casa Las Brisas.** Architect-owner Marc Lindskogh has created a nook
★ of nonchalant elegance, with updated country furnishings of wicker, leather, and wood; rock-floor showers without curtains or doors; and cheerful Pacific Coast architectural details. Mosquito netting lends romance to cozy, quilt-covered beds. Waves crashing onshore, their sound somehow magnified, create white noise that lulls you to sleep. In the morning, settle into a cushy chaise on your private patio to watch seabirds swim; at night watch the sun set behind Punta de Mita. These simple pleasures make this hideaway a winner. It doesn't hurt that the food is truly delicious, the bar is well-stocked with international labels, and it's all included in the room price. You can avoid the 10% surcharge for credit cards by using PayPal. ⊠*Playa Careyeros, Punta de Mita, Nayarit, 63734* ☎*329/298–4114* ⊕*www.mexicoboutiquehotels.com/casalasbrisas* ↻*7 rooms* ⚭*In-room: no phone, safe, refrigerator, no TV (some). In-hotel: restaurant, bar, pool, water sports, no elevator, concierge* †⊙*AI.*

$$$$ ⊞**Four Seasons Resort.** The hotel and its fabulous spa perch above a
Fodor'sChoice lovely beach at the northern extreme of Bahía de Banderas, about 45
★ minutes from the PV airport and an hour north of downtown Puerto Vallarta. Spacious rooms occupy Mexican-style casitas of one, two, and three stories. Each room has elegant yet earthy furnishings and a private terrace or balcony—many with a sweeping sea view. The Jack Nicklaus–designed championship golf course has a challenging, optional 19th-island hole; the gym is first rate; and a good variety of sporting and beach equipment is on hand. Just offshore, the Marietas Islands are great for snorkeling, diving, whale-watching, and fishing. This is the place for indulging golf and spa fantasies, exploring beaches and small towns to the north and south, or doing absolutely nothing. ⊠*Bahía de Banderas, Punta de Mita63734, Nayarit* ☎*329/291–6019, 800/322–3442 in U.S., 800/268–6282 in Canada* ⊕*www.fshr.com/puntamita* ↻*141 rooms, 27 suites* ⚭*In-room: safe, refrigerator, DVD, Ethernet. In-hotel: 3 restaurants, room service, bars, golf course, tennis courts, pool, gym, spa, beachfront, water sports, concierge, children's programs (ages 5–12), laundry service, public Internet, parking (no fee), no-smoking rooms* ▤*AE, DC, MC, V* †⊙*EP, BP.*

Continued on page 46

SPAAAHH

The trend of luxury spas in Mexico, and particularly in vacation hot spots like Puerto Vallarta, shows no signs of slowing. From elegant resort spas scented with essence of orange and bergamot to Aztec-inspired day spas, each has its own personality and signature treatments. Competition keeps creativity high, with an ever-changing menu of new treatments, many using native products like sage, chocolate, aloe vera, and even tequila.

Four Seasons Resort, Punta Mita

Spa Savvy

All of the spas listed here are open to nonguests, but reservations are essential. Guests of the hotel may get discounts. Spa customers can sometimes use other facilities at a resort, such as the restaurant, beach, pool, or gym. Ask when you book. Prices are generally on par with those of resort spas worldwide, but some deals are to be had, if you go with the less-expensive but still high-quality spas we lists. Or scout out hotel-spa packages and specials.

RESORT NAME	BODY TREATMENTS	SEASIDE TREATMENTS	TREATMENTS FOR TWO	FITNESS DAY PASS	HOT TUB	TEMAZCAL
Four Seasons	$80-$188	yes	yes	yes*	yes	yes
Gran Velas	$58-$178	yes	yes	$40	yes	no
Paradise Village	$69-$104	yes	yes**	$20	yes	no
El Tamarindo	$48-$152	yes	yes	no	no	yes
Terra Noble	$55-$65	no	yes	no	yes	yes

* a fitness day pass is free for Four Seasons guests; non-guests have access to all hotel facilities for half the room rate
** At El Tigre spa, at golf course

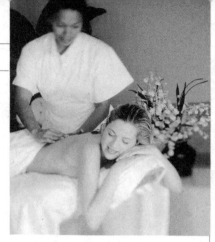

TOP SPOTS

Organically Yours

EL TAMARINDO
This *Gilligan's Island*–style spa has no sauna, whirlpool, or fancy extras. But it does have some of the best treatments and staff in Pacific Mexico, and one of the most authentic *temazcals* (*See* Glossary, *p. 46*) around. The vibe is more convivial warmth than nonchalant New Age. Products are often made with lemongrass, aloe vera, fresh coconut, and mineral-laced mud. Try the Tonameyotl Teocuitlatic facial, which employs a mixture of champagne and real gold.

Body Treatments & Services: Exfoliation; massage; wraps, scrubs and body treatments (11 types); temazcal sweat lodge; yoga and Chi-Kung classes; meditation.

Beauty Treatments: Facials, manicure, pedicure

Prices: Body treatments $67–$152; facials $86–$95; manicure/pedicure $38–$48

Carretera Melaque–*Puerto Vallarta (Carretera 200) km. 7.5, Cihuatlán. Tel. 315/351–5032* ⊕ *www.mexicoboutiquehotels.com/thetamarindo* ▭ *AE, MC, V.*

A Spa for All Seasons

FOUR SEASONS PUNTA MITA APUANE SPA
Professional service is the hallmark of this exclusive spa. An excellent kid's club allows you to enjoy spa treatments, knowing that your children are thoroughly engaged. The gym is first rate. An inspirational experience is a traditional temazcal ceremony, which takes place in a little building on a knoll near the sea.

Treatments are among the most expensive in the area, but everything is top drawer. Native products are used almost exclusively; the Punta Mita massage combines tequila and locally grown sage. And refreshing lime is mixed with tequila and salt for a margarita body scrub.

Body Treatments: Aromatherapy; facials; exfoliation; massage (10 types); Vichy hydrotherapy; wraps and scrubs (7 types); temazcal sweat lodge.

Beauty Treatments: Facials (7 types); manicure; pedicure; hair/scalp treatment.

Prices: Body treatments $83–$230; facials $95–$209; hair: $44–$95; manicure or pedicure $53–$125; waxing $27–$73.

Packages: Standard treatment combinations, such as the Mayan honeymoon ritual, with mini facial, skin softening wrap and milk bath for two. *Punta de Mita, Bahía de Banderas. Tel. 329/291–6000* ⊕ *www.fourseasons.com/puntamita.* ▭ *AE, DC, MC, V.*

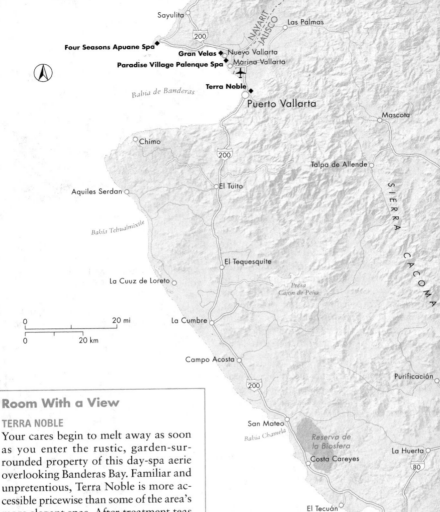

Sayulita
Las Palmas
200
Four Seasons Apuane Spa
Gran Velas Nuevo Vallarta
Paradise Village Palenque Spa Marina Vallarta
Bahía de Banderas
Terra Noble
Puerto Vallarta
Mascota
Chimo
Talpa de Allende
200
El Tuito
Aquiles Serdan
S
I
E
R
R
A
Bahía Tehualmixtle
El Tequesquite
C
A
C
O
M
A
La Cuuz de Loreto
*Presa
Cajón de Peña*
0 ___ 20 mi
La Cumbre
0 ___ 20 km
Campo Acosta
Purificación
200
San Mateo
Bahía Chamela
Reserva de
la Biosfera
La Huerta
Costa Careyes
80
El Tecuán
Bahía Tenacatita
Cihuatlán
El Tamarindo
Barra de Navidad

Room With a View

TERRA NOBLE

Your cares begin to melt away as soon as you enter the rustic, garden-surrounded property of this day-spa aerie overlooking Banderas Bay. Familiar and unpretentious, Terra Noble is more accessible pricewise than some of the area's more elegant spas. After-treatment teas are served on an outdoor patio with a great sea view. Two-hour temazcal sweat lodge rituals cleanse on three levels: physically, mentally, and spiritually. Or recharge with clay and painting classes, and Tarot readings.

Body Treatments: Reflexology; massage; several wraps and scrubs; temazcal sweat lodge; yoga/meditation.

Beauty Treatments: Facials; manicure; pedicure.

Packages: A few economical packages such as the Stress Recovery (a sea-salt body scrub, a massage, and a facial), for $145.

Prices: Body treatments $50–$65; manicure/pedicure $25–$30.
Av. Tulipanes 595, at Fracc. Lomas de Terra Noble, Col. 5 de Diciembre. Tel. 322/223-3530
🌐 *www.terranoble.com.* ▭ *MC, V.*

MORE TOP SPOTS

Something for Every Body

PARADISE VILLAGE PALENQUE SPA

On a peninsula between the beach and marina, this modern Maya temple of glass and marble is a cool, sweet-smelling oasis with separate wings for men and women; each is equipped with private hydrotherapy tubs, whirlpools, saunas, and steam rooms. The coed gym has state-of-the-art equipment and views of the ocean, plus aerobics classes in a separate studio and an indoor lap pool.

Spa designer Diana Mestre, an old hand in these parts, brings together ancient healing arts and the latest technologies. The reasonably priced therapy selections are extensive, from an anti-cellulite seaweed wrap to milk baths with honey, amaranth, and orange oil or the raindrop aromatherapy massage, employing clove, sage, bergamot, and other essential oils.

Body Treatments: Aromatherapy; facials; electro-acuscope anti-pain & stress therapy; Reiki; exfoliation; hot-stone massage; hydrotherapy; wraps, scrubs, and body treatments (14 types); reflexology; shiatsu.

Beauty Treatments: Facials (10 types), manicure, pedicure.

Prices: Body treatments $40–$119; facials $40–$119; manicure/pedicure $23–$63; hair $35–$97; waxing $6–$63.

Packages: A wide variety of packages that allow switching treatments in an equivalent price bracket. The basic plan combines three 50-minute treatments: marine body scrub, holistic massage, and hydrating facial.

Paseo de los Cocoteros 1 Nuevo Vallarta.
Tel. 322/226-6770 ⊕ *www.paradisevillage.com.*
▭ *AE, MC, V.*

Drama Queen

GRAN VELAS

The spa at Nuevo Vallarta's most elegant all-inclusive has the same dramatic architectural lines and artful use of marble, stone, teak, and tile. The 16,500-square-foot facility has 23 treatment rooms, and ample steam, sauna, and whirlpools. Lounge in the comfortable chaises in the "plunge lagoon" (with warm and cold pools) between or after treatments, with a cup of hot tea or cold chlorophyll water.

Reading the extensive menu of treatments can take hours—highlights are the chocolate, gold, or avocado wraps, Thai massage, European facial, cinnamon-sage foot scrub, and the challenging buttocks sculpt-lift. Adjoining the spa is an impressive fitness facility.

Body Treatments: Reflexology; massage (18 types); shiatsu; Vichy shower; exfoliation; wraps, scrubs, baths, and body treatments (32 types).

Beauty Treatments: Facials (12+); manicure/pedicure; hair care; waxing; makeup.

Prices: Body treatments: $58–$178; facials: $89–$148; manicure/pedicure: $20–$89; hair care: $29–$89; waxing: $29–$58; makeup: $78.

Packages: 10% discount for three or more treatments; otherwise, no packages.

Av. de los Cocoteros 98 Sur, Nuevo Vallarta.
Tel. 322/226-8000 ⊕ *www.grandvelas.com.*
▭ *AE, MC, V.*

GLOSSARY

acupuncture. Painless Chinese medicine during which needles are inserted into key spots on the body to restore the flow of *qi* and allow the body to heal itself.

aromatherapy. Massage and other treatments using plant-derived essential oils intended to relax the skin's connective tissues and stimulate the flow of lymph fluid.

ayurveda. An Indian philosophy that uses oils, massage, herbs, and diet and lifestyle modification to restore perfect balance to a body.

body brushing. Dry brushing of the skin to remove dead cells and stimulate circulation.

body polish. Use of scrubs, loofahs, and other exfoliants to remove dead skin cells.

hot-stone massage. Massage using smooth stones heated in water and applied to the skin with pressure or strokes or simply rested on the body.

hydrotherapy. Underwater massage, alternating hot and cold showers, and other water-oriented treatments.

reflexology. Massage on the pressure points of feet, hands, and ears.

reiki. A Japanese healing method involving universal life energy, the laying on of hands, and mental and spiritual balancing. It's intended to relieve acute emotional and physical conditions. Also called radiance technique.

salt glow. Rubbing the body with coarse salt to remove dead skin.

shiatsu. Japanese massage that uses pressure applied with fingers, hands, elbows, and feet.

shirodhara. Ayurvedic massage in which warm herbalized oil is trickled onto the center of the forehead, then gently rubbed into the hair and scalp.

sports massage. A deep-tissue massage to relieve muscle tension and residual pain from workouts.

Swedish massage. Stroking, kneading, and tapping to relax muscles. It was devised at the University of Stockholm in the 19th century by Per Henrik Ling.

Swiss shower. A multijet bath that alternates hot and cold water, often used after mud wraps and other body treatments.

Temazcal. Maya meditation in a sauna heated with volcanic rocks.

THE TEMAZCAL TRADITION

Increasingly popular at Mexico spas is the traditional sweat lodge, or *temazcalli*. Herb-scented water sizzles on heated lava rocks, filling the intimate space with purifying steam. Rituals blend indigenous and New Age practices, attempting to stimulate you emotionally, spiritually, and physically. For the sake of others, it's best to take a temazcal only if you're committed to the ceremony, or at least open-minded, and not claustrophobic.

Thai massage. Deep-tissue massage and passive stretching to ease stiff, tense, or short muscles.

thalassotherapy. Water-based treatments that incorporate seawater, seaweed, and algae.

Vichy shower. Treatment in which a person lies on a cushioned, waterproof mat and is showered by overhead water jets.

Watsu. A blend of shiatsu and deep-tissue massage with gentle stretches—all conducted in a warm pool.

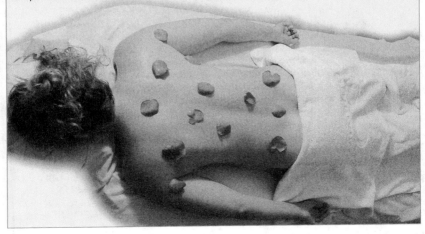

$$$$ ⌐Grand Velas. In scale and majesty, the public areas of this luxury brand compare to other Nuevo Vallarta all-inclusives like the Taj Majal to a roadside taco stand. Ceilings soar overhead, and the structure and furnishings are simultaneously minimalist and modern, yet earthy, incorporating stucco, rock, polished teak, and gleaming ecru marble. The spa is excellent, and the views—with the garden-shrouded pool in the foreground and the beach beyond—are striking. Rooms are sleek, with elegant furnishings and appointments. In terms of food and

> **PILLOW TALK**
>
> If you're picky about your pillow, Grand Velas, Presidente Intercontinental, Four Seasons, or another top-drawer accommodation might prove to be the hotel of your dreams. Some of the swankiest hotels in the area have pillow menus with a half-dozen or more styles to choose from. Go with whisper-soft eider-down or, if you're allergic to farm animals, 100% man-made materials.

drink, the high price entitles you to top-of-the-line spirits in minibars and restaurants, but the food, in our experience, is not exceptional, and for a rack rate of over $1,000 per couple per night, all-inclusive, it should be. ⌐Paseo de los Cocoteros 98 Sur, Nuevo Vallarta, Jalisco, 63735 ☎322/226–8000, 877/398–2784 in U.S., 866/355–3359 in Canada ⊕www.grandvelas.com ➟269 suites &In-room: safe, CD, DVD, Wi-Fi. In-hotel: 4 restaurants, room service, bars, tennis court, pools, gym, spa, beachfront, children's programs (ages 4–12), laundry service, public Internet, airport shuttle, parking (no fee), some pets allowed (fee) ▭AE, MC, V ⦿ΙAI.

$$$$ ⌐Marival. Rooms have strong air-conditioning and amenities like hair dryers, irons and ironing boards, and small tubs, but also demonstrate an uninspired attempt at modern decor, not to mention cheap doors. There's an extra charge, inexplicably, for the use of in-room safes. Only a few units have ocean views, but there are plenty of individual palapas and lounge chairs at the beach. Come here for the relatively inexpensive all-inclusive price and the wealth of activities. ⌐Paseo Cocoteros s/n at Blvd. Nuevo Vallarta, Nuevo Vallarta63735, Jalisco ☎322/226–8200 ⊕www.gomarival.com ➟373 rooms, 122 suites &In-room: kitchen (some). In-hotel: 6 restaurants, room service, bars, tennis courts, pools, gym, spa, beachfront, bicycles, children's programs (ages 4–17), public Internet, parking (no fee) ▭MC, V ⦿ΙAI.

$$$ ⌐Casa Obelisco. The vibe is warm and romantic, the cozy-chic rooms—endowed with original paintings, folk art, and super-comfortable king beds with pillowtop mattresses and mosquito nets—are perfect for spooning and honeymooning. Drinks by the pool, walks on the beach, and trips into town or down to Sayulita (5 km [3 mi] south) are about as ambitious as most guests get. Each ocean-facing patio (some private, some shared) has either a hammock or table with equipale (pigskin) chairs. American owners provide opinions and information about the area. Breakfasts are varied and expansive. Kahlua, the well-behaved doodle dog, is a boon to pet-starved guests. ⌐Calle Palmas 115, Fracc. Costa Azul, San Francisco63732, Nayarit ☎311/258–4316 ⊕www. casaobelisco.com ➟4 rooms &In-room: no phone, no TV. In-hotel:

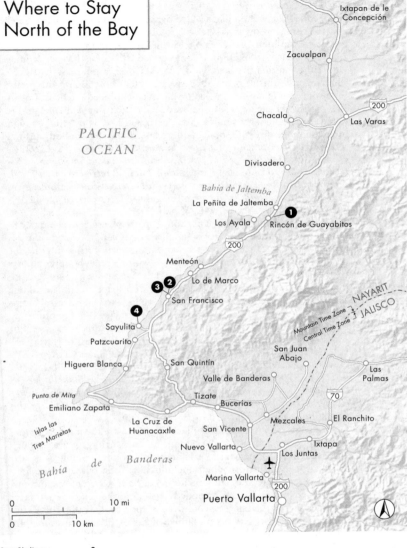

Where to Stay North of the Bay

Ixtapan de le Concepción

Zacualpan

PACIFIC OCEAN

Chacala

Las Varas

200

Divisadero

Bahía de Jaltemba

La Peñita de Jaltemba

Los Ayala

Rincón de Guayabitos ❶

200

Menteón

Lo de Marco

❸❷ San Francisco

❹ Sayulita

Patzcuarito

Higuera Blanca

San Quintín

San Juan Abajo

Valle de Banderas

Mountain Time Zone **NAYARIT** **JALISCO**
Central Time Zone

Las Palmas

Punta de Mita

Emiliano Zapata

Tizate

Bucerías

70

Islas las Tres Marietas

La Cruz de Huanacaxtle

San Vicente

Mezcales

El Ranchito

Nuevo Vallarta

Ixtapa

Bahía de Banderas

Los Juntas

Marina Vallarta

200

Puerto Vallarta

0 — 10 mi
0 — 10 km

restaurant, bar, pool, no elevator, no kids under 16 ▤*No credit cards* ⍭❙*BP* ⊘*Closed July–Sept.*

$$$ ⍨**Paradise Village.** Built like a Maya pyramid, this Nuevo Vallarta hotel
Ⅽ and time-share property is perfect for families, with lots of activities
geared to children. Many people love it, others complain of the over-
zealous time-share pitch and poor service. All suites have balconies
with either marina or ocean views; the smallest, a junior suite, is 700
square feet. Furnishings are attractive as well as functional, with pretty
cane sofa beds in a soothing palette and well-equipped kitchens. Locals
like to visit the clean, well-organized spa, which smells divine, and is
noted for its massages and facials. The beach here is tranquil enough
for swimming, although some small waves are suitable for bodysurfing.
⊠*Paseo de los Cocoteros 1, Nuevo Vallarta63732, Jalisco* ☎*322/226–
6770, 800/995–5714 Ext. 111 in U.S. and Canada* ⊕*www.paradisevil-
lage.com* ⌨*490 suites* ⅀*In-room: safe, kitchen, refrigerator. In-hotel:
4 restaurants, room service, bars, golf course, tennis courts, pools, gym,
spa, beachfront, children's programs (ages 4–11), concierge, public Wi-
Fi, parking (no fee)* ▤*AE, MC, V* ⍭❙*EP.*

$$–$$$ ⍨**Villa Bella.** Tranquillity reigns, and tropical plants give character to
this privately owned property on a hill above quiet La Cruz, just north
of Bucerías. Choose a garden-view room or ocean-facing suite in one
of two villas that share common rooms—with TV, telephone, computer
with Internet access, and DVD and CD players—as well as a swim-
ming pool and gardens. Other pretty shared spaces include a dining
area and kitchen in the guest villa, and second-story terraces off some
of the suites. A very Mexican village with a growing number of foreign
residents and snowbirds, Villa Bella is the perfect place to enjoy the
simple charms of earthy La Cruz. Payment is accepted only via Pay-
Pal. ⊠*Calle del Monte Calvario 12, La Cruz de Huanacaxtle 63732,
Nayarit* ☎*329/295–5161, 329/295–5154, 877/273–6244 toll-free
in U.S., 877/513–1662 toll-free in Canada* ⊕*www.villabella-lacruz.
com* ⌨*2 rooms, 4 suites* ⅀*In-room: no a/c (some), no phone, kitchen
(some), no TV (some). In-hotel: restaurant, bar, pool, no elevator, air-
port shuttle, no-smoking rooms* ▤*MC, V* ⍭❙*CP.*

$$ ⍨**Costa Azul.** What makes this place attractive are the many activities
Ⅽ offered: horseback riding, kayaking, hiking, surfing (with lessons),
and excursions to the Marietas Islands or La Tobara mangroves near
San Blas. The all-inclusive plan includes activities, but since the food
is mainly mediocre and San Pancho has several excellent restaurants,
the European Plan is recommended. Although the sandy beach faces
the open ocean, it curves around to a spot that's safer for swimming. Some guests have complained of disorganized and unhelpful
staff members, and hotel maintenance has declined in recent years.
⊠*Carretera 200, Km 118, Fracc. Costa Azul, San Francisco63732,
Nayarit* ☎*311/258–4210, 800/365–7613 in U.S.* ⊕*www.costaazul.
com* ⌨*24 rooms, 3 villas* ⅀*In-room: no phone, kitchen (some),
refrigerator (some), no TV. In-hotel: restaurant, bars, pool, beachfront, water sports, no elevator, laundry service, parking (no fee)*
▤*AE, D, DC, MC, V* ⍭❙*AI, EP, FAP.*

CLOSE UP

Don't Be (Time-Share) Shark Bait

In Puerto Vallarta, time-share sales-people are as unavoidable as death and taxes. And almost as dreaded. Although a slim minority of people actually enjoy going to one- to four-hour time-share presentations to get the freebies that range from Kahlua to rounds of golf, car rentals, meals, and shows, most folks find the experience incredibly annoying. For some it even casts a pall over their whole vacation.

The bottom line is, if the sharks smell interest, you're dead in the water. Time-share salespeople occupy tiny booths up and down main streets where tourists and cruise passengers walk. In general, while *vallartenses* are friendly, they don't accost you on the street to start a conversation. Those who do are selling something. Likewise, anyone calling you *amigo* is probably selling. The best solution is to walk by without responding, or say "No thanks" or "I'm not interested" as you continue walking. When they yell after you, don't feel compelled to explain yourself.

Some sly methods of avoidance that have worked for others are telling the tout that you're out of a job but dead interested in attending a presentation. They'll usually back off immediately. Or explaining confidentially that the person you're with is not your spouse. Time-share people are primarily interested in married couples—married to each other, that is! But our advice is still to practice the art of total detachment with a polite rejection and then ignoring the salesperson altogether if he or she persists.

Even some very nice hotels (like the Westin) allow salespeople in their lobbies disguised as the Welcome Wagon or information gurus. Ask the concierge for the scoop on area activities, and avoid the so-called "information desk."

Time-share salespeople often pressure guests to attend time-share presentations, guilt-tripping them ("My family relies on the commissions I get," for example) or offering discounts on the hotel room and services. The latter are sometimes difficult to redeem and cost more time than they're worth. And although it may be the salesperson's livelihood, remember that this is your vacation, and you have every right to use the time as you wish.

$$ ▥ **Decameron.** This high-volume hotel is at the south end of long and lovely Bucerías Beach and has beautifully manicured grounds. It also has quality entertainment, activities, and food, and strives to maintain high sanitary standards. Rooms are plain and not particularly modern or appealing, with laminate bathroom counters and textured stucco interior walls that have been painted over many times. Those in the older section have the best views since they were built along the water. Reservations must be made through a brick-and-mortar or online travel agency (e.g., Expedia.com, Travelocity.com, etc.). ✉ *Calle Lázaro Cárdenas, Bucerías63732, Nayarit* ☎ *329/298–0226, FunJet 888/558–6654* ⊕ *www.decameron.com* ➼ *620 rooms* ⚙ *In-room: safe (fee). In-hotel: 7 restaurants, bars, tennis courts, pools, bicycles, public Internet, parking (no fee)* ═ *MC, V* ⏱ *AI.*

$$ ▥ **Villa Amor.** What began as a hilltop home has slowly become an
★ amalgam of unusual, rustic-but-luxurious suites with indoor and out-

door living spaces. The higher up your room, the more beautiful the view of Sayulita's coast. The trade-off for such beauty? A long walk up a seemingly endless staircase and the dearth of room phones make contacting the front desk frustrating. Accommodations, managed by different owners, range from basic to honeymoon suites with terraces and plunge pools. Details like recessed color-glass light fixtures, talavera sinks in bathrooms, brick ceilings, wrought-iron table lamps, art in wall niches, and colorful cement floors add a lot of class. The property overlooks a rocky cove where you can fish from shore; a beautiful sandy beach is a few minutes' walk. The staff lends out bikes, kayaks, boogie boards, and snorkeling gear. The restaurant is closed in low season unless occupancy is unusually high. ⊠ *Playa Sayulita, Sayulita63842, Nayarit* ☎ *329/291–3010* ⊕ *www.villaamor.com* ⇝ *32 villas* �*In-room: no a/c (some), no phone, kitchen (some), refrigerator, no TV. In-hotel: restaurant, bar, water sports, bicycles, no elevator, laundry service, parking (no fee)* ⊟ *No credit cards* �†○† *EP.*

> ### OM AWAY FROM HOME
>
> **Via Yoga** (⊕ *www.viayoga.com*), based in Seattle, WA, offers week-long packages at Villa Amor that include twice-daily yoga classes with group activities, various disciplines of yoga, and, if you like, surfing classes and excursions.

$$ ▦ **Villa Varadero.** Kids under 10 stay and eat for free with the all-
☾ inclusive plan at this small, friendly, four-story hotel in Nuevo Vallarta.
★ What's the bottom line, then? Families can stay for less than $150 per night, including tax. Other pluses are the wide beach with gentle surf; the free use of bikes, kayaks, and boogie boards; and the chummy bar with its billiards salon, dart boards, dominoes, chess, and other games. Only a few of the compact, well-maintained units have tubs, and decor is standard, although walls are painted in cheerful hues. ⊠ *Retorno Nayarit, Lotes 83 and 84, Manzana XIII, Nuevo Vallarta63732, Jalisco* ☎ *322/297–0430* ⊕ *www.villavaradero.com.mx* ⇝ *29 rooms, 29 suites* �*In-room: safe, kitchen (some), refrigerator. In-hotel: restaurant, bars, pool, beachfront, bicycles, laundry service, parking (no fee)* ⊟ *AE, MC, V* †○† *AI, EP.*

$$ ▦ **Villas Buena Vida.** On beautiful Rincón de Guayabitos Beach, this property has three-story units, breeze-ruffled palms, and manicured walkways. Four guests are allowed in even the smallest rooms (which have two double beds and run-of-the-mill hotel furnishings), making this a deal for bargain hunters. Guayabitos is a Mexican resort town that's recently been attracting snowbirds and travelers looking for less-touristy digs. The bay has calm surf that's good for swimming, a long flat beach embraced by twin headlands (great for walking), and boat trips to the quiet coves and solitary beaches along Jaltemba Bay. Be prepared for the staff to count every spoon and spatula when you check in and out. ⊠ *Retorno Laureles 2, Rincón de Guayabitos63727, Nayarit* ☎ *327/274–0231* ⊕ *www.villasbuenavida.com* ⇝ *36 rooms, 9 suites* �*In-room: kitchen, refrigerator. In-hotel: restaurant, pools, no elevator, laundry facilities* ⊟ *MC, V* †○† *EP.*

2

$ Marco's Place Villas. Despite its name, this is a motel-like three-story property, and one of the few standard hotels in Bucerías, which is filled with apartment and condo rentals. Rooms are on the small side, with tiny baths, but beds are comfortable. Junior suites are slightly larger, with a tiled breakfast counter. The property is a block from the beach. ⊠ *Calle Juventino Espinoza 6–A, Bucerías63732, Nayarit* ☎ *329/298–0865* ⊕ *www.marcosplacevillas.com* ⤳ *15 rooms, 3 suites* ⚹ *In-room: kitchenette, refrigerator. In-hotel: pool, no elevator* ⊟ *No credit cards* ℗️*EP.*

GET YOUR ZZZ'S

Some accommodations in coastal Nayarit and Jalisco are along the main highway and experience heavy traffic. And resort hotels often have lobby bars in the middle of an open-air atrium leading directly to rooms, or rooftop discoteques, or outdoor theme nights with live music. When you book, request a room far from the noisiest part of the hotel.

¢–$ Palmeras. A block from the beach, in an area with lots of good restaurants, Palmeras has small rooms with brightly painted interior walls and modeled-stucco sunflowers serving as a kind of headboard behind the bed. Rooms on the second floor have a partial ocean view. There's plenty of space to socialize around the pool, basketball court, outdoor grill, and grassy picnic area, and a TV with satellite in the lounge for essential programs in English. The more expensive rooms are larger, newer, and have a sitting room and cable TV. ⊠ *Lázaro Cárdenas 35, Bucerías63732, Nayarit* ☎ *329/298–1288* ⊕ *www.hotelpalmeras.com* ⤳ *11 rooms* ⚹ *In-room: no phone, kitchen, refrigerator, no TV (some), Wi-Fi. In-hotel: pool, no elevator, no-smoking rooms* ⊟ *MC, V* ℗️*EP.*

¢ Bungalows Los Picos. Deep ochre walls are trimmed in cobalt blue and brick archways at this warm, two-story property. The value is even greater if you put several families in the two- and three-bedroom bungalows. Don't expect to be in town: this enclave of about a half-dozen hotels is on Playa del Beso at the north end of Bucerías. You'll need a car or a taxi if you plan on straying from the pool or the beautiful beach for grocery shopping, sightseeing, or dining out. Bungalow-style motels and related trailer parks fill up with Canadian and American snowbirds in winter, and with large Mexican families during school vacations. The restaurant is closed in low season. ⊠ *Carretera Tepic–Puerto Vallarta (Carretera 200), Km 140, Playa del Beso, Bucerías63732, Nayarit* ☎ *329/298–0470* ⊕ *www.lospicos.com.mx* ⤳ *56 bungalows for 4, 6, or 8 people* ⚹ *In-room: no a/c (some), kitchen (some), refrigerator (some). In-hotel: restaurant, no elevator, public Internet* ⊟ *No credit cards* ℗️*EP.*

COSTALEGRE

$$$$ Las Alamandas. Personal service and exclusivity lure movie stars and royalty to this low-key resort in a nature preserve about 1½ hours from both PV and Manzanillo. Suites are filled with folk art; their indoor-outdoor living rooms have modern furnishings with deliciously nubby fabrics in bright, bold colors and Guatemalan-cloth throw pillows. Request a TV, VCR, and movie from the library for an evening in; there's little else to do at night except socialize. There's lots more to do in the daytime, however, including picnics anywhere on the property (the thorn forest here is scrubby and dry rather than tropical and green) and boat rides on the Río San Nicolás. There's a 15% service charge and a two-night minimum; the average stay is seven nights. If you have to ask the price, you can't afford it. ⊠*Carretera 200, Km 85, Quemaro ✈83 km (52 mi) south of PV, 133 km (83 mi) north of Barra de Navidad* ☎*322/285–5500 or 888/882–9616* ⊕*www.mexicoboutiquehotels.com/lasalamandas* ⇆*14 suites* ⌂*In-room: refrigerator, DVD, VCR. In-hotel: restaurant, room service, bars, tennis court, pool, gym, spa, beachfront, water sports, bicycles, concierge, laundry service, public Internet, parking (no fee)* ☰*MC, V* ☯*EP, FAP.*

$$$$ ☷**Grand Bay Isla Navidad.** On a 1,200-acre peninsula between the Pacific and the Navidad Lagoon, this no-holds-barred resort cascades down to a private, though not terribly scenic, beach. An island unto itself, the lovely and rather snooty Grand Bay faces humble Barra de Navidad across the lagoon. Spanish arches, shady patios, cool fountains, and lush gardens contribute to the elegant architecture; tiered swimming pools are connected by slides and waterfalls. There's even a movie theater. If all this indulgence becomes too much, an inexpensive water taxi can take you over to the real world, two minutes away. There's a $15 per night service charge. ⊠*Isla Navidad, Barra de Navidad48987, Jalisco* ☎*315/331–0500, 800/996–3426 in U.S.* ☷*315/355–6071* ⊕*www.wyndham.com* ⇆*158 rooms, 41 suites* ⌂*In-room: safe, refrigerator, kitchen (some), Wi-Fi, Ethernet. In-hotel: 3 restaurants, room service, bars, golf course, tennis courts, pools, gym, spa, concierge, laundry service, public Internet, public Wi-Fi, airport shuttle, parking (no fee), no-smoking rooms* ☰*AE, MC, V* ☯*EP.*

$$$$ ☷**Hotelito Desconocido.** Although every inch of the place is painted, tiled,
★ or otherwise decorated with bright Mexican colors and handicrafts, the effect is distinctive rather than fussy. Perhaps that's because rooms and suites incorporate local building styles and materials, including plank floors, reed mats, bamboo walls, and palm-frond roofs. They're cooled by battery-powered fans and lighted by lanterns, candles, and low-wattage lamps. Rustic but lovely bathrooms bring the outdoors in through large open windows. Signal for morning coffee by running up the red flag. On a long stretch of beach, this isolated hotel is an idyllic escape for its clientele: about 60% American, 25% European, and 100% laid-back. There's an obligatory meal plan of $179 for two people. ⊠*Playón de Mismaloya s/n, Cruz de Loreto, Jalisco* ✈*97 km (60 mi) south of PV, 119 km (74 mi) north of Barra de Navidad* ☎*322/281–4010, 800/851–1143 in U.S., 322/281–4010, 01800/013–1313 toll-free in Mexico* ⊕*www.hotelito.com* ⇆*16 rooms, 13 suites* ⌂*In-room: no a/c, no phone, no TV. In-hotel: 2 restaurants, bar, pool, spa, beachfront, water sports, bicycles, no elevator, concierge, public Internet, airport shuttle, parking (no fee)* ☰*AE, MC, V* ☯*BP, FAP.*

$$$$ ☷**Punta Serena.** Guests come from New York and Italy to this adults-
★ only oasis of calm. Perched on a beautiful headland, "Point Serene" enjoys balmy breezes and life-changing views from the infinity hot tub;

COSTALEGRE HOTELS AT A GLANCE

HOTEL	Worth Noting	Cost	Rooms	Restaurants	On the Beach	Dive Shop	Pools	Spa	Golf Course	Tennis Courts	Health Club/Gym	Children's Program	Location
Las Alamandas	ultra-exclusive	$910	14	1	yes		1	yes		1	yes		Quemaro, Costalegre
El Careyes Beach Resort	impeccable decor	$305	80	1	yes		1	yes		2	yes		Careyes, Costalegre
Coconuts by the Sea	fab beach views	$105	4				1						Bahía Tenacatita
Grand Bay Isla Navidad	elegant but snooty	$382	199	3			3	yes	yes	3	yes		Barra de Navidad
Hotelito Desconocido	rustic-chic idyll	$395	29	2	yes		1	yes					Cruz de Loreto, Costalegre
La Paloma Oceanfront	well-equipped studios	$115	11	1			1						San Patricio-Melaque
Punta Serena	adults-only oasis	$333	24	1	yes		1	yes			yes		Bahía Tenacatita
Rancho Cuixmala	to-die-for views	$55	3	1									Costalegre
El Tamarindo	stunning good taste	$495	29	1	yes	yes	1	yes	yes	1	yes		Cihuatlán, Costalegre
Vagabundo	far from crowds	$51–$68	21	1			1						Punta Perula
Las Villas	on the waterfront	$78	9	1	yes								Barra de Navidad
Las Villitas	lovely bay	$78	10	1	yes		1						Bahía Tenacatita

the beach far below and pool are clothing optional. Spa treatments are inventive: roses and red wine promote moisturizing; carotene and honey contribute to a glowing tan; and the "Mayan Wrap" connects you herbally to the glowing god within. Shamans lead healing steam ceremonies on weekends; mud-and-music therapies are on the beach,

and activities like horseback riding, tennis (three courts), and nonmotorized water sports at the adjacent Blue Bay hotel are included in the price. Additionally, rooms have lovely furnishings and decor, and shared or private terraces, some with fab beach views. ⊠ *Carretera Barra de Navidad–Puerto Vallarta (Carretera 200), Km 20, Tenacatita 48989, Jalisco* ✛ *196 km (122 mi) south of PV, 20 km (12 mi) north of Barra de Navidad* ☎ *315/351–5427 or 315/351–5020* ⊕ *www.puntaserena. com* ➬ *12 rooms, 12 suites* ♿ *In-room: safe. In-hotel: restaurant, bar, pool, gym, spa, beachfront, laundry service, public Internet, parking (no fee), no kids under 18* ☰ *AE, MC, V* ⦿ *AI.*

$$$$
Fodor'sChoice
★

🏨 **El Tamarindo.** More than 2,000 acres of ecological reserve and jungle surround this magical resort along 16 km (10 mi) of private coast. The architecture utilizes simple design elements (with a Mediterranean flavor) and local building materials; world-renowned Ricardo Legorreta was one of the architects. Many villas have outdoor living rooms. All have dark-wood floors, king-size beds, wet bars, ample bathrooms, and patios with plunge pools, hammocks, and chaise longues. Sofas are upholstered in rich textured fabrics, and all furnishings and details are spare and classy. At night the staff lights more than 1,500 candles around the villas to create a truly enchanting setting. The hotel receives our highest accolade, Fodor's Choice, for its stunning location, gorgeous rooms, and excellent golf course. ⊠ *Carretera Melaque–Puerto Vallarta (Carretera 200), Km 7.5, Cihuatlán 48970, Jalisco* ✛ *204 km (127 mi) south of PV, 12 km (7 mi) north of Barra de Navidad* ☎ *315/351–5032, 888/625–5144 in U.S. or Canada* ⊕ *www.mexico-boutiquehotels.com/thetamarindo/* ➬ *29 villas* ♿ *In-room: safe, no TV. In-hotel: restaurant, room service, bar, gym, spa, golf course, tennis court, pool, beachfront, diving, water sports, bicycles, concierge, laundry service, public Internet, parking (no fee)* ☰ *AE, MC, V* ⦿ *EP.*

$$
★

🏨 **Coconuts By the Sea.** A friendly couple of American expats (he's a former Eastern Airlines pilot) own and run this charming cliff-top hideaway with a drop-dead gorgeous view of the ocean and Boca de Iguana Beach below. The furniture is stylish, and homey touches like lamps and fish-theme wall decorations make the snug apartments just right for holing up for a week or even a month. The two apartments upstairs, with thatched roofs and kitchen and living room open to the elements, are not usually available in summer due to the rain; the rest of the year they're highly coveted. One has an outdoor shower with a view. ⊠ *Playa Boca de Iguanas, 6 Dolphin Way, Bahía Tenacatita 48987, Jalisco* ✛ *195 km (121 mi) south of PV, 21 km (13 mi)*

2

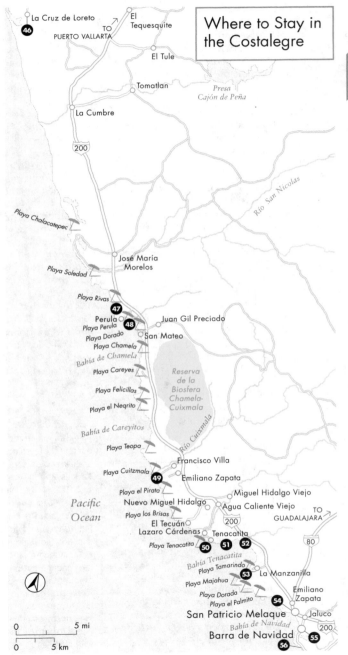

Where to Stay in the Costalegre

La Cruz de Loreto

46

TO PUERTO VALLARTA

El Tequesquite

El Tule

Tomatlan

Presa Cajón de Peña

La Cumbre

200

Playa Chalacatepec

José María Morelos

Playa Soledad

Playa Rivas

47

Perula
Playa Perula

48

Juan Gil Preciado

Playa Dorado

San Mateo

Playa Chamela

Bahía de Chamela

Playa Careyes

Reserva de la Biosfera Chamela-Cuixmala

Playa Felicillas

Playa el Negrito

Bahía de Careyitos

Río Cuixmala

Playa Teopa

Francisco Villa

Playa Cuitzmala

49

Emiliano Zapata

Playa el Pirata

Miguel Hidalgo Viejo

Pacific
Ocean

Nuevo Miguel Hidalgo

Agua Caliente Viejo

TO GUADALAJARA

Playa los Brisas

200

El Tecuán

Lazaro Cárdenas

Tenacatita

80

Playa Tenacatita

50 **51** **52**

Bahía Tenacatita

Playa Tamarindo

53

La Manzanilla

Playa Majahua

Playa Dorada

Emiliano Zapata

Playa el Palmito

54

San Patricio Melaque

Jaluco

Bahía de Navidad

200

Barra de Navidad

55

56

Río San Nicolas

0 ___ 5 mi

0 ___ 5 km

north of Barra de Navidad ☎314/338–6135 ⊕*www.coconutsbythe-sea.com* 🖵*4 rooms* ⬧*In-room: no phone, kitchen, refrigerator, Wi-Fi. In-hotel: pool, parking (no fee)* ⊟*No credit cards* Ⓞ*EP.*

$$ 🍴 **La Paloma Oceanfront Retreat.** Room prices are reasonable considering the small studio apartments have almost everything home does, and four of them face the beach (where the waves are often good for boogie boarding, and always great for long walks along the bay). Each room is configured differently, but all are uniformly bright and cheerful, with private patios and paintings by the owner (she gives lessons in high season). There's a large pool and patio for outdoor barbecuing facing the ocean. Unlike most hotels, La Paloma does not have off-season discounts. ⊠*Av. Las Cabañas 13, San Patricio–Melaque, 48980* ✛*6 km (4 mi) north of Barra de Navidad* ☎315/355–5345 ⊕*www.lapalomamexico.com* 🖵*11 studio apartments* ⬧*In-room: no a/c (some), no phone, kitchen, refrigerator, DVD (some). In-hotel: restaurant, pool, public Internet, public Wi-Fi, parking (no fee)* ⊟*No credit cards* ⓄCP.

$ 🍴 **Las Villitas Club & Marina.** Each of the small bungalows on the beach at Tenacatita has a small sitting room with two single beds doubling as couches, and a king-size bed in the separate bedroom. Cheerfully painted rooms have beach views and bathtubs as well as *equipale* (pigskin) tables and chairs and a large patio for outside lounging; doors and windows are screened. Ask to borrow the kayak; sometimes there are bikes to lend, too. This is a wonderful place to kick back on one of Pacific Mexico's most beautiful bays. Ask for discounts on stays Monday through Thursday. ⊠*Playa Tenacatita, Calle Bahía de Tenacatita 376, Bahía Tenacatita, Jalisco* ✛*183 km (114 mi) south of PV, 37 km (23 mi) north of Barra de Navidad* ☎315/355–5354, 01800/980–7060 *toll-free in Mexico* ⊕*www.lasvillitas.com.mx* 🖵*10 bungalows* ⬧*In-room: no phone, DVD (some), kitchen, refrigerator. In-hotel: pool, beachfront* ⊟*MC, V* ⓄEP.

$ 🍴 **Rancho Cuixmala.** This ecologically inspired ranch has views to die for, plus massage and birding. The owners are happy to give guests a tour of the property at no extra cost. Relaxation and communing with nature are what this 12-acre, thorn-forest retreat (in owner Mercedes Gargallo Chavez's family since the 19th century) is all about; cell phones don't work and there's no TV. The luxurious indoor-outdoor home on a cliff overlooking the ocean is lovely and belies the modest price. Guests share the common spaces: living room, dining room, kitchen, and outdoor patio. ⊠*Carretera Melaque–Puerto Vallarta (Carretera 200), Km 44 Jalisco, 48943*

TURTLES 911

Releasing tiny turtles into the sea, done in the evening when there are fewer predators, is a real thrill for kids, and for many adults as well. The Westin, Marriott Casa-Magna, Fiesta Americana, Velas Vallarta, and Dreams Resort in Puerto Vallarta; and Las Alamandas, Hotelito Desconocido, and El Tamarindo on the Costalegre have marine turtle conservation programs. They employ biologists to collect eggs from nests on nearby beaches, incubate them in protected sand pits, and help guests repatriate them into the wild blue sea.

✥171 km (106 mi) south of PV, 45 km (28 mi) north of Barra de Navidad ☎315/351–0272 ⊕www.ranchocuixmala.com ⌨3 rooms ♿In-room: no a/c, no phone, no TV. In-hotel: restaurant, no elevator ▭No credit cards †◯|BP.

$ ▦**Vagabundo.** This humble beach town on Chamela Bay is an excellent place off the gringo trail for swimming, fishing, or exploring the offshore islands. Simple hotel rooms surround a swimming pool in this motel-like, quiet, two-story hotel a block from the beach at Punta Perula. Bungalows have tiny but well-equipped kitchens; the restaurant serves breakfast and dinner. The hotel owner spent many years in the United States and speaks excellent English. ✉Calle Independencia 100, Punta Perula, Chamela Bay, Punta Perula, Jalisco ✥79 km (49 mi) south of PV, 137 km (85 mi) north of Barra de Navidad ☎315/333–9736 ⌨21 rooms ♿In-room: no phone, kitchen (some), refrigerator (some). In-hotel: restaurant, pool, no elevator, laundry service ▭No credit cards †◯|EP.

$ ▦**Las Villas.** Aside from the luxurious and costly Grand Bay Isla Navidad and the behemoth Hotel Alondra, Barra de Navidad has only basic hotels with few rooms, and not a particularly good value compared to similar hotels elsewhere. This hotel with a domed brick ceiling, comfortable beds, and remote control air-conditioning is among the best choices. Ask for a 25% discount between Easter and New Year's, and a free cot anytime for an additional guest. ✉Calle López de Legazpi 127, Barra de Navidad48987, Jalisco ☎315/355–5354, 01800/980–7060 toll-free in Mexico ⊕www.lasvillitas.com.mx ⌨9 rooms ♿In-room: no phone, Wi-Fi. In-hotel: restaurant, bar, beachfront, public Wi-Fi ▭MC, V †◯|EP.

Where to Eat

Food with a view.

WORD OF MOUTH

"There are so many great restaurants. Once you get to PV just ask around; you'll have umpteen recommendations."

—blondlady

"Each night we went to dinner at great restaurants like De Santos and Centro. The last night we went to Café des Artistes. Beautiful!"

—_Linda_

DINING PLANNER

Quick Take

Puerto Vallarta's restaurants are to die for, but what a misuse of earthly delights that would be. Variety, quality, and innovation are the norm whether you dine in a beachfront café or a swanky candlelighted restaurant. The best restaurants buy fresh fish and shellfish daily—and it's a great bargain. Vallarta's already superior restaurants really overachieve during the 10-day Festival Gourmet International in mid-November. More than three dozen establishments invite guest chefs to prepare special menus, some of which influence restaurant menus the following year.

Meals

PV restaurants cater to tourists with multicourse dinners, but traditionally, *comida* (late lunch) is the big meal of the day, usually consisting of soup and/or salad, bread or tortillas, a main dish, side dishes, and dessert. Traditional *cena* (dinner) is lighter; in fact, many people just have milk or hot chocolate and a sweet roll, or *tamales*.

Desayuno (breakfast) is served in *cafeterías* (coffee shops) and small restaurants. Choices might be hefty egg-and-chorizo or -ham dishes, enchiladas, or *chilaquiles* (fried tortilla strips covered in tomato sauce, shredded cheese, and meat or eggs). Tacos and quesadillas are delicious for breakfast; some of Vallarta's best taco stands set up shop by 9 AM.

Foodie Hot Spots

PV's biggest concentration of restaurants is in the Zona Romántica, mostly in Colonia Emiliano Zapata. Once called Restaurant Row, Calle Basilio Badillo now has as many shops as restaurants, but on the surrounding streets eateries continue to crop up. Downtown has its fair share of choice places, too. All in all, gourmets will be happiest here in Old Vallarta, where an appetizer, sunset cocktail, or espresso and dessert isn't more than a $3 cab ride away.

Bucerías has good restaurants in the center of town. Marina Vallarta's worthwhile eateries are mainly in the resorts and surrounding the marina. Punta de Mita's restaurant scene is diversifying to bring more than ceviche and fish fillets to the palapas at El Anclote.

Beer & Spirits

Jalisco is far and away Mexico's most important tequila producing state. Mexican beers range from light beers like Corona and Sol to medium-bodied, golden beers like Pacífico and the more robust Bohemia, to dark beauties Negra Modelo and Indio.

Mealtimes

Mexican mealtimes are generally as follows. Upon rising: coffee, and perhaps *pan dulce* (sweet breads). Schedule permitting, Mexicans love to eat a hearty *almuerzo*, a full breakfast, at about 10. *Comida*, typically between 2 and 5 PM, is the main meal. *Cena* is between 8 PM and 9 PM.

Restaurants have long hours in PV, though seafood "shacks" on the beach often close by late afternoon or sunset. Outside the resorts of PV, southern Nayarit, and the Costalegre, restaurants may close by 7 or 8 PM, be sure to check so you don't go without supper. Unless otherwise noted, the restaurants listed in this guide are open daily for lunch and dinner.

Taco Primer

In this region, a taco is generally a diminutive corn tortilla heated on an oiled grill and filled with one of many meats, shrimp, or batter-fried fish.

If your'e eating at an informal taco stand, your server may ask *"Preparadita?"*; he or she is asking if you want cilantro and onions. Then add your own condiments: salsa mexicana (chopped raw onions, tomatoes, and green chilies), guacamole, and pickled jalapeño peppers. Some restaurants go further with chopped nopal cactus and other items.

Reservations

Reservations are always a good idea. During low season, getting a table is usually a snap. But it's always wise to call ahead and make sure the place hasn't been reserved for a party.

What to Wear

We'd love to suggest resort casual or at least grunge chic, but not everyone likes to dress up.

The Mexicans are usually the best dressed, but even they forego jacket and tie for a nice button-down and slacks. The most elegant restaurants, like Café des Artistes, simply request that men wear T-shirts with sleeves.

If you enjoy looking like a million bucks, don't despair: looking good is always in style. The maitre d' *will* take notice.

What it Costs In U.S. Dollars

AT DINNER

$$$$	$$$	$$	$	¢
over $25	$18–$25	$12–$17	$5–$11	under $5

The restaurants we list are the cream of the crop in each category. Prices are for a main course at dinner, excluding tax and tip

Pricing

PV's extremely high number of excellent eateries—from corner taco stands to 5-star Diamond-Award winners—means competition is high, and that keeps prices reasonable. While some restaurants do charge as much as those in New York or L.A., there are tons of wonderful places ranging from moderate to downright cheap. To really experience Puerto Vallarta, try both ends of the spectrum, and everything in between.

Paying

Credit cards are widely accepted at pricier restaurants, especially MasterCard and Visa, and to a lesser extent American Express. More modest restaurants might accept cash only, and are leery of traveler's checks. Small eateries that do accept credit cards sometimes give a "discount" for cash (i.e., they charge a small fee for credit card use).

Tips on Tipping

Twenty years ago, leaving a tip in Puerto Vallarta meant pocketing the bills and leaving the loose change. Today, influenced by big tippers from the U.S., servers count on 10%–15%. In more humble establishments, where the bill is often shockingly low, tips are taken more casually than in the more prestigious restaurants. But in any case, we suggest tipping 15% for good service, a bit less for a flawed performance, and a bit more if the tab is ridiculously low.

3

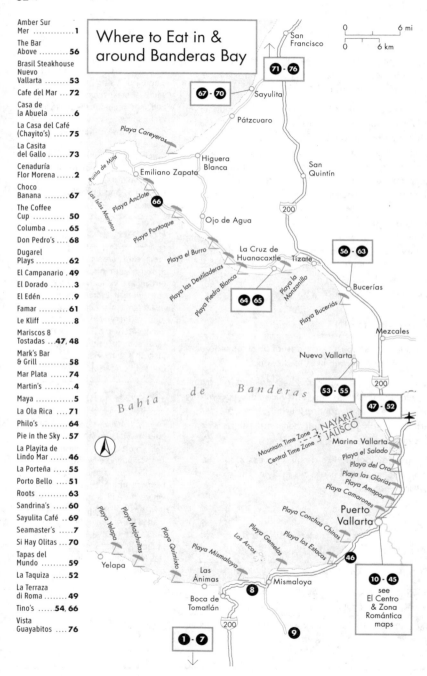

Where to Eat in & around Banderas Bay

San Francisco

Sayulita

Pátzcuaro

Playa Careyeros

Punta de Mita

Higuera Blanca

San Quintín

Emiliano Zapata

Las Islas Marietas

Playa Anclote

Playa Pontoque

Ojo de Agua

Playa el Burro

La Cruz de Huanacaxtle

Tizate

Playa la Manzanilla

Bucerías

Playa las Destiladeras

Playa Piedra Blanca

Playa Bucerías

Mezcales

Nuevo Vallarta

Bahía   de   Banderas

200

NAYARIT
JALISCO

Mountain Time Zone
Central Time Zone

Marina Vallarta

Playa el Salado

Playa del Oro

Playa las Glorias

Playa Amapas

Playa Camarones

Puerto Vallarta

Playa Yelapa

Playa Majahuitas

Playa Quimixto

Playa Conchas Chinas

Playa Gemelas

Playa los Estacas

Los Arcos

Playa Mismaloya

Yelapa

Las Ánimas

Mismaloya

Boca de Tomatlán

see
El Centro
& Zona
Romántica
maps

0   6 mi
0   6 km

PUERTO VALLARTA

AMERICAN–CASUAL

$ ✕**Andale.** Although many have been drinking, rather than eating, at this local hangout for years, the restaurant serves great burgers, fries, herb-garlic bread, black-bean soup, and jumbo shrimp, as well as daily lunch and nightly drink specials at the chummy bar. The interior is cool, dark, and informal; two rows of mini-tables line the sidewalk outside. Service is generally attentive, although that doesn't mean the food will arrive promptly. Plus-size patrons should beware the munchkin-size toilet stalls. ✉*Av. Olas Altas 425, Col. E. Zapata* ☎*322/222–1054* ⊟*MC, V.*

¢–$ ✕**Memo's Pancake House.** If your child can't find something he or she ☺ likes on the Pancake House menu, you might have an alien on your hands. There are 12 kinds of pancakes—including the Oh Henry, with chocolate bits and peanut butter—and eight kinds of waffles. Other breakfast items include machaca burritos, *chilaquiles,* and eggs Florentine, but these tend to be perfunctory: pancakes and waffles are your best bet. Waiters bustle around the large, fairly noisy dining room, which is bursting with local families on weekends and homesick travelers daily. The back patio—draped in pothos and serenaded by birds—experiences a greenhouse effect when the day heats up. ✉*Calle Basilio Badillo 289, Col. E. Zapata* ☎*322/222–6272* ⚲*Reservations not accepted* ⊟*No credit cards* ⊘*No dinner.*

BISTRO

$$–$$$ ✕**Vitea.** When chefs Bernhard Güth and Ulf Henriksson, of Trio, ★ needed a challenge they cooked up this delightful seaside bistro. So what if your legs bump your partner's at the small tables? This will only make it easier to steal bites off her plate. The decor of the open, casual venue is as fresh as the food. Appetizers include the smoked salmon roll with crème fraiche and the spicy shrimp tempura; crab manicotti and other entrées are light and delicious. Half portions are available, or make a meal of the bistro's soups, sandwiches, and appetizers. ✉*Libertad 2, near south end of Malecón, Centro* ☎*322/222–8703* ⊟*MC, V* ⊘*Closed 1 wk in late Sept.*

CAFÉS

¢–$ ✕**The Coffee Cup.** Coffee is sold in all its various presentations, including freshly ground by the kilo. You can munch on pastries, sandwiches, wraps, and breakfast breads, or get a fresh fruit smoothie. A chit gets you 10 minutes of free Internet around the corner, ostensibly to be used the same day. It's no relation to the Coffee Cup in Marina Vallarta. ✉*Calle Rodolfo Gómez 146–A, Col. E. Zapata* ☎*322/222–8584* ⊟*No credit cards* ⊘*No dinner Sun. Nov.–Apr.*

¢–$ ✕**A Page in the Sun.** This corner café in the middle of Olas Altas is always full of coffee drinkers reading newspapers and paperback books

MENU TRANSLATOR

Because eating is such an integral part of a Puerto Vallarta vacation, we've described here some of the dishes you're likely to find on area menus or in our reviews below. *Buen provecho!*

arrachera: skirt steak

carne asada: thin cut of flank or tenderloin (sometimes not *that* tender), grilled or broiled and usually served with beans, rice, and guacamole

carnitas: bites of steamed, fried pork served with tortillas and a variety of condiments

chilaquiles: pieces of corn tortillas fried and served with red or green sauce; good ones are crispy, not soggy, and topped with chopped onions and *queso cotija:* a crumbly white cheese

chile en nogada: a green poblano chili stuffed with a semi-sweet meat mixture and topped with walnut sauce and pomegranate seeds; the Mexican national dish, it's often served in September in honor of Independence Day

chile relleno: batter-fried green chili (mild to hot) stuffed with cheese, seafood, or a sweetish meat mixture; served in a mild red sauce

menudo: tripe stew

pozole: a rich pork- or chicken-based soup with hominy; a plate of accompanying condiments usually includes raw onions, radishes, cilantro, oregano, sliced cabbage, and tostadas

tostada: a crispy fried tortilla topped with beans and/or meat, cheese, and finely chopped lettuce or cabbage; or, the corn tortilla by itself, which is served with foods like ceviche and pozole

purchased here, or playing chess. The salads, sandwiches, and desserts on the menu are almost an afterthought. It's the location and the opportunity to hang out with one's friends that really count, plus the good coffee. ⊠ *Olas Altas 399, Col. E. Zapata* ☎ *322/222–3608* ⊟ *No credit cards.*

CONTINENTAL

$$$
★
✕ **Kaiser Maximilian.** Viennese and Continental entrées dominate the menu, which is modified each year when the restaurant participates in PV's culinary festival. One favorite is herb-crusted rack of lamb served with horseradish and pureed vegetables au gratin; another is venison medallions with chestnut sauce served with braised white cabbage and steamed vegetables. The adjacent café (open 8 AM–noon) has sandwiches, excellent desserts, and 20 specialty coffees—all of which are also available at the main restaurant. Because a stream of street peddlers is anathema to fine dining, eat in the charming, European-style dining room, where handsome black-and-white-clad waiters look right at home amid dark-wood framed mirrors, brightly polished brass, and lace café curtains. ⊠ *Av. Olas Altas 380, Col. E. Zapata* ☎ *322/223–0760* ⊟ *AE, MC, V* ⊘ *Closed Sun. No lunch.*

CUBAN

$-$$ ✕ **La Bodeguita del Medio.** Near the malecón's north end, this restaurant with a fun-loving atmosphere has a bit of a sea view from its second-floor dining room, and a Caribbean flavor. Specials vary by season; if possible, try the roast pork, the Cuban-style paella, or the pork loin in tamarind sauce; order rice, salad, or fried plantains separately. Like its Havana namesake, La Bodeguita sells Cuban rum and cigars, and the live music—like the cuisine—is pure *cubano*. A sextet performs most nights until past midnight. Try the Havana specialty drink *mojito*: a blend of lime juice, sugar, mineral water, white rum, and crushed fresh mint leaves. ⊠*Paseo Díaz Ordáz 858, Centro* ☎*322/223–1585* ⊟*AE, MC, V.*

DELICATESSENS

¢   ✕ **The Coffee Cup.** Early-risers and those heading off on fishing charters will appreciate the 5 AM opening time. There are fruit smoothies, and coffee in many manifestations, including frappés of Oreo cookie and German chocolate cake. Have a breakfast bagel (all day), wrap, deli sandwich, or homemade dessert. Located right on the marina, the café is filled with wonderful art for sale, and is open daily until 10 PM. ⊠*Condominios Puesto del Sol, Local 14–A, at marina, Marina Vallarta* ☎*322/221–2517* ⊟*MC, V.*

ECLECTIC

$$$-$$$$ ✕ **Le Kliff.** From a table on one of four tiers you can watch for whales in season or boats heading to the docks as the sun sets. Asian and Mediterranean flavors have been added to the recipes without great success. (The new chef, Everado Robles, may be able to set things right.) This open-air restaurant with an enormous palapa roof is best for sunset hors d'oeuvres and cocktails, as the food is not worth the inflated prices. Weddings are a big part of the business, so call ahead to make sure it's not booked, and to reserve a table on the lowest deck, closest to the water. ⊠*Carretera a Barra de Navidad, Km 17.5, just north of Boca de Tomatlán, Zona Hotelera Sur* ☎*322/224–0975* ⊟*MC, V.*

$$-$$$$ ✕ **Café des Artistes.** Several sleek dining spaces make up Café des Artistes,
★   the liveliest of which is the courtyard garden with modern sculpture. The main restaurant achieves a modern Casablanca feel with glass raindrops and tranquil music. Thierry Blouet's Cocina de Autor (closed Sunday and September) is the restaurant's latest innovation, and it was listed in Condé Nast's 2005 "80 hottest new restaurants in the world." The limited seating restaurant pairs four- to six-course tasting menus with appropriate wines. Decor is restrained, with a waterfall garden behind plate glass taking center stage. The clubby cigar bar has one of the structure's few original adobe walls; the Constantini Wine Bar has some 50 vintages by the glass as well as distilled spirits, appetizers, and live music Monday through Saturday nights. ⊠*Av. Guadalupe Sánchez 740, Centro* ☎*322/222–3229* ⊟*AE, MC, V* ⊘*No lunch.*

$$$
Fodor'sChoice
★
✕**Trio.** Conviviality, hominess, and dedication on the parts of chef-owners Bernhard Güth and Ulf Henriksson have made Trio one of Puerto Vallarta's best restaurants— hands-down. Fans, many of them members of PV's artsy crowd, marvel at the kitchen's ability to deliver perfect meal after perfect meal. Popular demand guarantees rack of lamb with fresh mint and for dessert, the warm chocolate cake. The kitchen often stays open until nearly midnight, and there's a back patio and rooftop terrace on which to dine in fair weather. Waiters are professional yet unpretentious; sommelier Cesar Porras can help you with the wine. But the main reason to dine here is the consistently fabulous food at great value. ✉*Calle Guerrero 264, Centro* ☎*322/222–2196* ▭*AE, MC, V* ☉*No lunch.*

> **WORD OF MOUTH**
>
> "La Palapa is the epitome of Mexican romantic restaurants. On the beach, excellent food and service, very good margaritas, and a little combo playing soft Mexican jazz. This is my idea of heaven, palapa style." –Bill

$$–$$$
✕**Chez Elena.** Frequented in its heyday by Hollywood luminaries and the who's who of PV, this downtown restaurant still has a loyal following. The patio ambience is simple, but the wholesome food is satisfying, and portions are generous. House specialties include fajitas and Yucatan-style pork. Elena's is also known for its killer, handcrafted margaritas and its flaming coffee drinks. ✉*Calle Matamoros 520, Centro* ☎*322/222–0161* ▭*MC, V* ☉*Closed Tues. May, Oct. Closed June–Sept. No lunch.*

$$–$$$
Fodor'sChoice
★
✕**Daiquiri Dick's.** Locals come for the reasonably priced breakfasts (the homemade orange-almond granola is great); visitors come (often more than once during a vacation) for the good service and consistent Mexican and world cuisine. The lunch-dinner menu has fabulous appetizers, including superb lobster tacos with a drizzle of béchamel sauce and perfect, tangy jumbo-shrimp wontons. On the menu since the restaurant opened almost 30 years ago is Pescado Vallarta, or grilled fish on a stick. Start with a signature daiquiri; move to the extensive wine list. The tortilla soup is popular, too. The very plain patio dining room frames a view of Playa Los Muertos. ✉*Av. Olas Altas 314, Col. E. Zapata* ☎*322/222–0566* ▭*MC, V* ☉*Closed Sept. and Wed. May–Aug.*

$$–$$$
★
✕**La Palapa.** This large, welcoming, thatch-roof place is open to the breezes of Playa los Muertos and filled with wicker chandeliers, art-glass fixtures, and lazily rotating ceiling fans. The menu meanders among international dishes in modern presentation: roasted stuffed chicken breast, pork loin, or seared yellowfin tuna drizzled in cacao sauce. The seafood enchilada plate is divine. For a pricey but romantic evening, enjoy one of several set menus (265 pesos for two; reserve in advance) at a table right on the sand. This is a popular place for breakfast daily after 8 AM, for a lingering Sunday brunch, or solo guitar or Latin jazz combo nightly between 9 and 11. ✉*Calle Púlpito 103, Playa Los Muertos, Col. E. Zapata* ☎*322/222–5225* ▭*AE, D, MC, V.*

$$–$$$
✕**River Cafe.** At night, candles flicker at white-skirted tables with comfortable cushioned chairs, and tiny white lights sparkle in palm trees

surrounding the multilevel terrace. This riverside restaurant is recommended for breakfast and for the evening ambience. Attentive waiters serve such international dishes as chicken stuffed with wild mushrooms and spinach or rack of lamb with polenta; the fish and shrimp combo with lobster sauce is especially recommended. If you're not into a romantic (some say overpriced) dinner, belly up to the intimate bar for a drink and—Thursday through Sunday evenings—a listen to the live jazz. ⊠*Isla Río Cuale, Local 4, Centro* ☎322/223–0788 ⊟*AE, MC, V.*

<aside>

WHERE DOGS HAVE THEIR DAY

If you travel with a lapdog instead of a laptop, PV is the place for you. Small breeds, like the universally popular chihuahua, are escorted into upscale restaurants on their own little pillows; big dogs accompany their owners to beachfront bistros. A few restaurants take issue; if you and Fifi are going to an unfamiliar eatery, call ahead.

</aside>

■TIP→ **A waiter would never consider bringing you your check before you ask for it; that would be rude. However, it's also considered inappropriate to dally in bringing that check once you do ask for it.**

$-$$ ⤫**Le Bistro.** Start off with a soup of Mexican or Cuban origin and then ★ on to one of the international main dishes, like the Mediterranean-style pasta on a bed of fresh spinach, herbed Cornish hen, or sea scallops with jicama coleslaw. The restaurant overlooks the Cuale River, and its eclectic decor draped in ferns and tropical plants is a knockout, with carved-stone columns, zebra chairs, wicker settees, and other sophisticated touches. ⊠*Isla Río Cuale 16–A* ☎322/222–0283 ⊕*www.lebistro.com.mx* ⊟*AE, MC, V* ☉*Closed Sun. and Aug. and Sept.*

$-$$ ⤫**La Playita de Lindo Mar.** A favorite breakfast spot any day, or for Sun-★ day brunch, this restaurant has a wonderful view of the waves crashing on or lapping at Conchas Chinas Beach. The breakfast menu wanders among savory crèpes, fritatta, omelets, and the tasty *huevos Felix:* eggs scrambled with fried corn tortillas, served with a grilled cactus pad, beans, and grilled serrano chilies. The multitude of lunch and dinner choices includes grilled burgers and chicken, shrimp fajitas, and lobster thermador. Open to the ocean air, the wood-and-palm front building looks right at home here. See the sign on Carretera a Mismaloya or follow your nose on the beach at Conchas Chinas. If you're driving, you can park in the hotel's lot across the highway and take the elevator down to the beach, or park in the lot near the beach. ⊠*Carrertera a Barra de Navidad 2.5, Playa Conchas Chinas, at Hotel Lindo Mar* ☎322/221–5511 ⊟*MC, V.*

$-$$ ⤫**El Repollo Rojo.** Better known as the Red Cabbage (its English name), this restaurant is by—but doesn't overlook—the Cuale River. It's hard to find the first time out, but it's worth the effort for the international comfort food. Homesick Canadians fill up on chicken with mashed potatoes, gravy, and cranberry sauce, while Italians indulge in pasta with fresh tomatoes; there are even a few Russian dishes. Frida's Dinner includes an aperitif of tequila followed by cream of peanut soup, white or red wine, *chile en nogada* (a mild chili decorated with colors of the

Mexican flag), a main dish from the Yucatán or Puebla, and flan for dessert. Romantic ballads fill the small space, and the walls are crowded with movie posters and head shots of international stars. Here's the quandary: some patrons rave about the service, and others lambaste it. ✉ *Calle Rivera del Río 204–A, El Remance* ☎*322/223–0411* ▭*No credit cards*. ⊘*No lunch. Closed Sept. and Sun. May–Oct.*

$ ✕**Fidensio's.** Let the tide lick your toes and the sand caress shoeless feet
ↄ   as simple yet tasty food is brought to your comfortable cloth, palapa-shaded chair right at the ocean's edge. Made when you order them, the shrimp enchiladas—served with rice, a small handful of piping hot fries, and a miniature salad—are simply delicious. Many expats come for breakfast, or before 6 PM for burgers, nachos, club or tuna sandwiches, or a fresh fish fillet. Service is relaxed and friendly, not overbearing or phony; the only soundtrack is the sound of the waves. ✉ *Pilitas 90, Los Muerto Beach, Col. E. Zapata* ☎*322/222–5457* ▭*No credit cards* ⊘*No dinner.*

FUSION

$$–$$$ ✕**Boca Bento.** This comely restaurant in the heart of the Romantic Zone represents fusion of Latin American and Asian elements. The feeling is simultaneously Eastern and modern, with contemporary music and artwork. The small-plates concept has been abandoned in favor of a more traditional menu of appetizers, soups, salads, and entrées with a side of starch and vegetables: try the rib-eye steak, pork ribs with a honey-chili glaze, or the cross-cultural mu shu carnitas with hoisin sauce. ✉ *Calle Basilio Badillo 180, Col. E. Zapata* ☎*322/222–9108* ⊕*www.bocabento.com* ▭*AE. MC, V* ⊘*No lunch.*

ITALIAN

$$–$$$ ✕**Porto Bello.** Yachties, locals, and other return visitors attest that everything on the menu here is good. And if you're not satisfied, the kitchen will give you something else without quibbling. Undoubtedly that's what makes Marina Vallarta's veteran restaurant its most popular as well. The dining room is diminutive and air-conditioned; the outdoor patio overlooking the marina is more elegant, with a white chiffon ceiling drape and white ceiling fans. Since there are no lunch specials and the Italian menu is the same then as at dinner, most folks come in the evening. ✉ *Marina del Sol, Local 7, Marina Vallarta* ☎*322/221–0003* ▭*MC, V.*

$$–$$$ ✕**La Terraza di Roma.** The small dining room is nondescript, although most evenings a pianist adds a bit of panache. The food is fine, with homemade pasta and individual pizzas as well as the usual Italian nosh. It's the square patio hanging right above the marina, amid the boats, that brings most people back. Breakfast is also served. ✉ *Condominios Puesta del Sol, Local 2, at marina, Marina Vallarta* ☎*322/221–0560* ▭*AE, MC, V.*

$–$$ ✕**La Piazzeta.** Locals come for the delicious Naples-style pizza (the crust not too thick, not too thin, and cooked in a brick oven), but there's also great pasta and a good variety of entrées, like the cream-based salmon with caviar and lemon. For appetizers try the top-heavy (*con molto tomate*) bruschetta or steamed mussels with lemon, parsley, and butter. Most folks choose to sit on the open patio, but La Piazzeta also has an intimate dining room. The personal attention of the owner, Mimmo, guarantees repeat business. It's open 4 to midnight. ⊠ *Calle Rodolfo Gómez 143, Col. E. Zapata* ☎ *322/222–0650* ☰ *MC, V* ☻ *Closed Sun. No lunch.*

MEXICAN

$$$–$$$$ ✕ **Los Xitomates.** Both fun and modern, Los Xitomates has bright white tablecloths and oxidized, cutout-figure wall sconces. This hip, tranquil place in the heart of downtown is worth a try if you want an upscale ambience and variations on traditional Mexican dishes. Some recipes, like the tomato soup, leave a little to be desired. Winners include the tortilla soup (a classic) and the rib-eye steak sautéed with wild mushrooms and seasoned with the distinctive herb *epazote*. Chef-owner Luis Fitch, of Oaxaca, is amenable to fixing meals for Rastafarians, Orthodox Jews, or others with specific dietary requirements, preferably with advance notice. High ceilings make it noisy when crowded and echoy at other times. ⊠ *Calle Morelos 571, Centro* ☎ *322/222–1695* ☰ *AE, MC, V* ☻ *No lunch.*

$$–$$$ ✕ **Agave Grill.** Mexico City chef Oscar Galván successfully concocts dishes that take advantage of the country's unique and flavorful ingredients, such as fresh vanilla, avocados, plantains, and a host of smoky and fresh chilies. Try one of the Veracruz-style seafood recipes or the five-course menu (soup, salad, appetizer, main course, and dessert), perhaps paired with one or more of the many fine tequilas from the expansive bar. There's tequila ice cream for dessert. Service can be disjointed, the space itself is plain, and tables are small. Come for the tasty and unusual dishes. ⊠ *Calle Morelos 589, Centro* ☎ *322/222–2000* ⊕ *www.agavegrill.com.mx* ☰ *AE, MC, V* ☻ *No lunch.*

$$–$$$ ✕ **El Andariego.** A few blocks past the north end of the malecón is this lively Mexican restaurant. Lovely paintings of the city brighten the walls, lighting is subdued, and the mood is romantic Mexico. The large menu includes numerous salads, pasta dishes, lots of variety in chicken and beef, and seafood and lobster prepared to your taste. You're allowed to choose your poison (beef, cheese, or chicken fillings) for the tacos and enchiladas on the combo plates. Enjoy live music (electric guitar versions of "My Way," or mariachi music) nightly between 3 and 11 PM. Breakfast is served, and there's

TACO PRIMER

In this region's informal eateries, a taco is generally a diminutive corn tortilla heated on an oiled grill filled with meat, shrimp, or batter-fried fish. If your server asks "¿Preparadita?", he or she is asking if you want it with cilantro and onions. Add-your-own condiments are salsa mexicana (chopped raw onions, tomatoes, and green chilies), liquidy guacamole, and pickled jalapeño peppers. Some restaurants include chopped nopal cactus and other signature items.

•

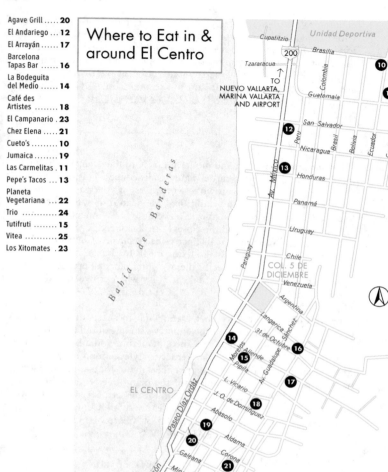

Where to Eat in & around El Centro

free wireless Internet in the restaurant and bar. ⊠ *Av. México 1358, at El Salvador, Col. 5 de Diciembre* ☎ *322/222–0916* ⊕ *www.elandariego.com* ⊟ *MC, V.*

$$-$$$
Fodor's Choice
★
✕El Arrayán. The oilcloth table covers, enameled tin plates, exposed rafters, and red roof tiles of this patio-restaurant conjure up nostalgia for the quaint Mexican home of

> **DAILY SPECIALS**
>
> To save money, **look for the fixed-menu lunch** called either a *comida corrida* or a *menú del día*, served from about 12:30 to 4 in restaurants throughout Mexico geared to working-class folks.

less frenetic times. Carmen Porras, the hip, cute co-owner (with her parents), masquerades as your waitress, dispensing interesting info about the origins of chiles en nogada (first prepared for Emperor Agustín Iturbide—who knew?) and the other Mexican comfort foods on her menu. Here you'll find the things *grandmamá* still loves to cook, with a few subtle variations. Highlights are chicken breasts stuffed with zucchini blossoms and chipotle-chili shrimp with a citrus sauce. For dessert how about caramel flan or a light pumpkin-caramel ice? ⊠ *Calle Allende 344, at Calle Miramar, Centro* ☎ *322/222–7195* ⊟ *MC, V* ⊙ *Closed Tues. and Aug. No lunch.*

$$
★
✕Las Carmelitas. Hawks soar on updrafts above lumpy, jungle-draped hills. The town and the big blue bay are spread out below in a breathtaking, 200-degree tableau. Under the palapa roof of this small, open restaurant romantic ballads play as waiters start you off with guacamole, fresh and cooked salsas, chopped cactus pad salad, and tostadas. Seared meats—served with grilled green onions and tortillas made on the spot—are the specialty, but you can also order seafood stew or soups. The restaurant opens at 1 PM. Don't despair about the $5 per person fee you pay to enter (apparently to discourage lookie-loos); it will be deducted from your tab. ⊠ *Camino a la Aguacatera, Km 1.2, Fracc. Lomas de Terra Noble* ☎ *322/303–2104* ⊟ *No credit cards.*

$-$$
✕El Brujo. The street corner on which the small restaurant is tucked means noise on either side. Service is reasonably attentive, although it sometimes seems grudging. Still, this is an expat favorite, and no wonder: the food is seriously good and portions generous. The *molcajete—* a sizzling black pot of tender flank steak, grilled green onion, and soft white cheese in a delicious homemade sauce of dried red peppers—is served with a big plate of guacamole, refried beans, and made-at-the-moment corn or flour tortillas. ⊠ *Venustiano Carranza 510, at Naranjo, Col. Remance* ☎ *No phone* ⬧ *Reservations not accepted* ⊟ *No credit cards* ⊙ *Closed Mon., 2 wks in late Sept., and early Oct.*

$-$$
✕Café de Olla. This earthy restaurant fills up as soon as it reopens for the season. Repeat visitors swear by the enchiladas and carne asadas. As reservations are not accepted, you may need to wait for a table, especially at breakfast and dinner. A large tree extends from the dining-room floor through the roof, local artwork adorns the walls, and salsa music often plays in the background. If you despair of waiting, the taco shop next door is reputedly very good. ⊠ *Calle Basilio Badillo 168–A, Col. E. Zapata* ☎ *322/223–1626* ⬧ *Reservations not accepted* ⊟ *No credit cards* ⊙ *Closed Tues. and Sept. 15–Oct. 15.*

3

$ ✕**Tía Catarina.** Co-owner Erin Gulliver used her interior decorator skills to create this beautiful, bright gem with an exhibition kitchen. Candles in blue glasses light tables, and reliquaries hang on vividly painted walls. Designed with the local's palate and budget in mind, the restaurant has some interesting vegetarian appetizers in addition to traditional dishes with a twist: beet soup with tequila, chile relleno stuffed with shrimp and cheese, ceviche, and tacos de arrachera. It's open for breakfast after 9 AM. ⊠*Calle Pino Suárez at Madero, Col. E. Zapata* 🕾*No phone* ▤*No credit cards* ⊘*Closed Sun. No lunch.*

> **BREAKFASTS OF CHAMPIONS**
>
> In PV, **Memo's Pancake House** is a favorite; ritzier **La Palapa** and **Dacquiri Dick's** serve breakfast at the beach. **Langostino's** and **Playita de Lindo Mar** have more casual, oceanside morning fare. In **Bucerías,** head to **Famar** for an excellent Mexican breakfast or **Chayito's,** in **San Francisco,** for good coffee, fruit smoothies, and eggs. In the **Costalegre,** try **Casa de la Abuela** for excellent coffee and jazzy tunes and **El Dorado** for a full breakfast at the beach.

¢–$ ✕**El Campanario.** This little jewel is increasingly popular with budget travelers. Egg dishes and chilaquiles are served 9–11 AM, and an inexpensive daily lunch menu is served 2–5 PM. Slightly less than $5 gets you soup, a main dish, drink, homemade tortillas, and dessert. Office workers come in for takeout, or drift in between 6 and 10 PM for tacos, *tortas* (Mexican-style sandwiches on crispy white rolls), or pozole. A recipe for the latter is given—along with a positive dining review—in a framed *Los Angeles Times* article from the 1980s. Fans swirl the air, doors are open to the street, and cheerful oilcloths cover wooden tables at this no-frills spot across from the cathedral. ⊠*Calle Hidalgo 339, Centro* 🕾*322/223–1509* ▤*No credit cards* ⊘*Closed Sun., and often between 5 and 6 PM.*

¢–$ ✕**Pepe's Tacos.** No longer the be-all and end-all of taco consumption in PV, Pepe's still can't be beat at 4 or 5 AM, when most sensible tacomakers are asleep. Although these diminutive tacos are a meat-lover's treat, there are quesadillas—and one taco with grilled onions and bell peppers, cheese, and canned mushrooms—for wayward vegetarians. Order tacos individually for about 70¢ each to try different types, or by the set. Or order one of several plates for two with a stack of tortillas. Expect plastic tablecloths and sports on several TVs at this open-door dive across from the Pemex station at the north end of Old Vallarta. ⊠*Honduras 173, between Avs. Peru and Mexico, Col. 5 de Diciembre* 🕾*322/223–1703* ▤*No credit cards* ⊘*Closed Mon. No lunch.*

¢–$ ✕**La Taquiza.** Here's a tip: Stop by this local's den on your way to the
★ airport (it's just across the street), and get food to go. Dollar, Budget, and Thrifty rental car storefronts surround this bright and shiny hole-in-the-wall. You can order food, drop off your rental car, and then get a shuttle to the airport. Or eat in at the brightly polished green Formica tables (with matching chairs). The tasty lime drink, lunch specials, pinto bean soup, and the house specialty—tacos—are served in or on old-fashioned red pottery plates, bowls, and mugs. ⊠*Blvd. Federico*

M. Ascencio s/n, Col. Las Flores ☎*No phone* ▭*No credit cards* ☉*Closed Sun. No dinner.*

¢–$ ✕**Tutifruti.** If you find yourself near the main square at lunchtime, consider having a taco at this little stand. While we can't exactly call this *fast* food, the quesadillas and machaca (shredded beef) burritos are delicious; you can also get a sandwich or burger. Consider sharing, because the portions are large. For breakfast, order up a *licuado* (smoothie) made from fresh fruit and milk. If you're lucky, you might get one of the few stools at the tiled counter. ✉*Calle Allende, between Av. Juaréz and Av. Guadalupe Sánchez, Centro* ☎*322/222–1068* ▭*No credit cards* ☉*Closed Sun. No dinner.*

PAN-ASIAN

$$–$$$ ✕**Archie's Wok.** This extremely popular South Side restaurant has a variety of Asian cuisines and dishes such as Thai garlic shrimp, *pancit* (Filipino stir-fry with pasta), and Singapore-style (lightly battered) fish, plus lots of vegetarian dishes. Thursday through Saturday 7:30 to 10:30 PM the soothing harp music of well-known local musican D'Rachel is the perfect accompaniment to your meal. It opens for lunch only after 2 PM. ✉*Calle Francisca Rodríguez 130, Col. E. Zapata* ☎*322/222–0411* ▭*MC, V* ☉*Closed Sun.*

SEAFOOD

$$–$$$ ✕**El Edén.** The location, a jungly riverside place where the movie *Predator* was filmed, is as much of a draw as the mainly seafood fare. This is a place to spend time, splashing in the river or zinging through the air on a canopy tour. Not on the menu but worth asking about is the Festival de Camarones: shrimp is prepared breaded, butterflied, sautéed in garlic, and served with rice, tortillas, homemade chips, and various salsas. You might catch a ride at El Edén's downtown PV office, when they transport their canopy tour patrons; otherwise, plan to drive or take a cab. If it's not too busy, the restaurant will sometimes return patrons to the highway, where buses frequently pass. ✉*Carr. al Edén, Predio el Venado, 10 mins. east of Mismaloya* ☎*No phone* ▭*No credit cards* ☉*No dinner.*

$–$$$ ✕**Langostino's.** Right on the beach just north of the pier at Playa Los Muertos, Langostino's is a great place to start the day with a heaping helping of Mexican rock, cranked up to a respectable volume. The house favorite at this professional and pleasant place is surf and turf, and the three seafood combos are a good value. The kids can play on the beach while you linger over coffee or suds. ⊠ *Los Muertos Beach at Calle Manuel M. Dieguez, Col. E. Zapata* ☎*322/222–0894* ⊟*No credit cards* ☉*No breakfast or lunch for 2 wks in Sept. (wks vary).*

$$ ✕**Cueto's.** Teams of engaging waiters, all family members, nudge aside
★ mariachi duos to refill beer glasses, remove empty plates, or bring more fresh tostadas and hot, crusty garlic bread. But don't fill up on nonessentials, as the recommended cream-based and mild-chili casseroles—with crab, clams, fish, shrimp, or mixed seafood—are so delicious you won't want to leave even one bite. You can have a complimentary margarita with dinner or a free digestif later on. Cueto's is a few blocks behind the Unidad Deportivo sports complex. Don't confuse this fabulous seafood restaurant with Cuates y Cuetes, on the beach at Los Muertos. ⊠*Calle Brasilia 469, Col. 5 de Diciembre (Zona Hotelera)* ☎*322/223–0363* ⊟*No credit cards.*

$$ ✕**Tino's.** Vine-covered trees poke through the roof of the breeze-blessed,
★ covered outdoor eatery overlooking the Río Ameca. The Carvajal family has worked hard to make this a favorite Nuevo Vallarta restaurant, though the Punta de Mita branch is also nice, on a pretty beach. Tino's is full even midweek, mainly with groups of friends or businesspeople leisurely discussing deals. A multitude of solicitous, efficient waiters proffer green-lipped mussels meunière, crab enchiladas, oysters, and the regional specialty, fish *sarandeado* (rubbed with herbs and cooked over coals). Concha de Tino is a dish with seafood, bacon, mushrooms, and spinach prettily presented in three seashells. ⊠*2a Entrada a Nuevo Vallarta, Km 1.2, Las Jarretaderas* ☎*322/297–0221* ⊟*MC, V* ⊠*Av. El Anclote 64, El Anclote, Punta de Mita* ☎*322/224–5584.*

$–$$ ✕**Mariscos 8 Tostadas.** Extremely popular with locals, this large restau-
★ rant hums with activity and a varied, upbeat soundtrack with tunes by icons such as Bob Marley and Frank Sinatra. The menu is oddly translated—tuna sashimi appears as *atun fresco con salsa rasurada,* or "tuna cut thick with shaved sauce, alone if there was fishing" (the latter meaning that it's only available if the fish was caught that day)—indicating that this is a spot geared to locals, not tourists. The freshly caught, raw tuna, which is thicker than in U.S. sushi houses, but not too thick, is served in a shallow dish with soy sauce, micro-thin cucumber slices, sesame seeds, green onions, chili powder, and lime. Eat with tostadas until fit to burst. Avoid the scallop tostadas, as the shellfish is virtually raw. The ceviche, however, couldn't be better—or fresher. There's a small storefront subsidiary in the parking lot at Plaza Marina; the charming original venue is behind Blockbuster Video in the Hotel Zone. ⊠*Calle Quilla at Calle Proa, Local 28–29, Marina Vallarta* ☎*322/221–3124* ⊟*No credit cards* ☉*No dinner* ⊠*Calle Niza 132 at Lucerna, Col. Versalles (Zona Hotelera)* ✛*Behind Blockbuster Video store* ☎*No phone* ⊟*No credit cards* ☉*Closed Sun. No dinner.*

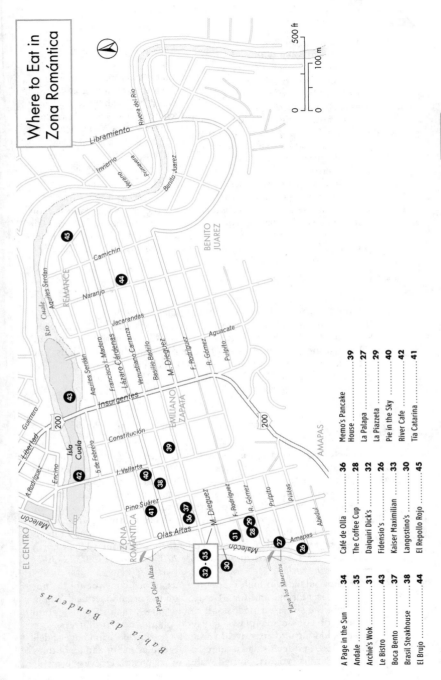

Where to Eat in Zona Romántica

BENITO JUAREZ

REMANCE

ZONA ROMÁNTICA

EL CENTRO

AMAPAS

Bahía de Banderas

500 ft

100 m

Barcelona Tapas Bar. One of the ∨ places in town with both great ·d and an excellent bay view, Barcelona has traditional Spanish tapas like *patatas alioli* (garlic potatoes), spicy garlic shrimp, and grilled mushrooms. In addition to traditional paella, the restaurant serves a seafood version. To start you off, attentive waiters bring a free appetizer and delicious homemade bread. The tasting menu lets you try soup, salad, and dessert as

---

HANGOVER CURES

For a hangover, menudo (tripe stew) and pozole are recommended, both with the addition of chopped fresh onions and cilantro, a generous squeeze of lime and as much chili as one can handle. Ceviche is another popular cure, with the same key ingredients: lime and chili.

---

well as tapas—choose your own or follow the chef's suggestions. You can sit in a small, relatively quiet room or the often crowded open-air patio. You'll have to pay for the patio view by walking up a few dozen stairs. ⊠*Matamoros at 31 de Octubre, Centro* ☎*322/222–0510* ⚐*Reservations essential* ▭*AE.*

STEAK

$$ ✕**Brasil Steakhouse.** Vallarta's most popular venue for grilled meat is this all-you-can-eat place, where you're treated to excellent barbecue, steak, pork, BBQ ribs, and grilled chicken. Waiters first bring soup and chicken wings, a shared plate of three different chopped salads, and then platters of meat of your choosing. Lunch begins after 2 PM. ⊠*Venustiano Carranza 210, Col. E. Zapata* ☎*322/222–2909* ⊠*Condominio Marina del Sol, Local 1, Marina Vallarta* ☎*322/221–5026* ▭*AE, MC, V.*

VEGETARIAN

$ ✕**Planeta Vegetariana.** Those who stumble upon this hog-less heaven
☾ can partake of the tasty meatless carne asada and a selection of main
★ dishes that change daily. Choose from at least three delicious main dishes, plus beans, several types of rice, and a daily soup at this buffet-only place. Though the selection of overdressed salads is good, the greens tend to get wilted or soggy. A healthful fruit drink, coffee, or tea, and dessert is included in the reasonable price. Eggs are not used; items containing milk products are labeled as such. It's about a block north of the cathedral, downtown. ⊠*Iturbide 270, Centro* ☎*322/222–3073* ▭*No credit cards.*

¢–$ ✕**Jumaica.** Salads win high marks for meticulous construction, if not artistic presentation, and for $1 extra you get organic lettuce. Young servers in the sweet-scented, small restaurant—which sprouts a good number of convincing plastic flowers, plants, and fruit trees—are accommodating and attentive. In addition to pancakes and bagels, deli sandwiches, and fruit salads, there's a large juice menu and smoothies made with milk, yogurt, bottled water, or ice cream. Delivery is avail-

Continued on page 82

Mar Plata restaurant

PV merges cooking styles and ingredients from all over the world

After huge cities like Guadalajara and Mexico City, Puerto Vallarta beats anywhere in the country for sheer number of excellent restaurants. Many talented chefs, drawn to this area by its natural beauty, have fallen in love with the place and opened restaurants, contributing to the varied world cuisine. Metaphorically duking it out, they create confits, reductions, tapanades, and tempuras. You, the visitor, are the clear winner, able to indulge in spring rolls or Filipino pancit, great pizza, melt-in-your-mouth beef carpaccio, and wonderful seafood dishes made with sea bass and tuna, shrimp, and shellfish plucked from local waters.

Competition creates excellence. "The high season is only five months long," says chef Bernhard Güth. "You have to be creative and good year-round to survive." PV doesn't have a signature cuisine—instead, it merges cooking styles and ingredients from all over the world. Traditional Mexican dishes are plentiful, but more often upscale restaurants use these as a springboard for their own specialties, infusing European techniques and classical recipes with new life. The most elegant restaurants present dishes so beautifully that you might dread the thought of disassembling these works of art.

TOP RESTAURANTS AND CHEFS

Stars among Puerto Vallarta's many fine chefs and restaurants, these trailblazers march to a different drummer.

Trio

Conviviality, hominess, and dedication on the parts of the chef-owners have made Trio one of Puerto Vallarta's best restaurants, hands-down. Fans, many of them members of PV's artsy crowd, marvel at the kitchen's ability to deliver perfect meal after perfect meal. Popular demand guarantees rack of lamb with fresh mint and for dessert, the warm chocolate cake.

Vitea

The chefs at Trio, opened this oceanfront bistro in 2005— which all but guaranteed its success. In addition to the great oceanfront location and upbeat Caribbean soundtrack, Vitea charms with its wide range of Mediterranean-inspired, contemporary sandwiches, soups, small plates, and full entrées—all at accessible prices.

THE DUO AT TRIO AND VITEA When you ask patrons why they love Trio, they almost universally mention the personal attention of high-energy but low-key owner–chef **Bernhard Güth** and his colleague, **Ulf Henriksson**. Güth says "Our mission here is to hug all of our clients, mentally, to make them feel more than welcome."

TOP: Fish Dish from Trio
ABOVE: Bernhard Guth &
Ulf Henriksson

Daiquiri Dick's

Visitors come often more than once during a vacation for the excellent service and consistent and innovative Mexican and world cuisine. The menu has fabulous appetizers and fish. Start with a signature daiquiri; move to the lingering wine list. Twin patios face the sea—one covered, one not.

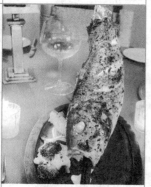

THE COLLABORATORS The fish on a stick has been around since Dick's was a palapa on the beach. But most of the stellar recipes originated with departed chef Rafael Nazario, and are now expertly executed by talented Mexican chef **Ignacio Uribe**. During high season, Seattle chef **Hnoi Latthitham** joins Uribe, adding sizzle and spice from her native Thailand.

Daquiri Dick's fish on a stick

La Ola Rica

Presentation is artful, portions generous, and the decor—a cross between whimsical and chic—is as yummy as the food. Owners Gloria Honan and Triny Palomera Gil scour the coast each day for fresh ingredients, fish, and bread, and preside over the restaurant each night to make sure the food's as good as it can be.

SELF-MADE CHEF In 1996 **Gloria Honan** and her partner were selling espresso from a lopsided wooden table inviting potential clients to sign up for a meal. But when the pasta primavera proved wildly successful, they opened La Ola Rica in Triny's family home. Their expertise is self-taught. "I've got to learn the names of the fish," Gloria laughs, "and then I can expand my repertoire."

Gloria Honan (chef-owner) and her partner Triny Palomero Gil (co-owner)

Mark's Bar & Grill

Standout dishes at this Bucerías restaurant include the homemade bread and pizza, great salads, and such entrées as macadamia-crusted fish fillets and lobster ravioli. The restaurant is cozy but chic, with glassware from Tonalá, special-order lamps from Guadalajara, and rocks from the local beach. Vie for the back patio, open to the stars.

NATURAL TALENT Creative New Zealand transplant **Jan Benton** spent happy childhood hours digging potatoes, shaking walnuts from trees, and roaming for wild mushrooms. Her appreciation for wholesome, natural foods shows in her cuisine, of which Jan says: "Everything has its own reason to be on the plate. You'll not find a repeat flavor."

Still Life No. 1: Mussels

Café Des Artistes

In Thierry Blouet's kitchen Mexican ingredients and European techniques produce such stellar dishes as cream of prawn and pumpkin soup, artichoke-and-potato terrine, and grilled tenderloin served with Camembert and smoky chipotle chile sauce.

THE MASTER Given the title of Master Chef of France in 2000, **Thierry Blouet** is well-spoken and confident, piling up the accolades and awards. Born in the Philippines to French parents, Chef Blouet describes his cooking as French cuisine with Mexican—and to a lesser extent, Asian—ingredients and spices. He is also president and co-founder of PV's Gourmet Festival, and in 2006 inaugurated Thierry's Prime Steakhouse.

Dessert as sculpture

THE DISH ON THE DISHES

Lobster Taco, Daquiri Dick's

Puerto Vallarta has dozens of wonderful restaurants, and diligent research has produced the following list of some of the most exciting plates this gourmet town has to offer.

AMAZING APPETIZERS

Daiquiri Dick's **lobster tacos** are divine, and its shrimp wonton's wonderful melange of flavors dance a merengue in your mouth. At Trio, try the **anise-infused Portobello mushrooms** with vegetable vinaigrette. La Ola Rica has delightful **garlic mushrooms** and the sweetest **coconut shrimp** around.

SEAFOOD, MEXICAN-STYLE

The **mixed-seafood enchiladas** at La Palapa are wonderful, the best thing on the menu. Daiquiri Dick's **fish on a stick**, called Pescado Vallarta, has been pleasing crowds for nearly 30 years.

A-LIST ASIAN

Archie's Wok is the best place on the bay for multi-ethnic Asian cuisine, including Filipino, Thai, and Chinese. Favorite dishes are the **spicy Thai noodles** and **pancit** (Filipino noodle stir-fry). It's also great for vegetarians, with several wonderful stir-fried veggie dishes.

CHOCOLATE A-GO-GO

Indulge in a delicious **chocolate fondue** served with nutmeg ice cream at Café des Artistes. For special occasions, it's prepared on an creatively decorated tray with spun sugar and a liquid chocolate greeting. Trio's **warm chocolate cake** is legendary in PV. Make a pit stop at Pie in the Sky, in Bucerías, for a bag of crunchy **chocolate chip cookies** for the road, or sit down for an addictive **chocolate brownie** *beso* (kiss), so rich it goes best with strong, black coffee.

IT'S ALL IN THE ATMOSPHERE

FOOD WITH A VIEW

Get a magnificent view of the city and bay, and a varied menu of excellent Spanish tapas at **Barcelona Tapas.**

DECADENT DECOR

Greco-Roman meets modern at **Le Bistro.** One of Vallarta's original gourmet restaurants, recently revitalized, has river-view dining among stone pillars and stands of towering bamboo. **Café des Artistes** has a magical,

multilevel garden of ferns and figs, mangos and palms. Open to the ocean, **Vitea** is a casually hip bistro with clever and chic glass-and-

Boca Bento

metal furnishings. Two rows of tables outdoors facing the beach and boardwalk impart a European flavor. **Boca Bento** is serene, sensual, and open, with modern and elegant artwork, a soothing waterfall, and lots of candles. Grandiose yet romantic, **Mar Plata** is saved from looking industrial by innovative installations, fixtures, and antiques.

EPICUREAN EVENTS

Chocolate fondant with tomato and basil sorbet and white chocolate and raspberry sauce, Café Des Artistes

INTERNATIONAL GOURMET FESTIVAL

Puerto Vallarta's dining scene owes its success in part to its annual gourmet festival, which has brought it international attention since 1994. During the eight-day food fling each November, chefs from Africa, Europe, South America, and the United States bring new twists on timeless classics. Starting with an elegant chef's cocktail reception, the festival continues with a full table of events. Each of the more than two dozen participating restaurants invites a guest chef to create special menus with wine pairings. Local and guest chefs teach cooking classes and seminars. The culmination is a gala dinner with live music, fireworks, and naturally, an over-the-top gourmet meal. ☎ *322/222–3229 Café des Artistes,* ⊕*www.festivalgourmet. com.*

RESTAURANT WEEK (The May Food Festival)

Most everyone in Vallarta works his or her tail off during the December to Easter high season. When *vallartenses* can finally take a breath—and then give a collective sigh of relief—they reward themselves with some reasonably priced nights out at the destination's best restaurants during this two-week (despite its name) event. In 2006 more than 30 restaurants participated, each offering prix-fixe meals (with choices among appetizers, entrées, and desserts) for either 159 or 259 pesos. ☎ *322/221–0106.*

FOOD FOR A CAUSE

As if our clothes weren't already bursting at the seams, some of PV's most benevolent gastronomes began teaming up at fundraising events for local charities in 2005. Local chefs now produce Palomazo Gastronómico, or the "Culinary Jam Session," several times a year. Along with four courses of haute cuisine, they serve up wine, song, and a warm and fuzzy feeling to boot. Cost is about $60 per person. ☎ 322/226–0000 or 322/222–1695.

able to downtown Vallarta. ⊠*Calle Aldama 162, Centro* ☎*322/222–9393* ▭*No credit cards.*

NORTH OF PUERTO VALLARTA

AMERICAN–CASUAL

¢–$ ╳**Choco Banana.** BLTs and burgers, omelets and bagels, and chicken with
☺   rice and chai tea are some of what you'll find here. Service isn't fast and
the setting is beyond casual, in keeping with laid-back Sayulita's surfer
attitude. This perennial favorite is almost always full of young people
eating and loafing; there's a kid's menu for the truly young. ⊠*Calle
Revolución at Calle Delfin, on plaza, Sayulita* ☎*329/291–3051* ☉*No
dinner Sun.*

ARGENTINE

$$–$$$ ╳**La Porteña.** Restaurants are a hard sell in all-inclusive-dominated
Nuevo Vallarta. Hopefully this one will break the mold. Every cut
of meat is grilled over mesquite, from the steaks to Angus prime rib
(both imported from Texas). The adventurous yet tasty *chinculinas*
(tender tripe appetizers) and chorizo turnovers certainly are authentic. Rice, veggies, and other sides must be ordered separately. The setting, an L-shape covered patio with kids' play equipment in the center,
is Mexican, but the food is pure Argentine. It opens for lunch only
after 2 PM. ⊠*Blvd. Nayarit Pte. 250, Nuevo Vallarta* ✛*Between highway to Bucerías and El Tigre golf course* ☎*322/297–4950* ▭*MC, V*
☉*Closed Mon.*

BISTRO

$$–$$$ ╳**Mark's Bar & Grill.** You can dine alone at the polished black-gran-
★   ite bar without feeling too lonely, or catch an important ball game.
But seemingly a world away from the bar and TV is the charming
restaurant known for its delightful decor and excellent cuisine. Both
are best appreciated on the back patio, open to the stars. Standouts
include the homemade bread and pizza, the salads, and the macadamia-
crusted fresh fish fillets with mushroom ragout. The restaurant is decorated with objets d'art, special-order lamps from Guadalajara, rocks
from the local beach, and shells from New Zealand. Order wine by
the glass from the extensive list. ⊠*Av. Lázaro Cárdenas 56, Bucerías*
☎*329/298–0303* ▭*MC, V* ☉*No lunch.*

CAFÉS

¢–$ ╳**The Bar Above.** This little place above Tapas del Mundo defies catego-
rization. It's a martini bar without a bar (the owner, Buddy, prefers that
people come to converse with friends rather than hang out at a bar) that
also serves dessert. Order from the day's offerings, maybe molten choco-

late soufflé—the signature dish—or a charred pineapple bourbon short-cake. Lights are dim, and there's an eagle's view of the ocean from the roof-top nest. ✉ *Corner of Av. Mexico and Av. Hidalgo, 2 blocks north of central plaza, Bucerías* ☎329/298–1194 ▭ *No credit cards* ⊘ *Closed Sun., Aug., Sept., and Mon. in June, July, Oct.*

¢–$ ✗**Pie in the Sky.** Although the cars
★ on the highway can be noisy, the lure of deliciously decadent mini-cheesecakes and fruit pies, pecan tarts, and crunchy chocolate cookies exerts a strong gravitational pull. The signature dessert here is the *beso*, a deep chocolate, soft-center brownie. Cakes, including gorgeous wedding cakes, are decorated by Zulem, a fine artist who excels with frosting as her medium. In addition to iced coffee and gourmet ice cream, Pie in the Sky has chicken potpie, spinach empanadas, and a spinach-and-cheese pizza. Sit a spell and take advantage of the free Wi-Fi. ✉ *Héroes de Nacozari 202, Bucerías* ☎329/298–0838 ✉ *Lázaro Cárdenas 247, at I. Vallarta, Col. E. Zapata* ☎322/223–8183 ▭ *AE, MC, V* ⊘ *Closed Wed.*

> **TIME IS OF THE ESSENCE**
>
> The state of Nayarit (Nuevo Vallarta and points north) is in the Mountain Standard Time zone, while Jalisco (Marina Vallarta to Barra de Navidad) is on Central Standard Time. But because tourism in Bucerías and Nuevo Vallarta has always been linked to that of Puerto Vallarta, many Nayarit businesses run on Jalisco time. When making dinner reservations or checking restaurant hours, ask whether the place runs on *hora de Jalisco* (Jalisco time) or *hora de Nayarit*.

CONTINENTAL

$$$–$$$$ ✗**Mar Plata.** Grandiose yet romantic, these impressive second-story digs have a celestial seasoning of stars on the ceiling in the form of tin lamps from Guadalajara. Dark-blue and deep terra-cotta walls juxtapose nicely; the huge space is saved from looking industrial by innovative installations and fixtures. Co-owner and chef Amadine's recipes wed traditional Argentine meats with updated Continental cuisine in a happy transcontinental marriage. Portions are smallish, and entrées exclude sides. There's live music Sunday and occasional flamenco shows or tango classes. ✉ *Calle de Palmas 30, Col. Costa Azul, San Francisco* ☎311/258–4424 ▭ *MC, V* ⊘ *Closed Mon. and Aug. and Sept. No lunch.*

$$ ✗**Amber Sur Mer.** A French woman from Provence brings a welcome addition to Barra's circumspect culinary scene, along with good thin-crust pizzas, escargot, crepes, and other tasty French and Italian fare. Of the many pasta dishes, the lasagna, cannaloni, and ravioli use pasta made from scratch. The restaurant's compact size and good tunes, along with the small bar in the middle and the few tables out on the street, give it a bistro feel. ✉ *Calle López de Legazpi 160, across from Hotel Alondra, Barra de Navidad* ☎315/355–8169 ▭ *No credit cards* ⊘ *No lunch.*

$$ ✕ **Don Pedro's.** Sayulita institution Don Pedro's has pizzas baked in a wood-fire oven, prepared by European-trained chef and co-owner Nicholas Parrillo. Also on the menu are reliable seafood dishes and mesquite-grilled filet mignon—served with baby vegetables and mashed potatoes accompanied by crusty, home-baked bread—which is just about the best around. The pretty second-floor dining room, with the better view, is open when the bottom floor fills up, usually during the high season (December–Easter). Call to find out about live music during the week—sometimes salsa, sometimes flamenco—during the dinner hour. This is a good spot for breakfast, too, after 8 AM. ⊠ *Calle Marlin 2, at beach, Sayulita* ☎329/291–3090 ▭MC, V ⊘ *Closed Aug. 15–Oct. 15.*

ECLECTIC

$$ ✕ **Cafe del Mar.** Chefs Eugene of Singapore and Amandine, a Belgian-Mexican, collaborate to create beautiful food focusing on seafood and chicken; the varied and excellent appetizers and desserts are especially recommended. The dishes blend Asian, Mediterranean, and haute Mexican cuisine in simple yet successful dishes. The setting itself is romantic and sophisticated. Tiny white lights and soft music accompany individual tables down the side of a hill to a vine-drenched trellis at the bottom. There's usually a guitarist serenading during Friday dinner; the restaurant is open for lunch as well. ⊠ *Av. China 9, San Francisco* ☎311/258–4251 ▭MC, V ⊘ *Closed Wed. and Aug. and Sept.*

$$ ✕ **La Ola Rica.** Oh. My. God. The food is good. *Really* good. Somehow
Fodor'sChoice   chef and co-owner Gloria Honan (with Triny Palomera Gil) makes garlic-
★   sautéed mushrooms (a huge portion) into a minor miracle on toast. The cream of poblano-chili soup is simply to die for: not too spicy, but wonderfully flavorful. And these are just the starters. The restaurant is understandably popular, and reservations are encouraged when there's live music, often jazz or Cuban. Locals come for the medium-crust pizzas; everyone laps up the lovely margaritas. ⊠ *Av. Tercer Mundo s/n, San Francisco* ☎311/258–4123 ▭MC, V ⊘ *Closed Sun. and Aug.– Oct. Closed weekends June and July. No lunch.*

$–$$ ✕ **La Casita del Gallo.** If a hole in the wall could be out of doors, this would be it. Frankly, it looks best by candlelight. But folks don't come for the decor; they come for the fab filet mignon, great fish and shrimp, and good pizza. The affable owner, Gallo, is also a musician who presents tunes (often blues or acoustic guitar) whenever possible, usually Friday through Sunday after 7:30 PM. Nightlife being the exception rather than the rule in San Pancho, this is a great locals' after-dark hangout. ⊠ *Av. Tercer Mundo 7, San Francisco* ☎311/258–4135 ▭ No credit cards ⊘ *Closed Tues. No lunch.*

$–$$ ✕ **Tapas del Mundo.** Here, worldly recipes of this and that are served in small plates perfect for sharing. Sit at one of three long bars around the open kitchen, soaking in the ambience created by the colorful American owners. Nosh on a hot pot of shrimp with guajillo chiles served with homemade tortillas, breaded olives, Anaheim chiles stuffed with goat cheese, or Oriental beef strips. Be apprised of the wonderful margaritas. The owners plan to open a new restaurant, Le Bistro, in San Sebastián: check it out. The Bar Above, upstairs (⇨*above*), sells desserts, coffee, and mixed drinks. ✉*Corner of Av. Mexico and Av. Hidalgo, 2 blocks north of central plaza, Bucerías* ☎*329/298–1194* ▤*No credit cards* ◔*Closed Sun. No lunch.*

$ ✕**Philo's.** Ambitious Philo does it all: breakfast, lunch, dinner. It's a bar with live music, a meeting place for local fundraisers and events, and a community center (there are computers, yoga, and Spanish classes). There are even a pool table in the back and a small swimming pool.

And if you were wondering, the food is good, although the menu of sandwiches, burgers, and pizza is less ambitious than it once was. Philo's special pizza has goat cheese, sundried tomatoes, onion, and pineapple. ✉*Calle Delfín 16, La Cruz de Huanacaxtle* ☎*329/295–5068* ▤*No credit cards.*

MEDITERRANEAN

$$ ✕**Sandrina's.** Canadian owner Sandy is as colorful as her wonderful art, which graces this locals' favorite. Dine on the back patio at night amid dozens of candles and tiny lights. The varied menu has plenty of salads and pasta dishes as well as such Mediterranean fare as chicken souvlaki and Greek-style chicken and pita bread with hummus. Order an espresso, delicious doctored coffee, or dessert from the bakery counter. It's open only after 3 PM. ✉*Av. Lázaro Cárdenas 33, Bucerías* ☎*329/298–0273* ⊕*www.sandrinas.com* ▤*MC, V* ◔*No lunch. Closed Tues. and 2 wks in Sept.*

MEXICAN

$–$$ ✕**Famar.** This unassuming restaurant gets the vote of just about everyone we queried in Bucerías: expats and locals alike. Breakfast in the noisy front room includes chilaquiles, waffles, and omelettes. It's more peaceful on the back patio where the top picks are beef fajitas and shrimp Famar: the chef's secret recipe, containing shrimp, bacon, cheese, and salsa. Consistency and friendly, familial service is the name of the game. ✉*Héroes de Nacozari 105, Bucerías* ☎*329/298–0113* ▤*No credit cards* ◔*Closed Sun.*

$–$$ ✕**Vista Guayabitos.** Portions are large but the cooking is predictable at best. This restaurant's beauty lies in the setting, which couldn't be more dramatic. Enjoy lovely views of a solitary beach, an unattended island, and the beaches of Guayabitos. The hawk's-eye ocean view is especially wonderful around sunset. ⊠ *Carretera a Los Ayala, Km 1.5, Rincón de Guayabitos* ☎*327/274–2580* ▭*MC, V.*

$ ✕**Sayulita Café.** The restaurant bills itself as "home of the perfect chile relleno," but it also serves other Mexican plates from Puebla and Oaxaca as well as Continental dishes like rib eye with baked potato. The restaurant and bar in this small, rather dark converted home look good by candlelight. From the sound system emerge jazz, classic, and Latin tunes; waiters with perfect English are the rule. ⊠ *Av. Revolución 37, Sayulita* ☎*329/291–3511* ▭*No credit cards* ⊘*Closed Sept. No lunch.*

$ ✕**Si Hay Olitas.** This simply decorated, open-front Mexican restaurant
☾ near tiny Sayulita's main plaza is the one most often recommended by locals for dependable Mexican and American fare. Order a giant burrito, vegetarian platter, burger or grilled chicken, or a seafood combo. There's a little of everything to choose from, and it's open for breakfast. The setting is casual and the menu has plenty of things that children will like. ⊠ *Av. Revolución 33, Sayulita* ☎*329/291–3203* ▭*No credit cards.*

¢–$ ✕**La Casa del Café (aka Chayito's).** Here's a casual little place for breakfast a few blocks from the beach in San Francisco, right next to La Ola Rica. Service inside or on the street-facing patio is easygoing but attentive. Between 8 and noon or 1 PM you can get the house favorites: huevos rancheros y chilaquiles as well as freshly squeezed orange juice, a banana strawberry smoothie, or an excellent fruit plate. ⊠ *Av. Tercer Mundo s/n, at Calle Mexico, San Francisco* ☎*329/258–4126* ▭*No credit cards* ⊘*Closed Tues. and May–Oct. No lunch or dinner.*

SEAFOOD

$$ ✕**Dugarel Plays.** Do they mean "Dugarel's Place"? No matter, of Bucerías's many beachfront eateries, this one gets extra points for longevity, attentive service, good views north and south along the bay, and the best breezes. The menu is not extensive: there are several beef plates and Mexican dishes, and a larger assortment of fresh fish and seafood served with the usual rice and toasted bread, as well as some underdone veggies. ⊠ *Av. del Pacífico s/n, Bucerías* ☎*329/298–1757* ▭*No credit cards.*

$ ✕**Columba.** Yearn for manta ray stew? Crave fresh tuna balls? Simply must have shark soup? The recipes here are geared to the local palate; if you're an adventurous eater with a hankering for fresh, strangely prepared (a lot of things are minced beyond recognition) seafood dishes, give Columba a try. It's on the road to the fishermen's beach in Cruz de Huanacaxtle. As a backup plan, have an appetizer here, then head for one of the

NATURAL THIRST-BUSTER

The guy on the malecón or in the main plaza with a giant gourd and a handful of plastic cups is selling *agua de tuba,* a refreshing, pleasant, yet innocuous drink made from the heart of the coconut palm. It's stored in a gourd container called a *huaje,* and served garnished with chopped walnuts and apples.

other picks in Bucerías. This restaurant closes at 7 PM, and serves only beer and sodas as beverages. It has the least expensive lobster around. ✉ *Calle Marlin 14, at Calle Coral, Cruz de Huanacaxtle* ☎ *329/295–5055* ▤ *No credit cards* ☾ *Closed Mon. and wk after Easter.*

STEAK

$$ ✕ **Brasil Nuevo Vallarta.** Although the food and presentation is the same as the steak house restaurant in downtown Vallarta *(⇨ above)*, this venue in Nuevo Vallarta's large, comprehensive mall has café seating on the corridor. Lunch is served only after 2 PM. ✉ *Paradise Village Mall, 2nd fl., Nuevo Vallarta* ☎ *322/297–1164* ▤ *AE, MC, V.*

VEGETARIAN

$ ✕ **Roots.** Young owner-chef Andrew Field apprenticed for two years at Fressen in Toronto. Although he's a vegan, he uses fresh cheese with a light hand. Other than that, you won't find any lacto-ovo products whatsoever. All of the sauces and stocks are vegan, too. To start, try the soup of the day or such small plates as avocado bruschetta and grilled asparagus with red-pepper coulis. Good main courses include Moroccan chickpea tart, Thai curry, eggplant ravioli, and veggie stir fry. The restaurant gets daily deliveries of produce from an inland farm. During high season (late November–April), the lounge at the back has live music on Friday and shows films Saturday, Sunday, and Tuesday at 8:30. It opens at 4:30 PM. ✉ *Lázaro Cárdenas 40, Bucerías* ☎ *329/298–2504* ▤ *MC, V* ☾ *Closed Thurs. and Sept. No lunch.*

COSTALEGRE

AMERICAN–CASUAL

¢–$ ✕ **Casa de la Abuela.** The amiable and service-oriented owner, Miguel, makes this one of the town's top choices for breakfast, snacks, or a light lunch. Listen to rock and jazz on the great sound system as you sip cappuccino and munch on the assortment of Mexican cookies that comes with it. Refills of the good American-style coffee are a given. Besides omelets, chilaquiles, fresh juices, and other breakfast food, Miguel and his family serve snacks like guacamole and chips, and burgers and fries for lunch. ✉ *Av. Miguel López de Legazpi 150, Barra de Navidad* ☎ *No phone* ▤ *No credit cards* ☾ *Closed Mon. No dinner.*

KNOW YOUR TORTILLAS

In PV, tortillas are made of boiled and milled corn, griddle cooked, and served with just about every traditional dish. Butter to accompany tortillas is offered to *gringos* only. Foreigners also are given their choice of corn or flour tortillas, the latter native to northern Mexico and typically offered only with certain dishes, like *queso fundido* (cheese fondue).

ECLECTIC

$-$$ ✕**Maya.** Two Canadian women have teamed up to bring sophistication
★   to San Patricio–Melaque's dining scene. East meets West in contemporary dishes such as tequila-lime prawns and grilled eggplant rollups.
Favorite entrées include Szechuan prawns and prosciutto-wrapped
chicken stuffed with spinach and goat cheese. Their hours of operation are complex and subject to change; it's best to check their Web
site or confirm by phone. ⊠*Calle Alvaro Obregón 1, Villa Obregón,
San Patricio–Melaque* ☎*315/355–6764* ⊟*No credit cards* ⊘*Closed
Mon. and Tues. in Nov.; mid-May–Oct. No lunch.*

MEXICAN

$-$$ ✕**Martin's.** This second-floor, palapa-roof restaurant is the most reliable
in town for food and good cheer, and for hours of operation, too, as it's
open year-round. There are Mexican- and American-style breakfasts,
fajitas and shrimp for lunch and dinner, and sporadic serenades. This
is as much a place for socializing as for eating; at the bar you can quaff
champagne, cognac, martinis, and wine. ⊠*Calle Playa Blanco 70, La
Manzanilla* ☎*315/351–5106* ⊟*No credit cards.*

¢-$ ✕**Cenaduría Flor Morena.** Some folks say these are the best enchiladas
★   they've ever eaten; others call it a "local institution." Locals and foreigners all pretty much agree that this hole in the wall on the
main square is the best place around to get good, inexpensive Mexican favorites like pozole, tamales, and tacos. ⊠*Facing main plaza below the
Catscan bar, San Patricio–Melaque* ☎*No phone* ⊟*No credit cards*
⊘*Closed Mon. and Tues. No lunch.*

SEAFOOD

$-$$ ✕**Seamaster's.** Although most of the ocean-facing restaurants in Barra
have a similar menu, this friendly family favorite is often recommended
above the others. Have a shrimp or fish burger, the catch of the day
bathed in garlic cream, or the house special: shrimp flambéed in brandy
and Kahlua served in a nubby pineapple. The bar sometimes stays
open late in high season, keeping clients around after the kitchen has
shut down. ⊠*Av. Miguel López de Legaspi 146, Barra de Navidad*
☎*315/355–5199* ⊟*No credit cards.*

$ ✕**El Dorado.** This is the best place in town for seafood with an ocean
view under a tall, peaked palapa roof. Besides seafood there are grilled
chicken with baked potato, beef tips with rice and beans, soups, quesadillas, great guacamole, and fries. It's open all day (8 AM until 10 PM)
and serves everyone from white-collar business types to families and
friends meeting for lunch, to tourists cleaned up for an evening out.
After your meal, kick your shoes off and take a walk on the beach.
⊠*Calle Gómez Farias 1, San Patricio–Melaque* ☎*315/355–5239 or
315/355–5770* ⊟*MC, V.*

Beaches

Ixtapa

WORD OF MOUTH

"Yelapa is gorgeous. It's in a cove, protected from wind and waves … with a small village all around the cove and climbing part way up the mountains. We passed Las Animas, Quimixto, Las Caletas, and Mahajuitas beaches on the way—Yelapa was the prettiest."

—balasteve

PUERTO VALLARTA SITS AT THE center of horseshoe-shape Bahía de Banderas (Banderas Bay), the second largest bay in North America (after the Hudson). Although Pacific Mexico's beaches are not the sugar-sand, crystal-water variety of the Caribbean, the beaches are lovely, the water unpolluted, and the coastline itself among the most majestic in Mexico.

Accounting for much of its beauty are the foothills that race down to meet the sea. Crowded with palms and cedars, the jungle's blue-green canopy forms a highly textured background to the deep blue ocean and creamy sand. Dozens of creeks and rivers follow the contours of these hills, creating estuaries, mangrove swamps, and other habitats for exploration. Exquisitely visible from cliff-side hotels and restaurants, the scalloped coast holds myriad coves and small bays perfect for shelling, sunning, swimming, and more strenuous activities.

At crowded Hotel Zone beaches and a few of the more popular stretches of sand north and south of town you can parasail, take boat rides, Jet Ski, kayak, boogie board, snorkel, and dive. If you want to explore the coast, some of the isolated beaches accessible by boat offer some of the above activities. Accessible by both land and sea are untouristy hideaways where there's little to distract you beyond the waves lapping at the shore. Almost any beach has at least one low-key seafood restaurant to provide simple fish lunches, cold beer, and warm pink sunsets.

GETTING ORIENTED

The mountainous backdrop of the beaches in Puerto Vallarta and to the north makes them beautiful—even though the water isn't translucent and the sand is grainy and brown, rather than powdery white. South of PV the mountains recede from the coast. The lovely yet lonely beaches and bay are fringed by dry tropical thorn forest with a wonderful variety of plant species. Several species of whales cruise down in winter and turtles spawn on the beaches. Throughout the region from southern Nayarit to the Costalegre, long, flat beaches invite walking and reefs and offshore breaks draw surfers; the omnipresent seafood shanties are perfect vantage points for sunsets on the sand.

BEACH REGIONS

PUERTO VALLARTA

Paralleling the Romantic Zone, Playa los Muertos is PV's most popular beach, with restaurants and bars with music; vendors selling barbecued fish on a stick; and people cruising the boardwalk. The beaches in the Hotel Zone and Marina Vallarta are a bit dull by comparison. At the south end of the bay are beautiful mountain-backed *playas* accessible only by boat.

NUEVO VALLARTA

One wide, flat, sandy beach stretches north of the Ameca River mouth for miles into the town of Bucerías. The generally calm water is good for swimming and, when conditions are right, bodysurfing or boogie

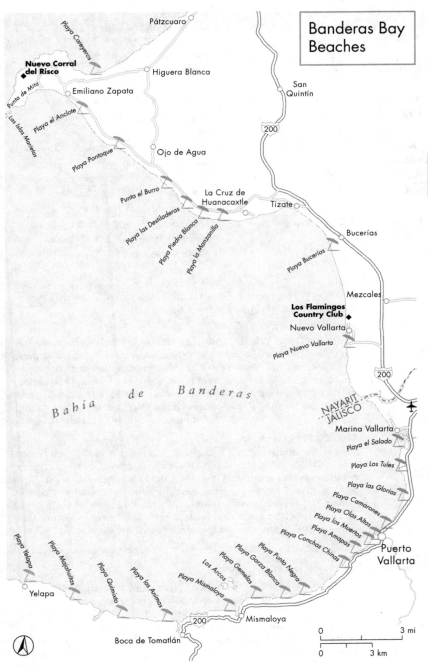

Banderas Bay Beaches

Pátzcuaro

Playa Careyeros

Nuevo Corral del Risco ◆

Punta de Mita

Higuera Blanca

San Quintín

Emiliano Zapata

Playa el Anclote

Las Islas Marietas

Playa Pontoque

Ojo de Agua

200

4

Punta el Burro

La Cruz de Huanacaxtle

Playa las Destiladeras

Tizate

Playa Piedra Blanca

Playa la Manzanilla

Bucerías

Playa Bucerías

Mezcales

Los Flamingos Country Club ◆

Nuevo Vallarta

Playa Nuevo Vallarta

200

Bahía   de   Banderas

NAYARIT
JALISCO

Marina Vallarta

Playa el Salado

Playa Los Tules

Playa las Glorias

Playa Camarones

Playa Olas Altas

Playa los Muertos

Playa Amapas

Playa Conchas Chinas

Puerto Vallarta

Playa Yelapa

Playa Majahuitas

Playa Quimixto

Playa las Ánimas

Playa Punta Negra

Playa Garza Blanca

Los Arcos

Playa Gemelas

Playa Mismaloya

Yelapa

200

Mismaloya

Boca de Tomatlán

0   3 mi

0   3 km

GO FOR:	IN PV	NORTH OR SOUTH OF PV
WILDLIFE	Los Arcos	Kayak adventures from La Manzanilla (Bahía Tenacatita); Islas Marietas (Punta de Mita)
SNORKELING	Los Arcos; Playa Conchas Chinas	Islas Marietas; Playa Mora
WALKING OR JOGGING	Playa los Muertos	Nuevo Vallarta; Bucerís; Barra de Navidad and San Patricio Melaque (Bahía de Navidad)
CALM, SWIMMABLE WATERS	Hotel pool, Conchas Chinas	Los Ayala, Rincón de Guayabitos (Bahía de Jaltemba); Playa Las Minitas; Boca de Naranjo; Playa Chalacatepec
SURFING	N/A	El Anclote (Punta de Mita); Sayulita; Quimixto; Barra de Navidad
EATING/DRINKING WITH LOCALS	Boca de Tomatlán	Chacala; Rincón de Guayabitos (Bahía de Jaltemba); Playa Tenacatita; Colimilla (Bahía de Navidad)

boarding. Activities are geared to all-inclusive hotel guests north of Paradise Village marina. Guys on the beach rent water-sports equipment, and most of the hotels rent equipment, too.

SOUTHERN NAYARIT

North of Nuevo Vallarta, rocky headlands sandwich scallops of sand from Bucerías to Chacala. These beaches attract boogie boarders, beachcombers, and those who make their own fun, as there are fewer services than in Vallarta. Surfing is big at Punta de Mita. Guayabitos, with its offshore island, is a vacation mecca for Mexican families and a refuge for (mainly) Canadian snowbirds. Off the main highway, long, sandy roads lead to more isolated beaches such as Destiladeras.

THE COSTALEGRE

This is the domain of the independent traveler and the well-heeled recluse. High-end hotels on picturesque, rock-framed beaches arrange fishing and other pastimes. Other long, sandy beaches—many on large, semi-protected bays—are frequented by fishermen and local people relaxing at seafood shanties, and allow shelling, snorkeling, fishing, and trips to offshore islands. Having a car is helpful for exploring multiple beaches, although local bus service is available.

PUERTO VALLARTA

PV beaches are varied. Downtown Vallarta's main beach, Los Muertos, is a fun scene, with shoulder-to-shoulder establishments for drinking and eating under the shade, and year-round action. The itinerant vendors can be annoying, however. Immediately north of Los Muertos is contiguous Olas Altas Beach, with the same grainy brown sand but fewer vendors and services and sometimes waves big enough to surf or boogie. North of Hotel Rosita, more stretches of unispired sand front minor hotels. Hotel Zone beaches to the north offer opportunities to play in the sun during high season, although sand was dredged away by Hurricane Kenna, in 2002. The beach at Marina Vallarta, between PV and Nuevo Vallarta, is swimmable but uninspired except for the beach toys and hotels that offer refreshments.

South of Vallarta proper are Conchas Chinas, a few smaller beaches, and Mismaloya. The wild beaches farther south (on the north side of Cabo Corriente, from Las Animas to Yelapa) didn't have electricity until the 1970s. They tend to fill up with day-trippers between December and April but are well worth a visit. At Los Muertos as well as beaches in the Hotel Zone and Marina Vallarta, you'll find Jet Skis, parasailing, and banana-boat rides in high season (December–April) and on weekends year-round.

> ## BEACH OF THE DEAD
>
> There are several versions of how Playa los Muertos got its name. One says that around the time it was founded, Indians attacked a mule train laden with silver and gold from the mountain towns, leaving the dead bodies of the muleteers on the beach. A version crediting pirates with the same deed seems more plausible. In 1935, anthropologist Dr. Isabel Kelly postulated that the place was an Indian cemetery.

GETTING THERE
The only public beach access (with on-street parking) at Marina Vallarta is between the airport and Condominios Grand Bay. There's little to stop you from walking through the major hotels, though, if you take a bus or cab to the area. The Hotel Zone and Centro beaches are easily accessed from the street. Take a bus or a cab, or drive your car; there's curbside parking but no parking lots to speak of.

DOWNTOWN PUERTO VALLARTA

Playa los Muertos is PV's original happenin' downtown beach. Facing Vallarta's South Side (south of the Río Cuale), this flat beach runs about 1½ km (1 mi) south to a rocky point called El Púlpito. Joggers cruise the cement boardwalk (interrupted by sandy areas) early morning and after sunset; vendors stalk the beach nonstop, hawking kites, jewelry, and sarapes as well as hair-braiding and alfresco massage. Their parade can range from entertaining (good bargainers can get excellent deals) to downright maddening. Restaurant-bars run the length of the beach; the bright blue umbrellas near the south end of the beach belong to the Blue Chairs resort, the hub of PV's effervescent gay scene.

The surf ranges from mild to choppy with an undertow; the small waves crunching the shore usually discourage mindless paddling. Strapping young men occasionally occupy the lifeguard tower, and local people fish from the small pier at the foot of Calle Francisca Rodríguez or cast nets from waist-deep water near the south end of the beach. Jet Skis zip around, but stay out beyond the small breakers, and are not too distracting to bathers and sunbathers. Guys on the beach offer

banana-boat and parasailing rides.
■TIP→ The steps (more than 100) at
Calle Púlpito lead to a lookout with a
great view of the beach and the bay.

Playa Olas Altas means High Waves
Beach, but the only waves suitable
for body surfing or boogie boarding are near the Cuale River, at
the north end of this small beach.
Although Olas Altas more often
refers to the neighborhood of bars
and businesses near the ocean south
of the Río Cuale, it is also the name
of a few blocks of sand between
Daiquiri Dick's restaurant and the
Río Cuale. It attracts fewer families
than Los Muertos, but is otherwise an extension of that beach. Facing
Olas Altas Beach near leafy Lázaro Cárdenas Plaza are open-air stands
selling beach accessories, small grocery stores, and easy access to beach-
facing bars and restaurants.

> **BEACH BLANKET BOTHER**
>
> Although it might feel rude, it's
> culturally permissible to simply
> ignore itinerant vendors, especially
> if you're in the middle of a conver-
> sation. However, being blatantly
> impolite (i.e., shouting at the
> vendor to take a hike) *is* rude—no
> matter where you're from. A wide
> grin and a firm *"No, gracias,"* with
> no further eye contact, is the best
> response—apart from "Yes, please,
> I'll take it," that is!

The rock-strewn beach paralleling the malecón and the beach hotels
like Rosita and El Pescador just north of it is **Playa Camarones.** Hurricane Kenna (2002) stole *mucho arena* (a lot of sand), however, and
most people prefer to walk along the cement boardwalk than the beach
here. Likewise, although the waves are gentle, the ocean floor is rocky
and most bathers opt for the hotel pool. What you see here most often
are small groups of men and boys surf casting, more for diversion than
for hopes of great catches.

NORTH OF DOWNTOWN

The high-rise-backed **Zona Hotelera and Marina Vallarta beaches** have
several names—**Playa Las Glorias** to the south, **Playa Los Tules** in the
middle (around the Holiday Inn and Fiesta Americana), and **Playa El
Salado** to the north. Most people, however, just refer to each beach by
the hotel that it faces. These gray-beige, coarse-sand beaches are generally flat with a slope down to the water. Major winds and tides sometimes strew them with stones that make it less pleasant. (The Sheraton
and its beachfront, at the south end of the strip, were hit hard by Hurricane Kenna in 2002, and tons of sand were trucked in, in 2005. The
beach in front of it is therefore sandier than its neighbors, although still
pocked with smooth, egg-size rocks.)

At Marina Vallarta, Playa **El Salado**—facing the Grand Velas, Meliá,
Marriott, Mayan Palace, and the Westin—is pleasantly sandy. Colorful in high season with parasailers and with windsurfers rented or lent
at area hotels, these beaches are actually more fun when crowded than
when solitary. During fine weather and on weekends, and daily during
high season, you can rent Jet Skis and pack onto colorful banana boats

for bouncy tours of 10 minutes or longer. Some hotels rent small sailboats, sailboards, and sea kayaks to guests and to nonguests.

NAYARIT

At the northern end of Bahía de Banderas and farther into Nayarit state, to the north, are long, beautiful beaches fringed with tall trees or scrubby tropical forest. Only the most popular beaches like those of Nuevo Vallarta and Rincón de Guayabitos have much in the way of water-sports equipment rentals, but even the more secluded ones have stands or small restaurants serving cold coconut water, beer, and grilled fish with tortillas.

GETTING THERE

In Nuevo Vallarta, park on the street or in the parking lot of the tourism office, between Gran Velas and Maribal hotels. Buses arrive here as well, but the all-inclusives that predominate cater to guests only, so bring your own supplies. It's a cinch to install yourself anywhere on Bucerías's long beach, with easy streetside parking. As most of the beaches north of here are off the main road, they are easiest to access by car (or taxi).

A new road (rather, the improvement of an old, narrow dirt-and-gravel road) connects Punta de Mita with Sayulita, San Francisco, and points to the north. However, if your destination is north of Punta de Mita, there's no need to follow the coast road to the point. Simply bear right instead of left after Bucerís, continuing on Carretera 200.

NUEVO VALLARTA TO PUNTA DE MITA

Several kilometers of pristine, if plain, beach face the hotels of **Playa Nuevo Vallarta.** The wide, flat, sandy beach is perfect for long walks: in fact, you could walk all the way to Bucerías, some 8 km (5 mi) to the north. Most of the hotels here are all-inclusives, so guests generally move between their hotel pool, bar, restaurant, and the beach in front. The same all-inclusive program means that nonguests are generally barred from the bars and restaurants.

☙ **Bucerías.** Eighteen kilometers (11 mi) north of Nuevo Vallarta, the substantial town of Bucerías attracts a loyal flock of snowbirds, which has encouraged the establishment of apartments for rent and good restaurants. The beach here is endless: you could easily walk along its medium-coarse beige sands all the way south to Nuevo Vallarta. The surf is gentle enough for swimming, but also has body-surfable waves, and beginning surfers occasionally arrive with their longboards.

☙ Just north of Bucerías, **La Cruz de Huanacaxtle,** better known as simply "La Cruz," has a fishing fleet but not much of a beach. A marina is being developed as part of the Escalera Nautica program: a "ladder" of marinas meant to encourage sailing and boating on the Sea of Cortez and the coast of northern-to-central Pacific Mexico. Like other Vallarta–Nayarit beaches, homey La Cruz is growing and becoming somewhat more sophisticated. On the north side of La Cruz, **Playa la Manzanilla** is a crescent of soft, gold sand where kids play in the shallow water while their parents sip cold drinks at one of several seafood shacks. It's somewhat protected by the Piedra Blanca headland to the north.

A few miles north of Piedra Blanca headland, **Destiladeras** is a 1½-km-long (1-mi-long) beach with white sand and good waves for bodysurfers and boogie-boarders. There's nothing much here except for a couple of seaside *enramadas* (thatch-roof shelters) serving fillets of fish and ceviche. **Punta el Burro,** at the north end of the beach, is a popular surf spot often accessed by boat from Punta de Mita.

> **A SHADY DEAL**
>
> You can spread a blanket on the sand, but because the strong sun can burn you to a crisp or even cause sunstroke, it's a better idea to rent a *palapa* (typical shade structure of wood and palm thatch) for shade. These generally cost around $5 a day, with no deals for shorter stays. Beachfront hotels and restaurants have their own tables and chairs on or near the sand for those who order at least a soda.

☺ **Punta de Mita,** about 40 km (25 mi) north of Puerto Vallarta, is home to the posh Four Seasons and the boutique resort Casa Las Brisas; other exclusive developments, condo complexes, and private villas are under construction. Just a few minutes past the entrance to the Four Seasons, the popular beach at **El Anclote** has a string of restaurants—once simple shacks but today of increasing sophistication. This is a primo spot for viewing a sunset. Artificially calmed by several rock jetties and shallow for quite a ways out, it's also a good spot for children and average to not-strong swimmers to paddle and play, but there's a long slow wave for surfing, too. Most of the jewelry and sarape sellers and fishermen looking for customers have moved—or been moved—off the beach to more official digs in buildings along the same strip or facing the Four Seasons.

Accessible from El Anclote or the adjacent town of **Nuevo Corral del Risco,** Punta de Mita has the most surf spots in the region, nearly a dozen, and the long swells here pump year-round. Divers favor the fairly clear waters and abundance of fish and coral on the bay side of the **Islas Marietas** about a half-hour offshore from El Anclote. In winter, especially January through March, these same islands are also a good place to spot orcas and humpback whales, which come to mate and give birth. Las Marietas is the destination for fishing, diving, and snorkeling; in addition, sealife viewing expeditions set out from El Anclote and Nuevo Corral de Risco as well as from points up and down Banderas Bay.

NORTH OF BANDERAS BAY

As is happening up and down the Pacific Riviera, real estate north of the bay is booming. Mexicans are selling family holdings, jaded gringos are building private homes, and speculators from around the globe are grabbing what land they can, on and off the beach. For now, however, the Nayarit coast continues to enchant, with miles of lovely beaches bordered by arching headlands and Pacific hamlets drowsing in the tropical sun.

★ The increasingly popular town and beach of **Sayulita** is about 45 minutes north of PV on Carretera 200, just about 19 km (12 mi) north of Bucerías, and 35 km (22 mi) north of the airport. Until a few years ago, people liked to say it was like PV was 40 years ago. But today the sounds of construction ring through its narrow, sandy streets, which are now clogged with traffic in high season. Despite the growth, this small town is still laid-back. Fringed in lanky palms, Sayulita's heavenly beach curves along its small bay. A decent shore break here is good for beginning or novice surfers; the left point break is a bit more challenging. Skiffs on the beach have good rates for surfing or fishing safaris in area waters.

★ Ten minutes north of Sayulita, **San Francisco** is known to most people by its nickname: San Pancho. Just beginning to be developed, it stretches between headlands to the north and south, and is accessed at the end of the town's main road: Avenida Tercer Mundo. You'll see men fishing from shore with nets as you walk the 1½-km-long (1-mi-long) beach of coarse beige sand. There's an undertow sometimes, but otherwise nothing to discourage reasonably strong swimmers. Its small waves occasionally support longboard surfing (especially in September), but this isn't a surf spot. In fact its small waves—too big for family splashing and too small for surfing—have probably maintained its innocence ... until now. Popular with a hip crowd of European artists and intellectuals, San Pancho has just a few hotels but a growing number of good restaurants. Of the few beachfront restaurants in San Pancho, **La Perla**—serving burgers, tacos, fish fillets, and lobster—is the most dependable.

About 8 km (5 mi) north of San Pancho, **Lo de Marcos** is a humble town of quiet, wide streets that sometimes fill up on weekends and holidays with Mexican families renting the nondescript, bungalow-style motel rooms that predominate. After entering town on the main street, head left on the last road before the beach to reach **Playa las Minitas,** a small brown-sand beach on a pretty little cove framed by rocks. When not camped out at a half-dozen seafood shanties specializing in barbecued fish, local people bob in the super-tranquil surf. Continue another ½ km (¼ mi) along the road to **Playa los Venados,** which like Las Minitas, is a good spot for both swimming and snorkeling.

WATER-TOY PRICES

Prices for water toys in and around Vallarta are fairly consistent:

wave runners: $45–$50 per half hour (one or two riders)

parasailing: $35 for a 10-minute ride

banana-boat rides: $15 for a 10-minute ride (usually 4-person minimum)

Hobie Cat or small sailboat: $30–$45 per hour

4

From south to north, the main beaches of **Bahía de Jaltemba** are: Los Ayala, Rincón de Guayabitos, and La Peñita.

A mini version of Guayabitos (⇨ *below*), **Playa los Ayala** has a level beach, mild surf, and an excellent view of **Isla del Coral,** to which glass-bottom boats ferry passengers for about $6 per person. On weekends, holidays, and in high season take a ride on a banana boat; most any time you can find a skiff owner to take you to **Playa Frideritas** or **Playa del Toro,** two pretty beaches for bathing that lie around the headland to the south, accessible only by boat. You can walk, however, over the hill at the south end of the beach to a seafood restaurant on a small scallop of beach called **Playa Frideras.**

> **TURTLE RESCUE**
>
> In San Pancho, **Grupo Ecológico de la Costa Verde** (*Green Coast Ecological Group* ⊠ *Av. Latino América 102, San Pancho* ☎ *311/258–4100* ⊕ *www.project-tortuga.org*) works to save the olive ridley, leatherback, and eastern Pacific green turtles that once swamped area beaches. Encouraged to dedicate two to six months to the cause, volunteers patrol beaches, collect eggs, maintain the nursery, tabulate data, and educate the public about their program.

☾ ★ A couple of kilometers north of Ayala along the highway, **Rincón de Guayabitos** bustles with legions of Mexican families on weekends and holidays; foreigners take up residence during the winter months. The main street, Avenida Nuevo Sol, has modest hotels, inexpensive restaurants, and shops that all sell the same cheap bathing suits and plastic beach toys. One block closer to the sea are more hotels along with some vacation homes right on the sand. Colorfully painted stands on the beach sell fresh chilled fruit and coconuts; others serve up fresh seafood. This lovely beach bounded by headlands and the ocean is tranquil and perfectly suited for swimming.

Contiguous with Guayabitos, **La Peñita,** at the north end of the bay, has fewer hotels and the beach is often nearly abandoned except for a few fishermen. Its name means "little rock." The center for area business, La Peñita has banks, shoe stores, and ice-cream shops; a typical market held each Thursday offers knock-off CDs, polyester clothing, and fresh fruits and vegetables.

A few kilometers north of Peñita, a dusty road leads to **Boca de Naranjo,** a long, secluded sandy beach with excellent swimming. The rutted dirt road from the highway, although only about 4 km (2½ mi) long, takes almost a half hour to negotiate in most passenger cars. Enjoy great views of the coastline from one of nearly a dozen seafood shanties. Turtles nest here in August and September.

Some 30 km (19 mi) north north of Rincón de Guayabitos, **Chacala** is another 9 km (5 mi) from the highway through exuberant vegetation. Although most people are content to dine or drink at the handful of eateries right on the beach while imbibing the soft-scented sea air and the sight of the green-blue sea, you can bodysurf and boogie board here, too. Swimming is safest under the protective headland to the north of the cove; surfing is often very good, but you have to hire a boat to access the point break.

SOUTH OF PUERTO VALLARTA

While coastal Nayarit is jumping on the development bandwagon, the isolated beaches of Cabo Corriente and those of southern Jalisco—some surrounded by ecological reserves—continue to languish for the time being in peaceful abandon. Things here are still less formal, and aside from the super-posh resorts like El Tamarindo, the Careyes, and Las Alamandas, whose beaches are off-limits to nonguests, words like "laid-back" and "run-down" or "very basic" still apply, much to the delight of adventurous types.

GETTING THERE

Catch a green bus to Conchas Chinas, Mismaloya, or Boca de Tomatlán from the southwest corner of Calle Basilio Badillo and Constitución, Col. E. Zapata in Puerto Vallarta. Give the driver sufficient notice when you want to get off; pulling over along the narrow highway is challenging.

There are several ways to reach the beaches of southern Banderas Bay. Party boats (aka booze cruises) and privately chartered boats leave from Marina Vallarta's cruise-ship terminal *(⇨ Chapter 7)* and generally hit Las Animas, Quimixto, Majahuitas, and/or Yelapa. You can also hire a water taxi from Boca de Tomatlán ($6 one-way, usually on the hour 9 AM through noon, and again in early afternoon), from the pier at Los Muertos ($20 round-trip, 11 AM and in high season at 10:15 and 11 AM), or from the tiny pier next to Hotel Rosita ($20 round-trip, 11:30 AM). ■ TIP→ **If not full, the water taxi from Hotel Rosita will stop at Los Muertos to pick up passengers.** You can catch the 4 PM taxi from Los Muertos to Yelapa if you're planning to spend the night; it will not return until the next day. *Pangas* (skiffs) for your party only can be hired at Boca, Mismaloya, or Los Muertos. The price depends on starting and ending points, but runs about $35 per hour for up to eight passengers.

It's best to have your own car for exploring the Costalegre, as many beaches are a few kilometers—down rutted dirt roads—from the highway. However, if you want to hang out in the small but tourist-oriented towns of San Patricio–Melaque and Barra de Navidad, you may not need wheels.

SOUTHERN BANDERAS BAY & CABO CORRIENTES

★ Frequented mainly by visitors staying in the area, **Playa Conchas Chinas** is a series of rocky coves with crystalline water. Millions of tiny white shells, broken and polished by the waves, form the sand; rocks that resemble petrified cowpies jut into the sea, separating one patch of beach from the next. These individual coves are perfect for reclusive sunbathing and, when the surf is mild, for snorkeling around the rocks;

bring your own equipment. It's accessible from Calle Santa Barbara, the continuation of the cobblestone coast road originating at the south end of Los Muertos Beach, and also from Carretera 200 near El Set restaurant. Swimming is best at the cove just north of La Playita de Lindo Mar, below the Hotel Conchas Chinas (where the beach ends), as there are fewer rocks in the water. You can walk—be it on the sand, over the rocks, or on paths or steps built for this purpose—from Playa Los Muertos all the way to Conchas Chinas. The beach does not have services.

Though **Punta Negra**, about a mile south of Conchas Chinas, lost a lot of sand and allure during Hurricane Kenna, waves usually break gently on shore and the water is usually glassy and nice for swimming. It is accessible from Carretera a Mismaloya (Carretera 200) down a somewhat steep stone-and-cement path. Park off the highway at the north end of Condominios Jalisco Vacactional, near the blue Playa Punta Negra sign. The beach is mainly big round rocks, with little sand. There's shade under several tall trees sprouting from an old foundation, but there's sometimes trash from previous picnics. The beach has no facilities.

Playa Garza Blanca, or "White Heron Beach," is a mirror image of Punta Negra Beach about half a mile away at the opposite end of the narrow cove. It's also signed, and accessible on foot by a dirt path. The beach does not have facilities.

Playa Mismaloya is the cove where *The Night of the Iguana* was made. Unfortunately, the big, tan Hotel La Jolla de Mismaloya looms large over the once-pristine sand, and Hurricane Kenna stole much of Mismaloya's white sand. Nonetheless, the place retains a certain cachet. It also has views of the famous cove from a handful of full-service seafood restaurants on the south side of a wooden bridge over the mouth of the Río Mismaloya. Sun-seekers kick back in wooden beach chairs, waiters serve up food and drink, massage techs offer their (so-so) services alfresco, and Chico's Dive Shop sells dive packages and boat trips. The tiny village of Mismaloya is on the east side of Carretera 200, about 13 km (8 mi) south of PV.

Boca de Tomatlán is the name of both a small village and a rocky cove that lie at the mouth of the Río Tomatlán, about 5 km (3 mi) south of Mismaloya and 17 km (10½ mi) south of PV. Water taxis leave from Boca to the southern beaches; you can arrange snorkeling trips to Los Arcos. Five seaside cafés cluster at the water's edge.

There's lots to do besides sunbathe at **Playa las Ánimas,** a largish beach 15 minutes south of Boca de Tomatlán by boat, so it tends to fill up with families on weekends and holidays. The usual seafood eateries line the sand, and you can also rent Jet Skis, ride a banana boat, or soar up into the sky behind a speedboat while dangling from a colorful parachute.

Between the sandy stretches of Las Animas and Majahuitas, and about 20 minutes by boat from Boca de Tomatlán, rocky **Quimixto** has calm, clear waters that attract boatloads of snorkelers. There's just a narrow beach here, with a few seafood eateries. Day-trippers routinely rent horses ($15 round-trip; ask at the restaurants) for the 25-minute ride—or only slightly longer walk—to a large, clear pool under a waterfall. You can bathe at the fall's base, and then have a cool drink at the casual restaurant. There's a fun, fast wave at the reef here, popular with surfers but because of its inaccessibility, rarely crowded.

Majahuitas—between the beaches of Quimixto and Yelapa and about 35 minutes by boat from Boca de Tomatlán—is the playground of people on day tours and guests of the exclusive Majahuitas Resort.

> ## SNORKELING SANCTUARY
>
> Protected area **Los Arcos** is an offshore group of giant rocks rising some 65 feet above the water, making the area great for snorkeling and diving. For reasonable fees, local men along the road to Mismaloya Beach run diving, snorkeling, fishing, and boat trips here and as far north as Punta de Mita and Las Marietas or the beach villages of Cabo Corrientes. Restaurants at Playa Mismaloya can also set you up.

The beach has no services for the average José; the lounge chairs and bathrooms are for hotel guests only. Palm trees shade the white beach of broken, sea-buffed shells. The blue-green water is clear, but tends to break right on shore.

★ The secluded village and ½-km-long (¼-mi-long) beach of **Yelapa** is about an hour southeast of downtown or a half hour from Boca de Tomatlán. Several seafood *enramadas* (thatch-roof huts) edge its fine, clean, grainy sand. During high season, parasailers float high above it all. From here you can hike 20 minutes into the jungle to see the small Cascada Cola del Caballo (Horse's Tail Waterfall), with a pool at its base for swimming. (The falls are often dry near the end of the dry season, especially April–early June.) A more ambitious expedition of several hours brings you to less-visited, very beautiful Cascada del Catedral (Cathedral Falls).

But, for the most part, Yelapa is *tranquilisimo:* a place to just kick back in a chair on the beach and sip something cold. Seemingly right when you really need her, Cheggy the pie lady will show up with her fantastic homemade pies.

Phones and electricity arrived in Yelapa around the turn of the 21st century. ■TIP→ **But bring all the money you'll need, as there is nothing as formal as a bank.**

Just south of the end of Banderas Bay are the lovely beaches of pristine, wonderful, fairly inaccessible **Cabo Corrientes.** These take an effort to visit, and preferably, a four-wheel-drive vehicle, although a sturdy, high-clearance vehicle will do. Public transportation goes there and back once a day from the small town of El Tuito (40 km [25 mi] south of Puerto Vallarta) along a rutted dirt road.

A somewhat difficult 40 km (25 mi) from the highway, the tiny town of **Aquiles Serdán** lies between the ocean and a river-fed lagoon. Boats hired here give access to miles of solitary, sandy beaches where primitive camping is permitted—providing you bring all of your own supplies and clean up after yourself. To get to Aquiles Serdán, bear right at the fork just past the village of Los Conejos.

Bearing left (and then right) just past Los Conejos brings you to bucolic **Tehualmixtle**, a sheltered cove that has, in addition to several restaurants, places to camp and basic rooms to rent. The pristine beach invites snorkeling and diving (bring your own equipment). Or you can explore the inland area with the help of an experienced guide at CandelaRío's palapa (☎no phone).

THE COSTALEGRE

Most people come to the Costalegre—dubbed "The Happy Coast" by Jalisco's tourism authorities—to stay at luxury accommodations on lovely, clean beaches: Hotelito Desconocido, Las Alamandas, the Careyes, and El Tamarindo. Others head to southern Jalisco State without reservations to explore the coast at their leisure. Whether you kick back at an elegant resort or explore the wild side, the area between Cabo Corrientes and Barra de Navidad, the latter at the southern extreme of Jalisco state, will undoubtedly delight.

GETTING THERE

It's optimum to explore the beaches of southern Jalisco by car, SUV, or small RV. Camping is permitted on most beaches, and these are often down a long dirt road from the highway. Fill up with gas at every opportunity, as gas stations are numbered. If you're in a rental car, reset the odometer and look for the kilometer signs at the side of the road. If you're driving a car marked in miles, not kilometers, the road signs are still useful, as many addresses are simply "Carretera 200" or "Carretera a Barra de Navidad" along with the number of kilometers the place is from Puerto Vallarta.

Buses leave from the **Central Camionero** (✉ *Carretera Puerto Vallarta—Tepic [Carretera 200], Km 9, Col. Las Mojoneras* ☎*322/290–1009*) in Puerto Vallarta.

COSTALEGRE

Some of the nicest beaches, with services, are now the private domain of Gran Turismo (5-star-plus) hotels. However, there are some delightful, pristine, and mainly isolated beaches along the Costalegre, most with few services aside from the ubiquitous seafood enramadas serving fish fillets and fresh ceviche.

A sylvan beach with no services, **Playa Chalacatepec** lies down a packed dirt road about 82 km (50 mi) south of El Tuito and 115 km (70 mi) south of Puerto Vallarta. The road to the beach is rutted and negotiable only by high-clearance passenger cars and smallish RVs. The reward for 8 km (5 mi) of bone-jarring travel is a beautiful rocky point, Punta Chalacatepec, with a sweep of protected white-sand beach to the north perfect for swimming, bodysurfing, and hunting for shells. Admire the tidepools at the point during low tide; take a walk of several kilometers along the open-ocean beach south of the point, where waves crash more dramatically, discouraging swimming. To get here, turn right into the town of José María Morelos (at Km 88). Just after 8 km (5 mi), leave the main road (which bears right) and head to the beach over a smaller track. From there it's less than a 1½ km (1 mi) to the beach.

The handful of islands just offshore of lovely **Bahía de Chamela,** about 131 km (81 mi) south of PV, protects the beaches from strong surf. The best place on the bay for swimming is **Playa Perula** (turnoff at Km 76, then 3 km [2 mi] on dirt road), in the protective embrace of a cove just below the Punta Perula headland. Fishermen there take visitors out to snorkel around the islands or to hunt for dorado, tuna, and mackerel; restaurants sitting on the coarse beige sand sell the same as fresh fillets and ceviche. The sand curves the length of the 8-km-long (5-mi-long) bay to **Playa Negrita,** with camping and RV accommodations and plenty of opportunities for shore fishing, swimming, and snorkeling. Almost every pretty beach in Mexico has its own humble restaurant; this one is no exception.

About 11 km (6½ mi) south of Bahía Chamela, **Playa Careyes** is a lovely soft-sand beach framed by headlands. When the water's not too rough, snorkeling is good around the rocks, where you can also fish.

You can walk south from Playa Careyes along the dunes to **Playa Teopa,** although guards protect sea turtle nests by barring visitors without written permission during the summer and fall nesting seasons. A road from the highway at Km 49.5 gains access to Playa Teopa by car; ask for written permission at Hotel El Careyes, a few kilometers to the north, or just roll up in your car and try your luck.

★ Named for the bay on which it lies, **Playa Tenacatita** is a lovely beach of soft sand about 34 km (20 mi) north of San Patricio Melaque and 172 km (106 mi) south of Puerto Vallarta. Dozens of identical seafood shacks line the shore; birds cruise the miles of beach, searching for their own fish. Waves crash against clumps of jagged rocks at the north end of the beach, which curves gracefully around to a headland. The water is sparkling blue. There are camping for RVs and tents at Punta Hermanos, where the water is calm, and local men offer fishing excursions. ■TIP→ **Of the string of restaurants on the beach, La Fiesta Mexicana is especially recommended.**

★ On the north end of Playa Tenacatita, **Playa Mora** has a coral reef close to the beach, making it an excellent place to snorkel.

A little more than 6 km (4 mi) south of Bahía de Tenacatita at Km 20, is the entrance to down-at-the-heels **Bahía de los Angeles Locos** all-inclusive hotel. It may be tacky and have a buffet that serves mediocre food, but it's got a great location and such amenities as tennis and banana boats. Sharing the property and some of the services is the buffed-out naturalistic resort at Punta Serena. Nearby Coconuts by the Sea guesthouse enjoys lovely breezes and excellent views from its breezy hilltop perch.

Farther south along Tenacatita Bay, **Playa Boca de Iguanas** is a wide, flat beach of fine gray-blond sand that stretches for several kilometers north of Playa Tenacatita. Gentle waves make it great for swimming, boogie boarding, and snorkeling, but beware the undertow. There are two RV parks here, and a couple of beach restaurants. The entrance is at Km 17.

☾ Two-kilometer-long (1-mi-long) **Playa la Manzanilla** is little more than a kilometer in from the highway, on the southern edge of Bahía de Tenacatita, 193 km (120 mi) south of Puerto Vallarta and 25 km (15½ mi) north of Barra de Navidad (at Km 14). Informal hotels and restaurants are interspersed with small businesses and modest houses along the main street of the town. Rocks dot the gray-gold sands and edge both ends of the wide beach. The bay is calm. At the beach road's north end, gigantic, rubbery-looking crocodiles lie heaped together just out of harm's way in a mangrove swamp. The fishing here is excellent; boat owners on the beach can take you fishing for snapper, sea bass, and others for $20–$25 an hour.

Twenty-one kilometers (13 mi) south of La Manzanilla, **Bahía de Navidad** represents the end of the Costalegre at the border with Colima State. First up (from north to south) is **San Patricio–Melaque,** the most populous town on the Costalegre, with about 12,000 people. (The town is actually two towns that have now met in the middle.) While parts of town look dilapidated or abandoned, its long, coarse-white-sand beach is rather beautiful, with gentle waves. ∎TIP→ **The best swimming and boogie boarding is about half the length of town, in front of El Dorado restaurant.**

Fishermen congregate at the west end of San Patricio–Melaque, but it's most common to hire a panga for fishing at **Barra de Navidad** (usually called just "Barra"), a laid-back little town with sandy streets. At any time but at high tide you can walk between San Patricio and Barra, a distance of about 6 km (4 mi). It's about 4½ km (3 mi) on the highway from one town to the other.

Most of Barra is comprised of two streets on a long sand bar. Calle Veracruz faces the vast lagoon and **Isla Navidad,** now home to the posh Gran Bay resort. Water taxis take folks to the Gran Bay's golf course or marina, or to the seafood restaurants of **Colimilla,** on the lagoon's opposite shore. Avenida Miguel de Legazpi faces Barra's sloping brown-sand beach and the ocean. These and connecting streets have small shops, simple but charming restaurants, and—like everywhere along Mexico's Pacific coast—a host of friendly townspeople. ∎TIP→ **Surfers look for swells near the jetty, where the sea enters the lagoon.**

Lingering in Yelapa

If you can't tear yourself away at the end of the day (or you miss the last water taxi), consider renting one of the locally run rustic accommodations near the beach. Modest but charming, Hotel La Lagunita (closed in the rainy season) has rooms right over the water. "Rustic chic" describes La Verana hotel, a five-star property represented by Mexico Boutique Hotels; it normally doesn't accept walk-ins, but you might try if you're stranded with just the clothes on your back and a credit card.

If you're lucky enough to be staying in Yelapa, there's plenty to do beyond the beach. Splash across the shallow lagoon or catch the water taxi to the main pier for a jungly walk past private homes and small shops; this is the Yelapa most folks never see.

Back in Yelapa, check out the candlelit Club Yates disco on the south side of the estuary (Wednesday and Saturday nights during high season [December through Easter week] and holidays). Or ask around for one of several yoga classes, schedule a therapeutic massage with Claudia (☎ 322/209–508; 💳 $50), or hire a local *pangero* (panga operator) for a trip to a secluded southern beach for swimming and a trek to a clandestine waterfall.

But the best part of staying in Yelapa is that after the booze cruises decamp and the water taxis put in for the night, you'll have the cool and groovy place to yourself.

4

Shopping

Huichol bowls

WORD OF MOUTH

"PV has lots to choose from. Nice, expensive stores to booths along the river to guys strolling the beaches. A popular craft is the Huichol bead or yarn art. I also try to look for local artisan goods. Jewelry, particularly silver, is common. You will have no trouble finding places to shop."

–MichelleY

IT'S HARD TO DECIDE WHICH is more satisfying: shopping in Puerto Vallarta, or feasting at its glorious restaurants. There's enough of both to keep a bon vivant busy for weeks. But while gourmands return home with enlarged waistlines, gluttonous shoppers need an extra suitcase for the material booty they bring home.

Puerto Vallarta's highest concentration of shops and restaurants shares the same prime real estate: Old Vallarta. But as construction of hotels, time-shares, condos, and private mansions marches implacably north up the bay, new specialty stores and gourmet groceries follow the gravy train. To the south, the Costalegre is made up primarily of modest seaside towns and self-contained luxury resorts, and shopping opportunities are rare.

More than a half dozen malls line "the airport road," Boulevard Francisco M. Ascencio, which connects downtown PV with the hotel zone, the marina area, Nuevo Vallarta, and towns to the north. There you'll find folk art, resort clothing, and home furnishing stores amid supermarkets, and in some cases bars, movie theaters, and banks.

A 15% value added tax, locally called IVA, officially the *impuesto al valor agregado (see Taxes)*, is levied on most purchases, though it's often included in the price; it's usually disregarded entirely by market vendors.

SMART SOUVENIRS

ARTS & CRAFTS

Puerto Vallarta is an arts and crafts paradise, particularly if you're fond of ceramics, masks, fine art, and Huichol folk art (⇨ *"The Art of the Huichol," below)*. Occasionally you'll find vivid handwoven and embroidered textiles from Oaxaca and Chiapas, and comfortable, family-size hammocks from Yucatán State. Handmade or silkscreened, blank greeting cards make inexpensive and lovely framed prints.

GLASS & PEWTER

Glassblowing and pewter were introduced by the Spanish. A wide range of decorative and utilitarian pewter items is produced in the area, as well as distinctive deep blue goblets, emerald-rimmed, chunky drinking glasses, and other glassware. All are excellent buys today.

JEWELRY

Many PV shop owners travel extensively during the summer months to procure silver jewelry from Taxco, north of Acapulco. For more information see box "One Man's Metal."

POTTERY

After Guadalajara and its satellite towns Tlaquepaque and Tonalá—which produce ceramics made using patterns and colors hundreds of years old—Puerto Vallarta is the best place in the region to buy pottery, and at reasonable prices. PV shops also sell Talavera (majolica or maiolica) pottery from Puebla.

UNUSUAL GIFTS

For less-than-obvious souvenirs, go traditional and consider a *molinillo*, a carved wooden beater for frothing hot chocolate; you can find these at street vendors or traditional markets for about $1.50. A set of 10 or so *tiras de papel* (string of colored tissue-paper cuts) in a gift shop will only set you back about $2. Handmade huaraches (traditional sandals) are hard to break in (get them wet and let them dry on your feet), but last for years.

TIPS & TRICKS

Better deals are often given to cash customers—even though credit cards are nearly always accepted—because stores must pay a commission to the credit-card companies. U.S. dollars are almost universally accepted, although most shops pay a lower exchange rate than a bank (or ATM) or *casa de cambio* (money exchange). You may have to pay 5% to 10% more on credit-card purchases.

Bargaining is expected in markets and by beach vendors, who may ask as much as two or three times their bottom line. Occasionally an itinerant vendor will ask for the real value of the item, putting the energetic haggler into the awkward position of offering far too little. One vendor says he asks *norteamericanos* "for twice the asking price, since they always want to haggle." The trick is to **know an item's true worth** by comparison shopping. It's not common to bargain for already inexpensive trinkets like key chains or quartz-and-bead necklaces or bracelets.

Shop early. Though prices in shops are fixed, smaller shops may be willing to bargain if they're really keen to make a sale. Anyone even slightly superstitious considers the first sale of the day to be good luck, an auspicious start to the day. If your purchase would get the seller's day started on the right foot, you might just get a super deal.

HOURS OF OPERATION

Most stores are open daily 10–8 or even later in high season. A few close for siesta at 1 PM or 2 PM, then reopen at 4 PM. Perhaps half of PV's shops close on Sunday; those that do open usually close up by 2 or 3 in the afternoon. Many shops close altogether during the low season (August or September through mid-October). We've noted this whenever possible; however, some shops simply close up for several weeks if things get excruciatingly slow. In any case, low season hours are usually reduced, so call ahead during that time of year.

WATCH OUT   Watch that your credit card goes through the machine only once, so that no duplicates of your slip are made. If there's an error and a new slip needs to be drawn up, make sure the original is destroyed. Another scam is to ask you to wait while the clerk runs next door ostensibly to use another business's phone or to verify your number—but really to make extra copies. Don't let your card leave a store without you. While these scams are not common in Puerto Vallarta and we don't advocate excessive mistrust, taking certain precautions doesn't hurt.

SHOPPING IN SPANISH

bakery: *panadería*	health-food store: *tienda naturista*
bookseller: *librería*	jewelry store: *joyería*
candy store: *dulcería* (often sells piñatas)	market: *mercado*
	notions store: *mercería*
florist: *florería*	stationery store: *papelería*
furniture store: *mueblería*	tobacconist: *tabaquería*
grocery store: *abarrotes*	toy store: *juguetería*
hardware store: *ferretería*	undergarment store: *bonetería*

Don't buy items made from tortoiseshell or any sea turtle products: it's illegal and many of Mexico's turtle species are endangered or threatened. These items are also not allowed into the U.S., Canada, or the U.K. Cowboy boots, hats, and sandals made from the leather of endangered species such as crocodiles may also be taken from you at customs, as will birds, or stuffed iguanas or parrots. Both the U.S. and Mexican governments also have strict laws and guidelines about the import–export of antiquities. Check with customs beforehand if you plan to buy anything unusual or particularly valuable.

Although Cuban cigars are readily available, American visitors aren't allowed to bring them into the U.S. and will have to enjoy them while in Mexico. However, Mexico produces some fine cigars from tobacco grown in Veracruz. Mexican cigars without the correct Mexican seals on the individual cigars and on the box may be confiscated.

PUERTO VALLARTA

DEPARTMENT STORES

LANS (⊠ *Calle Juárez 867, at Pípila, Centro* ☎ *322/226–9100* ⊠ *Plaza Caracol, near Gigante supermarket, Blvd. Francisco M. Ascencio 2216, Zona Hotelera* ☎ *322/226–0204*) is a multilevel department store with clothing for men, women, and children: look for Perry Ellis khakis, Levi's, Lee, and Dockers shirts and trousers, and jeans from Colombia. The store also sells housewares; purses and Swatch watches; Samsonite luggage; ladies' perfume and makeup (Chanel, Gucci, Estée Lauder); and men's undies.

GROCERIES

If you crave country-style Texas sausage and other comfort foods from north of the border, try **AgroGourmet** (⊠ *Calle Basilio Badillo 222, Col. E. Zapata* ☎ *322/222–5357* ⊠ *Blvd. Francisco M. Ascencio 2820, Zona Hotelera* ☎ *322/221–2656*). You can find oils (sesame, grapeseed, nut, virgin olive), locally made pastas, homemade spaghetti sauce, lox, real maple syrup, and agave "honey." A nice gift is the Mexican vanilla, in blown-glass containers.

The most convenient market to the Romantic Zone, **Gutiérrez Rizo** (✉ *Av. Constitución 136, between 5 de Febrero and Aquiles Serdan, Col. E. Zapata* ☎*322/222–1367*) has an ample liquor section, American-brand cereals, canned food, condiments, good produce, and ground-to-order coffee. **Ley** (✉*Av. México 1150, at Veracruz, Col. 5 de Diciembre* ☎*322/223–2878*), a small standard grocery store with the usual supplies, is convenient to Colonia 5 de Diciembre and downtown Vallarta.

MALLS

PV's most popular mall with locals, **Plaza Caracol** (✉*Blvd. Federico M. Ascencio, Km 2.5, Zona Hotelera, across from Fiesta Americana hotel* ☎*322/224–3239*), aka Gigante Plaza, is lively and full on weekends and evenings, even when others are dead. Its anchors are the Gigante supermarket and the adjacent LANS department store. Surrounding these are tiny stores dispensing electronics and ice cream, fresh flowers, manicures, and inexpensive haircuts. Adding to the commercial center's appeal is the sixplex movie theater. A few worthwhile jewelry shops still reside at **Plaza Genovesa** (✉*Blvd. Federico M. Ascencio s/n, Zona Hotelera* ☎*322/224–4763*), though the mall has suffered since Hurricane Kenna in 2002, and many shops are still empty. A string of beachwear, curio, and jewelry shops faces the mall on the south side.

Plaza Marina (✉*Carretera al Aeropuerto, Km 8, Marina Vallarta* ☎*322/221–0490*), one long block north of Plaza Neptuno, has ATMs, dry cleaning, photo developing, a pharmacy, a café, and several bars. The mall is anchored by the Comercial Mexicana supermarket. **Plaza Neptuno** (✉*Carretera al Aeropuerto, Km 7.5, Marina Vallarta* ☎*No phone*) is a small mall in the heart of the marina district with a number of fine-home-furnishing shops, several classy clothing boutiques, and just behind it, a few good, casual restaurants.

MARKETS

In the **Mercado de Artesanías** (✉*Calle Francisca Rodríguez, between Calles Matamoros and Miramar, at base of bridge* ☎*No phone*), flowers, piñatas, produce, and plastics share space in indoor and outdoor stands with souvenirs and lesser-quality crafts. Upstairs, locals eat at long-established, family-run restaurants. Small shops and outdoor market stalls sell an interesting mix of wares at the informal and fun **Mercado Isla Río Cuale** (✉*Dividing El Centro from Colonia E. Zapata, access at Calle Morales, Calle I. Vallarta, Calle Matamoros, Calle Constitución, Calle Libertad, and Av. Insurgentes* ☎*No phone*). Harley-Davidson kerchiefs, Che paintings on velvet, and Madonna icons compete with the usual synthetic lace tablecloths, shell and quartz necklaces, and silver jewelry amid postcards and key chains. The market is partially shaded by enormous fig and rubber trees and serenaded by the rushing river; a half dozen cafés and restaurants provide sustenance.

SPECIALTY STORES

ART

★ **Galería 8 y Más** (⊠ *Calle Miramar 237, Centro* ☎ *322/222–7971* ⊕ *www.artismexico.com*) started with eight Guadalajara artists and has expanded under new ownership to almost 50 artists from or residing in Jalisco. The large old building (which lacks air-conditioning) has glass, bronze, chalk, and oil paintings. **Galería Arte Latinoamericana** (⊠ *Calle Josefa O. de Domínguez 155, Centro* ☎ *322/222–4406*) sells contemporary art, primarily paintings. There are representative Indian portraits by Marta Gilbert and chunky village scenes—a cross between the Flintstones and Chagall—by Celeste Acevedo.

Galería Corona (⊠ *Calle Corona 164, Centro* ☎ *322/222–4210* ⊕ *www.galeria-corona.com*) is a small shop with some sculpture and art jewelry as well as etherial and painterly portraits and landscapes in various genres. **Galería Em** (⊠ *Blvd. Francisco M. Ascencio 2758, Marina Vallarta* ☎ *322/221–1728* ⊠ *Las Palmas II, Local 17, Marina Vallarta* ☎ *322/221–2856*) sells art glass, stained glass, glass sculpture, and jewelry made of glass. You can commission a piece, or watch the artisans work, at the Las Palmas workshop.

Contemporary painters based in Oaxaca are represented by **Galería Gradiva** (⊠ *Av. Ignacio L. Vallarta 179, Centro* ☎ *322/222–7143*), which is open by appointment only in September and October. The artist who created the whale sculpture at the entrance to Marina Vallarta produces more portable pieces shown in **Galería Octavio** (⊠ *Av. México 1115, Col. 5 de Diciembre* ☎ *322/223–3492* ⊕ *www.octavio-arteenbronce.com*). The lifelike bronze whales, dolphins, sea turtles, and sea lions range from table or desk size, on a wooden base, to larger, free-standing garden or patio models. The gallery is closed Sunday and often from August through October; call ahead.

Fodor'sChoice **Galleria Dante** (⊠ *Calle Basilio Badillo 269, Col. E. Zapata* ☎ *322/222–*
★ *2477*) is a 6,000-square-foot gallery (PV's largest) and sculpture garden with classical, contemporary, and abstract works by more than 50 Latin American artists. A pioneer in Puerto Vallarta, **Galería Pacífico** (⊠ *Calle Aldama 174, Centro* ☎ *322/222–1982* ⊕ *www.galeriapacifico.net*), open since 1987, features the sculpture of Ramiz Barquet, who created the bronze *Nostalgia* piece on the malecón. Patrick Denoun is among the representational portrait artists; Brewster Brockmann paints contemporary abstracts. The gift shop sells less expensive items, including art books, figurines, and posters.

You'll find wonderful, varied art in many mediums at **Galería Uno** (⊠ *Calle Morelos 561, Centro* ☎ *322/222–0908*). Owners Jan Lavender and Martina Goldberg love to showcase local talent, and during the season host individual shows that change up to three times a month. National and international artists represented include João

Rodriguez, Esaú Andrade, and Daniel Palmer. **Galería Vallarta** (⊠ *Av. Juárez 263, Centro* ☎*322/222–0290* ⊕*www.galeriavallarta.com*) is notable since, in addition to a large cadre of fine artists showing watercolors, oils, mixed media, and sculptures of bronze, wood, and ceramics, it has a comprehensive collection of lithographs and art prints, from the likes of Frida Kahlo and Diego Rivera to contemporaries such as Marta Gilbert.

Internationally known **Sergio Bustamante** (⊠ *Av. Juárez 275, Centro* ☎*322/223–1405* ⊠*Paseo Díaz Ordáz 716, Centro* ☎*322/222–5480* ⊕*www.sergiobustamante.com.mx*)—the creator of life-size brass, copper, and ceramic animals, mermaids, suns, and moons—has a team of artisans to execute his never-ending pantheon of creative and quirky objets d'art, such as pots shaped like human torsos that sell for more than US$1,000. Paintings and jewelry are sold here as well.

BOOKS & PERIODICALS

English-language books and magazines are found at **The Book Store** (⊠ *V. Carranza 334–A at Av. Insurgentes, Col. E. Zapata* ☎*322/223–9437*). Owner Tom Barrett stocks a little of everything in his diminutive storefront, mainly "beach reads" in the fiction department and books of self-discovery in the nonfiction arena. Some 200 books are special-ordered each week. **Librería Guadalajara** (⊠ *Plaza Genovesa, Av. Francisco M. Ascencio s/n, Zona Hotelera* ☎*332/224–9084*) sells books in English and Spanish, and educational toys.

★ **Libros Libros Books Books** (⊠ *31 de Octubre 127, Centro* ☎*322/222–7105*) has more than 50 magazine titles in English, plus a small but respectable selection of English-language nonfiction and fiction. Folks read books they've bought or traded at outdoor café **A Page in the Sun** (⊠ *Calle Olas Altas 399, Col. E. Zapata* ☎*322/222–3608*). The shelves tend to be full of romance novels and other light reading. **Seven Deli** (⊠ *Plaza Marina, 2 doors down from McDonald's, Marina Vallarta* ☎*322/221–0177*) has the *Miami Herald* as well as *Cosmo, GQ, Vogue, People,* and *Marie Claire* in English, along with many Spanish-language magazines.

CERAMICS, POTTERY & TILE

★ **Alfarería Tlaquepaque** (⊠ *Av. México 1100, Centro* ☎*322/223–2121*) is a large store with a ton of red-clay items traditional to the area—in fact, their predecessors were crafted before the 1st century AD. Talavera and Talavera-style pottery are available at good prices. The 300 or so potters from the village of Juan Mata Ortiz add their touches to the intensely—sometimes hypnotically—geometric designs of their ancestors from Paquimé. The

WALKING AND GAWKING

On Wednesday evenings during high season (late October–end of April), the PV art community hosts Old Town artWalk (⇨ *Chapter 8*). Participating galleries welcome lookie loos as well as serious browsers between 6 PM and 10 PM; most provide at least a cocktail. Look for signs in the windows of participating galleries, or pick up a map at any of them ahead of time.

place to buy this wondrous pottery is **Galería de Ollas** (⊠ *Calle Corona 176, Centro* ☎ *322/223–1045* ⊕ *www.galeriadeollas.com*). Pieces range from about $60 to $10,000, with an average of about $400. Stop in during artWalk, or at the branch in Paradise Plaza if you're based in Nuevo Vallarta.

Before you buy rustic ceramic plates, bowls, and cups, ask if there's lead in the glaze, unless you plan to use them for decoration only and not for food service.

★ **Majolica Antica** (⊠ *Calle Corona 191, Centro* ☎ *322/222–5118*) sells just that, which, according to knowledgeable shop owner Antonio Cordero, is also called Talavera or tin-glazed pottery. You get a certificate of origin with each piece of beautiful ornamental tile, utilitarian pitcher, plate, or place setting. It's open until 5 PM during the week and until 3 PM on Saturday; it's closed Sunday. Buy machine-made tiles from Monterrey, painted locally, for about 60¢ each at **Mundo de Azulejos** (⊠ *Av. Venustiano Carranza 374, Col. E. Zapata* ☎ *322/222–2675* ⊕ *www.talavera-tile.com*). Slightly sturdier at about $1 each are the handmade tiles. You can get mosaic tile scenes (or order your own design), a place setting for eight, hand-painted sinks, or any number of soap dishes, cups, saucers, plates, or doodads. Around the corner and run by family members, Mundo de Cristal *(⇨ below)* has more plates and tableware in the same genre.

★ Jackie Kilpatrick, who owns **Talavera Etc.** (⊠ *Av. Ignacio L. Vallarta 266, Col. E. Zapata* ☎ *322/222–4100*), is happy to share her knowledge of Talavera pottery. She sells the exclusive Uriarte line, the oldest maker of Talavera in Mexico (est. 1805), as well as reproductions of tiles from Puebla churches and small gift items. Look in the book to choose made-to-order pieces. The shop is closed Sunday, during lunch, and for two weeks in September.

CIGARS

La Casa del Habano (⊠ *Aldama 170, Centro* ☎ *322/223–2758*) sells only Cuban cigars, starting at $3.50 each and topping out at $44 for a Cohiba Millenium 2000. You can smoke your stogey downstairs in the casual lounge while sipping coffee or a shot of liquor. **Guantanamera** (⊠ *Calle Corona 186B, Centro* ☎ *322/223–3513*) sells Mexican and Cuban cigars. The Mexican tobacco, from Veracruz, is hand-rolled here in Vallarta. Drinks and coffee are served in the small bar. It's closed Sunday.

■TIP➔ **If you're bringing any Mexican cigars back to the States, make sure they have the correct Mexican seals on both the individual cigars and on the box. Otherwise, they may be confiscated.**

EXPAT HUMOR

The co-owner of Lucy's CuCú Cabana is Gil Gevens, who writes quirky epistles, often at his own expense, or the expense of other expats, about life in Puerto Vallarta. Gil writes regularly for the weekly English-language paper *Puerto Vallarta Tribune*, and you can buy his tongue-in-cheek books around town or at Lucy's.

CLOTHING

★ **La Bohemia** (✉ *Calle Constitución, at Calle Basilio Badillo, Col. E. Zapata* ☎ *322/222–3164* ✉ *Plaza Neptuno, Av. Francisco M. Ascencio, Km 7.5, Plaza, Marina Vallarta* ☎ *322/221–2160*) sells elegant clothing, some of it designed by the equally elegant owner, Toody. You'll find unique jewelry, accessories, and the San Miguel shoe—the elegant yet comfortable footware designed for walking on cobblestone streets like those of San Miguel and Puerto Vallarta. It's closed Sunday. **Boutique Osiris** (✉ *Plaza Marina, Local F–6, Marina Vallarta* ☎ *322/221–0732*) has simple gauze, cotton, and linen clothing for day or evening wear, although it's more practical than formal or fancy. The specialty is plus sizes.

Caprichoso (✉ *Plaza Neptuno, Av. Federico M. Ascencio, Km 7.5, Marina Vallarta* ☎ *322/221–3067*) sells sizes from XS to 2X. This is the only store in PV to stock the Oh My Gauze line of women's resort wear, and also sells Dunes, Juanita Banana, and unusual clothing by Chalí, with cut-out, painted flowers. Most of the inventory is cotton, including a smaller selection of clothing for men. **D'Paola** (✉ *Calle Basilio Badillo 258, Col. E. Zapata* ☎ *322/223–2742*) has a large and somewhat unusual selection of pashmina, purses, and shawls and lots of muslin clothing. It's surrounded by other interesting shops. It's closed Sunday. Diminutive **Etnica Boutique** (✉ *Av. Olas Altas 388, Col. E. Zapata* ☎ *322/222–6763*) has a well-edited collection of cotton and linen dresses, shawls, purses, hats, sandals, and jewelry. A few items from Indonesia are mixed in with things from different regions of Mexico and Central America.

☾ **Gecko** (✉ *Condominios Puesto del Sol, Marina Vallarta* ☎ *322/221–2165*) is the place to go for beach togs for kids and teens. The selection of any one type of item isn't large, but there are bikinis, sunglasses, flip-flops, nice ball caps, and T-shirts. Board shorts and rash guards are stocked for surfers and wannabes. **Mar de Sueños** (✉ *Calle Basilio Badillo 277-B, Zona Romántica, Centro* ☎ *322/222–7362*) carries classy Italian threads, including the stylish La Perla brand. The selection of linen blouses and exquisitely cut linen pants is perfect for PV's sultry climate. Or choose from Lycra™ tops, sexy silk lingerie, and several lines of bathing suits. Everything is top-notch and priced accordingly. It's closed Sunday.

★ **María de Guadalajara** (✉ *Puesta del Sol condominiums, Local 15–A, Marina, Marina Vallarta* ☎ *322/221–2566* ✉ *Calle Morelos 550, Centro* ☎ *322/222–2387* ⊕ *www.mariadeguadalajara.com*) has inspired jewelry and a fabulous line of women's cotton clothing. It's DIY chic here: you choose the colorful triangular sash of your liking, miraculously transforming pretty-but-baggy dresses into flattering and stylish frocks. The color palette is truly inspired. The selection for men is limited. **Manta Maya** (⊠*Basilio Badillo 300, at Av. Constitución, Col. E. Zapata* ☎*322/223–5915*) has mainly white- and cream-color women's and men's clothing, with the occasional brightly colored blouse or skirt tossed in for contrast. Like its sister stores in other resort cities, this small shop has smart clothes at reasonable prices.

☉ **Myskova Beachwear Boutique** (⊠*Calle Basilio Badillo 278, Col. E. Zapata* ☎*322/222–6091*) has its own line of bikinis, plus cover-ups, nylon slacks, and some items for children (sunglasses, bathing suits, flip-flops). There's a small line of jewelry, and Brazilian flip-flops for adults in a rainbow of colors. **Oahu** (⊠*Calle Juárez 314, Centro* ☎*322/223–1058*) has men's surf and casual wear, including well-made flip-flops, high-quality T-shirts, as well as pint-size Hawaiian shirts for children. In fact, this is one of the best places to shop for children's casual wear and for water gear like board shorts and rash guards.

FodorsChoice **Rebeca's** (⊠*Olas Altas 403, Col. E. Zapata* ☎*322/222–2320*), open
   ★ daily, has a large selection of beachwear, including shorts, pseudo-Speedos, and bathing trunks for men; and sandals and fashionable flip-flops, attractive tankinis, lots of bikinis, and a few one-piece suits for women. Most of the goods are manufactured in Mexico. For over-the-top ethnic clothing, stamped leather purses from Guadalajara and belt buckles from San Miguel, as well as clunky necklaces and bracelets of quartz, amber, and turquoise, head to **Serafina** (⊠*Calle Basilio Badillo 260, Col. E. Zapata* ☎*322/223–4594*), which also sells wonderful tchotchkes.

★ Worth a look for women with eclectic tastes is **Sirenas** (⊠*Basilio Badillo 252B, Col. E. Zapata* ☎*322/223–1925*), a sister store to Serafina. Here, creative sisters from Tamaulipas State create chic and unusual, exuberant fantasy jewelry. Colorful clutches and makeup bags made from recycled packaging are an innovation from Mexico City. At this writing, the shop is filled with tight-fitting ribbed T-shirts edged in sequins and an assortment of ethnically inspired yet edgy and contemporary blouses and skirts from Indonesia and elsewhere. It's closed Sunday.

Long-established **La Surtidora** (⊠*Morelos 256, at Guerrero, Centro* ☎*322/222–1439*) may not have the most trendy clothes, but it does have men's guayabera shirts and ladies cotton and muslin blouses in a wide range of styles. **Ucho Bali** (⊠*Calle Lázaro Cárdenas 330, Col. E. Zapata* ☎*322/222–7175* ⊠*Plaza Marina, Local 119, Marina Vallarta* ☎*322/209–0800*) is a great place to purchase inexpensive, cool, beachy clothing for women, imported from Indonesia. There's an extensive collection of Bali batiks made into dresses of all lengths, long straight skirts, and sexy top-and-trouser outfits. The lightweight cotton shawls come in an array of colors, with same-color embroidery and sequins. There are outfits in sheer material and stacks of lovely sarongs. Most items are $20 or less.

FOLK ART & CRAFTS

In addition to pewter, **Alas de Aguila** (✉ *Av. Juárez 547, at Calle Corona, Centro* ☎*322/222–4039* ⊗*Closed Sun.*) has a wide selection of Talavera-style objects—from soap holders and liquid soap dispensers to pitchers, platters, and picture frames—in a variety of patterns. Quality is middle-of-the-road; prices are excellent.

Expansive **Galería Indígena** (✉ *Av. Juárez 628, Centro* ☎*322/223–0800*) has an assortment of handicrafts: Huichol yarn paintings and beaded bowls and statuettes, real Talavera ceramics from Puebla, decorative pieces in painted wood, and many other items. **El Instituto de la Artesanía Jalisciense** (✉*Calle Juárez 284, Centro* ☎*322/222–1301*) promotes Jalisco State's handicrafts, selling burnished clay bowls signed by the artist, blown glass, plates and bowls from Tonalá, and other items at fair prices. That said, Bustamante knockoffs and Huichol pieces in less-than-traditional themes (smiley faces not being one of the Huichols' typical motifs) are indications that quality is slipping. Still, there's a representative sampling of the state's ceramics, blue and red glassware, and *barro bruñido*: clay pieces finished by burnishing only. It's cater-corner from La Plaza de Armas, and is open 9 to 9 daily.

★ Shop for inexpensive, one-of-a-kind folk art from Guerrero, Michoacán, Oaxaca, and elsewhere at **Lucy's CuCú Cabana** (✉*Calle Basilio Badillo 295, Col. E. Zapata* ☎*322/222–1220*). Note that Lucy closes during lunch, on Sunday, and September through mid-October. Young artist Mateos Gamboa, of Tonalá, creates hand-painted scenes using multiple tiles for **México Místico** (✉*Lazaro Cardenas 175, Col. E. Zapata* ☎*322/223–1021*), across from Plaza Lázaro Cárdenas. Themes are traditional, like pastoral scenes with donkeys and white-washed villages. Stained glass can be custom ordered, or purchased ready-made with traditional motifs such as hummingbirds, bearded irises, lighthouses, and angelfish; or less-traditional motifs, such as the Harley-Davidson logo.

Purchase glassware from Jalisco and Guanajuato states in sets or individually at **Mundo de Cristal** (✉*Av. Insurgentes 333, at Calle Basilio Badillo, Col. E. Zapata* ☎*322/222–1426*). Also available are Talavera place settings and individual platters, pitchers, and decorative pieces. Look in the back of the store for high-quality ceramics with realistic portrayals of fruits and flowers. You can have your purchase packed, but shipping is left to you. It's closed Sunday and after 2 PM Saturday. Relatives of the owners of Mundo de Cristal and Mundo de Azulejos (⇨*above*) own **Mundo de Pewter** (✉*Av. Venustiano Carranza 358, Col. E. Zapata* ☎*322/222–0503*), which is wedged in between the other two stores. Attractive, lead-free items in modern and traditional designs are sold here at reasonable prices. The practical, tarnish-free pieces can go from stovetop or oven to the dining table and be no worse for wear.

Olinalá (✉*Av. Lázaro Cárdenas 274, Col. E. Zapata* ☎*322/222–4995 or 322/228–0659*) sells mainly painted ceremonial masks and a limited selection of other folk art from throughout Mexico. It's closed Sunday

One Man's Metal

In less than a decade after William Spratling arrived in the mining town of Taxco—275 mi (170 km) north of Acapulco—he had transformed it into a flourishing silver center, the likes of which had not been seen since colonial times. In 1929 the writer-architect from New Orleans settled in the then-sleepy, dusty village because it was inexpensive and close to the pre-Hispanic Mexcala culture that he was studying in Guerrero Valley.

In Taxco—Mexico's premier "Silver City"—marvelously preserved white-stucco, red-tile-roof colonial buildings hug cobblestone streets that wind up and down the foothills of the Sierra Madre. Taxco (pronounced tahss-ko) is a living work of art. For centuries its silver mines drew foreign mining companies. In 1928 the government made it a national monument.

For hundreds of years Taxco's silver was made into bars and exported overseas. No one even considered developing a local jewelry industry. Journeying to a nearby town, Spratling hired a couple of goldsmiths and commissioned them to create jewelry, flatware, trays, and goblets from his own designs.

Ever the artist with a keen mind for drawing, design, and aesthetics, Spratling decided to experiment with silver using his designs. Shortly afterward, he set up his own workshop and began producing highly innovative pieces. By the 1940s Spratling's designs were gracing the necks of celebrities and being sold in high-end stores abroad.

Spratling also started a program to train local silversmiths; they were soon joined by foreigners interested in learning the craft. It wasn't long before there were thousands of silversmiths in the town, and Spratling was its wealthiest resident. He moved freely in Mexico's lively art scene, befriending muralists Diego Rivera (Rivera's wife, Frida Kahlo, wore Spratling necklaces) and David Alfaro Siqueiros as well as architect Miguel Covarrubios.

The U.S. ambassador to Mexico, Dwight Morrow, father of Anne Morrow, who married Charles Lindbergh, hired Spratling to help with the architectural details of his house in Cuernavaca. American movie stars were frequent guests at Spratling's home; once, he even designed furniture for Marilyn Monroe. Indeed, when his business failed in 1946, relief came in the form of an offer from the United States Department of the Interior: Spratling was asked to create a program of native crafts for Alaska. This work influenced his later designs.

Although he never regained the wealth he once had, he operated the workshop at his ranch and trained apprentices until he died in a car accident in 1969. A friend, Italian engineer Alberto Ulrich, took over the business and replicated Spratling's designs using his original molds. Ulrich died in 2002, and his children now operate the business.

Each summer PV shop owners travel to Taxco to procure silver jewelry. Viva is one shop that carries such items, including Spratling pieces.

and September and October. **Queru-bines** (✉ *Av. Juárez 501–A, at Calle Galeana, Centro* ☎ *322/223–1727*) has woven goods from Guatemala and southern Mexico, including tablecloths, napkins, placemats, and *rebozos* (stoles) made of rayon, silk, and cotton. The shop is in an old house that once belonged to Jesús Langarica, PV's first mayor. The structure's stone, cement, and brick floors make interesting backdrops for painted gourds from Michoacán and carved gourds from the Costa Chica (northern Oaxaca coast), and Talavera pottery.

> **ALL THAT GLITTERS ISN'T SILVER**
>
> There's a great selection of Mexican silver in PV, but watch out for "German silver" (aka *alpaca* or *chapa*): an alloy of iron, zinc, and nickel. Real silver is weightier, and is marked "925" (indicating a silver content of at least 92.5%) for sterling and "950" (at least 95% silver content) for finer pieces. When size permits, the manufacturer's name and the word "Mexico" should also appear.

HOME FURNISHINGS

★ *Also see Folk Art & Crafts, above.* The American owners of **Banderas Bay** (✉ *Lázaro Cárdenas 263, Col. E. Zapata* ☎ *322/223–4352* ✉ *Constitución 319A, Col. E. Zapata* ☎ *322/223–9871*), who also own Daiquiri Dick's restaurant *(⇨ Chapter 3)*, travel around the country for months in search of antiques, collectibles, handicrafts, and unique household items. About two-thirds of the merchandise is new. The shop, which will pack and ship your purchases, is closed Sunday. **Ponciana** (✉ *Basilio Badillo 252–A, Col. E. Zapata* ☎ *322/222–2988*) has things you won't find at all the other stores, like porcelain replicas of antique dolls. The "antique" cupboards may have only original doors, but that's a common practice. Other antiques, perhaps an old reliquary, are transformed into wall art. You can also find tablecloths and placemats from Michoacán, place settings, arty statuettes, matchboxes decorated with Frida Kahlo and Mexican movie themes, and other decorative items.

JEWELRY

★ The jewelers at **Alberto's** (✉ *Av. Juárez 185, Centro* ☎ *322/222–8317*), family to jewelers of the same surname in Zihuatanejo, are happy to explain, in English, which pieces carry authentic stones and which are composites or synthetics. Prices are reasonable and the selection is impressive. It's closed Sunday. **La Brisa** (✉ *Condominios Puesta del Sol, Local 11–B, Marina Vallarta* ☎ *322/221–2516*) is one of several silver stores owned by the same family. All have fair prices and no pressure; this one also has Talavera pottery for sale.

La Piedra (✉ *Av. Mexico 1087, Centro* ☎ *322/223–2242*) has fine stones and beads for jewelry makers as well as findings and other bits needed for jewelry-making. Spend as little as $5 or as much as $5,000 on anything and everything jade at **Jades Maya** (✉ *Leona Vicario 226-A, Centro* ☎ *322/222–0371* ⊕ *www.jadesmaya.com*). The shop is open daily until 10 PM in high season. In addition to jewelry made from the 20 different colors of jade, there are replicas of ancient Mayan masks.

Joyería El Opalo (✉ *Local 13–A, Plaza Genovesa, Col. Las Glorias* ☎ *322/224–6584*), a bright spot in a nearly abandoned mall, has managed to remain afloat through its cruise ship contacts. Silver jewelry ranges in price from $1.50 per gram for simpler pieces to $6 a gram for the lighter, finer quality and more complex pieces. There's high-grade "950" silver jewelry in addition to the usual 0.925 sterling silver, and gold settings as well. Most of the semi-precious stones—amethyst, topaz, malachite, black onyx, and opal in 28 colors—are of Mexican origin. The diamond-cut necklaces are magnificent. **Joyas Finas Suneson** (✉ *Calle Morelos 593, Centro* ☎ *322/222–5715*) specializes in silver jewelry and objets d'art by some of Mexico's finest designers. Most pieces have modern rather than traditional motifs, and designs are creative and unusual. It's closed Sunday.

Fodor'sChoice
★ Manager Ramon Cruz of **Joyería Yoler** (✉ *Calle Olas Altas 391, Col. E. Zapata* ☎ *322/222–8713 or 322/222–9051*) proudly shows off the store's collection of the Los Castillo family's silver jewelry made with lost-wax casting as well as hammering and burnishing techniques, small silver pitchers with lapis lazuli dragonfly handles, napkin rings, abalone pill boxes, and other lovely utilitarian pieces. The merchandise—which includes an extensive yet not overwhelming array of silver and semi-precious-stone jewelry—is nicely arranged in the ample shop.

Fodor'sChoice
★ The worldly **Viva** (✉ *Calle Basilio Badillo 274, Col. E. Zapata* ☎ *322/222–4078* ⊕ *www.vivacollection.com*) represents hundreds of jewelry designers from around the globe, and so achieves an impressive diversity. The store also sells unique espadrilles, flats, and sandals as well as beach clothing, magnifying sun glasses, and accessories for men and women.

LEATHER, SHOES & HANDBAGS

Aranpelli (✉ *Morelos 600–A, between Calles Aldama and Corona, Centro* ☎ *322/223–2854*) is a small shop with a classy selection of handbags, day packs, valises, wallets, and other leather goods (but no shoes). The fun, stamped-leather purses come in various colors and modern designs from Spain; other handbags hail from Italy and Colombia. The shop also has coin purses, penknife cases, and other small gift items. It's closed Sunday.

★ Longtime visitors to Puerto Vallarta will remember **Huarachería Fabiola** (✉ *Av. Ignacio L. Vallarta 145, Col. E. Zapata* ☎ *322/222–9154*). Buy huaraches off the rack or order custom sandals for men or women. Most styles can be made in one to three days. Credit cards are not accepted. Try **Rolling Stones** (✉ *Paseo Diaz Ordáz 802, Centro* ☎ *322/223–1769*) for custom-made boots, sandals, and shoes (or off the rack).

WINE, BEER & SPIRITS

Run by the sommelier at Trio, **Anfitrión de México** (✉ *Calle Guerrero 278–A, Centro* ☎ *322/222–8130*) sells imported wine.

La Playa (✉ *Blvd. Francisco M. Ascencio, Km 1.5, Zona Hotelera* ⊹ *across from IMSS [Mexican Social Security Agency]* ☎ *322/224–*

7130) has tequila; wines from Chile, California (Gallo), and Spain; imported vodka and other spirits; and the cheapest beer around.

NORTH & SOUTH OF PUERTO VALLARTA

GROCERIES

Don Chuy's Wine & Deli (⊠ *Calle Tercer Mundo s/n, San Pancho* ☎*311/258–4487*) has an assortment of food, condiments, and wines. **Frutería Chabacano** (⊠ *Calle Hidalgo 25, Bucerías* ☎*329/298–0692*) has the freshest fruits and vegetables in town. **El Indio** (⊠ *Av. América Latina 23 at Av. Mexico, San Pancho* ☎*311/258–4010*) is the most convenient place in San Pancho to get liquor, wine, milk, water, and Mexican brands of condiments and other necessities. **Mi Tiendita** (⊠ *Calle Marlin 44–A, Sayulita* ☎*329/291–3145*) sells deli sandwiches and groceries, as well as wine and beer. **Super La Peque** (⊠ *Morelos 7, Bucerías* ☎*329/298–0598*) has wine, liquor, cleaning supplies, junk food, and fresh fruit.

MALLS

Paradise Plaza (⊠ *Paseo de los Cocoteros 85 Sur, Nuevo Vallarta* ☎*322/226–6770*) is the most comprehensive plaza north of Marina Vallarta, with a food court, hair salon, Internet café, clothing and handcraft boutiques, and a bank, but no movie theater.

SPECIALTY STORES

ART

Galería La Manzanilla (⊠ *Calle Playa Perula 83, La Manzanilla* ☎*315/351–7099* ⊕*www.artinmexico.com*) has a cadre of more than a dozen fine artists from Mexico, Canada, and the U.S. It's closed September through mid-October. Hours are 10–2 and 4–6 Monday through Saturday; Sunday 10–2.

BOOKS & PERIODICALS

Try **Gringo's Books & Coffee** (⊠ *Calle Morelos 7–A, Bucerías* ☎*329/298–1767*) for novels a-go-go, including lots of beach reading. It's closed Sunday. **Librería Sayulita** (⊠ *Calle Manuel Navarrete 3, Sayulita* ☎*329/291–3382*) has new books in Spanish, used paperbacks in English, and magazines.

CLOTHING

★ Shop for dressier dresses and casual, unique resort wear in linen and cotton at **D'Paola** (⊠ *Paradise Plaza, Local 11* ☎*322/297–1030*). **Ruly's Boutique** (⊠ *Paradise Plaza, Local 10, Paseo de los Cocoteros 85 Sur, Nuevo Vallarta* ☎*322/297–1724*) has the choicest men's clothing around. They have nice trousers, shirts, and shorts in a wide selection of handsome yet vibrant colors, as well as accessories, underwear,

Continued on page 127

The intricately woven and beaded designs of the Huichols' art are as vibrant and fascinating as the traditions of its people, best known as the "Peyote People" for their traditional and cermonial use of the hallucinigenic drug. Peyote-inspired visions are thought to be messages from God, and are reflected in the art.

THE ART OF THE HUICHOL

Like the Lacandon Maya, the Huichol resisted assimilation by Spanish invaders, fleeing to inhospitable mountains and remote valleys. There they retained their pantheistic religion in which shamans lead the community in spiritual matters and the use of peyote facilitates communication directly with God.

Huichol is pronounced wee-CHOL; the people's name for themselves, however, is Wirarika (we-RAH-ri-ka), which means "healer."

Roads didn't reach larger Huichol communities until the mid-20th century, bringing electricity and other modern distractions. The collision with the outside world has had pros and cons, but art lovers have only benefited from the Huichols' centuries-long mastery of intricately patterned woven and beaded goods. Today the traditional souls that remain on the land— a significant population of perhaps 6,000 to 8,000—still create votive bowls, prayer arrows, jewelry, and bags, and sell them to finance elaborate religious ceremonies. The pieces go for as little as $5 or as much as $5,000, depending on the skill and fame of the artist and quality of materials.

Bead-covered wooden statuette

UNDERSTANDING THE HUICHOL

When Spanish conquistadors arrived in the early 16th century, the Huichol, unwilling to work as slaves on the haciendas of the Spanish or to adopt their religion, fled to hard-to-reach mountains and valleys of the Sierra Madre. They lived there, disconnected from society, for nearly 500 years. Beginning in the 1970s, roads and electricity made their way to tiny Huichol towns. The reintroduction to society has come at a high price: at least one ill-advised government project encouraged Huichol farmers to sell their land, and with it, their traditional lifestyle, in favor of a city existence. Today, about half of the population of perhaps 12,000 continues to live in ancestral villages and *rancheritas* (tiny individual farms).

THE POWER OF PRAYER

Spirituality and prayer infuse every aspect of Huichol life. They believe that without their prayers and offerings the sun wouldn't rise, the earth would cease spinning. It is hard, then, for them to reconcile their poverty with the relative easy living of "free-riders" (Huichol term for nonspiritual freeloaders) who enjoy fine cars and expensive houses thanks to the Huichols efforts to sustain the planet. But rather than hold our reckless materialism against us, the Huichol add us to their prayers.

Huichol craftsmen, Cabo San Lucas

Huichol yarn artist at work

THE PEYOTE PEOPLE

Visions inspired by the hallucinogenic peyote plant are considered by the Huichol to be messages from God, and to help in solving personal and communal problems. Indirectly, they provide inspiration for their almost psychedelic art. Just a generation or two ago, annual peyote-gathering pilgrimages were done on foot. Today the journey is still a man's chief obligation, but they now drive to the holy site at Wiricuta, in San Luis Potosi State. Peyote collected is used by the entire community—men, women, and children—throughout the year.

SHAMANISM

A Huichol man has a lifelong calling as a shaman. There are two shamanic paths for the Huichol: the path of the wolf, which is more aggressive, demanding, and powerful (wolf shamans profess the ability to morph into wolves); and the path of the deer, which is playful—even clownish—and less inclined to prove his power. A shaman chooses his own path.

SMART SHOPPING TIPS

Huichol Art, Sun Face

BEADED ITEMS: The smaller the beads, the more delicate and expensive the piece. Beads with larger holes are fine for stringed work, but if used in bowls and statuettes cheapen the piece. Items made with iridescent beads from Japan are the priciest. Look for good-quality glass beads, definition, symmetry, and artful use of color. Beads should fit together tightly in straight lines, with no gaps.

YARN "PAINTINGS": Symmetry is not necessary, although there should be an overall sense of unity. Thinner thread results in finer, more costly work. Look for tightness, with no visible gaps or broken threads. Paintings should have a stamp of authenticity on the back, including artist's name and tribal affiliation.

PRAYER ARROWS: Collectors and purists should look for the traditionally made arrows of brazilwood inserted into a bamboo shaft. The most interesting ones contain embroidery work, or tiny carved icons, or are painted with copal symbols indicative of their original, intended purpose, for example protecting a child or ensuring a successful corn crop.

WHERE TO SHOP

SUPPORTING HUICHOL TRADITIONS

Families that continue to work the land may dedicate a few hours a day to crafts production, working to maintain their ceremonies, not to pay the cable bill. Buying directly from them can ensure a higher degree of artistry: the Huichol who make art to supplement farming work more slowly and with less pressure than their city-dwelling brethren. Shopping at stores like Peyote People and Hikuri supports artisans who live in their ancestral villages and practice the ancient traditions.

Peyote People treats the Huichol as a people, not a product. At their downtown Vallarta shop, the owners—a Mexican-Canadian couple—are happy to share with cus-

tomers their wealth of info about Huichol art and culture. They work with just a few farming families, providing all the materials and then paying for the finished product. ⊠ *Calle Juárez 222, Centro* ☎ *322/222-2303.*

Hikuri At the north end of Banderas Bay, is run by a British couple that pays asking prices to their Huichol suppliers and employs indigenous men in the adjoining carpentry and screen-printing shops. The men initially have little or no experience, and the jobs give them a leg up to move on to more profitable work. The excellent inventory includes fine yarn paintings. ⊠ *Calle Coral 66A, La Cruz de Huanacaxtle* ☎ *329/295-5071.*

The Huichol Collection Native artisans working on crafts and wearing their stunning and colorful clothing draw customers in. The shop has an excellent inventory, with some museum-quality pieces. Though the merchandise is genuine, the shop is also venue for time-share sales—albeit with a soft sales pitch. ⊠ *Paseo Diaz Ordaz 732, Centro* ☎ *322/223-0661b* ⊠ *Morelos 490, Centro* ☎ *322/223-2141.*

Galería Huichol sells yarn paintings, beaded bowls and statuettes, and some smaller items like beaded jewelry and Christmas ornaments. ⊠ *Paradise Plaza, 2nd fl., Nuevo Vallarta* ☎ *322/297-0342*

TRADITION TRANSFORMED

The art of the Huichol was, for centuries, made from undyed wool, shells, stones, and other natural materials. It was not until the 1970s that the Huichol began incorporating bright, zingy colors, without sacrificing the intricate patterns and symbols used for centuries. The result is strenuously colorful, yet dignified.

YARN PAINTINGS

Dramatic and vivid yarn paintings are highly symbolic, stylized visions of life.

MASKS AND ANIMAL STATUETTES

Bead-covered wooden or ceramic masks and animal statuettes are other adaptations made for outsiders.

PRAYER ARROWS

Made for every ceremony, prayer arrows send petitions winging to God.

VOTIVE BOWLS

Ceremonious votive bowls, made from gourds, are decorated with bright, stylized beadwork.

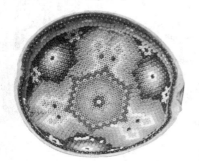

WOVEN SHOULDER BAGS

Carried by men, the bags are decorated with traditional Huichol icons.

For years, Huichol men as well as women wore BEADED BRACELETS; today earrings and necklaces are also made.

Diamond-shape GOD'S EYES of sticks and yarn protect children from harm.

HOW TO READ THE SYMBOLS

Spiders that come out at dawn are thought to welcome the rising sun.

The deer is the animal manifestation of the god Kahumari, who intercedes in heaven on earthlings' behalf.

Anything with horns or antlers symbolizes communion and oneness with God.

Yarn painting

■ The trilogy of corn, peyote, and deer represent three aspects of God. According to Huichol mythology, peyote sprang up in the footprints of the deer. Depicted like stylized flowers, peyote represents communication with God. Corn, the Huichol's staple

Corn symbol

food, symbolizes health and prosperity. An image drawn inside the root ball depicts the essence of god within it.

■ The double-headed eagle is the emblem of the omnipresent sky god.

Peyote

■ A nierika is a portal between the spirit world and our own. Often in the form of a yarn painting, a nierika can be round or square.

■ Salamanders and turtles are associated with rain; the former provoke the clouds. Turtles maintain underground springs, and purify water.

■ A scorpion is the soldier of the sun.

Scorpion

■ The Huichol depict raindrops as tiny snakes; in yarn paintings they descend to enrich the fields.

Snakes

José Benítez Sánchez, (1938–) may be the elder statesman of yarn painters, and has shown in Japan, Spain, the U.S., and at the Museum of Modern Art in Mexico City. His paintings sell for upward of $3,000 a piece.

hats, and so on. The owner of Ruly's designs the clothing sold here and supervises its construction.

FOLK ART

Galería Corazón (✉ *Av. América Latina 1, at Av. Tercer Mundo, San Pancho* ☎ *311/258–4170*) specializes in high-end arts and crafts from Michoacán. Take note of the "beyond bankers" hours: Thursday, Friday, and Saturday noon to 4 and Tuesday 3–7. It's closed mid-May through October, however.

DO WEAR THEM OUT

Huaraches are woven leather sandals that seem to last several lifetimes. Traditionally worn by peasants, they're now sold by fewer shops, but in a slightly larger assortment of styles. Once broken in—and that takes a while—this classic, sturdy footwear will be a worthwhile addition to your closet.

★ **La Hamaca** (✉ *Calle Revolución 110, Sayulita* ☎ *329/291–3039*) has a wonderful inventory of folk art and utilitarian handicrafts; each piece is unique. Scoop up masks and pottery from Michoacán, textiles and shawls from Guatemala, hammocks from the Yucatán, and lacquered boxes from Olinalá. The items aren't cheap, but the store is wonderful. Best yet, the store is open daily 9 to 9.

Shop for pottery, small housewares, tin frames sporting Botero-style fat ladies, and other gifts at **Jan Marie's Boutique** (✉ *Lázaro Cárdenas 56, Bucerías* ☎ *329/298–0303*). The Talavera pottery is both decorative and utilitarian. This is not the place for bargain hunters. **La Aldaba** (✉ *Paradise Plaza, 2nd fl., Nuevo Vallarta* ☎ *322/297–0903*) has an interesting collection of gifts and small decorative items and housewares: Bustamante-inspired cat and moon candles, subtly painted sheet metal candleholders and wall art, and glass vases.

HOME FURNISHINGS

The flamboyant, displaced Brit and owner of **Anthony Chetwynd Collection** (✉ *Calle Las Palmas 30, Col. Costa Azul, San Francisco* ☎ *311/258–4373*) travels to estates and villages all over Mexico to stock his antiques shop. About half the inventory is antique masks, chandeliers, reliquaries … whatever he can get his hands on. The rest are copies of the same, and some furnishings and housewares imported from Asia.

After Dark

Mariachi

WORD OF MOUTH

"I merrily ate and drank my week away [in PV]! Oh, how I miss those mango margaritas at 5:30 PM!"

—baglady

"There is definitely some fun nightlife [in PV] without being quite so spring breakish [as Cancún]. People tend to be a little older than in Cancún (when I was there I think the average age was 17 at most clubs)."

—Bain05

ORGANIC, OUTDOORSY VALLARTA SWITCHES GEARS after dark and rocks into the wee hours. After the beachgoers and sightseers have been showered and fed, Vallarta kicks up its heels and puts the baby to bed. Happy hour in martini lounges sets the stage for evening entertainment that might include a show, live music, or just hobnobbing under the heavens at a rooftop bar.

Many hotels have Mexican fiesta dinner shows, which can be lavish affairs with buffet dinners, folk dances, and even fireworks. Tour groups and individuals—mainly middle-age and older Americans and Canadians—make up the audience at the Saturday night buffet dinner show at Playa Los Arcos and other hotels. *Vaqueros* (cowboys) do rope tricks and dancers perform Mexican regional or pseudo-Aztec dances. The late-late crowd gets down after midnight at dance clubs, some of which stay open until 6 AM.

The scene mellows as you head north and south of Puerto Vallarta. In Punta de Mita, Bucerías, Sayulita, and San Francisco (aka San Pancho), local restaurants provide live music; the owners usually scare up someone good once or twice a week in high season. Along the Costalegre, tranquillity reigns. Most people head here for relaxation, and nightlife most often takes the form of stargazing, drink in hand. If you're visiting June through October (low season), attend live performances whenever offered, as they are few and far between.

Although there's definitely crossover, many Mexicans favor the upscale bars and clubs of the Hotel Zone and Marina Vallarta hotels, while foreigners tend to like the Mexican flavor of places downtown and the south side (the Zona Romántica), where dress is decidedly more casual.

⇨ *For more nightlife options, see "Gay Puerto Vallarta" (Chapter 10).*

BARS & PUBS

Like any resort destination worth its salt—the salt on the rim of the margarita glass, that is—PV has an enormous variety of watering holes. Bars on or overlooking the beach sell the view along with buckets of beer. Martini bars go to great lengths to impress with signature drinks, and sports bars serve up Canadian hockey and Monday-night football. Hotels have swim-up bars and lobby lounges, and these, as well as restaurant bars, are the main options in places like Nuevo Vallarta, Marina Vallarta, and most of the small towns to the north and south. ⇨ *For gay bars, see Chapter 10.*

ALL-PURPOSE BARS

Andale (⊠*Av. Olas Altas 425, Col. E. Zapata* ☎*322/222–1054*) fills up most nights. Crowds spill out onto the sidewalk as party-hearty men and women shimmy out of the narrow saloon, drinks in hand, to the strains of Chubby Checker and other vintage tunes. For a laugh, intoxicated or less inhibited patrons sometimes take a bumpy ride on the burro just outside Andale's door (a handler escorts the burro).

★ It's difficult to categorize **The Bar Above** (✉*Av. México at Av. Hidalgo, 2 blocks north of central plaza, Bucerías* ☎*329/298–1194*), a little place above Tapas del Mundo. It's a martini bar without a bar (the owner, Buddy, prefers that people

come to converse with friends at tables rather than "hang out" at a bar) that also serves dessert. Molten chocolate soufflé—the signature dish— or charred pineapple bourbon shortcake may be on the menu. Lights are dim, the music is romantic, and there's an eagle's view of the ocean from the rooftop crow's nest. It's closed every Sunday and in August and September. At other times, it's open 6 PM–11 PM.

Right on the sand across from Parque Lázaro Cárdenas, restaurant-bar **Burro's Bar** (✉*Av. Olas Altas at Calle Lázaro Cárdenas, Col. E. Zapata* ☎*No phone*) has bargain brewskis (three beers for three bucks) and equally inexpensive fruity margaritas by the pitcher. The seafood is less than inspired, but nachos and other munchies are good accompaniments to the drinks. Watch the waves and listen to Bob Marley and the Gypsy Kings among lots of gringo couples and a few middle-age Mexican vacationers. It opens daily at 10 AM.

Second-floor **La Cantina** (✉*Morelos 709, at J.O. de Dominguez, Centro* ☎*322/222–1734*), while not especially hip, has a good view of Banderas Bay and the boardwalk as well as canned Mexican tunes, especially *ranchera*, *grupera*, and *cumbia*.

The rooftop bar of **Chez Elena** (✉*Hotel Los Cuatro Vientos, Matamoros 520, Centro* ☎*322/222–0161*) is plain as can be, but the margaritas are first rate and the bay view expansive. It's disconcerting though, when you're the only one up there.

Geckos Pub (✉*Calle Morelos, between Calles Madero and Av. Cárdenas Bucerías* ☎*329/298–1861*) is an unassuming local watering hole with a billiards table. It's the kind of place a single woman can enter without feeling weird or being hassled as bartenders tend to keep an eye out for them in the small venue.

The tallest building around, **Hotel Alondra** (✉*Calle Sinaloa 16, Barra de Navidad* ☎*315/355–8372*), has a rooftop bar that's great for sunset cocktails.

FodorśChoice **Memories** (✉*Calle Mina 207, at Av. Juárez, Centro* ☎*322/205–7906*) ★ is a wonderful little second-story nightspot. Right in downtown PV near the main plaza, it is frequented mainly by locals. The space is darkly romantic and a great place for a date, but still ideal for groups of friends, or for singles with a book. The extensive drink list includes "hair of the squirrel," with Frangelica, and lots of specialty alcoholic and nonalcoholic coffees. The classic-rock soundtrack pays homage to John Lennon, the Eagles, and Bob Marley; black-and-white posters and photos honor other rock and rollers.

Called simply "Frog's" by the locals, **Señor Frog's** (⊠ *V. Carranza 218, at Ignacio I. Vallarta, Col. E. Zapata* ☎322/222–5171) is a good old-fashioned free-for-all for the young and the restless. There are black lights on the walls, sawdust on the floor, and a giant-screen TV above the tiny dance floor. Expect a foam party at least once a week, and other shenanigans.

Party Lounge (⊠ *Av. Mexico 993, across from Parque Hidalgo, Centro* ☎*No phone*) is open daily after 1 PM for stop-and-go drinks: mainly *litros*, that is, 32-ouncers of tequila sunrise, Long Island ice tea, piña colada, and the like. Because they have '70s, '80s, and lounge music rather than electronic music, the upstairs bar, open 8 PM to 4 AM, is popular with the middle-age and older set, foreign and domestic, as well as with the younger crowd.

We Be Sausage Roadhouse Bar & Grill (⊠ *Av. de los Picos 102, Bucerías* ☎*329/298–0954* ⊕*www.webesausage.com*) is a pub owned by a Canadian sausage lover; have one of their excellent Italian-sausage sandwiches with your suds. Ball games are usually on the tube. It's closed Monday and Tuesday.

KARAOKE BAR

There's no cover at **La Regadera** (⊠ *Morelos 666, Centro* ☎322/222–3970), where you can dazzle or frazzle your fellow karaoke fans with songs in English or Spanish. It's open daily between 8 PM and 4 AM, but things don't begin to bounce until around midnight.

MARTINI BARS

★ **Apaches** (⊠ *Olas Altas 439, Col. E. Zapata* ☎322/222–4004) is gay friendly, lesbian friendly, *people* friendly. Heck, superwomen Mariann and her partner Endra would probably welcome you and your pet python with open arms, give you both a squeeze. PV's original martini bar, Apaches is the landing zone for expats reconnoitering after a long day, and a warm-up for late-night types. When the outside tables get jam packed in high season, the overflow heads into the narrow bar and the adjacent, equally narrow bistro. It opens after 5 PM; happy hour is 5 to 7. If you're alone, this is the place to make friends of all ages.

Garbo (⊠ *Pulpito 142, Olas Altas, Col. E. Zapata* ☎322/223–5753) is open nightly after 6. This is not the kind of place where you'll strike up a conversation; rather it's an upscale place to go with friends for a sophisticated, air-conditioned drink or two. Cigarette smoke perfumes the air, and a musician plays gentle electric guitar music Thursday through Saturday evenings 7 to 10.

The cozy **Kit Kat Club** (⊠ *Calle Púlpito 120, Col. E. Zapata* ☎ *322/223–0093*) has great martinis and a retro feel. Both straights and gays are drawn to this elegant lounge, which has full meals as well as millions of $6 martinis. Most popular include the Peggy Lee (vodka, orange, and cranberry juices, and banana liqueur) and the Queen of Hearts (vodka, amaretto, cranberry juice, and 7UP).

PIANO BARS

Bon vivants should head for **Constantini Wine Bar** (⊠ *Café des Artistes, Av. Guadalupe Sánchez 740, Centro* ☎ *322/222–3229*), the latest innovation of hot-shot restaurant Café des Artistes. Order one of 50 wines by the glass (more than 300 by the bottle, from 10 countries) and snack on caviar, bruschetta, and carpaccio—or go directly to dessert. Wine tastings are scheduled from time to time. There's live music Monday through Saturday. Weekdays it's piano music from 7:30 to 11:30 PM; Friday and Saturday nights there's jazz and blues between 8:30 and midnight.

At romantic **El Faro** (⊠ *Royal Pacific Yacht Club, Marina Vallarta* ☎ *322/221–0541*) you can admire the bay and marina from atop a 110-foot lighthouse. There's often live guitar or other music in the evening, and happy hour is from 6 to 7 PM. It's mainly a baby-boomer crowd.

6

RESTAURANT BARS

★ Soon after its 2004 inauguration, the sophisticated **Nikki Beach** (⊠ *Westin hotel, Paseo de la Marina Sur 205, Marina Vallarta* ☎ *322/226–1150*) hosted several events during the *Maxim* magazine model competition, guaranteeing instant name recognition … although much of its glamour has since worn off for the locals. Just about everything under the palapa roof is white, and hanging beds and furnishings encourage lounging. In the restaurant, hard-body waiters deliver dishes from Continental to Mediterranean to Asian, including sushi.

Vallartans decided that **Tribu** (⊠ *Paseo de la Marina 220, Mayan Palace Marina, Marina Vallarta* ☎ *322/226–6000*) was a bit out of the way to become a serious hot spot, but travelers in the Marina district still find it a dark and atmospheric space. DJ-spun music pulses house, lounge, techno or disco, and ''80s music … whatever the crowd demands. There are also two billiard tables. It's open 6 PM to 2 AM, and there's no cover.

Victor's Place (Café Tacuba) (⊠ *Condominios Las Palmas, Local 9, Marina Vallarta* ☎ *322/221–2808*) is an excellent, inexpensive restaurant but doubles as a fun bar, well tended by the owner. Beer for a buck and inexpensive tequila-with-beer-chasers are practically a house rule. Nightly until 11 PM.

Continued on page 138

A cross-section of la piña (the heart) of the blue agave plant

¡TEQUILA!

If God were Mexican, tequila would surely be our heavenly reward, flowing in lieu of milk and honey. Local lore asserts that it was born when lightning hit a tall blue agave, cooking its heart.

Historians maintain that, following Spanish conquest and the introduction of the distillation process, tequila was developed from the ancient Aztec drink *pulque*. Whatever the true origin, Mexico's national drink long predated the Spanish, and is considered North America's oldest intoxicating spirit.

Conjuring up tequila, what might come to mind is late-night teary-eyed confessions or spaghetti-Western-style bar brawls. But tequila is more complex and worldly than many presume. By some accounts it's a digestive that reduces cholesterol and stress. Shots of the finest tequilas can cost upward of $100 each, and are meant to be savored as ardently as fine cognacs or single-malt scotches.

Just one of several agaves fermented and bottled in Mexico, tequila rose to fame during the Mexican Revolution when it became synonymous with national heritage and pride. Since the 1990s tequila has enjoyed a soaring popularity around the globe, and people the world over are starting to realize that tequila is more than a one-way ticket to a hangover.

The Blue Agave

Tequila is made from the blue agave plant (not from a cactus, as is commonly thought), a member of the lily family. Nearly 100,000 acres of blue agave are grown in Mexico today; the plant is native to the Sierra Madre region, still the center for agave fields and tequila production.

After the blue agave plant matures (which takes 8–12 years), its spiky leaves are removed and the heart cooked up to three days in a traditional pit oven (or convection oven) to concentrate the sugars. Seeping blood-red juice, the hearts are then ground and strained, then fermented and distilled at least two or three times.

Workers harvest *Agave tequilana Weber azul*

Mezcal

Liquor distilled from any maguey (agave) plant is called mezcal, so technically, tequila is a type of mezcal. But mezcal is usually used to describe a liquor made from any agave *except* the blue agave from which tequila is made. Originally hailing from Oaxaca, mezcal is as popular as tequila in Mexico, if not more so. Like tequila, quality varies widely from cheap firewater to smooth (and expensive) varieties with complex flavors. The type of maguey used influences the quality greatly.

At the fermentation stage, the agave is added to water.

Effortless Education

You can chat with your local bartender about the blue agave revolution, but the information you get may be flawed. Close to *casa*, you can learn a lot at **La Casa del Tequila** (⊠ Calle Morelos 589, Centro ☎ 322/ 222–2000.) Ask the owner to educate you as you taste a few of the 150 tequilas on hand.

TEQUILA TOURS

Near Boca de Tomatlán, **Agave Don Crispín** (⊠ Las Juntas y Los Veranos, 10 mi south of PV ☎ 322/223–6002) is a small but proud producer of 100% agave tequila that also sells *raicilla,* an unsophisticated liquor made from green agave. Learn the basics of tequila production, and see the pit ovens and old-fashioned stills. If you're serious about tequila, you must go to tequila country. One of the most complete tours is with **Hacienda San José del Refugio** (⊠ Amatitán, about 400 km [250 mi] east of PV, ☎ 33/3613–9585), producer of the Herradura brand. On the 9-hour **Tequila Express** (☎ 33/3880–9090 or through Ticketmaster at 33/3818–3800) train ride, blue agave fields zip by as you sip tequila and listen to roving mariachis. After a distillery tour, there's lunch, folk dancing, and *charro* (cowboy) demonstrations.

An assembly-line worker fills tequila bottles

José Cuervo is Mexico's largest tequila maker

6

TEQUILA!

CHOOSING A TEQUILA

Line 'em up!

Connoisseurs recommend imbibing nothing but 100% pure agave—with no added sugar or chemicals—even for mixed drinks. A tequila's quality is most directly related to the concentration of blue agave, and a higher agave content adds significantly to the price. The cheapest varieties have 49% of their alcohol derived from sugars other than blue agave. (The max allowed by law.) This fact will be clearly marked on the label as TEQUILA 100% DE AGAVE or TEQUILA 100% PURO DE AGAVE.

Aging tequila changes the flavor, but doesn't necessarily improve it. Whiskey and scotch inspired the aging process in oak barrels, which instills a smoky taste or imparts one of many other subtle bouquets. Some experts consider the unmitigated flavor of *blanco* (silver) superior to, or at least less influenced by Yankee and European tastes than that of *reposado* (aged) or *añejo* (mature).

Distinctions you should know (from—generally speaking—least to most expensive) are:

BLANCO (SILVER): Also known as white tequila (though "silver" is the official name), tequila blanco is clear as water. It is unaged—bottled immediately after distillation—and therefore has the purest agave taste of the tequila varieties.

ORO (GOLD): Also called *joven* (young) tequila, this is tequila blanco to which colorants or flavorings have been added, or that has been mixed with tequila aged in oak barrels, giving it a golden hue. Additives (all strictly regulated) such as caramel, oak tree extract, glycerin, and sugar syrup simulate the flavor of tequila aged in oak barrels.

REPOSADO (AGED): Aged in oak barrels 2 to 11 months, reposado is smoother and more flavorful than blanco, as it has acquired some of the oak flavor.

AÑEJO (EXTRA-AGED): Tequila aged more than one year in oak barrels; may also be called "mature tequila." This is the smoothest tequila variety, and the one that most resembles cognac or whiskey—ideal for sipping. Some feel that the agave taste is less noticeable.

CREAM OF THE CROP

In the tequila business, innovation and young energy aren't as successful as age and experience. Traditional *tequilera* families like those behind Don Julio, Sauza, and José Cuervo tend to get the most outstanding results, having pursued perfection for generations. All of our top picks are 100% blue agave.

El Tesoro de Don Felipe Platinum: Triple distilled, and produced the old-fashioned way, the agave hearts crushed with a stone grinder and baked in a brick oven

Don Eduardo: Youthful, crisp, and jubilant, with herby notes; triple distilled

Sauza's Tres Generaciones Blanco: Clean and balanced with hints of cinnamon

Chinaco Blanco: International World Spirits Competition judges proclaimed it "the epitome of tequila character, ... with a lively finish"

Amatitlán Reposado: A complex spirit with a suggestion of nutmeg and spice; awarded best in class at the 2005 International World Spirits Competition

Penacho Azteca Reposado: Another award winner by the same distillery as Amatitlán Reposado

Three faces of tequila. . .

Chinaco Reposado: Medium-dry rested tequila with an oak-spice bite and subtle fruit and flower aromas

Don Julio 1942: Exquisite, complex tequila with the aroma of toffee and vanilla

José Cuervo's Reserva de la Familia: Aged for three years in new oak barrels; rich flavor with touches of vanilla and herbs, and a long, graceful finish

Arette Gran Clase: Ultrasmooth, one of the suavest tequilas anywhere; aged for a full three years, it goes for nearly $200 a bottle

6

TEQUILA!

A TEQUILA BY ANY OTHER NAME ISN'T TEQUILA

To be called "tequila" a drink must meet the following strict requirements, as put forth by Consejo Regulador de Tequila (Tequila Regulatory Council; CRT):

- made entirely in Mexico, and from blue agave grown in certain regions of Mexico (though it can be bottled elsewhere)

- distilled twice; some varieties are distilled three times

- contains at least 51% alcohol derived from Weber blue agave plant

- bears the official stamp of the CRT on the label

- if it is 100% blue agave, it must be bottled in Mexico at the plant at which it was made

SPORTS BAR

With NASCAR on Sunday morning, NFL on Monday night, hockey, indispensable motocross, and welterweight fights, **Steve's Sports Bar** (⊠*Basilio Badillo 286, Col. E. Zapata* ☎*322/222–0256*) is a sports mecca. Multiple satellite connections guarantee broadcasts of many sporting events from various continents, simultaneously. There are piles of board games, too, and the burgers and crinkle fries couldn't be better.

LIVE MUSIC

Most of Puerto Vallarta's live music is performed in restaurants and bars, often on or overlooking the beach. ■TIP→ **Musical events happening anywhere in Vallarta are listed in** *Bay Vallarta.* This twice-monthly rag is an excellent source of detailed information for who's playing around Old Vallarta, the Zona Hotelera Norte, Marina Vallarta, and even as far north as Bucerías. More detail-oriented than most similar publications, *Bay Vallarta* lists showtimes, venues, genres, and cover charges. Live music is much less frequent in the smaller towns to the north and south of PV; to find out what's happening there, ask in tourist-oriented bars, restaurants, or hotels.

LATINO

FodorśChoice
★

Blanco y Negro (⊠*Calle Lucerna at Calle Niza, behind Blockbuster Video store, Zona Hotelera* ☎*322/293–2556*) is a wonderful place to have a drink with friends. The intimate café-bar is comfortable yet rustic, with *equipale* (leather-and-wood) love seats and traditional round cocktail tables. The music, which begins at 10:30, is *trova* (think Mexican Cat Stevens) by Latino legends Silvio Rodríguez and Pablo Milanés; some songs composed and sung by the owner are thrown in. There's never a cover. It's closed Sunday. **La Bodeguita del Medio** (⊠*Paseo Díaz Ordaz 858, Centro* ☎*322/223–1585*) is a wonderful Cuban bar and restaurant with a friendly vibe. People of all ages come to dance salsa (and drink mojitos made with Cuban rum), so the small dance floor fills up as soon as the house sextet starts playing around 9 PM. There's no cover.

Claudio's Meson Bay (⊠*Lázaro Cárdenas 17, by footbridge, Bucerías* ☎*329/298–1634*) is a casual, open-sided, ocean-facing restaurant with live music (usually marimba). Musicans show up daily to tap out these lighthearted melodies after 5 PM—which coincides with excellent all-you-can-eat buffets Monday, Wednesday, and Friday. Start off with a happy-hour drink between 5 and 6 PM.

Cuates y Cuetos (⊠*Francisca Rodriguez 101, Playa los Muertos* ☎*322/223–2724*) is a great outdoor venue where you can have a drink while watching the sun set and the people promenade. After 8 PM listen to live music, usually a seductive guitarist, romantic trio, or more lively version of folk music, like trova or samba rhythms.

An institution for Mexican breakfast, **La Paloma** (⊠*Paseo Diaz Ordaz, at Aldama, Centro* ☎*322/222–3675*) has otherwise average food but is recommended for sunset cocktails with live marimba and, later, mariachi music.

The privileged location overlooking the malecón and the sea is reserved for dining, but **Tequila's** (⊠*Paseo Diaz Ordaz at Galeana, Centro* ☎*322/222–5725*) is still a good place to sip a hand-crafted margarita made with your favorite brand. Sit in the second-floor cantina to absorb the full flavor of mariachis nightly (except Monday, their day off) between 8 and 10:30 PM. There's no cover.

ROCK, JAZZ & BLUES

Philo's (⊠*Calle Delfín 15, La Cruz de Huanacaxtle* ☎*329/295–5068* ⊕*www.philosbar.com*) is the unofficial cultural center and meeting place of La Cruz, with music, food, a large-screen TV, a diminutive swimming pool, and pool table. The namesake owner, a former record producer, also has a small recording studio here. The space is plain but there's excellent live music after 9 PM Thursday through Saturday year-round. Get down with rhythm and blues, country, and rock; or chow down on good pizza or on Thursday evenings, barbecue.

Qué Pasa (⊠*Olas Altas 351, Col. E. Zapata* ☎*No phone*) means "What's Happening." What's happening is that when it's hot—especially Tuesday and Thursday nights, when there's good live music, usually rock or country—it's hot, but when it's not—mainly low season—it's dead. The vibe is 100% American. Some call it a baby-boomer pickup spot; others call it a casual spot for a drink with friends. In addition to live music at least three nights a week, the bar has open mike and movie nights, great BBQ, and dance classes. Check out the whiteboard downstairs for weekly events.

With the ambience (or lack thereof) of a small auditorium, **Roxy/Route 66** (⊠*Av. Ignacio L. Vallarta 217, Col. E. Zapata* ☎*322/223–2404*) is a hit with locals and foreigners who like live blues, rock, reggae, and a little pop, mostly played by cover bands. The club doesn't begin to rock until around 10 PM, when the variable—but always small—cover charge begins. It's closed Sunday but is otherwise open until 4 AM.

At the malecón in the heart of downtown, second-floor **Viejo Vallarta** (⊠*Morelos 484, Centro* ☎*322/222–0589*), open nightly in high season, is popular with locals for live blues, rock, and reggae from 11 PM to 4 AM.

DANCE CLUBS

You can dance salsa with the locals, groove to rock in English or *en español,* or even tango. Things slow down in the off-season, but during school vacations and the winter clubs stay open until 3, 5, or even 6 AM. Except those that double as restaurants, clubs don't open until 10 PM. ■TIP➜If you care about looking hip, don't show up at a club before midnight—it will most likely be dead. Arriving around 10 PM, however, could save you a cover charge.

> **ROCK ON**
>
> The sound system at de Santos is top-notch, not surprising since one of the principal partners is Alex González, the drummer from Mexico's venerable rock band Maná.

Have a late and leisurely dinner, take a walk on the beach and get some coffee, then stroll into the club cool as a cucumber at 12:30 AM or so.

Carlos O'Brien's (⊠*Paseo Diaz Ordaz 796, Centro* ☎*322/222–1444*) is the destination of choice for Vallarta's very young people—a mix of local teens and foreigners come after midnight to mingle and party, especially on weekends. Music is a bit of everything: rock, house, techno, banda, hip-hop, disco, you name it. The ground floor fills up from early afternoon, however, with cruise-shippers and other travelers seeking food and drinks in a relatively familiar atmosphere. There's an $8 cover on weekend nights and also during the week during high season. When the place is hopping it stays open until dawn.

★ **Christine** (⊠*Krystal Vallarta, Av. de las Garzas s/n, Zona Hotelera* ☎*322/224–6990 or 322/224–0202*) has spectacular light shows set to bass-thumping music that ranges from techno and house to disco, rock, and Mexican pop. Most people (young boomers and Gen-Xers) come for the duration (it doesn't close until 6 AM), as this is the top of the food chain for the PV dancing experience. Cover is usually $10 for women and $20 for men, except on Thursday and Sunday, when it's $40 per person for open bar until 4 AM. It's closed Monday and Tuesday, and opens at around 10 PM other nights.

Fodor'sChoice In addition to pretty good Mediterranean dinners in the ground-floor
★ restaurant, **de Santos** (⊠*Calle Morelos 701, at Leona Vicario, Centro* ☎*322/223–3052*) starts the evening with chill out and lounge music that appeals to a mixed, though slightly older, crowd. Later, local and guest DJs spin the more danceable, beat-driven disco and house tunes that appeal to slightly younger folks. If the smoke and noise get to you, head upstairs to the rooftop bar, where you and your friends can fling yourselves on the giant futons for some stargazing. This is a see-and-be-seen place for locals.

Popular with young, hip *vallartenses,* **Hilo** (⊠*Paseo Díaz Ordaz 588, Centro* ☎*322/223–5361*) attracts a mix of locals and visitors. It's mainly a young crowd, serving up house, techno, hip-hop, electronic, and Top 40. The ceiling is several stories high, and enormous bronze-colored statues give an epic feeling. It's open from 10 PM to 4 or 6 AM, but doesn't get rolling until midnight. The cover is $7–$10, or $30 with open bar.

★ **J.B.** (✉ *Blvd. Francisco M. Ascencio 2043, Zona Hotelera* ☎ *322/224–4616*), pronounced "Hota Bay," is the best club in town for salsa. The age of the crowd varies, but tends toward thirty- and fortysomethings. J.B. is serious about dancing, so it feels young at heart. There's usually a band Thursday through Saturday nights, DJ music the rest of the week. Those with *dos patas zurdas* (two left feet) can attend salsa lessons Wednesday through Friday 9:30–10:30 PM; cost is $2 with no additional cover; otherwise, the cover is $9 (except Monday and Tuesday) after 10:30 PM.

Ready to party? Then head to **The Zoo** (✉ *Paseo Díaz Ordaz 630, Centro* ☎ *322/222–4945*) for DJ-spun techno, Latin, reggae, and hip-hop. The adventurous can dance in the cage. It attracts a mixed crowd of mainly young locals and travelers, though after midnight the median age plunges. It's open until 6 AM when things are hopping. The restaurant is full in the early evening with cruise-ship passengers.

FILM

Movie tickets here are less than half what they are in the U.S. and Canada. Many theaters have discounted prices on Wednesday. See theater Web sites or ⊕ www.vallartaonline.com/cinema.

Cine Bahía (✉ *Insurgentes 63, Centro* ☎ *322/222–1717*) is in Old Puerto Vallarta. It has five screens and numerous English-language choices. Tickets are $3.50.

Cinépolis (✉ *Plaza Soriana, Av. Francisco Villa 1642–A, Pitillal* ☎ *322/297–6763* ⊕ *www.cinepolis.com.mx*) was, until Cinemark showed up, PV's newest theater. Next to Soriana department stores at the south entrance to El Pitillal, it has 15 screens and shows in English and Spanish. Tickets are about $4.

Easy to access in the heart of the Hotel Zone, **Cinemark** (✉ *Ave. de los Tules 178, Plaza Caracol, Zona Hotelera* ☎ *322/224–8927*) is on the second floor at the south end of Plaza Caracol. The latest films are shown on its 10 screens. Tickets are about $3.50.

Versalles (✉ *Av. Francisco Villa 799, Col. Versalles* ☎ *322/225–8766*) has six screens. Tickets: $4.

Mexican Rhythms & Roots

Salsa, merengue, *cumbia* ... do they leave you spinning, even off the dance floor? This primer is designed to help you wrap your mind around Latin beats popular in Pacific Mexico. Unfortunately, it can't cure two left feet.

These and other popular Latin dance rhythms were born of African drumming brought to the Caribbean by slaves. Dancing was vital to West African religious ceremonies; these rhythms spread with importation of slaves to the New World. Evolving regional tastes and additional instruments have produced the Latin music enjoyed today from Tierra del Fuego to Toronto, and beyond.

While the steps in most dances can be reduced to some basics, these flat-footed styles of dancing are completely foreign to most non-Latins. Dance classes can definitely help your self-esteem as well as your performance. In Puerto Vallarta, the dance club J.B. *(F below)* is the place to go for lessons.

From Colombia, wildly popular **cumbia** combines vocals, wind, and percussion instruments. With a marked rhythm (usually 4/4 time), the sensual music is relatively easy to dance to. Hip-hop and reggae influences have produced urban cumbia, with up-tempo, accordion-driven melodies. Listen to Kumbia Kings, La Onda, Control, and Big Circo to get into the cumbia groove.

Fast-paced and with short, precise rhythms, **merengue** originated in the Dominican Republic. Although the music sounds almost frantic, the feet aren't meant to keep pace with the melody. Check out Elvis Crespo's 2004 album *Saboréalo.*

Born in Cuba of Spanish and African antecedents, **son** is played on accordion, guitar, and drums. The folkloric music was translated to various dialects in different parts of Mexico. "La Bamba" is a good example of *son jarrocho* (from Veracruz).

American Prohibition sent high-rollers sailing down Cuba way, and they came back swinging to son, mambo, and rumba played by full orchestras—think Dezi Arnaz and his famous song "Babalou." In New York these styles morphed into **salsa**, popularized by such luminaries as Tito Puente and Celia Cruz and carried on today by superstars like Marc Anthony. Wind instruments (trumpet, trombone), piano, guitar, and plenty of percussion make up this highly spiced music.

Mexicans love these African-inspired beats, but are especially proud of homegrown genres, like **música norteña**, which has its roots in rural, northern Mexico (in Texas, it's called *conjunto*). The traditional instruments are the *bajo sexto* (a 12-string guitar), bass, and accordion; modern groups add the trap drums for a distinctive rhythmic pulse. It's danced like a very lively polka, which is one of its main influences. Norteña is the music of choice for working-class Mexicans and Mexican-Americans in the United States.

A subset of música norteña is the **corrido**, popularized during the Mexican Revolution. Like the ballads sung by wandering European minstrels, corridos informed isolated Mexican communities of the adventures of Emiliano Zapata, Pancho Villa, and their compatriots. Today's "narco-corridos" portray dubious characters: the drug lords who run Mexico's infamous cartels. Popular norteño artists include

Michael Salgado and the pioneering Los Tigres del Norte, whose album *Americas Sin Fronteras* was terrifically popular way back in 1987.

But the quintessential Mexican music is **mariachi**, a marriage of European instruments and native sensibilities born right here in Jalisco, Mexico. Guitars, violins, and trumpets are accompanied by the *vihuela* (a small, round-backed guitar) and the larger, deep-throated *guitarrón*. Professional mariachis perform at birthdays and funerals, engagements, anniversaries, and life's other milestones. You won't find mariachi music at nightclubs, however; the huapango, jarocho, and other dances the music accompanies are folk dances. F *For more about mariachi, see "Mariachi: Born in Jalisco" in Chapter 9.*

For concerts, clubbing, and dancing, Mexicans look to the contemporary music scene. Latin jazz was born when legendary Cuban musician Chano Pozo teamed up with the great bebop trumpeter Dizzy Gillespie. Current Latin jazz acts worth applauding are Puerto Ricans Eddie Palmieri and David Sanchez; representing pop, Obie Bermúdez also hails from that Caribbean mecca of music. Check out Latin pop by Cuba's Bebo Valdez, and rock en español by Colombian-born Juanes as well as Mexico's own los Jaguares, El Tri, Ely Guerra, Molotov, and the veteran band Maná.

MORE AFTER-DARK OPTIONS

Enjoy a dinner show or sunset cruise or see silver-studded mariachis in their fancy dress uniforms. Most of the large hotels have live lounge music. Drag shows (⇨ *Chapter 10)* are crowd pleasers—whether the crowd is straight or gay.

COFFEEHOUSES

⇨ *For more coffeehouses, see "Where to Eat" in Chapter 3.* **Pie in the Sky Vallarta** (⊠ *Lázaro Cárdenas 247, Col. E. Zapata* ☎ *322/223–8183)* serves excellent coffee as well as *the* most scrumptious pies, cookies, and cakes. There's free Wi-Fi for those with their trusty laptops.

Dark and romantic, albeit open to the four winds, **Café San Angel** (⊠ *Av. Olas Altas 449, at Calle Francisca Rodriguez, Col. E. Zapata* ☎ *322/223–1273)* is always pleasantly crowded. It has tables along the sidewalk and comfortable couches and chairs within. The menu holds soups, sandwiches, salads, and a great frappuccino.

DINNER CRUISES

⇨ *See "Cruises" in Chapter 7.*

SHOWS

In addition to those listed here, many hotels have buffet dinners with mariachis, charros, and folkloric dancers. All-inclusive hotels generally include nightly entertainment in the room price. ⇨ *For more dinner shows, see "Theater" in Chapter 8.*

Enjoy Vallarta's original dinner show Thursday or Sunday at **La Iguana** (⊠ *Calle Lázaro Cárdenas 311, Col. E. Zapata* ☎ *322/222–0105).* Large troops of professional mariachis entertain, beautiful women dance in colorful costumes, couples dance, kids whack piñatas, and fireworks light up the sky. The simulated cockfight is supposed to be painless for the roosters, and nearly so for alarmed foreign visitors. There's an open bar, and the buffet has 40 selections. Most folks deem this party worth the price of $62 per person.

El Mariachi Loco (⊠ *Lázaro Cárdenas 254, Centro* ☎ *322/223–2205)* is the place to see silver-studded mariachi musicians. The mariachis begin at 9 PM Monday through Wednesday; the rest of the week an organ player and drummer warm up the crowd before the mariachis come onstage at around 11:30 PM. On weekends a comedian and ranchera group are added to the mix at around 1 AM. Cover is $5.

Playa Los Arcos (⊠ *Av. Olas Altas 380, Col. E. Zapata* ☎ *322/222– 1583)* has a theme dinner show most nights 6:30–10:30 PM. The show, which costs $18, includes a buffet and Mexican beer and spirits. The most popular theme night is Saturday's Mexico Night, with mariachis, a charro doing rope tricks, and folkloric dance.

Adventure

Snorkeling

WORD OF MOUTH

"I can recommend an activity I participated in. It was a canopy tour. You ride on zip lines from treetop to treetop through the jungle. So thrilling, scary and just fun!!!! I had such a blast on this—I am definitely going to do it again when I go back."

—Ivitaly

"Great whale watching, mellow atmosphere, amazing snorkeling [at Marietas Islands]. I highly recommend it."

—dabblingman

www.fodors.com/forums

PUERTO VALLARTA IS THE BEST adventure-vacation destination on Mexico's Pacific Coast, at least for the sheer variety of activities. The water's warm and swimmable year-round, although downright bath-like July through September. The big blue bay attracts sea turtles, humpback whales, several species of dolphins, and a growing number of snorkelers and divers. The fishing is excellent—from deep-sea angling for gigantic marlin and sailfish to trolling near shore for roosters and red snapper. Banderas Bay and the beaches to the north and south have waves for surfing as well as plenty of calm bays and inlets for swimming.

Among the lush subtropical mountains—so close to the coast and laced with streams and rivers rushing to the ocean—are challenging mountain biking trails for the fit, and, for those who prefer gas-driven excitement, dune and ATV safaris into the hills. Many family-owned ranches have horse-riding tours at reasonable prices—lasting from an hour or two to overnight forays into the Sierra.

Most tour operators provide transportation from strategic pickup points, usually in downtown Puerto Vallarta, Marina Vallarta, and Nuevo Vallarta and sometimes in Conchas Chinas, but you'll save traveling from one end of the bay to the other by choosing an outfitter near your neck of the woods. Party boats and private yachts are great for accessing gorgeous and hard-to-reach beaches, primarily south of Vallarta along Cabo Corrientes.

Most of the tour operators are in Puerto Vallarta, but whenever possible we've listed some of the companies springing up to meet the needs of visitors staying north and south of town.

OUTDOOR ACTIVITIES & SPORTS

ATV & DUNE BUGGY TOURS

There's an increasing number of ATV, dune buggy, and jeep tours heading to the hills around Puerto Vallarta. Sharing a vehicle with a partner means a significant savings. Also take into consideration location; some head south of PV proper, others to the north. Most rides are to small communities, ranches, and rivers north, south, and east of Puerto Vallarta.

LOGISTICS

A valid driver's license and a major credit card are required. Wear lightweight long pants, sturdy shoes, bandanna (some operators provide one as a keepsake) and/or tight-fitting hat, sunglasses, and both sunscreen and mosquito repellent. In rainy season (July–October) it's hotter and wetter—ideal for splashing through puddles and streams; the rest of the year is cooler but dusty. In either season, prepare to get dirty. Four-hour tours go for $75–$120; full-day trips to San Sebastián cost about $165 for one or $175 for two riders.

MULTI-ADVENTURE OUTFITTERS

Don't see what you want here? Try one of these outfitters, whose multitude of tours includes bird-watching, ATV tours, whale-watching, biking, hot-air ballooning, sailing, and much, much more.

Ecotours (☎ *322/223–3130 or 322/222–6606* ⊕ *www.ecotoursvallarta.com*). **Immersion Adventures** (✉ *La Manzanilla* ☎ *315/351–5341* ⊕ *www.immersionadventures.com*).

Tours Soltero (✉ *San Patricio Melaque* ☎ *315/355–6777* ✐ *raystoursmelaque@yahoo.com*). **Vallarta Adventures** (☎ *322/297–1212 Nuevo Vallarta, 322/221–0657 Marina Vallarta, 888/303–2653 from U.S. and Canada* ⊕ *www.vallartaadventures.com*). **Wild Vallarta** (☎ *322/224–2118 or 322/225–6105* ⊕ *www.wildpv.com*).

OUTFITTERS

Adventure ATV Jungle Treks (✉ *Basilio Badillo 400, Col. E. Zapata* ☎ *322/223–0392*) leads four-hour dune buggy tours and three-hour ATV tours that head into the hills behind Vallarta, daily. Convenient to Marina Vallarta and Nuevo Vallarta, **Best Ride** (✉ *Orquidia 117, Col. Villa Las Flores* ☎ *322/221–3066* ⊕ *www.magiic.com*) runs custom tours in addition to twice-daily, three-hour ATV and dune buggy tours; kids under 11 ride free with a parent.

★ **Wild Vallarta** (✉ *Calle Cardenal 160, Col. Los Sauces* ☎ *322/224–2118 or 322/225–6105* ⊕ *www.wildpv.com*) has full-day and half-day tours in Honda four-wheel ATVs and open-frame, five-speed buggies with VW engines. The long and rugged ATV tour to San Sebastián, high in the Sierra, requires some experience, but four-hour trips to the tequila-producing factory Hacienda Doña Engracia are fine for beginners. (Consider riding two per ATV for the tequila tasting, solving the drinking-and-driving conundrum.) Based in the north part of the bay, the company has a pickup point in Conchas Chinas, too, but it's a longish ride through Vallarta.

CANOPY TOURS

Puerto Vallarta's newest thrill is canopy tours, which are better described as high-octane thrill rides. On a canopy tour you'll "fly" from treetop to treetop, securely fastened to a zip line. Despite the inherent danger of dangling from a cable hundreds of feet off the ground, the operators we list have excellent safety records. It's permissible to take photos while zipping along so if you're brave, bring your camera along, with a neck strap to leave hands free.

LOGISTICS

■TIP→ **Don't take a tour when rain threatens.** A thunderstorm isn't the time to hang out near trees attached to metal cables, and rain makes the activity scary to say the least. Even during the rainy season, however, mornings and *early* afternoons are generally sunny. Check with each operator regarding maximum weight (usually 250 pounds) and minimum ages for kids.

OUTFITTERS

★ **Canopy El Edén** (⊠ *Office: Basilio Badillo 370, Col. E. Zapata* ☎*322/222–2516* ⊕*www.canopyeleden.com*) has daily trips to the spirited Mismaloya River and adjacent restaurant. During the 3½-hour adventure ($77), which departs from the downtown office, you zip along 10 lines through the trees and above the river. To take full advantage of the lovely setting (bring your swimsuit) and good restaurant, take the first tour (they depart at 9, 11, and 1 daily, more often in high season); if there's room, you can return with a later group. Otherwise if you wish to stay longer at the river or restaurant, you can return to Vallarta by taxi, or ask the restaurant staff for a lift to the highway, where buses frequently pass.

Fodor'sChoice
★ Vallarta's top canopy tour is **Canopy Tour de Los Veranos** (⊠ *Office: Calle Francisca Rodríguez 336, Centro* ☎*322/223–0504* ⊕*www.canopytours-vallarta.com*). Slightly more expensive than its competitors ($79), Los Veranos also has the most zip lines (15), the longest zip line (600 feet), the highest zip line (500 feet off the ground), and the most impressive scenery: crossing the Rio Los Horcones half a dozen times on several miles of cables. Departures are from the office, across from the Pemex station at the south side of Puerto Vallarta, on the hour between 9 and 2, with reduced hours in low season (June through November). It's the only PV tour company that doesn't require helmets. After your canopy tour, there's time to scale the climbing wall, play in the Los Horcones River, eat at the restaurant, or hang out at the bar overlooking the river, but check to make sure that a ride back to town is available.

Luis Verdin of **Rancho Mi Chaparrita** (⊠ *Manuel Rodriguez Sanchez 14, Sayulita* ☎*329/291–3112*) runs a 10-zip-line tour on his family ranch. Access the ranch on his lively, healthy horses via the beach and backcountry for a complete adventure. Canopy tours are $50; a canopy tour plus the horseback ride is $75.

The most convenient canopy tour if you're staying in Nuevo Vallarta is **Vallarta Adventures** (⊠ *Paseo de las Palmas 39–A, Nuevo Vallarta* ☎*322/297–1212, 888/303–2653 in U.S. and Canada* ⊠*Edifício Marina Golf, Local 13–C, Calle Mástil, Marina Vallarta* ☎*322/221–0657* ⊕*www.vallarta-adventures.com*), although it's not the best show in town. Participants use gloved hands rather than a braking device to slow down or stop, and must return to town right after their zip line canopy adventure with no time for other activities. It's $70 per person.

FISHING

Sportfishing is excellent off Puerto Vallarta, and fisherfolk have landed monster marlin well over 500 pounds. Surf casting from shore nets snook, roosters, and jack crevalles. Hire a *panga* (skiff) to hunt for Spanish mackerel, sea bass, amberjack, snapper, bonito, and roosterfish on full- or half-day trips within the bay. Yachts are best for big-game fishing: yellowfin tuna; blue, striped, and black marlin; and dorado. Hire them for 4 to 10 hours, or overnight. Catch-and-release of billfish is encouraged. If you don't want to charter a boat, you can also join a "party" boat.

Most sportfishing yachts are based at Marina Vallarta; only a few call "home" the marina at Paradise Village, in Nuevo Vallarta. Pangas can be hired in the traditional fishing villages of Mismaloya and Boca de Tomatlán, just south of town; in the Costalegre towns of La Manzanilla and Barra de Navidad; and in the north, La Cruz de Huanacaxtle, as well as at El Anclote and Nuevo Corral del Risco, Punta de Mita. The resort hotels of the Costalegre and Punta de Mita arrange fishing excursions for their guests. Bass fishing at Cajón de Peña, about 1½ hours south of Vallarta, nets 10-pounders on a good day.

SEASONAL CATCHES
Sailfish and dorado are abundant practically year-round. (Though dorado drop out a bit in early summer and sailfish dip slightly in spring.)
Winter: bonito, dorado, jack crevalle, sailfish, striped marlin, wahoo
Spring: amberjack, jack crevalle, grouper, mackerel, red snapper
Summer: grouper, roosterfish, yellowfin tuna
Fall: black marlin, blue marlin, sailfish, striped marlin, yellowfin tuna, wahoo

LOGISTICS
Most captains and crews are thoroughly bilingual, at least when it comes to boating and fishing.

LICENSES Licenses are necessary, but don't worry about procuring yours on your own. If the captain hasn't arranged it ahead of time, he will make sure that a SEMARNAP official is on hand to sell you one before the boat departs. Cost is about $12 per day; there are no weekly rates.

PRICES Prices generally range $300–$400 for four hours on a yacht to $600–$1,050 for a day-long cruise for four to eight anglers. A longer trip is recommended for chasing the big guys, as it takes you to prime fishing grounds like Los Bancos and Cobeteña.

Party boats range from $125 to $140 per person for an eight-hour day. Drinking water is generally included in the price; box lunches and beer or soda may be sold separately or included, or sometimes it's BYOB. Pangas and superpangas, the latter with shade and a head of some sort, charge $185 to $400 for four to eight hours and generally accommodate one to three or four anglers. For a boat and round-trip transportation to Cajón de Peña, an all-day affair, expect to pay $150 to $600 per person.

OUTFITTERS
CharterDreams (✉ *Marina Las Palmas II, Locales 11 and 12, Marina Vallarta* ☎ *322/221–0690* ⊕ *www.charterdreams.com*) has a variety of excursions, from trips with one to three people in *pangas* (skiffs) for

bass fishing to cruises with up to eight people aboard luxury yachts. Although most fisherfolk choose to leave around the smack of dawn, you set your own itinerary. The same rates apply for whale-watching or private sightseeing or snorkeling tours. Aboard group boats—aka party boats—belonging to **Cruceros Princesa** (⊠ *Faro de la Marina, Marina Vallarta* ☎ *322/224–4777*), you'll get a reliable boat, knowledgeable crew, and a box lunch to boot. Equipment, live bait, box lunch, water, and a soft drink or two are included. The eight-hour tour departs from the maritime pier. Yachts from 38 to 46 feet are available for individual charter as well.

In Barra de Navidad, at the southern end of the Costalegre, contact **Gerardo Kosonoy** (☎ *044–315/354–2251* ✎ hakunakosonoy@yahoo. com) for honest fishing excursions. Alternately, you can easily round up a fisherman with a panga from one of the two large fishing co-ops on the lagoon side of town. There's usually at least one representative hoping for clients at the water taxi dock. Gerardo and the other fishermen charge 400 pesos ($37) per hour for one to four passengers.

★ **Master Baiter** (⊠ *Puesto del Sol Condominiums, near lighthouse, Marina Vallarta* ☎ *322/209–0498 or 322/209–0499* ⊕ *www.mbsportfishing. com* ⊠ *Calle 31 de Octubre 107, across from McDonald's, Centro* ☎ *322/222–4043*) is a comprehensive fishing outfitter with a proven track record. Its superpanga fleet consists of 26-foot skiffs with shade and bathroom; some have GPS. The 8-, 10-, and 12-hour yacht charters allow enough time to fish El Morro, Corbeteña, and beyond. An overnight trip ($2,650) allows further exploration, and includes meals and drinks. Both storefronts (downtown Vallarta and Marina Vallarta) sell fishing tackle, although there's a better selection at the Marina store.

Do you remember the seductive-looking divers in *Night of the Iguana?* Well, their progeny might be among the local guys of **Mismaloya Divers** (⊠ *Road to Mismaloya Beach, Mismaloya* ☎ *322/228–0020*). Panga trips here are comparatively inexpensive, usually around $185 within the bay or $230 to the Marietas (five lines, one to four passengers), including lunch and drinks. Local fishermen at Punta de Mita have formed the **Sociedad Cooperativa de Servicios Turísticos** (*Tourist Services Cooperative* ⊠ *Av. El Anclote 1, Manz. 17, Nuevo Corral del Risco* ☎ *329/291–6298* ⊕ *www.prodigyweb.net.mx/cooperativapuntamita*). The families who run this co-op were forcibly relocated from their original town of Corral del Risco due to the development of luxurious digs like the Four Seasons. The guides may not speak English as fluently as the more polished PV operators, but they know the local waters, and the fees go directly to them and their families. Sportfishing costs about $46 per hour, with a four-hour minimum, for up to four people. Two hours of whale-watching or snorkeling around the Marietas Islands, for up to eight people, costs $111. Kids older than six but younger than 60 pay $2 for a wristband allowing entrance to the Marietas, a national aquatic park.

Captain Peter Vines of **Vallarta Tour and Travel** (⊠ *Marina Los Palmas Local 4, in front of Dock B, Marina Vallarta* ☎☎ *322/209–0005;*

ANNUAL EVENTS

FEBRUARY
Hundreds of bikes roar into PV for **Bike Week** (⊕ *www.bikeweek.com*) and its rallies, parties, and motorcycle parades.

MARCH
The entire month is dedicated to racing and boating activities, beginning with the **Banderas Bay Regatta** (☎ *322/297–2222* ⊕ *www.banderasbayregatta.com*), which starts in San Diego, California, and ends here with a great awards banquet. Throughout the month there are cocktail parties, charity events, receptions, seminars, additional races, and boat parades.

MAY
Begun in the early '90s, the five-day **Annual Sports Classic** (☎ *322/226–0404 Ext. 6038 [Veronica Alarcon at the Sheraton Buganvilias]*) invites amateurs, pros, and semi-pros to compete in disc golf, basketball, softball, soccer, tennis, and an aerobics marathon. Most events take place at the Agustin Flores Contreras Stadium or Los Arcos Amphitheater.

NOVEMBER
The **Puerto Vallarta International Half Marathon** (⊕ *www.maratonvallarta.com*), held in early November, gets bigger each year, with nearly 1,000 participants in 2005, its third year.

The **International Puerto Vallarta Sailfish and Marlin Tournament** (☎ *322/225–5467* ⊕ *www.fishvallarta.com*) celebrated its 50th anniversary in 2005. The entry fee is more than $1,000 per line, but the prizes and prestige of winning are great. Categories are dorado, tuna, marlin, and sailfish.

866/682–1971 in U.S. and Canada) can accommodate eight fisherfolk with top-of-the-line equipment, including the latest electronics, sonar, radar, and two radios. Rates are very reasonable, especially because they include lunch, beer, soda, and fish-cleaning service at the end of the day. Transportation from your hotel is included in the full-day bass-fishing expedition to Cajón de Peña.

GOLF

"Not a bad mango in the bunch" is how one golf aficionada described Puerto Vallarta's courses. From the Four Seasons Punta Mita to the Gran Bay at Barra de Navidad, the region is a close second to Los Cabos in variety of play at a range of prices. Well-known designers are represented, including Jack Nicklaus and Tim Weiskopf.

LOGISTICS
Most of these courses offer first-class services including driving ranges and putting greens, lessons, clinics, pro shops, and clubhouses.

COURSES
★ Joe Finger designed the 18-hole course at **Marina Vallarta** (✉ *Paseo de la Marina s/n, Marina Vallarta* ☎ *322/221–0545 or 322/221–0073*); the $128 green fee includes practice balls and a shared cart. It's the area's second-oldest course and is closest and most convenient for golfers

staying in the Hotel Zone, Old Puerto Vallarta, and Marina Vallarta. Very flat, it's way more challenging than it looks, with lots of water hazards. Speaking of hazards, the alligators have a way of blending into the scenery. They might surprise you, but they supposedly don't bite. Some of the best views in the area belong to the aptly named **Vista Vallarta** (⊠*Circuito Universidad 653, Col. San Nicolás* ☎*322/290–0030 or 322/290–0040*). There are 18 holes designed by Jack Nicklaus and another 18 by Tom Weiskopf. The green fee for the course, which is a few miles northwest of the Marina Vallarta area, is $174. A shared cart and tax are included.

★   At the Paradise Village hotel and condo complex, **El Tigre** (⊠*Paseo de los Cocoteros 18, Nuevo Vallarta* ☎*322/297–0773, 866/843–5951 in U.S., 800/214–7758 in Canada* ⊕*www.eltigregolf.com*) is an 18-hole course with 12 water features. The green fee of $138 includes a shared cart and practice balls but not 15% tax. Don't be surprised if you see a guy driving around with tigers in his truck: the course's namesake and mascot is the passion of the club's director. El Tigre has a fun island par 3. **Four Seasons Punta Mita** (⊠*Punta de Mita* ☎*329/291–6000* ⊕*www.fourseasons.com*) was designed by Jack Nicklaus. Nonguests are permitted, but not *encouraged*, to play the 195-acre, par-72 course; advance reservations are essential. The club's claim to fame is that it has perhaps the only natural island green in golf. Drive your cart to it at low tide; otherwise hop aboard a special amphibious vessel (weather permitting) to cross the water. There are seven other oceanfront links, as well as an optional par 3, the resort's signature hole.

Designed by Percy Clifford in 1978, PV's original course, **Los Flamingos Country Club** (⊠*Carretera a Bucerías, Km 145, 12 km [8 mi] north of airport, Nuevo Vallarta* ☎*329/296–5006* ⊕*www.flamingosgolf.com. mx*), has been totally renovated. The 18-hole course at the northern extremity of Nuevo Vallarta has new irrigation and sprinkler systems to maintain the rejuvenated greens. The green fee is $130, including a shared cart and a bucket of balls. The $149 green fee for the 18-hole course at **Mayan Palace** (⊠*Paseo de las Moras s/n, Fracc. Nautico Turistico, Nuevo Vallarta* ☎*322/226-4000 Ext. 4600*) includes a golf cart for each player. Twilight fees (after 1 PM) are almost half that price, at $89.

Fodor'sChoice   About two hours south of Vallarta on the Costalegre is the area's best
★   course. At least six of the holes at **El Tamarindo** (⊠*Carretera Melaque– Puerto Vallarta, Careterra 200, Km 7.5, Cihuatlán* ☎*315/351–5032 Ext. 113*) play along the ocean; some are cliffside holes with fabulous views, others go right down to the beach. On a slow day, golfers are encouraged at tee time to have a swim or a picnic on the beach during their round, or to play a hole a second time if they wish. Designed by David Fleming, the breathtaking course is the playground of birds, deer, and other wildlife. It's an awesome feeling to nail the course's most challenging hole, the 9th: a par-3 with a small green surrounded by bunkers. The green fee is $210, including cart and tax. Resort guests get priority for tee times; call up to a week ahead to check availability. **Isla Navidad** (⊠*Isla Navidad, Barra de Navidad* ☎*314/337–9006* ⊕*www.islanavi-*

dad.com) must have the best variety of play in the area, with three 9-hole courses of different flavors: mountain, lagoon, and ocean. Designed by Robert VanHagge, the course is beautifully sculpted, with lovely contours. Green fees are $184 for 9 holes or $207 for 18, including driving range practice, cart, and tax.

HORSEBACK RIDING

Most of the horse riding outfits are based on family ranches in the foothill towns of the Sierra like Las Palmas. Horses are permitted on the beach in smaller towns like Sayulita and San Francisco, but not in Vallarta proper, so expect to ride into the hills for sunset-viewing there.

LOGISTICS

Outfitters pick you up either from the hotel or strategic locations north and south of town and return you to your hotel or to the pickup point. Short rides depart morning and afternoon, while longer rides are generally in the morning only, at least during winter hours of early sunset.

Ask at the beachfront restaurants of tiny towns like Yelapa, Quimixto, and Las Animas, south of PV, to hook up with horses for treks into the jungle. Horses are generally well cared for, and some are exceptionally fit and frolicky.

OUTFITTERS

Hacienda de Doña Engracia (⊠ *Carretera a las Palmas, Km 10, La Desembocada* ☎ *322/224–0410* ⊕ *www.haciendadonaengracia.com*) has, among other activities, a three-hour horseback excursion ($56 per person). After the river has receded at the end of the wet season (this dry period usually lasts from late November through June), you ride one hour to a series of three hot springs, where you spend an hour before heading back, crossing a river mid-trip. In rainy season, the tour through jungly hills is impressive but, because you often can't cross the swollen streams, it doesn't go to the hot springs. Some of the large stable of horses are of Arabian stock. At the hacienda, you can fish in the small artificial lake, do a tequila tasting, go mountain biking, or lunch at the restaurant. Most people arrive as part of a cruise-ship excursion or dune buggy tour with Wild Vallarta (⇨ *ATV Tours, above*) or other adventure companies, but you can drive on your own as well.

★ **Rancho Charro** (☎ *322/224–0114* ⊕ *www.ranchoelcharro.com*) provides transportation to and from your hotel for rides to rivers and waterfalls. Choices include three-hour ($56), five-hour ($69), and all-day rides ($100), and several multiday camping-riding combos.

★ The friendly folks at family-owned **Rancho Manolo** (⊠ *Highway 200, Km 12, at Mismaloya bridge, Mismaloya* ☎ *322/228–0018 day, 322/222–3694 evening*) take you into the mountains they know so well. The usual tour is to El Edén, the restaurant-and-river property where the movie *Predator* was filmed. The three-hour trip (45 minutes each way, with 1½ hours for a meal or for splashing in the river) costs just $33.

The horses of **Rancho Ojo de Agua** (✉ *Cerrada de Cardenal 227, Fracc. Aralias, Puerto Vallarta* ☎ *322/224–0607*) are part Mexican quarter horse and part thoroughbred; according to proud owner Mari González, the stock comes from the Mexican cavalry. The family-owned business conducts sunset and half-day horseback rides (three to five hours, $58 and $71), the latter including lunch and time for a swim in a mountain stream. Also available is a full-day excursion (seven hours, most of which on the horse) into the Sierra Madre ($95) or an overnight ($250), which includes four meals and either tent or cabin camping.

> **PICKUP POLO**
>
> Rent a pony and join a game of polo at the **Club de Polo Costa Careyes** (✉ *Km 53.5 Carretera 200, Carretera a Barra de Navidad, El Careyes* ☎ *315/351–0320* ⊕ *www.mexicopolo.com*). The cost is $80 per game per player. Spectators are welcome, too, at no charge, to watch the various tournaments (mid-April–November). Ask about packages including accommodations, clinics (mid-February through mid-March only), and lessons.

Manuel, of **Rancho Manuel** (✉ *Calle 33, Gringo Hill, Sayulita* ☎ *322/132–7683*), rents horses for riding on the beach or in the hills behind Sayulita. You can find him on the beach at San Pancho or Sayulita, or give him a call ahead to arrange. Though the trail rides at **Club de Polo Costa Careyes** (✉ *Km 53.5, Carretera 200, Carretera a Barra de Navidad, El Careyes* ☎ *315/351–0320* ⊕ *www.mexicopolo.com*) are expensive at $80 for 45 minutes to an hour, you know you're getting an exceptional mount. Trips leave in early morning or around sunset. Tours are mid-November through mid-April only.

KAYAKING

Except on very calm, glassy days, the open ocean is really too rough for enjoyable kayaking, and the few kayaking outfitters there mainly offer this activity in combination with snorkeling, dolphin-watching, or boating excursions to area beaches. The best places for kayaking-and-birding combos are the mangroves, estuaries, large bays, and islands of the Costalegre, south of Puerto Vallarta.

LOGISTICS

Many of the larger beachfront hotels—especially the all-inclusives—rent or loan sea kayaks to their guests. Double kayaks are easier on the arms than single kayaks. As the wind usually picks up in the afternoon, morning is generally the best time to paddle. Stick to coves if you want to avoid energy-draining chop and big waves. Kayaks range from $9 to $12 an hour or $23 to $35 per day.

Rent kayaks or take a half-day, full-day, or two-day paddling and birding tour with **Immersion Adventures** (✉ *Entrada Camino a La Manza-*

nilla, La Manzanilla ☎*315/351–5341* ⊕*www.immersionadventures.
com*). Although the company has an office on the entrance road to La
Manzanilla, it's best to book your excursions at least a week ahead of
your arrival. Opportunities include trips to offshore islands Cocinas
and Iglesias, the riparian environment of Ríos Purificación or Cuixmala, or five- to six-hour coastal forays with time for snorkeling.

In addition to its other curricula, **Ecotours** (✉*Ignacio L. Vallarta 243,
Col. E. Zapata* ☎*322/223–3130 or 322/222–6606* ⊕*www.ecotours-
vallarta.com*), in downtown Vallarta, has kayaking tours from Boca de
Tomatlán. After paddling around a rocky point you end at tiny Playa
Colomitos, where there's time for snorkeling and then a snack. You'll
spend 1½ to 2 hours kayaking and though it's fun being on the water,
the scenery is not exactly breathtaking.

Vallarta Adventures (✉*Paseo de las Palmas 39–A, Nuevo Vallarta*
☎*322/297–1212, 888/303–2653 in U.S. and Canada* ✉*Edifício
Marina Golf, Local 13–C, Calle Mástil, Marina Vallarta* ☎*322/221–
0657* ⊕*www.vallarta-adventures.com*) includes kayaking in its boat
trip to Las Caletas, the company's private beach; the coastline here is
fun to explore. The only other option is on dolphin-watching trips to
Las Marietas Islands, where there are about five kayaks per boatload
of up to 100 passengers, most of whom choose to snorkel.

MOUNTAIN BIKING

Although the tropical climate makes it hot for biking, the Puerto Vallarta area is lovely and has challenging and varied terrain. Based in
Puerto Vallarta, the major biking operators lead rides up river valleys,
to Yelapa, and from the old mining town of San Sebastian (reached via
plane; included in price), high in the Sierra, back to Vallarta. It's about
45 kilometers of downhill.

In the rainy season, showers are mainly in the late afternoon and evening, so bike tours can take place year-round. In summer and fall rivers and waterfalls are voluptuous and breathtaking. A popular ending
point for rides into the foothills, they offer a place to rest, rinse off,
and have a snack or meal. During the dry season, it's cooler and less
humid—although still hot and humid. The very best months for biking
are January through March: the weather is coolest and the vegetation,
rivers, and waterfalls still reasonably lush after the end of the rainy
season in October.

LOGISTICS

PRICES Four- to five-hour rides average $45 to $70; Yelapa costs $115–$140.
The ride down from San Sebastián, including one-way plane trip, goes
for around $220. Rides of more than a half day include lunch, and all
include helmet, gloves, and bikes.

OUTFITTERS

Oscar del Díos of **Bike Mex** (✉*Calle Guerrero 361, Centro* ☎*322/223–
1834 or 322/223–1680*) can tailor rides to your level of fitness and
ability. He has a technical, single-track ride for the very advanced,

local rides for beginners to advanced, and an all-day downhill from San Sebastian. Take the plane one way and ride back for $220, or pay $68 for the round-trip "killer donkey" experience. Excursions include guide, gear (24-speed mountain bikes), and light breakfast and snacks. Multiday excursions can be arranged. A few streets behind Vallarta's cathedral, **Eco Ride** (⊠ *Calle Miramar 382, Centro* ☎ *322/222–7912* ⊕ *www.ecoridemex.com*) caters to intermediate and expert cyclists. Rides start at the shop and go up the Río Cuale, passing some hamlets along single tracks and dirt roads. A few rides include time at local swimming holes; the Yelapa ride ($130)—with two 10-km (6-mi) uphills and a 20-km (12-mi) downhill—returns by boat.

Family-operated **Vallarta Bikes** (⊠ *Fransico Villa 1442, Col. Los Sauces* ☎ *322/293–1142* ⊕ *www.vallartabikes.com*) has custom tours of up to 10 days. More common, however, are set itineraries for beginner to advanced cyclists. A three- to four-hour beginner's ride to La Pileta is popular, as the departure point is near the town center and the destination a year-round swimming hole. This easy downhill includes lunch, as do all Vallarta Bikes' tours. The six-hour, 35-km (22-mi) tour to Yelapa is more physical, but the reward is lunch overlooking Yelapa's beautiful beach and returning by water taxi. Owner-guide Alejandro González leads groups whenever possible. He will certainly push you, but don't expect him to hold your hand.

MULTISPORT TOURS

Natura Tours (⊠ *Carretera Aeropuerto, Km 5.5, Zona Hotelera* ☎ *322/224–0410*) has nature-oriented excursions, including bass and deep-sea fishing, scuba diving, hiking, horseback riding, and biking.

Canadian expat Ray Calhoun and his wife Eva run **Tours Soltero** (⊠ *Privada Las Cabañas 26, San Patricio Melaque* ☎ *315/355–6777* ✐ raystoursmelaque@yahoo.com). They rent mountain bikes, snorkeling equipment, and boogie boards ($10 per day), and lead active tours from their base in San Patricio Melaque to neighboring beaches and towns. Typical tours are snorkeling in Tenacatita with boogie boarding at Boca de Iguana, 10–5 ($27), and a day trip to the state capital, Colima, which includes lunch and a stop at a typical hacienda cum museum ($54). Tours run any day, all year with a minimum of four customers.

SAILING

Although large Bahía de Banderas and towns to the north and south have lots of beautiful beaches to explore and wildlife to see, there are few sailing adventures for the public. Most boating companies don't want to rely on the wind to get to area beaches for the day's activities. The companies below are recommended for their true sailing skills and reliable vessels.

LOGISTICS

For insurance reasons, companies or individuals here don't rent bare-boat (uncrewed) yachts even to seasoned sailors. Those who want to crew the ship themselves can do semi-bareboat charters, where the captain comes along but allows the clients to sail the boat.

OUTFITTERS

Recommended by Pat Henry (now retired) of the Coming About School of Sailing is **Dos Amantes** (⊠*Marina Vallarta* ☎*044322/140–3171* ✐*dos_amantes_lacey@hotmail.com*). The easy-going owners, Joe and Lori Lacey, will tailor a day or overnight of sailing to their clients' wishes: giving sailing tips or sailing the boat themselves, providing gourmet food, snorkeling and sunset-viewing opportunities, and most anything else.

Vallarta Adventures (⊠*Paseo de las Palmas 39–A, Nuevo Vallarta* ☎*322/297–1212, 888/303–2653 in U.S. and Canada* ⊠*Edifício Marina Golf, Local 13–C, Calle Mástil, Marina Vallarta* ☎*322/221–0657* ⊕*www.vallarta-adventures.com*) has day and sunset sails during high season for about $85 and $70 per person, respectively. They'll do individual charters as well. Another option for chartering your own private sailboat is to contact captain Andre Schwartz of **Casa Naval** (⊠*El Faro de la Marina, Marina Vallarta* ☎*044–322/100–4154* ✐*zenigma_1947@yahoo.com*). The captain-owner has a comfortable Beneteau Oceanis 390 called the *Dèjá-Vu Again,* a 39-foot vessel that accommodates eight for trips of four hours to several days. He charges $75 per hour for up to 10 passengers.

SCUBA DIVING & SNORKELING

The ocean isn't nearly as clear as the Caribbean, but the warm, nutrient-rich water attracts a varied community of sea creatures. Many of the resort hotels rent or loan snorkeling equipment and have introductory dive courses at their pools. The underwater preserve surrounding Los Arcos, a rock formation off Playa Mismaloya, is a popular spot for diving and snorkeling. The rocky bay at Quimixto, about 32 km (20 mi) south of PV and accessible only by boat, is a good snorkeling spot. *Pangeros* based in Boca and Yelapa can be hired to take you to spots off the tourist trail.

On the north side of things, Punta de Mita, about 80 km (50 mi) north of PV, has the Marietas Islands, with lava tubes and caves and at least 10 good places to snorkel and dive, including spots for advanced divers. El Morro Islands, with their big fish lurking in the underwater pinnacles and caves, are also suitable for experienced divers.

LOGISTICS

June through September is the very best time for snorkeling and diving, although it's fine all year long. In summer, however, the water is not only its warmest and calmest but visibility is best—80 to 120 feet on a good day—and you can spot gigantic manta rays, several species of eel, sea turtles, large and many species of colorful fish. In winter, although conditions are less favorable, some luck will yield orca and humpback whale sightings, an awesome experience.

OUTFITTERS

For PADI- or NAUI-certification, equipment rentals, and one- or two-tank dives, contact **Chico's Dive Shop** (✉ *Paseo Díaz Ordáz 772, Centro* ☎ *322/222–1895* ✉ *Mismaloya Beach, in front of Barceló La Jolla de Mismaloya, Mismaloya* ☎ *322/228–0248* ⊕ *www.chicos-diveshop. com*). Trips to Los Arcos accommodate snorkelers ($36) as well as those who want a one- or two-tank dive ($54 and $84, respectively). From the Mismaloya shop, you can rent Wave Runners ($46 per half hour). Kayaks and mountain bikes rent by the hour, day, or week ($10 per hour, $32 per day; bikes rent for $41 per week). In Nayarit, **CIS-BAB** (✉ *Héroes de Nacozarí 152, Bucerías* ☎ *329/298–2364* ⊕ *www. vallartaundersea.com*) teaches PADI dive courses; runs dive trips; and sells, rents, and repairs dive equipment.

★ **Ecotours,** an authorized equipment dealer, has English-speaking PADI dive masters. Two-tank dives run $80 to $100; longer trips to Corbeteña cost $120. All two-tank trips include lunch, refreshments, and gear. The PADI dive masters at **Pacific Scuba** (✉ *Blvd. Francisco Medina Ascencio 2486, Zona Hotelera* ☎ *322/209–0364* ⊕ *www.pacificscuba. com.mx*) teach courses, rent equipment, and arrange trips. A two-tank package to one of at least six sites (including Los Arcos, Marietas Islands, or Corbeteña) costs $79 to $148 and includes lunch and all gear. Three-day packages are available, too.

★ Tours with **Sociedad Cooperativa de Servicios Turísticos** (✉ *Av. El Anclote 1, Manz. 17, Nuevo Corral del Risco* ☎ *329/291–6298* ⊕ *www.prodigyweb.net.mx/cooperativapuntamita*) are a great deal if you have a group: two hours of snorkeling around the Marietas Islands, for up to eight people, costs just $111. **Vallarta Adventures** (✉ *Paseo de las Palmas 39–A, Nuevo Vallarta* ☎ *322/297–1212, 888/303–2653 in U.S. and Canada* ✉ *Edifício Marina Golf, Local 13–C, Calle Mástil, Marina Vallarta* ☎ *322/221–0657* ⊕ *www.vallarta-adventures.com*) has daylong, two-tank tours of the Marietas Islands ($90), El Morro Islands ($115), El Corbeteña ($125), and other sites. The latter two are for advanced divers only and offered usually just once a week. Their expert PADI guides accommodate snorkelers as well as divers. They also have introductory dive classes for children and adults ($35), and open-water certification.

SURFING

The main surfing areas are in the north, in Nayarit State, including (from south to north) Destiladeras, Sayulita, and nearly a dozen breaks off Punta de Mita, where offshore breaks for intermediate and advanced surfers are best accessed by boat. The best spots for beginners are shore breaks like those at El Anclote and Sayulita; in the south, Barra de Navidad is also appropriate for beginners.

LOGISTICS

SEASONS Waves are largest and most consistent between June and December; the water is also warmest during the rainy season (late June–October), averaging nearly 80° July through September.

PRICES Surfboard rentals start at $5 an hour or $25 a day. Surfing trips run around $40 per hour, usually with a three- or four-hour minimum. Shops sell rash guards (no need for a full wet suit here), boogie boards, wax, and other necessities. For good info and links check out ⊕*www.surf-mexico.com.*

OUTFITTERS

On the beach at Sayulita is **Captain Pablo** (⊠*Calle Las Gaviotas at beach, Sayulita* ☎*329/291–2070 early morning and evenings only* ✍pandpsouthworth@hotmail.com), where you can rent equipment or take surfing lessons with Patricia: $25 should get you to your feet (board included). Surf tours, gear included, cost $160 for four hours (up to four surfers). You can take lessons from **Oscar's Rental** (⊠*El Anclote beach, Punta de Mita* ☎*329/291–6284*), which has a stand right on the beach. The cost is a bit steep: $80 for two hours of instruction. Surfboard rentals go for $8 an hour, $30 a day, or $150 per week. Oscar's also runs surfing trips for up to eight people that last an average of three hours. If you're not up to surfing, try a boogie board, which rents for $20 a day.

Although there's not much surf at its beach, **San Pancho Surf Shop** (⊠*Av. Tercer Mundo 37, San Francisco* ☎*311/258–4215*) sells and rents boards (surfboard rentals go for $7 an hour, $28 a day) and other surfing equipment. Lessons ($30 per hour) are generally taught at Sayulita, 10 minutes south of town, where the shore break is gentle. The shop sells organic coffee as well as a small selection of bikinis, flip-flops, and board shorts. On the beach at Sayulita, **Sininen** (⊠*Calle Delfín 4–S, Sayulita* ☎*329/291–3186*) rents and sells surfboards and surf paraphernalia. In Barra look for **South Swell Surf Shop** (⊠*Hotel La Alondra, Suite 2, Calle Sinaloa 16, Barra de Navidad* ☎*044–315/354–5497 cell*) for all your ripping requirements.

WILDLIFE-WATCHING

Banderas Bay and the contiguous coast and inland areas are blessed with abundant species of birds and beasties. Diverse habitats from riparian forests to offshore islands are home to a wide range of native and migratory birds, including about two dozen endemic species. Beyond birds, most of the wildlife spotting is marine: whales (late November through end of March), dolphins, marine turtles, and giant manta rays, among many other species.

WHEN TO CATCH A WAVE

Locals have lots of folk wisdom about when to catch the best waves. Some say it's best right before a good rain, others believe it's when the tide is moving toward an extreme high or low.

BIRD-WATCHING

Although there aren't a lot of dedicated birding operators here, this region is perfect for the pastime, as Vallarta has more than 350 species in a wide variety of habitats, including shoreline, rivers, marshes, lagoons, mangroves, and tropical and evergreen forests. In the mangroves, standouts are the great blue heron, mangrove cuckoo, and vireo. Ocean and shore birds include brown and blue-footed boobies and red-billed tropic birds. Military macaws patrol the thorn forests, and songbirds of all stripes serenade the pine-oak forests.

LOGISTICS   Most people come on trips through birding clubs or organizations like those below, or hire a private birding guide. Outfitters charge $45–$60 for half-day tours and $100–$125 for full-day tours.

OUTFITTERS   **Ecotours** (⊠ *Ignacio L. Vallarta 243, Col. E. Zapata* ☏*322/223–3130 or 322/222–6606* ⊕*www.ecotoursvallarta.com*) runs a six-hour tropical forest tour approximately four days per week for $63. Bring plenty of insect repellent, especially in the rainy months. Clients of **Immersion Adventures** (⊠ *Entrada Camino a La Manzanilla, La Manzanilla* ☏*315/351–5341* ⊕*www.immersionadventures.com*) sneak up on their idols via kayak, accessing mangrove swamps and riparian environments as well as hiking along jungle trails. **Victor Emanuel Nature Tours** (☏*512/328–5221, 800/328–8368 in U.S. and Canada* ⊕*www.ventbird.com*) has several yearly small-group birding tours of the Puerto Vallarta from Rancho Primavera, just south of PV proper.

Mark Stackhouse, of **Westwings Birding Tours** (⊕*www.westwings.com*), divides his time evenly between the U.S. and San Blas, Nayarit. According to Mark, a 30-year birder, it's possible to see about 25% of the birds found throughout Mexico on day trips from a San Blas Hotel. Contact Mark with plenty of lead time to arrange private birding tours. **Wings** (☏*520/320–9868, 888/293–6443 in U.S. and Canada* ⊕*www.wingsbirds.com*) leads several weeklong tours each year to the mangroves and tropical forest around San Blas.

DOLPHIN ENCOUNTERS

Many folks find the idea of captive dolphins disturbing; others cherish the opportunity to interact with these intelligent creatures that communicate through body language as well as an audible code we humans have yet to decipher. Decide whether you support the idea of captive-dolphin encounters, and act accordingly. Listed below are operators with captive dolphin programs as well as one that has an open-ocean encounter. As these gregarious mammals are fond of bow-surfing, most bay-tripping boats will encounter dolphins as they motor along the bay, providing more opportunities to see dolphins as well as leaping manta rays and other sea life.

LOGISTICS   Dolphins are abundant in the bay year-round, though not 24/7. Dolphin encounters limit the number of humans per encounter, and usually allow just two visits a day, so call early in your stay to book.

OUTFITTERS   For both the Dolphin Encounter ($69) and the Dolphin Swim ($99)
★   with **Dolphin Discovery** (⊠ *Sea Life Park, Carretera a Tepic, Km 155,*

Nuevo Vallarta ☎*322/297–0724)* you spend about 30 of the 45-minute experience in the water interacting with dolphins. In the Royal Dolphin Swim ($139), you still get only 30 minutes in the pool, but at a higher ratio of cetaceans to humans, you get more face time. Mexican-owned **Wildlife Connection** (✉*Calle Francia 140, Col. Versalles, Puerto Vallarta* ☎*322/225–3621* ⊕*www. wildlifeconnection.com*) uses two-motor skiffs equipped with listening equipment to find pods of dolphins in the wild blue sea. You can then jump in the water to swim with these beautiful creatures in their own environment. The most common destination is around the Marietas Islands. The cost is $65 per person for a four-hour tour, including travel time.

> **CAUTION**
>
> Several organizations, including Greenpeace, the Humane Society (U.S.), and the Whale and Dolphin Conservation Society have spoken out against captive dolphin encounters, asserting that some water parks get dolphins from restricted areas, and that the confined conditions at some parks put the dolphins' health at risk. Consider putting the $100-plus fee toward a snorkeling, whale-watching, or noncaptive dolphin encounter, where you can see marine life in its natural state.

HIKING

The coastal fringe and the hills behind Vallarta—with streams and rivers heading down from the mountains—are beautiful areas for exploring, but few tour operators have hiking and walking trips. If you plan an impromptu exploration, it's best to take along a local familiar with the area.

LOGISTICS Some of the biking tour operators (⇨*Biking, above)* will lead hiking outings as well, if you ask.

OUTFITTERS **Ecotours** (✉*Ignacio L. Vallarta 243, Col. E. Zapata* ☎*322/223–3130 or 322/222–6606* ⊕*www.ecotoursvallarta.com*) leads a very short hike (about one hour total hiking) or a three-hour hike around El Nogalito River with a pit stop at a rocky, waterfall-fed pool for a dip. En route to either you'll see a small number of birds, butterflies, and tropical plants.

Vallarta Adventures (✉*Paseo de las Palmas 39–A, Nuevo Vallarta* ☎*322/297–1212, 888/303–2653 in U.S. and Canada* ✉*Edifício Marina Golf, Local 13–C, Calle Mástil, Marina Vallarta* ☎*322/221–0657* ⊕*www.vallarta-adventures.com*) has an outdoor adventure tour combining a speedboat ride and mule trek with rappelling, hiking, and a partial canopy tour. Although hikes are generally led by knowledgeable naturalists, the emphasis is on physical activity rather than flora and fauna sightings. Participants must be 12 or over and 220 pounds or under.

TURTLE-WATCHING & REPATRIATION

Mexico has seven of the eight sea turtle species in the world. Three of those species live in and around Banderas Bay. The most prevalent is the olive ridley, or *golfina*. The fastest growing and earliest to mature of the Pacific Coast turtles, they are much more numerous than the Careyes and leatherbacks; the latter are the least frequently sighted. Researchers estimate there are 1 to 10 leatherbacks for every 1,000 olive ridleys in the Puerto Vallarta area. The tour companies listed offer educational programs combined with hands-on activities.

After the female turtle creates a nest in the sand, the eggs incubate for approximately 60 days. The babies must bust out of eggs and earth on their own, and with luck they will head for the ocean under cover of night. Birds, crabs, and other wild animals are relentless predators. For every 1,000 baby turtles born, only one survives to adulthood. Fortunately the average nest holds several hundred eggs. For every 1,000 baby turtles born, only one survives to adulthood.

LOGISTICS   Tours run from summer through late fall. Wear shoes or sandals that are comfortable for walking in the sand, bring a sweatshirt or light jacket, and plan to stay out late in the evening for most turtle repatriation programs, as that is when predators are less active. Most tours cost $46–$50 per person and last three to four hours.

OUTFITTERS   Learn about and interact with nature through **Ecotours** (✉ *Ignacio L. Vallarta 243, Col. E. Zapata* ☎ *322/223–3130 or 322/222–6606* ⊕ *www.ecotoursvallarta.com*), which offers three-hour turtle tours. Depending on the time of year, you may walk the beach searching for females depositing their eggs in the sand and help remove these eggs for safekeeping. Whether or not you find egg-laying females, there are always little turtles for releasing to the wild at the end of the evening. Tours are Monday through Saturday. Trained biologists from **Wildlife Connection** (✉ *Calle Francia 140, Col. Versalles, Puerto Vallarta* ☎ *322/225–3621* ⊕ *www.wildlifeconnection.com*) lead turtle repatriation programs. During the four-hour tours you'll drive ATVs to the beach to find and collect recently deposited eggs, if possible, and then blast over to Boca de Tomates Beach to liberate tiny turtles under the relative protection of darkness.

WHALE-WATCHING

Most of the boats on the bay, whether fishing boats or tour boats, also run whale-watching tours (December–mid-March). Some boats are equipped with hydrophones for listening to the whales' songs and carry trained marine biologists; others use the usual crew and simply look for signs of cetaceans. The species you're most likely to see are humpback and killer whales (a gray whale occasionally), false killer whales, and bottlenose, spinner, and pantropic spotted dolphins (yup, dolphins are whales, too!).

LOGISTICS   Whale-watching is only available December through mid-March. Prime breeding grounds are around the Marietas Islands. The larger boats leave from Marina Vallarta, but fishermen in villages like Corral del Risco, Mismaloya, Boca de Tomatlán, and even Yelapa and Las Animas can be hired for less formal, more intimate trips to look for whales. The larger boats are more likely to have radio equipment useful for communicating with others about the location of whale pods. Some outfitters offer a discount if you sign up online.

Ecotours (✉*Ignacio L. Vallarta 243, Col. E. Zapata* ☎*322/223–3130 or 322/222–6606* ⊕*www.ecotoursvallarta.com*) operates excursions aboard boats with hydrophones. After a brief lecture about cetacean ecosystems, board a boat at Punta de Mita for a three-hour tour. Tours are daily in season (mid-December–mid-March) and cost $74. **Sociedad Cooperativa de Servicios Turísticos** (✉*Av. El Anclote 1, Manz. 17, Nuevo Corral del Risco* ☎*329/291–6298* ⊕*www.prodigyweb.net.mx/cooperativapuntamita*) has whale-watching around the Marietas Islands ($115 for one to eight people). You search until whales are spotted, and then have a half-hour of viewing time before returning to dry land.

Vallarta Adventures (✉*Paseo de las Palmas 39–A, Nuevo Vallarta* ☎*322/297–1212, 888/303–2653 in U.S. and Canada* ✉*Edifício Marina Golf, Local 13–C, Calle Mástil, Marina Vallarta* ☎*322/221–0657* ⊕*www.vallarta-adventures.com*) has professional guides who assist you in spotting dolphins and whales as you snorkel, dive, or kayak around the Marietas Islands. Sailing trips for seeking cetaceans are also available ($68–$85). Professional biologists at **Wildlife Connection** (✉*Calle Francia 140, Col. Versalles, Puerto Vallarta* ☎*322/225–3621* ⊕*www.wildlifeconnection.com*) are dedicated to educating the public about area wildlife; the outfit gives tours in season ($74).

OTHER ADVENTURES

7

CRUISES

Daytime bay cruises generally begin with a quick jaunt to Los Arcos Underwater Preserve, off Mismaloya Beach. There's about a half hour for snorkeling or swimming—sometimes with legions of little jellyfish in addition to the turtles that feed on them. Cruises then proceed to Yelapa, Quimixto, or Playa las Ánimas, or to Islas Marietas for whale-watching (in winter), snorkeling, swimming, and lunch. Horseback riding might be available at an additional cost (about $15).

There are plenty of similar tours available; the following are among the most popular and professional.

LOGISTICS

Buy your ticket from licensed vendors at Parque Lázaro Cárdenas, just north of the Cuale River, along the boardwalk at Los Muertos Beach, and at sportfishing operators such as Master Baiters.

Prices are somewhat fluid; like car salespeople, the ticket sellers give discounts or jack up the price as they see fit. Full-day booze cruises cost about $45–$70 per person, including open bar, Continental breakfast, lunch, snorkeling, and/or kayaks. Dinner cruises cost $75–$80. Expect to pay a small port fee (less than $2) at the maritime pier in addition to the cost of the ticket.

OUTFITTERS

Cruceros Princesa (✉ *Terminal Marítima, Marina Vallarta* ☎ *322/224–4777*) has full-day trips to the beaches of southern Bahía de Banderas with snorkeling, beach time, and lunch. Daytime bay cruises generally go to Los Arcos, Yelapa, Quimixto, or Playa las Ánimas, as well as to Islas Marietas for half-day whale-watching

(in winter), snorkeling, swimming, and lunch. Most trips depart from the Terminal Marítima at around 9 AM; they return around mid-afternoon and cost about $37–$47. **Cruceros Santamaría** (✉ *Paseo de la Marina Sur 161, Interior 14, Las Palmas I Condominiums, Marina Vallarta* ☎ *322/221–2511* ⊕ *www.santamariacruises.com*) has two different full-day tours to Los Arcos and Las Ánimas with visits to either Quimixto or Yelapa. It also rents boats for large private parties. You can buy tickets from their office or booth vendors.

☺ A really-and-truly sailing vessel that has circumnavigated the world more than once, the *Marigalante* (✉ *Paseo Díaz Ordáz 770, Centro* ☎ *322/223–0309 or 322/223–1662* ⊕ *www.marigalante.com.mx*) has a pirate crew that keeps things hopping for preteens and even older kids with fun and games. The dinner cruise, with open bar and pre-Hispanic show, is geared for adults and has some bawdy pirate humor. Women who don't want to be "kidnapped" may prefer the day cruise or another operator.

★ **Vallarta Adventures** (✉ *Paseo de las Palmas 39–A, Nuevo Vallarta* ☎ *322/297–1212, 888/303–2653 in U.S. and Canada* ✉ *Edifício Marina Golf, Local 13-C, Calle Mástil, Marina Vallarta* ☎ *322/221–0657* ⊕ *www.vallarta-adventures.com*) has day or evening cruises to Caletas Beach, its exclusive domain. Although the day cruise can accommodate 150 passengers, there's plenty of room to spread out: boulder-bordered coves, sandy beaches, hammocks in the shade, and jungle trails ensure that you won't feel like a cow about to be branded "tourist." The Caletas by Day cruise includes snorkeling, kayaking, yoga, hiking, and lunch. The Rhythms of the Night evening cruise includes dinner on the beach and a show at the amphitheater. Most folks love the show—men and women dressed as voluptuous natives do a modern dance to dramatic lighting and music. Kids under 10 are not allowed.

WATER PARK

☺ Traditionally more popular with Mexican families than foreigners, **Sea Life Park** *(formerly Splash)* has added dolphin encounters *(⇨above)* to attract a wider audience. Kids love the place just as it was: They can still plummet down enormous waterslides, swim, and play on playground equipment and carnival rides. There are restaurants and bars; to take advantage of the three shows (birds, sea lions, and dophins), arrive by noon, as they're presented once only between then and 1:10 PM. ⊠*Carretera a Tepic, Km 155, Nuevo Vallarta* ☎*322/297–0724* 🎟*$12* ⊙*Daily 10–6.*

7

Culture

Huichol artisan

WORD OF MOUTH

"We lucked out because it was a festival week—the Virgin of Guadalupe. There were processions every night which were clearly not aimed at tourists."

—epi

"The most culture you can find [in PV] is to become friendly with local peoples."

—pschatz

IN THE 1950S, PUERTO VAL-LARTA was like an extended family: everyone knew everyone else. Most of the inhabitants were from related families who had come down from the mountain mining towns after the turn of the century. People sat in front of their houses in the evening, chatting; the action was in the street. Until the explosion of outside interest, most of PV's intellectual and artistic life has centered around traditional Mexican culture, which is synonymous with the Catholic religion. Today there are plenty of bars and nightclubs, but less live theater and music than locals would like. The fine arts scene, however, is thriving. Local and foreign artists are established and respected painters and sculptors, represented by PV's finest galleries. High season is the time to see these artists at their best, especially on Wednesday evenings, when everyone in town turns out for artWalk.

> **GET THE SCOOP**
>
> One of the best sources of information for upcoming events is *Bay Vallarta*, published twice a month. The free bilingual publication gets scooped up fast from hotels, restaurants, car rental agencies, and other places frequented by visitors.

ARCHITECTURE

La Iglesia de Nuestra Señora de Guadalupe (*Church of Our Lady of Guadalupe*) is dedicated to the patron saint of Mexico and of Puerto Vallarta. The holy mother's image, by Ignacio Ramírez, is the centerpiece of the cathedral's slender marble altarpiece. The brick bell tower is topped by a lacy-looking crown that replicates the one worn by Carlota, short-lived empress of Mexico. The wrought-iron crown toppled during an earthquake that shook this area of the Pacific Coast in October 1995, but was soon replaced with a fiberglass version, supported, as was the original, by a squadron of stone angels. ⊠ *Calle Hidalgo, Centro* ☎ *No phone* ⊘ *7:30* AM–8 PM.

THE ARTS

DANCE

Under the direction of Professor Carlos Enrique Barrios Limón at the Centro Cultural Cuale, **Grupo Folklorico Municipal Xiutla** (☎ *322/223–0095*) is a talented troupe of folkloric dancers. During the group's career of more than a decade, the 250 young people have performed at various venues around PV as well as elsewhere in Mexico, Canada, the United States, and Europe. Performances are sporadic and announced through the usual channels (*Bay Vallarta*, flyers, etc.).

PUBLIC HOLIDAYS

Post offices, government and private offices, and banks are closed on public holidays (ATMs are plentiful, however). On Labor Day even tourist-related businesses like restaurants may be closed, as they prefer to give all employees the day off with pay. Public holidays include:

January 1: Año Nuevo (New Year's Day)

February 5: Día de la Constitución (Constitution Day)

March 25: Aniversário de Benito Juárez (Juárez's Birthday)

May 1: Día del Trabajador (Labor Day)

September 15: Día de la Independencia (Independence Day)

November 20: Día de la Revolución Mexicana (Mexican Revolution Day)

FILM

Biblioteca Los Mangos (⊠*Av. Francisco Villa 1001, Col. Los Mangos* ☎*322/224–9966*) shows art films, musicals, and blockbusters. The current schedule is Friday at 7 PM and Saturday at 4 PM, but call to check showtimes; tickets are $1.50.

At different times throughout the year, movies of various genres are shown at an outdoor theater Friday at 7 PM at **Cine en el Cuale** (⊠*Centro Cultural Isla Río Cuale, east end of island, Río Cuale* ☎*322/223–0095*).

PV's original extravaganza for movie buffs and movie stars alike is the **Festival Internacional de Cine de Puerto Vallarta** (☎*322/223–0095* ⊕*cine-fest.pv.udg.mx*). Held during six days each March/April, the festival honors the best full-length feature film with a "golden iguana" award. Full-length, documentary, and short-subject films are shown around town at Cinépolis (about $4 each) or under the stars at Los Arcos Amphitheater; flyers all over town advertise the movies, or contact the movie houses directly (⇨*Chapter 6*). The public is invited to attend lectures and listen to discourses on local radio programs. In 2005, dozens of movies from Mexico, Argentina, Chile, Peru, Cuba, and elsewhere were shown.

Beginning in late November or early December, the public is welcome to see movies of many genres, at reasonable prices, during the six-day **Vallarta Film Festival** (☎*322/222–*

FOLKLORIC DANCE

Zapateado, the dancing characterized by rhythmical foot-stomping, is accompanied by *sones*, narrative, and up-tempo mariachi songs written specifically for the dances. Anywhere between 200 and 300 sones are known to exist, but the best-known is the *Jarabe Tapatío* (Mexican Hat Dance), whose dance includes the emblematic move of the male dancer putting his sombrero on the ground as a sign of respect to his female companion.

3593 or 322/222–3674 ⊕*www.vallartafilmfestival.com*). Films and seminars are held at the Cinemark Plaza Caracol (Plaza Caracol, Zona Hotelera ☎322/224–8927). Film industry types come to hobnob and honor each other with awards for best director, picture, cinematographer, and actor.

FINE ART

See Chapter 5 for art gallery descriptions and locations. An artist of worldwide renown, **Evelyn Boren** (✉*Casa Bugambilla, Calle Bouganvillea s/n, Sayulita* ☎*329/291–3095*) lives and works in Sayulita each winter. Represented by Galeria Café des Artistes and other Puerto Vallarta shops, Ms. Boren shares her colorful landscapes with the public each Wednesday afternoon between 1 and 4 (Nayarit time) December through April. Her house is on the beach just south of the plaza.

The late Manuel Lepe's 1981 mural depicting Puerto Vallarta as a fanciful seaside fishing and farming village is painted above the stairs on the second floor of the **Palácio Municipal** (✉*Av. Juárez, on Plaza de Armas, Centro* ☎*322/222–4565*), PV's city hall. Lepe is known for his blissful, primitive-style scenes of the city, filled with smiling angels. This one is rather tired, and the naïf work has been surpassed by his devotees. Still, Lepe is considered the father of PV naïf, and the mural is worth a quick look. The interior hallways surrounding the government building's central plaza sometimes host photography or fine art exhibitions. The tourism office is on the first floor. The Palácio is open weekdays 9–5.

An annual event since 1996, **Old Town artWalk** (☎*322/222–1982*) has expanded to 18 galleries. The galleries stay open late, usually offering an appetizer or snack as well as wine, beer, or soft drinks. Browse paintings, jewelry, ceramics, glass, and folk art while hobnobbing with some of PV's most respected artists. If you don't have a map, pick one up from one of the perennially participating galleries, which include Galería Arte Latinoamericano, Galería Corona, Galería 8 y Más, Galería Pacífico, Galería Uno, Galería Vallarta, and Leonardo Galerías *(⇨Chapter 5)*. This walk is held 6 PM–10 PM, from the last week of October until mid- or late-April.

MUSIC

Under the direction of Professor Carlos Enrique Barrios Limón, the 21-piece **Orquestra Vallarta** (☎*322/223–0095*) consists of local residents and a few "stringers": foreigners who come to Vallarta in winter. They have no set schedule but often play at **Auditorio CECATI** (*Centro de Capacitación Turística e Industrial* ✉*Calle Hidalgo 300, Centro* ☎*322/222–4910*). Tickets generally cost about $10 for adults, half that for kids.

Vallarta's *banda municipal* (☎*322/ 223–2500*) serenades its citizens Thursday and Sunday evenings between 6 and 7, sometimes a bit later. Couples dance around the main plaza to *cumbias* (a distinctive style

FLIGHT OF THE VOLADORES

A relatively new phenomenon on the malecón are performances by *los voladores de Papantla,* the Papantla "flyers" near Los Arcos. Dressed in exquisite costumes of red velveteen pants decorated with sequins, mirrors, embroidery, and fringe, five men climb a 30-meter (98-foot) pole. Four of them dive from the top of the platform as the leader "speaks" to them from the pinnacle with fife and drum. Held by a rope tied to one foot, the men wing around the pole exactly 13 times before landing on the ground. The total number of revolutions adds up to the ritualistically significant number of 52. Native to Veracruz State, this traditional performance is held Thursday and Sunday evenings at 6 PM and 8 PM in low season, and every hour on the hour from 6 PM to 9 PM in high season (December through April).

of popular Latin dance music that originated in Colombia), emanating from the central kiosk. Everyone's welcome to join in, and most of the dancers are just regular folks, both visitors and vallartenses, having some fun. Some days, however, the band plays *danzón,* a complicated, stylized box-step that originated in Cuba and is best left to those who know the steps.

THEATER

The small **Santa Barbara Theater** (⊠ *Olas Altas 351, Col. E. Zapata* ☎ *322/223–2048*) is the place to see English-language shows, mainly musicals, November through April. It's community theater, not high art, but the productions are fun. A four-course dinner and a show are usually $32; tickets for the show alone run about $18.

Inexpensive or free musical and theatrical events are often presented at **Centro Universitario de la Costa** (*CUC* ⊠ *Carretera a Ixtapa, Km 2.5, Ixtapa* ✦ *Outskirts of Ixtapa* ☎ *322/226–2263*). Performances include experimental and classical theater. Productions are in Spanish, but because they are very visual, they're enjoyable even if you don't speak the language. Check the principal newspapers *El Tribunal de la Bahía* and *Vallarta Opina* for upcoming events. Tickets are usually $5–$10.

CLASSES & WORKSHOPS

A good source of information for current classes is the bimonthly, free *Bay Vallarta,* which always lists a Web page or phone number for further information.

You can matriculate mid-session at the informal **Centro Cultural Río Cuale** (⊠ *East end of Isla Río Cuale, Centro* ☎ *322/223–0095*) for classes like painting, drawing, and acting for children and for adults. Most of the instructors speak some English, others are fluent.

English-speaking artist Alicia Buena gives ceramics and painting classes for individuals or groups at **Terra Noble** (⊠ *Av. Tulipanes 595,*

LIZ + RICHARD

The affair between Richard Burton and Elizabeth Taylor practically ignited tourism to PV, which was an idyllic beach town when the couple first visited in 1963. Taylor tagged along when Burton starred in *The Night of the Iguana*, shot in and around Mismaloya beach. The fiery Welsh actor purchased Casa Kimberley (on Calle Zaragoza, a few blocks behind the cathedral) for Liz's 32nd birthday and connected it to his home across the street with a pink-and-white "love bridge." Taylor's relationship with PV lasted longer than that with her fellow actor and two-time husband; she owned the house for 26 years and left most of her possessions behind when she sold it. Casa Kimberely later became a B&B; in 2007 litigation regarding ownership shut it—and tours of it—down.

Fracc. Lomas de Terra Noble, Col. 5 de Diciembre ☎*322/223–3530* ⊕*www.terranoble.com*). The cost is $55 per person for the 2- to 2½-hour class. To schedule, call Terra Noble two days before you'd like to attend a class.

MUSEUMS

Pre-Columbian figures and Indian artifacts are on display at the **Museo Arqueológico** *(Archeological Museum)*. There's a general explanation of Western Pacific cultures and shaft tombs, and abbreviated but attractive exhibits of Aztatlan and Purepecha cultures and the Spanish conquest. ✉ *Western tip of Isla Río Cuale, Centro* ☎*No phone* ✉*By donation* ⊗*Mon.–Sat. 10–7.*

CULTURAL CENTERS

The **Centro Cultural Cuale** (✉*East end of Isla Río Cuale, Aquiles Serdán 437, Int. 38, Centro* ☎*322/223–0095*) sells the work of local artists, has art and dance classes *(⇨Classes, below)*, and hosts cultural events. Cost of classes is nominal and cultural events are free. The free bimonthly *Bay Vallarta*, available at tourist-oriented shops, hotels, and restaurants, is the best source of information on current classes.

Biblioteca Los Mangos (✉*Av. Francisco Villa 1001, Col. Los Mangos* ☎*322/224–9966*) has lots of reasonably priced art classes *(⇨Classes and Workshops, above)*, and free or inexpensive monthly events, such as dance performances. Themed performances are scheduled around Day of the Dead, Christmas, Easter, and other holidays.

CULTURAL TOUR

Puerto Vallarta Tours (☎*866/217–9704* ⊕*www.puertovallartatours. net)* runs twice-weekly all-day guided bus tours from Puerto Vallarta to Tepic, Nayarit for sightseeing, shopping, and learning about the spiritually atuned culture of the Huichol Indians.

Philo's (✉ *Calle Delfin 15, La Cruz de Huanacaxtle* ☎ *329/295–5068*) is the unofficial cultural center of La Cruz, north of Bucerís. It has free yoga classes on Thursday at 9 AM. Spanish classes are Thursday and Saturday at noon for beginners and at 10:30 AM for intermediate speakers. Classes are free, but donations are greatly appreciated.

FESTIVALS & EVENTS

WINTER

FEBRUARY

The two-day **Festival de Música San Pancho** (*San Pancho Music Festival* ☎ *311/258–4135*) is an amalgam of the area's best local musicians. Some folks come down especially for the free jamboree, usually held in mid- to late February. Look for flyers around town that describe events and their venues. San Pancho is about 50 minutes north of downtown Puerto Vallarta.

Tours, hotel rooms, works of art, and dinner at participating restaurants are auctioned during the **Beneficio Annual Para la Biblioteca Los Mangos,** a benefit to support the city's only public library. Contact Ricardo Murrieta (☎ *322/224–9966*) for more information. *Charros* (cowboys) from all over Mexico compete in the **Campeonato Charro Nacional** (*National Charro Championship* ☎ *322/224–0001*) at Mojoneras. In addition to men's rope and riding tricks and the female competitors, there are mariachis, a parade, and exhibitions of charro-related art. Admission is $5–$10.

MARCH

Held for the first time in 2005, the **Perrotón** (*Dog Show* ☎ *322/223–2500*) hopes to become an annual event. In addition to lectures, there are contests (ugliest dog, dog and owner who most resemble each other, most beautiful dog, and exhibitions of agility and obedience).

SPRING

APRIL

★ The **International Film Festival of Puerto Vallarta** (⇨ *Film, above*) is a huge event that draws filmgoers from around the globe. Most of the events and ceremonies are for filmmakers, but the public can enjoy the art and blockbuster films shown during the weeklong event.

MAY

★ **Las Fiestas de Mayo** (*May Festivals* ☎ *322/223–2500*) is a traditional three-week fair with fireworks and regional crafts and foods that is

THE RICOS Y FAMOSOS

Three-hour **villa tours** (☎ *322/222–5466*), arranged by the International Friendship Club, get you inside the garden walls of some inspiring PV homes. Tours depart promptly at 11 AM (arrive by 10:30) from the Hotel Posada Río Cuale (Calle Aquiles Serdán 242) on Wednesday and Thursday mid-November through the end of April. The $35 fee benefits local charities.

more popular with locals than visitors. Here in Jalisco, no such festival would be complete without *charreadas* (rodeos) and cockfights. Restaurants lower their prices for two weeks at the beginning of low season during **Restaurant Week** (⇨ *"Mexico's Gourmet Town," in Chapter 3*), also known as the May Food Festival.

SUMMER

JUNE

June 1 is **Dí de la Marina** (☎ *322/224–2352*). Like other Mexican ports, PV celebrates Navy Day with free boat rides (inquire at the Terminal Marítima or the XII Zona Naval Militar, just to the south). Watch colorfully decorated boats depart from here to make offerings on the water to sailors lost at sea.

JULY AND AUGUST

During school vacations, **children's events** (☎ *322/223–2500*), like the release of baby marine turtles, are scheduled to educate, entertain, and heighten awareness of ecological issues.

Barra de Navidad celebrates its patron saint, **San Antonio de Padua,** the week preceding July 13 with religious parades, mass, street parties, and fireworks. **Cristo de los Brazos Caídos** is honored August 30–September 1 in much the same way as Saint Anthony.

FALL

SEPTEMBER

The **Celebration of Independence** is held on September 15 and 16, beginning on the evening of September 15 with the traditional *Grito de Dolores*. It translates as "Cry of Pain," but also references the town of Dolores Hidalgo, where the famous cry for freedom was uttered by priest Miguel Hidalgo. Late in the evening on September 15 there are mariachis, speeches, and other demonstrations of national pride. On September 16, witness parades and more charros on horseback along the length of the boardwalk.

NOVEMBER

FodorsChoice The **Festival Gourmet International**
★ is one of PV's biggest events (⇨ *"Mexico's Gourmet Town," in Chapter 3*). The **Vallarta Film Festival** (⇨ *Film, above*) is an opportunity to see great indie films.

THREE KINGS DAY

El Día de los Santos Reyes (January 6) was the traditional day of gift-giving in Latin America until Santa Claus invaded from the North (or North Pole, depending on your beliefs). Although many families now give gifts on Christmas or Christmas Eve, Three Kings Day is still an important family celebration. The children receive token "gifts of the Magi." Atole (a drink of finely ground rice or corn) or hot chocolate is served along with the *rosca de reyes,* a ring-shape cake. The person whose portion contains a tiny baby Jesus figurine must host a follow-up party on Candlemass, February 2.

CLOSE UP

On the Boardwalk

Fodor's Choice Puerto Vallarta's **malecón** is the Champs Élysées of PV—only shorter, warmer, and less expensive. Along the half-mile cement walkway bordering the sea, small groups of young studs check out their feminine counterparts, all in meticulously pulled-together casual clothes; cruise-ship passengers stretch their legs; and landlocked tourists take a walk before dinner. Even those who have lived here all their lives come out to watch the red sun sink into the gray-blue water beyond the bay. Every night and weekend is a parade. Vendors sell *agua de tuba,* a refreshing coconut-palm-heart drink. Empanada, corn-on-the-cob, and fried banana stands congregate near the Friendship Fountain and its trio of leaping bronze dolphins. Peddlers sell helium balloons and cotton candy. Clowns, magicians, and musicians entertain in the Los Arcos amphitheater.

Some of PV's most endearing art pieces are not in galleries, but here *en pleine aire.* Stretching along the seawalk is a series of bronze sculptures that are constantly touched, photographed, and climbed on. These nonstop caresses give a bright bronze luster to strategic body parts of "Neptune and the Nereid," a mermaid and her man. Higher up on its pedestal, Puerto Vallarta's well-known seahorse icon retains a more traditional (and dignified) patina.

The three mysterious figures that compose "In Search of Reason," by world-famous artist Sergio Bustamante, are just as otherworldly as the jewelry, painting, and statuettes sold in his three Vallarta shops. Look for the pillow-headed figures climbing a ladder to the sky. Across from Carlos O'Brien's restaurant, Ramiz Barquet's "Nostalgia" is an ode to the artist's reunion with the love of his life at this very spot. You can find more of Barquet's work at Galería Pacífico.

"Rotunda on the Sea," a wacky grouping of chair-people by Alejandro Colunga, is a good spot to sit and watch the sea and the swirl of people enjoying life, although around sunset, others waiting their turn make it hard to linger.

✉ *Extending south from Calle 31 de Octubre to Los Arcos outdoor amphitheater and the town square.*

8

NOVEMBER 28–DECEMBER 12

★ Puerto Vallarta's most important celebration of faith—and also one of the most elaborate spectacles of the year—is **Fiestas de la Virgin of Guadalupe** (☎ *322/223–2500*), designed to honor the Virgin of Guadalupe, the city's patron saint and the patroness of all Mexico. Exuberance fills the air as the end of November approaches and each participating business organizes its own procession. The most elaborate ones include allegorical floats and giant papier-mâché *matachines,* or dolls (for lack of a better word), and culminate in their own private mass. Throughout the afternoon and evening, groups snake down Calle Juárez between Woolworths and the Cathedral in Old Vallarta.

Overnight Excursions

Guadalajara

WORD OF MOUTH

"Downtown Guadalajara puts you in the heart of a living, breathing Mexican city. ... The maze of interlocking plazas, cathedrals, and major buildings which make up the Centro Histórico are a walker's and looker's mecca."

—ETee

"We would strongly recommend the San Blas jungle tour. Lots of fun and alligators."

–Gilles

EXCURSIONS FROM PUERTO VALLARTA

TOP REASONS TO GO

★ **Alchemic atmosphere:** San Blas's basic but charismatic attractions—beaches, markets, churches, and boat trips—combine like magic for a destination that's greater than the sum of its parts.

★ **Highland rambles:** Drop-dead-gorgeous hills and river valleys from Talpa to San Sebastián get you out into nature and away from coastal humidity.

★ **Amazing photography:** In the mountain towns, even amateur photographers can capture excellent small-town and nature shots.

★ **Palatable history:** Soak up Mexican history and culture in Guadalajara's churches, museums, and political murals.

★ **Getting the goods:** From megamalls to entire pre-Hispanic townships, Guadalajara has excellent housewares and handcrafts at great prices.

1 San Blas. Change happens slowly in San Blas, which has yet to experience a tourism boom. Cruise wide dirt streets on one-speed bikes, read books in the shade, dig your toes in the sand, and just enjoy life—one lazy day at a time. Blue mountains and green hills provide a beautiful backdrop.

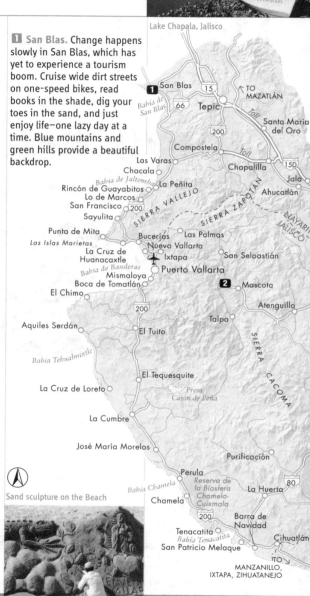

Sand sculpture on the Beach

2 The Mountain Towns. Former mining and supply towns **Talpa, Mascota,** and tiny **San Sebastián** were isolated for centuries by narrow roads and dangerous drop-offs and remain postcards of the past. Soak up the small-town atmosphere and alpine air.

3 Greater Guadalajara. Home to cherished archetypes like mariachi, charrería (elegant "rodeos"), and tequila, Guadalajara is often called "the Mexican's Mexico." The metropolitan area includes former farming community **Zapopan,** and two districts known for crafts: **Tlaquepaque** and neighboring **Tonalá.** Outside the city are unique archaeological digs at **Teuchitlán,** lakeside retreat **Chapala,** artists' and expats' enclave **Ajijic,** and **Tequila,** famous for . . . do we even need to say it?

GETTING ORIENTED

About 156 km (95 mi) north of PV, mountain-backed San Blas has beaches and birding. Inland 340 km (211 mi) or so from PV, Jalisco capital Guadalajara (pop. 4 million) sits in the Atemajac Valley, circled by Sierra Madre peaks. Sleepy mountain towns Talpa, Mascota, and San Sebastián lie about halfway between PV and Guadalajara; each offers a glimpse of rural life from centuries long gone.

9

Tonalá Ceramics

EXCURSION PLANNER

Coming and Going

If you plan to visit both Puerto Vallarta and Guadalajara, consider flying into one and out of the other. It costs little more than a round-trip ticket to either city. To do the trip one-way, go by bus ($32–$37), as drop-off charges for rental cars are steep. (Leave extra time if you're flying the same day.) Half-hour charter flights from PV offer painless access to the mountain towns, but then you've no car for sightseeing. The bus from PV is a long trip, but drivers are experts at navigating mountain roads, which are often in disrepair. Access to Mascota and Talpa from Guadalajara is shorter, more direct, and fully paved. The road from PV is sometimes impassable in rainy season. Buses take you directly from PV to San Blas, or you can get off at nearby beaches, but a car is handier for exploring the coast. The mostly two-lane PV–San Blas road is curvy but otherwise fine.

■ TIP→ **Most small towns that don't have official stations sell gas from a home or store. Ask around before heading out on the highway low on gas.**

Driving Times from PV

San Blas	3–3½ hours
San Sebastián	1¼–2 hours
Mascota	2½–3 hours
Talpa de Allende	3–3½ hours
Guadalajara	4½–5 hours

Day Trips versus Extended Stays

The San Blas area is best as an overnight unless you go with an organized tour (⇨ Tour Companies), though you could easily drive to Platanitos, south of San Blas, for a day at the beach.

If busing or driving to the mountain towns, plan to overnight unless you take the day tour with Vallarta Adventures. Alternately, you can fly on your own with **Aerotaxis de la Bahía** (☎ 322/221–1990) for a quick day trip or an overnight stay.

Guadalajara is too far to go for the day from Vallarta or San Blas, and at least two days is recommended.

How Much Can You Do?

What you can (physically) do and what you should do are very different things. To get the most out of your excursion from Puerto Vallarta, don't overdo it. It's a vacation—it's supposed to be fun, and possibly even relaxing! If you'll be in the Sayulita, San Francisco, and Chacala areas in Nayarit, it's easy to do an overnight jaunt up to San Blas, enjoying the myriad beaches and small towns as you travel up and back. Or make San Blas your base and explore from there.

You could also feasibly spend one night in San Blas and two in Guadalajara, about four hours driving and five hours by bus. For true nature and adventure junkies, two to three nights in the mountain towns gives you ample time to explore San Sebastián, Mascota, and Talpa as well as the surrounding countryside. Or you could spend one night in the mountains and continue to Guadalajara the next day. To fully appreciate Guadalajara, plan to spend at least two nights.

Tour Companies

Eco San Blas Safari (☏ 322/222–1922) leads all-day tours ($100 per person) Tuesday through Thursday from PV to San Blas with a boat trip to La Tovara. It's a full day, but at least you're not driving. Contact the **Cámera de Comercio** (Chamber of Commerce ✉ Av. Vallarta 4095, Zona Minerva, Guadalajara ☏ 33/ 3121–0378 or 33/3122–7701) for information about the all-day tour aboard the **Tequila Train**. The cost is about $70, including lunch, mariachi serenades, and tequila.

Highly recommended **Vallarta Adventures** (✉ Edifício Marina Golf, Local 13–C, Calle Mástil, Marina Vallarta, Puerto Vallarta ☏ 322/297–1212 or 322/ 221–0657, 888/303–2653 in U.S. and Canada ⊕ www.vallarta-adventures.com) has daily, seven-hour jeep tours to San Sebastín ($75). It also runs air trips to San Sebastián on Tuesday, Thursday and Saturday ($155) with occasional jaunts to Mascota and Talpa. On Monday is a flight to and day tour of San Blas ($255), followed by land trips to several other Nayarit villages, including the island Mexitlán, possible homeland of the Aztec empire.

With a day's notice, **Viajes Panoramex** (✉ Av. Federalismo Sur 944, Centro Histórico, Guadalajara ☏ 33/3810–5057 or 33/3810–5109 ⊕ www. panoramex.com.mx) has four- to five-hour tours to Tequila ($22), Chapala and Ajijic ($18), and the main sights of Guadalajara ($14) with time for shopping at Tlaquepaque at the end of the day.

While focusing mainly on vacation rentals, **Vista Travel Tours** (✉ Av. Olas Altas 250, Col. E. Zapata, Puerto Vallarta ☏ 866/256–2745 ⊕ www.vistatours. com.mx) also leads all-day trips to San Blas ($100) with a tour of the city and a motorboat ride into the mangroves to see the local fauna and flora.

When to Go

With its springlike climate, Guadalajara can be visited any time of year, though in winter pollution can cause raw throats, sore eyes, and sinus irritation. Book well in advance to visit during the October Festival or other holidays. Because roads can be dangerous during summer rains, June through October aren't the best time to visit Mascota and the mountain towns by land.

San Blas and the coast begin to heat up in May; during the late June through October rainy season both the ambient and ocean temps are highest. Make hotel reservations far in advance for Christmas, Easter, and the San Blas Festival (February 3).

FESTIVALS & SPECIAL EVENTS
Guadalajara's major events include a May cultural festival; suburb Tlaquepaque celebrates itself during the June ceramics festival.

The International Mariachi and Tequila Festival, in September, teams mariachi bands with the philharmonic orchestra.

Also in Guadalajara, the entire month of October is given up to mariachis, *charreadas* (rodeos), soccer matches, and theater; the blessed Virgin of Zapopan is feted the week preceding October 12.

In the Sierra Madre, Talpa's equally admired icon brings the faithful en masse four times a year for street dances and mariachi serenades.

At the San Blas Festival (February 3), a statue of the town's patron saint gets a boat ride around the bay.

9

SAN BLAS & ENVIRONS

The cool thing about San Blas and the surrounding beaches—if you like this sort of thing—is that they're untouristy and authentic. Sure, there's an expat community, but it's minuscule compared to that of Puerto Vallarta. Parts of San Blas itself are deliciously disheveled, or should we say, ungentrified. The lively square is a nice place to polish off an ice-cream cone and watch the world. If you're looking for organized activities and perfect English speakers, this isn't the place for you.

2–3 DAYS IN SAN BLAS & ENVIRONS

Most people come to the San Blas area for basic R&R, to enjoy the long beaches and seafood shanties. The town's sights can be seen in a day, but stay for a few days at least to catch up on your reading, visit the beaches, and savor the town as it deserves. La Tovara jungle cruise through the mangroves should not be missed.

LOGISTICS & TIPS
To really go native, rent a bike from Wala Wala Restaurant, a half block up from the plaza on Calle Juárez, and cruise to your heart's content. To get to the beaches south of town, to Matanchén Bay, and to the village of Santa Cruz, take a bus (they usually leave on the hour) from the bus station behind the church on the main plaza. To come back, just stand by the side of the road and flag down a passing bus.

Buses depart in the morning and again in the afternoon for Puerto Vallarta, and on the hour for Tepic, Nayarit's state capital. To get to Platanitos Beach, about an hour south of San Blas, take the Puerto Vallarta bus. ■TIP→ **Always check the return schedule with the driver when taking an out-of-town bus.** A car is handy for more extensive explorations of the coast between Puerto Vallarta and around San Blas. Within San Blas, the streets are wide, traffic is almost nonexistent, and with the exception of the streets immediately surrounding the main plaza, parking is easy.

SAN BLAS

Travelers come here looking for Old Mexico, or the "real Mexico," or the Mexico they remember from the 1960s. New Spain's first official Pacific port has experienced a long, slow slide into obscurity since losing out to better-equipped ports in the late 19th century. But there's something to be said for being a bit player rather than a superstar. Industrious but not overworked, residents of this drowsy seaside city hit the beaches on weekends and celebrate their good fortune during numerous saints' days and civic festivals. You can, too.

WHAT TO SEE

San Blas has a few fun places to visit, but don't expect to be bowled over.

Check out the outside of the chaste little **Templo de San Blas,** called *La Iglesia Vieja* (the Old Church) by residents, on the town's busy plaza. It's rarely open these days, nevertheless you can admire its diminutive beauty and look for the words to Henry Wadsworth Longfellow's poem

"The Bells of San Blas," inscribed on a brass plaque. (The long-gone bells were actually at the church dedicated to the Virgin of the Rosary, on Cerro de San Basilio.)

Browse for fruits or good photo-ops at the market, **Mercado José María** (⊠ *Calle H. Battalón de San Blas, between Calles Sonora and Sinaloa*), where you can take a load off at Chito's for a milkshake or fresh fruit juice.

> **CAUTION**
>
> The fierce biting *jejenes* (no-see-ums) of San Blas are legendary, but not everyone reacts to their sting.

The old **Aduana** (*Customs House* ⊠ *Calle Juárez, near Calle del Puerto*) has been partially restored and is now a cultural center with sporadic art or photography shows and theatrical productions.

For a bird's-eye view of town and the coast, hike or drive up Calle Juárez, the main drag, to Cerro de San Basilio. Cannons protect the ruined **Contaduría** (*Counting House* ⊠ *Cerro de San Basilio*), built during colonial times when San Blas was New Spain's first official port.

Continuing down the road from the Contaduría brings you to **El Templo de la Virgen del Rosario.** Note the new floor in the otherwise ruined structure; the governor's daughter didn't want to soil the hem of her gown when she married here in 2005. A bit farther on, San Blas's little cemetery is backed by the sea and the mountains.

WHERE TO STAY & EAT

$ ✕**Casa del Canibal.** How does grilled chicken served with mashed potatoes and big hunks of steamed broccoli sound? Or a big Caesar salad with garlic toast? There are also beef stroganoff, penne primavera, and a few other international dishes. The small bar, more popular with gringos than with locals, closes down by 9 or 10 PM. ⊠ *Calle Juárez 53* ☏ *323/285–1412* ▤ *No credit cards* ◷ *No lunch. Closed Mon. and Tues., and July–Sept.*

$ ✕**La Isla.** Shell lamps; pictures made entirely of scallops, bivalves, and starfish; shell-drenched chandeliers … every inch of wall space is decorated in different denizens of the sea. Service isn't particularly brisk (pretty much par for the course in laid-back San Blas), but the seafood, filet mignon, and fajitas are all quite good. Afterward stroll over to the main plaza a few blocks away. ⊠ *Calle Mercado s/n* ☏ *323/285–0407* ▤ *No credit cards* ◷ *Closed Mon.*

$$ ✕▦**Hotel Garza Canela.** Opened decades ago by a family of dedicated
★ bird-watchers, this meandering, three-story hotel with expansive grounds is the home base of choice for birding groups. Rooms have small balconies and polished limestone floors; junior suites have large whirlpool tubs. Betty Vasquez, who runs the French restaurant here, studied at Le Cordón Bleu in France; she prepares elegant and very tasty meals. ⊠ *Calle Paredes 106 Sur, San Blas 63740* ☏ *323/285–0112 or 323/285–0480* ⊕ *www.garzacanela.com* ⇆ *44 rooms, 6 suites* ♿ *In-room: no phone. In-hotel: restaurant, pool, no elevator, public Internet, parking (no fee)* ▤ *AE, MC, V* ⼝*EP.*

9

$ ⛬**Hacienda Flamingos.** Built in 1882, this restored mansion-turned-hotel was once part of a large hacienda. The restoration is stunning: surrounding a pretty, plant-filled courtyard is a covered veranda of lovely floor tiles, with lazily rotating ceiling fans, antique furniture, and groupings of chairs for a casual conversation. Opening off the veranda, elegant suites have also been restored to their original glory. It's amazingly lacking in guests given the low price. It's right across from the cultural center and near the market and town plaza. ⊠*Calle Juárez 105, San Blas63740* ☎*323/285–0485* ⊕*www.sanblas.com.mx* ⤙*20 rooms* ♿*In-room: cable TV, CD, DVD, no phone. In-hotel: pool, gym, no elevator, laundry facilities, parking (no fee)* ⊟*MC, V* ⏺*EP.*

¢ ⛬**Casa Roxanna.** This is an attractive little enclave of cozy, very clean (and painted yearly) cottages with screened windows. Full kitchens with lots of pots and pans invite cooking; lovingly tended gardens surround the lodgings, the covered patio, and the sparkling, three-lane lap pool. If you love it, settle in a while; monthly rates are usually available. ⊠*Callejón El Rey 1, San Blas, 63740* ☎*323/285–0573* ⊕*www.casaroxanna.com* ⤙*6 cottages* ♿*In-room: no phone, kitchen (some), refrigerator (some). In-hotel: pool, laundry facilities, parking (no fee), public Wi-Fi* ⊟*No credit cards* ⏺*EP.*

OUTDOOR ACTIVITIES & SPORTS

BOAT TOUR
★
☪
A series of narrow waterways wends through the mangroves to **La Tobara,** San Blas's most famous attraction. Turtles on logs, crocs that look like logs, birds, iguanas, and exotic orchids make this maze of mud-brown canals a magical place. Begin the tranquil ride ($10 per person; four-person minimum) at the El Conchal Bridge, at the entrance-exit to San Blas, or the village of Matanchén. Boats depart when there are enough customers, which isn't usually a problem. Either way you'll end up, after a 45-minute to 1-hour boat ride, at the freshwater pool fed by a natural spring. Rest at the snack shop overlooking the water or jump in using the rope swing, keeping an eye out for the allegedly benign resident croc. There's an optional trip to a crocodile farm.

ECOTOUR
Singayta (⊠*8 km [5 mi] from San Blas on road to Tepic* ☎*323/282–7019* ⊕*www.singayta.com*) is a typical Nayarit village that is attempting to support itself through simple and un-gimmicky ecotours. The basic tour includes a look around the town, where original adobe structures compete with more practical but less picturesque structures with corrugated tin roofs. Take a short guided hike through the surrounding jungle, and a boat ride around the estuary. Or rent mountain bikes ($3 per hour) or canoes ($5) to check out a broader area. This is primo birding territory. The easiest way to book a tour is to look for English-speaking Juan Bananas, who sells banana bread from a shop called Tumba de Yako (look for the sign on the unmarked road Av. Batallón

> **BEHIND THE MUSIC**
>
> If you're a fan of the rock group Maná, it's interesting to note that the song "Muelle de San Blas" ("San Blas's Wharf") refers to a tiny dock and a few wooden posts hosting friendly looking pelicans, just south of the Aduana.

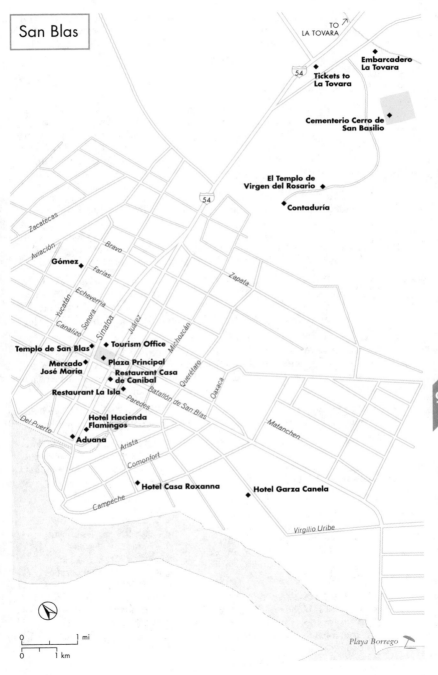

San Blas

TO
LA TOVARA

Embarcadero
La Tovara

54 Tickets to
La Tovara

Cementerio Cerro de
San Basilio

El Templo de
Virgen del Rosario

54

Contaduría

Zacatecas

Aviación

Bravo

Gómez Farías

Echeverria

Zapata

Yucatán

Canalizo Sonora Sinaloa

Juárez

Michoacán

Templo de San Blas Tourism Office

Mercado Plaza Principal
José María Restaurant Casa
de Canibal

Querétaro

Oaxaca

Restaurant La Isla

Paredes Batallón de San Blas

Del Puerto

Hotel Hacienda
Flamingos

Matanchen

9

Aduana Arista

Comonfort

Hotel Casa Roxanna Hotel Garza Canela

Campeche

Virgilio Uribe

0   1 mi
0   1 km

Playa Borrego

de San Blas, en route to Playa Borrego). He will set up the visit and guide you there. Otherwise, groups of five or more can call ahead to make a reservation with Juan or with Camilo Paz; call at least a day ahead if you want to have a meal.

THE BEACHES NEAR SAN BLAS

Like San Blas itself, the surrounding beaches attract mostly local people and travelers fleeing glitzier resort scenes. Beaches here are almost uniformly long, flat, and walkable, with light brown sand, moderate to largish waves, and seriously bothersome no-see-ums, especially around sunrise and sunset (and during the waxing and waning moons). Almost as ubiquitous as these biting bugs are simple *ramadas* (open-sided, palm-thatch-roof eateries) on the beach whose owners don't mind if you hang out all day, jumping in the ocean and then back in your shaded hammock to continue devouring John Grisham or leafing through magazines. Order a cold lemonade or a beer, or have a meal of fillet of fish, ceviche, or chips and guacamole. Don't expect a full menu, rather what's fresh and available. All these beaches are accessible by bus from San Blas's centrally located bus station.

Fodor's Choice
★
☾
You can walk or ride a bike to long, lovely **Playa Borrego,** just 1 km (½ mi) south of town. Rent a surfboard at Stoners' or Mar y Sol restaurant to attack the year-round (but sporadic) shore or jetty breaks there, or stroll down to the southern end to admire the lovely, palm-fringed estuary.

About 6 km (4 mi) south of Playa Borrego, at the northern edge of Bahía de Matanchén, **Playa Las Islitas** used to be legendary among surfers for its long wave, but this has diminished in recent years; the beach is now suitable for swimming, body surfing, and boogie boarding.

★ At the south end of the Matanchén Bay, **Playa Los Cocos and Playa Miramar** are both great for long walks and for hanging out at ramadas.

Adjacent to Miramar Beach is the well-kept fishing village of **Santa Cruz.** Take a walk on the beach or around the town; buy a soft drink, find the bakery and pick up some banana bread. Or, on a Saturday evening, head to the diminutive central plaza for the weekly dance.

★ Beyond Matanchén Bay the road heads inland and reemerges about 8 km (5 mi) later at **Playa Platanitos,** a lovely little beach in a sheltered cove. Fisherman park their skiffs here, and simple shacks cook up the catch of the day.

WHERE TO STAY & EAT

¢ ✕⊞ **Casa Mañana.** Some of the pleasant rooms overlook the beach from a balcony or terrace, but most people stay here for easy access to

---

BIRDER'S PARADISE

More than 500 species of birds settle in the San Blas area; 23 are endemic. Organize a birding tour through Hotel Garza Canela (⇨ *above*). In January, you can attend the **International Festival of Migratory Birds** for bird-watching tours and conferences with experts and fellow enthusiasts.

the good burgers, guacamole, and seafood platter for two ($14) at the adjoining **El Alebrije** restaurant. The bar, with its cool, brick-floor interior open to the beach, is also popular. Other perks: the long beach, large pool, and hiking and other outdoor activities. ⊠*South end of Playa Los Cocos, 13 km (8 mi) south of San Blas* ☎*323/254–9090* ⊕*www.casa-manana.com* ↪*26 rooms* ☐*In-hotel: restaurant, bar, pool, beachfront, parking (no fee)* ☐*MC, V* ⊙*EP.*

> **BEST BEACH BITE**
>
> For a marvelous albeit simple barbecue fish feast, visit **Enramada Ruiz,** a sinfully simple yet sublime seafood shanty on Playa Platanitos.

SAN BLAS & ENVIRONS ESSENTIALS

TRANSPORTATION

BY AIR If you want to head directly to San Blas from outside Mexico, fly to Tepic (via Mexico City or direct from Tijuana), 69 km (43 mi) from San Blas. But the majority of visitors going to PV start there, and road-trip up to San Blas. To get to San Blas from Tepic, Nayarit, head north on Highway 15D, then west on Highway 11. Mexicana de Aviación and Aeromexico do the Mexico City–Tepic route, while Avolar flies direct from Tijuana.

Contacts **AeroCalifornia** (☎800/237–6225 ⊕ www.aerocalifornia.com). **Aeromexico** (☎800/237–6639 in U.S. and Canada, 01800/021–4000 in Mexico ⊕ www.aeromexico.com). **Mexicana** (☎800/531–7921 in U.S., 866/281–3049 in Canada, 01800/502–2000 in Mexico ⊕ www.mexicana.com).

BY BUS The Puerto Vallarta bus station is less than 5 kilometers (a couple of miles) north of the PV airport; there are four daily departures for San Blas ($13; 4 hours). These buses generally don't stop, and they don't have bathrooms. Departure times vary throughout the year, but at this writing, there are no departures after 3 PM.

Contacts **Transportes Norte de Sonora** (☎323/285–0043 in San Blas, 322/290–0110 in Puerto Vallarta).

BY CAR From Puerto Vallarta, abandon Highway 200 just past Las Varas in favor of the coast road (follow the sign toward Zacualpan, where you must go around the main plaza to continue on the unsigned road. Ask locals "¿San Blas?", and they'll point you in the right direction). The distance of about 160 km (100 mi) takes 3½ to 4 hours.

From Guadalajara, you can take 15D (the toll road, about $40) to the Miramar turnoff to San Blas. It's actually much faster and less congested, however, to take Highway 15 at Tequepexpan and head west through Compostela on Highway 68 (toll about US$3); merge with Highway 200 until Las Varas, then head north on the coastal route (Highway 66) to San Blas.

BY TAXI A taxi from the Puerto Vallarta airport costs $50–$60; it's about $100 from Puerto Vallarta proper.

9

CONTACTS & RESOURCES
Hotlines **Police** (☎ *323/285–0221*).

Medical Center **Centro de Salud San Blas** (✉ *Calle H. Batallón at Calle Yucatán, San Blas* ☎ *323/285–0232*).

Pharmacies **Farmacia Económica** (✉ *Calle H. Batallón at Calle Mercado, San Blas* ☎ *323/285–0111*) closes between 2 and 4:30 PM and for the night at 9 PM.

Contacts **Banamex** (✉ *Calle Juárez 36, 1 block east of plaza, San Blas* ☎ *323/285–0031* ⊕ *www.banamex.com.mx*).

Post Office **Correos** (✉ *Corner of Calles Echevarrí and Sonora, San Blas* ☎ *323/285–0295*).

VISITOR
INFORMATION
In *la presidencia* (city hall), the fairly useless Oficina de Turismo de San Blas supposedly attends to visitors Monday through Friday 9 to 3, though they're rarely at their posts and rarely have staffers who speak English. Look for a booth with maps and info in the plaza across the street. The Web site **www.visitsanblas.com** is very helpful for planning.

Contacts **Oficina de Turismo de San Blas** (✉ *Calles Canalizo and Sinaloa in Municipal Palace, 2nd floor, on main plaza San Blas* ☎ *323/285–0221 or 323/285–0005*).

THE MOUNTAIN TOWNS

A trip into the Sierra Madre is an excellent way to escape the coastal heat and the hordes of vacationers. The Spanish arrived to extract ore from these mountains at the end of the 16th century; after the Mexican Revolution the mines were largely abandoned in favor of richer veins. The isolation of these tiny towns has kept them old-fashioned.

The air is crisp and clean and scented of pine, the valley and mountain views are spectacular, and the highland towns earthy, unassuming, and charming. Whitewashed adobe homes radiate from town plazas where old gents remember youthful exploits. Saturday night boys and girls court each other alfresco while oom-pah bands entertain their parents from the bandstand. Although most of the hotels in the region have only basic amenities (continued work on the road from PV is encouraging entrepreneurs, however), the chill mountain air and kilos of blankets can produce a delicious night's sleep.

1–2 DAYS IN THE MOUNTAIN TOWNS

Fodor'sChoice **Vallarta Adventures** (☎ *322/297–1212* ⊕ *www.vallarta-adventures.*
★ *com*) has excellent day tours to either San Sebastián or to Mascota and
🕒 Talpa. The small-plane ride provides a wonderful photo op and aerial introduction to the Sierra Madre.

If you're not joining an organized day tour, there are many possible itineraries, depending on whether you leave from PV or from Guadalajara, your tolerance for driving mountain roads, and your desire to explore (i.e., either to see lots or just relax and enjoy the tranquillity, mountain-and-valley views, and quaint lifestyle).

From Puerto Vallarta, consider a two-day trip to the area beginning in San Sebastián and returning to PV (or Guadalajara) from Talpa de Allende. There are many ways to go; keys are not driving at night and enjoying the slow pace. Drive to San Sebastian, enjoying the mountain scenery en route. After a look around the quaint old mining village and an early lunch, continue to Mascota, the area's largest town and a good base. Spend the night in Mascota or at the lodge on Lake Juanacatlán, which serves excellent food. Or visit Lake Juanacatlán as a day trip. If you prefer, take a day trip from Mascota to Talpa de Allende, whose raison d'être is the tiny, beloved Virgin statue in the town's ornate basilica.

Each of the three towns has hills to be climbed for excellent vistas and photos. Otherwise, activities include wandering the streets, visiting small museums and Catholic churches, tasting regional food, and drinking in the mountain air and old-fashioned ambience. Make sure you get where you're going before dark, as mountain roads are unlighted, narrow, and in many cases have sheer drop-offs.

LOGISTICS & TIPS

From Guadalajara to Talpa or Mascota, it's a scenic drive along a paved but serpentine mountain road. The route to San Sebastián (from Mascota) is part paved, part dirt. It takes about 1¼ hours when in good condition. From Puerto Vallarta (on a good day), it's a 1½- to 2-hour drive to San Sebastián, 2½ to Mascota, and about 3 to Talpa by car. The road is paved and finished as far as the turnoff to San Sebastian at La Estancia. A suspension bridge was inaugurated in early 2007 to cover the last 8 km (5 mi) of the road leading to San Sebastián and Mascota, which used to get washed out regularly in the rainy season. (Note: this road should still be avoided in the rainy season, when it becomes a heart-stopping narrow dirt track with gullies and drop-offs.) Lago Juanacatlán is an hour from Mascota on a rough one-lane road of dirt and rock.

9

SAN SEBASTIÁN

If, physically, there are only about 80 treacherous km (50 mi) between Puerto Vallarta and San Sebastián, metaphorically they're as far apart as the Earth and the moon. Sleepy San Sebastián is the Mayberry of Mexico, but a little less lively. It's the kind of place where you feel weird walking past people without saying hello, even though you don't know them from Adam. The miners that built the town have long gone, and more recently, younger folks are drifting away in search of opportunity. Most of the 800 or so people who have stayed seem perfectly content with life as it is, although rat-race dropouts and entrepreneurs are making their way here along improved roads.

WHAT TO SEE

The most interesting thing to see in San Sebastián is the town itself. Walk the cobblestone streets and handsome brick sidewalks, admiring the white-faced adobe structures surrounding the plaza. Take any side street and wander at will. Enjoy the enormous walnut trees lining the road into town, and diminutive peach trees peaking over garden walls.

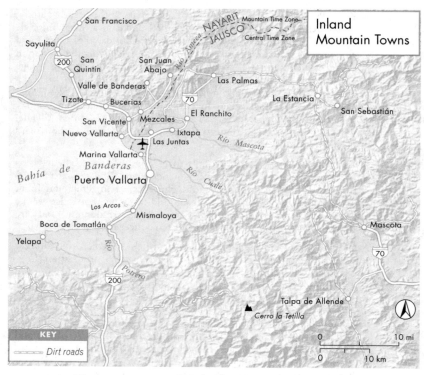

The reason to go to this cozy, lazy, beautiful town at 5,250 feet above sea level is to look inward, reflecting on life, or outward, greeting or chatting as best you can with those you meet. Look anywhere, in fact, except a laptop or if possible, a television screen. That's just missing the point.

San Sebastián has a few things to do, although none of them is the reason to visit.

Stop in the *abarrotes* (general store) on the north side of the square for a beverage or a spool of thread; then head directly behind it to **Iglesia de San Sebastián** a typically restored 1800s-era church that comes to life in the days preceding its saint's day, January 20.

You're welcome any time at the **Casa Museo de Doña Conchita** (⊠ *Calle Juárez 2* ☎ *322/297–2860* ☐ *$1*). The aged but affable lady loves to show visitors photos of her venerable family—which she traces back six generations. See bank notes from the mining days, bloomers, shirts made by hand by the lady for her many children, and other old memorabilia. If you speak Spanish, ask Doña Conchita to tell you about the ghosts that haunt her house, which is right on the square between the basketball court and *la presidencia,* or town hall.

WHERE TO STAY & EAT

¢–$ ✕**Fonda de Doña Lupita.** Typical food of the countryside—enchiladas, tamales, pozole, beefsteak with beans and tortillas, and so on—is served in an equally typical family home. The house has been enlarged to welcome guests, and the friendly owner does her part. Straw-bottom chairs are comfortable enough, and the oilcloths shiny and new. The small bar is at the back behind the large, open kitchen. It's open for breakfast, too. ⊠*Calle Cuauhtemoc 89* ☎*322/297–2803* ▭*No credit cards.*

> ### WARM CUPPA CORN?
>
> For an authentic experience, pop into any *fonda* or *lonchería* (simple eateries, the former usually in someone's home, the latter open for lunch only) for a typical *atole con piloncillo* (hot corn drink sweetened with unrefined brown sugar) and a simple meal. Some, like the **Fonda Doña Leo** (⊠*Calle Paso del Norte* ☎*322/297–2909*), down the street from the basketball court, don't even have signs out front.

$$ ⌂**La Galerita de San Sebastián.** A pair of displaced *tapatios* (Guadalajarans) have created a cluster of pretty cabins on their property about four blocks from the plaza. Lie on the comfortable futon (in each room) for a nap, or to view satellite TV on the small computer screen. The double-sided fireplace heats the bedroom and adjoining sitting room. Bed coverings and matching drapes of earthy, muted colors are all good quality. This is the most modern and stylish place to stay in San Sebastián, and is geared to adults. ⊠*Hacienda La Galería 62, Barrio La Otra Banda, San Sebastián46990* ☎*322/297–3040* ⊕*www.lagalerita.com.mx* ⇆*6 bungalows* ⌂*In-room: no a/c, no phone, refrigerator. In-hotel: restaurant, parking (no fee)* ▭*No credit cards* ⦿*EP.*

$ ⌂**Real de San Sebastián.** Small rooms are dominated by snug king beds in curtained alcoves in this interesting B&B. It has a (somewhat cramped) shared main living space with a cushy plush couch facing a large-screen satellite TV, and more formal round tables where afternoon coffee or hot chocolate is served. Take coffee and rolls in bed before emerging for a full breakfast in the dining room. The manager, Margarito, is friendly and solicitous. ⊠*Calle Zaragoza 41, San Sebastián46990* ☎*322/297–3223* ⊕*www.sanSebastiandeloeste.com* ⇆*6 rooms* ⌂*In-room: no a/c, no phone, no TV. In-hotel: restaurant, no elevator* ▭*No credit cards* ⦿*BP.*

OUTDOOR ACTIVITIES & SPORTS

Local men can be hired for a truck ride up to **La Bufa,** a half-dome visible from the town square. One such man is Obed Dueña (☎*322/297–2864*), who charges about $30 for the trip, whether for two or 16 people. It's the same price if you ride with him or hike back. The truck will wait while you climb—about 15 minutes to the top—and enjoy the wonderful view of the town, surrounding valleys, and, on a clear day, Puerto Vallarta. San Sebastián was founded as a silver-and-gold mining town; ask the driver to stop for a quick visit to a mine en route. The excursion takes about 3 hours all told. Or you can hike both ways; it takes most folks 2 to 2½ hours to reach the top, and half to two-thirds that time to return. Another great destination for a walk is **Hacienda**

9

Jalisco *(⇨above)*, a 15- to 20-minute walk from San Sebastián's plaza; ask the owner to show you around the property.

MASCOTA

Mascota's cool but sunny climate is perfect for growing citrus, avocados, nuts, wheat, corn, and other crops. Fed by the Mascota and Ameca rivers and many springs and year-round streams, the blue-green hills and valleys surrounding town are lusciously forested; beyond them rise indigo mountains to form a painterly tableau. This former mining town and municipal seat is home to some 13,000 people. Its banks, shops, and a hospital serve surrounding villages. On its coat of arms are a pine tree, deer, and rattlesnake. The town's name derives from the Nahuatl words for deer and snake.

WHAT TO SEE

★ Mascota's pride is **La Iglesia de la Preciosa Sangre** *(Church of the Precious Blood)*, started in 1909 but unfinished due to the revolution and the ensuing Cristero Revolt. Weddings, concerts, and plays are sometimes held here under the ruins of Gothic arches. Note the 3-D blood squirting from Jesus's wound in the chapel—you could hardly miss it.

Walk around the **plaza**, where old gents share stories and kids chase balloons. Couples dance the stately *danzón* on Thursday and Saturday evenings as the band plays in the wrought-iron bandstand. The town produces *huaraches* (woven leather sandals), ceramics, saddles, and *raicilla,* a relative of tequila.

On one corner of the plaza is the town's white-spire **Iglesia de la Virgen de los Dolores.** The Virgin of Sorrow is feted on September 15, which segues into Mexican Independence Day on the 16th.

A block beyond the other end of the plaza, the **Museo de Mascota** (✉ *Calle Morelos, near Calle Allende*) is worth a look. Open Monday through Saturday 10–2 and 4–8, the museum closes between 3 and 5.

Around the corner from the Mascota Museum, the **Casa de la Cultura** (✉ *Calle Allende 115*) has rotating exhibits of photography and art. It's open 10–2 and 4–7 Monday through Saturday.

WHERE TO STAY & EAT

$ ✕ **La Casa de Mi Abuela.** Everyone and his mother likes "Grandma's House," which is conveniently open all day (and evening), every day, starting at around 8 AM with breakfast. In addition to beans, rice, *carne asada,* and other recognizable Mexican food, there are backcountry recipes that are much less familiar to the average traveler. ✉ *Calle Corona, at Calle Zaragoza, Mascota* ☎ *No phone.*

MASCOTA'S MARTYR

In 1927, during the anti-clerical Cristero movement, Mascota's young priest refused to abandon his post. Soldiers peeled the skin from his hands and feet before forcing him to walk to a large oak tree, where he was hanged. Mascota's hero, José María Robles was canonized in 2000 by Pope John Paul II.

$$$$ ⊞**Sierra Lago.** An hour north of Mascota, this lodge of knotty pine is a tranquil lakeside retreat. Sail or kayak or just read a book in the steamy hot tub. Drinks are included, as are activities like fishing, horseback riding, and mountain biking. The clean mountain air is sure to give your appetite a boost; if he has time, the chef will cook up your freshly caught fish. ✉*Domicilio Conocido, Lago Juanacatlán* ☎*322/224–9350 or 877/845–5247* ⊕*www.sierralago.com* ➳*23 cabins* &*In-room: no phone, CD (some). In-hotel: restaurant, bar, tennis court, pool, bicycles, parking (no fee)* ▭*MC, V* ⟨○⟩*AI.*

$ ⊞**Mesón de Santa Elena.** Beautiful rooms in this converted 19th-century
★ house have lovely old tile floors, beige cotton drapes covering huge windows, rag-rolled walls, and wonderful tile floors and sinks. The dining room has old-fashioned cupboards and there are dining tables inside and out on two patios festooned with flowers and large potted plants. Second-floor rooms have views of fields and mountains to the west. ✉*Hidalgo 155, Mascota* ☎*388/386–0313* ⊕*www.mesondesan-taelena.com* ➳*10 rooms, 2 suites* &*In-room: no a/c, no phone, no TV. In-hotel: restaurant, no elevator, public Internet, public Wi-Fi* ▭*No credit cards* ⟨○⟩*AI, BP, EP.*

OUTDOOR ACTIVITIES & SPORTS

★ The beautiful countryside just outside town is ideal for hikes and drives. From Mascota's plaza you can walk up Calle Morelos out of town to **Cerro de la Cruz.** The hike to the summit takes about a half hour and rewards with great valley views. The newish **Presa Corinches,** a dam about 5 km (3 mi) south of town, has bass fishing, picnic spots (for cars and RVs), and a restaurant where locals go for fish feasts on holidays and weekend afternoons. To get to the dam, head east on Calle Juárez (a block south of the plaza) and follow the signs to the reservoir. Take a walk along the shore or set up a tent near the fringe of pine-oak forest coming down to meet the cool blue water, which is fine for swimming when the weather is warm. **Lago Juanacatlán** is a lovely lake in a volcanic crater at 7,000 feet above sea level. Nestled in the El Galope River valley, the pristine lake is surrounded by alpine woods, and the trip from Mascota past fields of flowers and self-sufficient *ranchos* is bucolic. Walk along the lakeshore or just enjoy it from the restaurant of the rusti-chic Sierra Lago lodge, where you can rent kayaks and small sailboats.

SHOPPING

Stores in town sell homemade preserves, locally grown coffee, raicilla (an alcoholic drink of undistilled agave), and sweets. A good place to shop for local products and produce is the **Mercado municipal** (✉*Calle P. Sánchez, at Hidalgo, 1 block west of plaza*).

TALPA DE ALLENDE

Another tranquil town surrounded by pine-oak forests, Talpa, as it's called, has just over 7,000 inhabitants but welcomes 4 million visitors a year. They come to pay homage or ask favors of the diminutive Virgen del Rosario de Talpa, Jalisco's most revered Virgin. Some people walk three days from Puerto Vallarta as penance or a sign of devotion; others come by car or truck but return annually to show their faith.

WHAT TO SEE

★ On the large town plaza, the **Basilica de Talpa** is the main show in town. The twin-spire limestone temple is Gothic with neoclassic elements. After visiting the diminutive, royally clad Virgin in her side chapel, stroll around the surrounding square. Shops and stalls sell sweets, miniature icons of the Virgin in every possible presentation, T-shirts, and other souvenirs. *Chicle* (gum) is harvested in the area, and you'll find small keepsakes in the shapes of shoes, flowers, and animals made of the (nonsticky) raw material.

HOLY CITY

During several major annual fiestas, the town swells with visitors. The Fiesta de la Candelaria culminates in Candlemass, February 2. The town's patron saint, St. Joseph, is honored March 19. May 12, September 10, September 19, and October 7 mark rituals devoted to the Virgin del Rosario de Talpa.

WHERE TO STAY & EAT

$ ✕ **Casa Grande.** This excellent steakhouse also serves grilled chicken and seafood. Under a roof but open on all sides and with an incredible view, it's highly recommended by visitors and locals. Lunch is served after 2 PM, and the kitchen stays open until 10:30. ⊠ *Calle Juárez 53, Talpa de Allende* ☎ *388/385–0709* ⊟ *MC, V* ⊙ *Closed Tues.*

¢ ✕▦ **Hacienda Jacarandas.** The charming, two-story building has high ceilings, wide corridors, and comfortable guest rooms with fine and folk art. Bougainvillea in shades of purple and pink climb up the cream-color exterior walls, and the rooftop terrace—with a terrific view—is a nice place to laze away a morning or afternoon, in the sun or under the covered portion. The 62-acre property has a small lake. ⊠ *Rancho Portrellos, just over bridge at southeast end of town, Talpa de Allende 48200* ☎ *333/447–7366* ⊕ *www.haciendajacarandas.com* ⇆ 6 *rooms* △ *In-hotel: restaurant, bar, pool, no elevator* ⊟ *No credit cards* ⊙ *Closed Easter–June* ℮ *BP, MAP.*

MOUNTAIN TOWNS ESSENTIALS

TRANSPORTATION

For an effortless excursion, go on a Vallarta Adventures day tour *(⇨ Overnight Excursions Planner).* For more flexibility or to spend the night in a cozy, no-frills hotel or a refurbished hacienda, fly on your own through Aerotaxis de la Bahía.

BY AIR Aerotaxis de la Bahía in PV has charter flights aboard twin-engine Cessnas to all three towns. For one to seven passengers the rate is about US$450 split among them to San Sebastián, US$465 to Mascota, and $510 to Talpa de Allende. Add to these fares 15% sales tax and US$20 per person air travelers' tax. ■TIP➔ **The return flight is free if you fly back with the pilot within three hours of arrival.**

Contact **Aerotaxis de la Bahia** (☎ *322/221–1990*).

BY BUS   ATM (Autotransportes Talpa–Mascota) buses depart from their bus station in PV (Calle Lucerna 128, Col. Versalles) three times a day at around 9 AM, 2:30, and 6 PM, stopping at La Estancia (11 km [7 mi] from San Sebastián; 1½ hours), then Mascota (2 to 2½ hours) and Talpa (3½ hours). Buses also depart several times a day from Guadalajara's new bus station (Entronque carretera libre a Zapotlanejo, Modules 3 and 4). Note that the bus does not enter San Sebastián; you can usually find a cab (or someone heading to town) for about $12, sharing the cab with others to split the cost. You'll be dropped at a small rest area at the side of the road, where local men in trucks or taxis usually are available to transport you to town.

Contact **Autotransportes Talpa–Mascota** (*ATM* ☎ *322/222–4816 in Puerto Vallarta, 388/386–0093 in Mascota, 388/385–0015 in Talpa, 33/3600–0588, 33/3600–0098 in Guadalajara*).

BY CAR   Mascota is 190 relatively carefree km (120 mi; 3 hours) from Guadalajara on a paved, two-lane but circuitous highway; it's about the same distance to Talpa. From Puerto Vallarta it's about 80 km (50 mi; 2½ hours) to San Sebastián, 1½ to Mascota, and an additional 30 minutes to Talpa.

BY TAXI   Taxis are easily found near the main square in Talpa, Mascota, and San Sebastián.

CONTACTS & RESOURCES

EMERGENCIES   For most problems in these small towns, seek assistance at the tourism office or la presidencia (the town hall). Medical services are available in Mascota's government-sponsored health clinic. If you get sick in Talpa or San Sebastián, ask for help at the pharmacy or town hall.

Pharmacies **Farmacia Estrella** (✉ *Calle 5 de Mayo, at Calle Ayuntamiento, Mascota* ☎ *388/386–0285*). **Farmacia del Oeste** (✉ *Calle Cuauhtemoc at Calle López Mateos, across from plaza, San Sebastián* ☎ *322/297–2833*). **Farmacia San Miguel** (✉ *Calle Independencia, at Calle Anahuac, across from square, Talpa* ☎ *388/385–0085*).

Medical Center **Centro de Salud de Mascota** (✉ *Calle Dávalos 70, Mascota* ☎ *388/386–0174*).

EXCHANGE SERVICES   There are banks with ATMs in Mascota and Talpa, but it's best to bring plenty of cash just in case; most businesses don't accept credit cards. San Sebastián has no bank, and businesses don't accept credit cards.

Contacts **Bancomer** (✉ *Calle Constitución at Calle Hidalgo, Mascota* ☎ *388/386–0387*). **Banco HSBC** (✉ *Calle Independencia, across from la presidencia [town hall], Talpa* ☎ *388/385–0197*).

INTERNET & MAIL   Mail any postcards or packages from Puerto Vallarta or Guadalajara. Mascota has an Internet café.

Contact **Cyber Center** (✉ *Calle Ayuntamiento, catercorner from plaza near Calle Constitución, Mascota*).

VISITOR INFORMATION   In small towns like these, the *presidencia* (town hall or mayor's office) is the place to get tourist information or to locate a specific service. Tourism offices are generally open weekdays 9–5, with a lunch closing around 1 (Mascota) or 3 (San Sebastián, Talpa), but hours tend to be flexible.

Contacts **Oficina de Turismo de Mascota** (⊠ *La Presidencia [Town Hall], Calle Ayuntamiento, at Calle Constitución, facing plaza, Mascota* ☎ *388/386–1179).* **Oficina de Turismo de San Sebastián** (⊠ *Calle López Mateos, around corner from la presidencia (town hall), San Sebastián* ☎ *322/297–2938).* **Oficina de Turismo de Talpa** (⊠ *La Presidencia (Town Hall), Calle Independencia s/n, 2 blocks north of plaza, Talpa de Allende* ☎ *388/385–0009 or 388/385–0287).*

THE GUADALAJARA REGION

Guadalajara rests on a mile-high plain of the Sierra Madre Occidental, surrounded on three sides by rugged hills and on the fourth by the spectacular Oblatos Canyon. Mexico's second largest city has a population of 4 million and is the capital of Jalisco State. This cosmopolitan if traditional and quintessentially Mexican city offers a range of activities. Shop for handicrafts, housewares, and especially fine ceramics in smart shops or family-owned factories. Dress up for drinks, dinner, and dancing in smart Zona Minerva, in downtown Guadalajara, or put on your comfy walking shoes to visit satellite neighborhoods of indigenous origin. For shoppers and metropolis lovers, this is a great complement to a Puerto Vallarta vacation.

An hour's drive in just about any direction from Guadalajara will bring you out of the fray and into the countryside. Due south is Lake Chapala, Mexico's largest natural lake. Bordering it are several villages with large expat communities, including Chapala and Ajijic, a village of bougainvillea and cobblestone roads. Tequila, where the famous firewater is brewed, is northwest of Guadalajara. Teuchitlán, south of Tequila, has the Guachimontones ruins. The placid lakeside area makes for a weeklong (expats would say lifelong) getaway, while Tequila and Teuchitlán are great for day-trippers.

2–3 DAYS IN THE GUADALAJARA REGION

The four primary municipalities of metropolitan Guadalajara are Guadalajara, Zapopan, Tlaquepaque, and Tonalá. With the exception of Zapopan, they can each be navigated on foot in a few hours, though each deserves at least half a day. Zapopan requires more time since it's a sprawling suburb with lots of shopping. Due west of Guadalajara's Centro Histórico, Zona Minerva is the place to go for great restaurants and after-dark action. Plan on a third day if you want to visit outlying areas like Lake Chapala and Teuchitlán.

On the morning of Day 1, visit historic Guadalajara, checking out the cathedral and other landmarks on the interconnecting plazas. Enormous Mercado Libertad (aka Mercado San Juan de Dios) is several long blocks east of Plaza Fundadores, or take the subway two blocks south of the cathedral on Avenida Juárez. If it's Sunday, see a charreada; otherwise head to Zapopan to see the basilica, the Huichol Museum, and the Art Museum of Zapopan, and spend 15 minutes at *la presidencia municipal* (city hall) to admire the leftist-theme mural inside. If you have more time, check out the market, two blocks west at Calles Eva Briseño and Hidalgo, and a couple of surrounding churches before grabbing a drink or a bite on Paseo Teopinztle, two blocks south. Freshen up at your hotel, then dine in downtown Guadalajara or the Zona Minerva.

Spend the second day shopping and visiting churches and museums in the old towns of Tonalá and in more compact, walkable Tlaquepaque. If you're here on Thursday or Sunday, don't miss the Tonalá crafts market, with its super deals. El Parián in Tlaquepaque is a great place to enjoy a mariachi serenade with a cool refreshment. Have Mexican food for lunch or dinner in one of Tlaquepaque's charming restaurants. If you don't want to shop, consider spending the day hiking in Barranca de Oblatos or visiting the playground, park, and gardens at Parque Azul. Arrive in the morning to avoid crowds; leave before dark.

If you've got three days in Guadalajara, you'll have time to visit Tequila or Lake Chapala. It's a refreshing change to get out of the city and admire the relatively dry hills and valleys, noting the fields of blue agave that are Tequila's reason for being. Tequila is en route to San Blas and Puerto Vallarta. Lake Chapala and the towns on the shore work well as a day excursion if you have a car.

LOGISTICS & TIPS — Allot a minimum of three hours for the Centro Histórico, longer if you really want to enjoy the sculptures and street scene. Mornings are generally the least crowded time of day, although the light is particularly beautiful in the afternoons when jugglers, street musicians, and other informal entertainers tend to emerge.

Beware of heavy traffic and *topes* (speed bumps). Traffic circles are common at busy intersections.

Tonalá's crafts market and Mercado Libertad are the region's top two marketplaces. Allot yourself plenty of time and energy to explore both. El Trocadero is a weekly antiques market at the north end of Avenida Chapultepec. Feel free to drive a hard bargain at all three.

9

GUADALAJARA

Metropolitan Guadalajara's sights are divided into four major areas: Guadalajara, Zapopan, Tlaquepaque, and Tonalá. Within Guadalajara are many districts and neighborhoods. Of most interest to visitors is the Centro Histórico (Historic District), a rather small section of town that's part of the larger downtown area (El Centro). Outside the Centro Histórico, Guadalajara resembles any large, sometimes polluted city with gnarly traffic. On the west side are Zona Minerva, the most modern section of the city and the place to go for dining, dancing, shopping in large malls, and high-rise hotels. The Centro Histórico, Tlaquepaque, and Tonalá can each be navigated on foot in a few hours, though they deserve at least half a day. Zapopan's high-end hotels, bars, shops, and cafés are spread out, but historic Zapopan is reasonably compact. Likewise, Tonalá is a lot more spread out than more tourist-oriented, walkable Tlaquepaque.

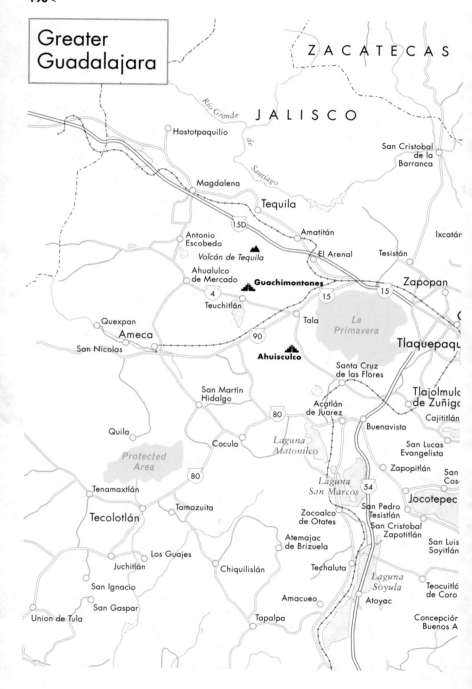

Greater Guadalajara

Z A C A T E C A S

J A L I S C O

Río Grande

Hostotpaquilio

San Cristobal
de la
Barranca

de

Santiago

Magdalena

Tequila

15D

Amatitán

Ixcatán

Antonio
Escobedo

Volcán de Tequila

El Arenal

Tesistán

Ahualulco
de Mercado

Guachimontones

Zapopan

4

15

15

Teuchitlán

Tala

La
Primavera

Quexpan

Ameca

90

Ahuisculco

Tlaquepaqu

San Nicolas

Santa Cruz
de las Flores

Tlajolmulc
de Zuñig

San Martín
Hidalgo

Acatlán
de Juarez

Cajititlán

80

Quila

Buenavista

San Lucas
Evangelista

*Laguna
Atotonilco*

Cocula

Zapopitlán

San
Cos

*Protected
Area*

*Laguna
San Marcos*

54

Jocotepec

Tenamaxtlán

Tamazuita

Zocoalco
de Otates

San Pedro
Tesistlán

Tecolotlán

San Cristobal
Zapotitlán

San Luis
Soyitlán

Atemajac
de Brizuela

Juchitlán

Los Guajes

Chiquilislán

Techaluta

*Laguna
Soyula*

Teocuitlá
de Coro

San Ignacio

Amacueo

Atoyac

San Gaspar

Union de Tula

Tapalpa

Concepciór
Buenos A

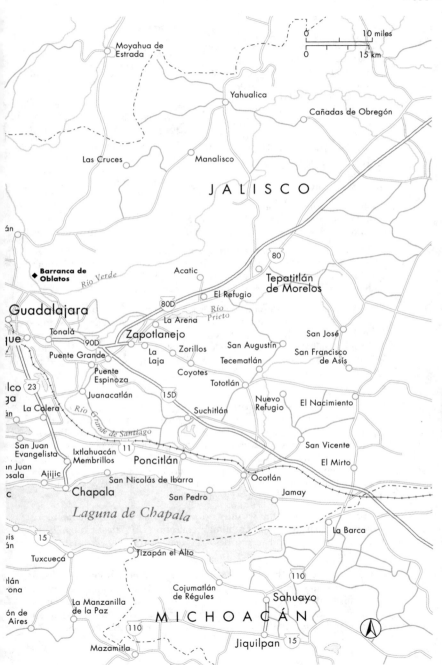

CITY TOURS

With a day's notice, take a free, three-hour **artisan-studio walking tour** (☎*33/3284–3092 or 33/3284– 3093*) given by the Tonalá Municipal Tourist Office. Tours depart daily (except Sunday and Thursday) at 10 AM from the Casa de los Artesanos (⊠*Av. Tonalteca Sur 140, between Calles Matamoros and 16 de Septiembre, Tonalá* ☎*33/3284–3092*). Ten guests or more can request an English-speaking guide by prior arrangement.

HORSING AROUND

Calandrias (horse-drawn carriages) take in the sights of the Centro Histórico; it's $20 for a long tour and $12 for a short one. Tapatío Tour, an open-top, double-decker bus, loops Zona Rosa ($9; daily 10 AM–8 PM). Get on and off as much as you like to explore the sights. The bus departs from the Rotunda, a plaza on the Cathedral's north side.

Viajes Panoramex has a five-hour **historic and cultural tour** (☎*33/3810–5057 or 33/3810–5005* ⊕*www. panoramex.com.mx*) that ends up in Tlaquepaque for some shopping.

You can hire a **horse-drawn carriage,** or *calandria* in front of the Museo Regional, the Mercado Libertad, or Parque San Francisco. It's about $15 for a shorter tour for up to five; $20 for an hour. Few drivers speak English. There are no reservations, just show up.

A free, 2½-hour **walking tour** (☎*33/3616–9150 or 33/3615–1182* ⊕*http://vive.guadalajara.gob.mx*) is given by the Guadalajara Municipal Tourism Office every weekend, starting at 10 AM at the Palacio Municipal Palace (English guide available with advance reservation only). Saturday evenings at 7 there's a 1½-hour tour accompanied by mariachis or minstrels.

WHAT TO SEE

EL CENTRO & THE CENTRO HISTÓRICO

Guadalajara's historical center is a blend of modern and old buildings connected by a series of large plazas radiating from the Cathedral. Many colonial-era structures were razed; others stand crumbling, as there's no money for restoration. But overall there are many colonial- and Republican-era buildings with impressive carved limestone facades, tiled steeples and domes, magnificent wooden doors, and wrought-iron grills. The surrounding parks, plazas, and fountains have Corinthian columns and a great sense of community.

For a taste of how the wealthy once lived, visit the **Casa-Museo López Portillo,** a mansion with a stunning collection of 17th- through 20th- century furniture and accessories. ⊠*Calle Liceo 177, Centro Histórico* ☎*33/3613–2411* 💲*Free* 🕙*Tues.–Sat. 10–6, Sun. 10–5.*

★ Construction was begun in 1561 on the **Catedral,** a downtown focal point and an intriguing mélange of Baroque, Gothic, and other styles. Exquisite altarpieces line the walls. In a loft above the main entrance is a magnificent late-19th-century French organ. ⊠*Av. Alcalde, between Av. Hidalgo and Calle Morelos, Centro Histórico* 🕙*Daily 8–8.*

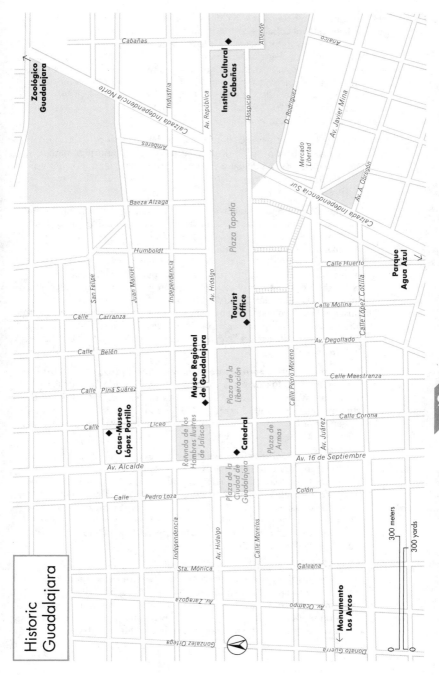

Historic Guadalajara

Zoológico Guadalajara

Cabañas

Instituto Cultural Cabañas

Allende

Hospicio

D. Rodríguez

Analco

Av. Javier Mina

Av. A. Obregón

Mercado Libertad

Calzada Independencia Sur

Industria

Calzada Independencia Norte

Av. República

Amberes

Baeza Atzaga

Plaza Tapatía

Humboldt

Calle Huerto

Parque Agua Azul

San Felipe

Juan Manuel

Independencia

Av. Hidalgo

Tourist Office

Calle Molina

Calle López Cotilla

Calle Carranza

Av. Degollado

Calle Belén

Museo Regional de Guadalajara

Plaza de la Liberación

Calle Maestranza

Calle Pedro Moreno

Calle Piña Suárez

Calle Corona

Casa-Museo López Portillo

Liceo

Rotunda de los Hombres Ilustres de Jalisco

Catedral

Plaza de Armas

Av. Juárez

Calle

Av. 16 de Septiembre

Av. Alcalde

Plaza de la Ciudad de Guadalajara

Calle Pedro Loza

Colón

Independencia

Av. Hidalgo

Calle Morelos

300 meters

300 yards

Sta. Mónica

Galeana

Av. Zaragoza

Monumento Los Arcos

Av. Ocampo

Gonzalez Ortega

Donato Guerra

0

0

9

FodorśChoice　Originally a shelter for the elderly and orphans, the neoclassical-style
★　**Instituto Cultural Cabañas** has 106 rooms and 23 flower-filled patios that
☾　now house art exhibitions. Kids love the murals by Orozco, as well as
his smaller paintings and cartoons and the labyrinthine compound in
general. Large-scale theater, dance, and musical performances occasionally take place on a patio here. The Tolsá Chapel hosts more intimate events. ✉*Calle Cabañas 8, Centro Histórico* ☎*33/3668–1647*
✉*$1; free Sun.* ☾*Tues.–Sat. 10:30–5:30, Sun. 10:15–2:30; occasionally closed for maintenance.*

★　Artifacts from prehistoric times through the Spanish conquest and an
impressive collection of European and Mexican paintings make the
Museo Regional de Guadalajara, a grand former seminary, worth a visit.
✉*Calle Liceo 60, Centro Histórico* ☎*33/3614–5257* ✉*$3; free Sun.*
☾*Tues.–Sun. 9–5:45.*

☾　Popular **Parque Agua Azul** has playgrounds, caged birds, an orchid
house, and acres of trees and grass crisscrossed by walking paths. There
aren't many butterflies in the huge, geodesic butterfly sanctuary, but the
semitropical garden inside still merits a visit. The Museo de la Paleontología (✉*Av. Dr. R. Michel 520, Centro Histórico* ☎*33/3619–7043*),
on the park's east side, has plant and animal fossils as well as exhibits on the origin of the planet. Admission is 70¢, and the museum is
open Tuesday through Saturday 10–6 and Sunday 11–6. (There's no
museum entrance inside Agua Azul; you must walk to the park's north
side.) ✉*Calz. Independencia Sur, between González Gallo and Las
Palmas, south of Centro Histórico, El Centro* ☎*33/3619–0333* ✉*40¢*
☾*Daily 10–6.*

North of El Centro, **Barranca de Oblatos** is a multipronged, 2,000-foot-
deep ravine with hiking trails and the narrow Cascada Cola de Caballo
(Horsetail Waterfall), named for its horsetail shape. A portion of the
canyon complex, called Barranca de Huetitán (Huetitán Canyon), has
a steep, winding, 5-km (3-mi) trail to the river below. The trails are less
strenuous at the Barranca de Oblatos entrance.

☾　The city's zoo, **Zoológico Guadalajara,** on the edge of the jagged Barranca
de Huetitán, has more than 1,500 animals representing 360 species.
There are two aviaries, a kids' zoo, and a herpetarium with 130 species of reptiles, amphibians, and fish. For 50¢ you can take a train tour
of the grounds. Admission to the adjacent amusement park is $1.30.
✉*Paseo del Zoológico 600, off Calz. Independencia, Zona Huentitán* ✛*North of town near Barranca de Oblatos* ☎*33/3674–4488*
✉*$3.50* ☾*Wed.–Sun. 10–5.*

TLAQUEPAQUE　Another ancient pueblo that's gone upscale is crafts-crazy Tlaquepaque.
Fabulous shopping for fine ceramics coupled with the attractive town's
compact size make it appealing to Guadalajarans and visitors. Along
its cobblestone streets are a wealth of mansions converted to shops and
restaurants. B&Bs with jungly gardens, warming fires, and reasonable
prices easily convince many travelers to make this their base.

LIVE PERFORMANCE

The State Band of Jalisco and the Municipal Band sometimes play at the bandstand on Tuesday around 6:30 PM. Small, triangular Plaza de los Mariachis, south of the Mercado Libertad, was once the ideal place to tip up a beer and experience mariachi, the most Mexican of music, at about $15 a pop. Now boxed in by a busy street, a market, and a run-down neighborhood, it's safest to visit in the day or early evening. For less money and a more tourist-friendly atmosphere, mariachis at El Parián, in Tlaquepaque, will treat you to a song or two as you sip margaritas at this enormous, partly covered conglomeration of 17 cantinas diagonal from the town's main plaza. Once a marketplace dating from 1883, it has traditional *cazuela* drinks, which are made of fruit and tequila and served in ceramic pots.

The internationally acclaimed **Ballet Folclórico of the University of Guadalajara** (☎ *33/3614–4773 or 33/3616–4991* ⊕ *www.ballet.udg.mx*) performs traditional Mexican folkloric dances and music in the Teatro Degollado most Sundays at 10 AM; tickets are $3–$25. The state-funded **Orquesta Filarmónica de Jalisco** (*Philharmonic Orchestra of Jalisco* ☎ *33/3658–3812 or 33/3658–3819* ⊕ *www.ofj.com.mx*) performs pieces by Mexican composers mixed with standard orchestral fare. When in season (it varies), the OFJ performs Sunday at 12:30 PM and Friday at 8:30 PM; tickets are $6–$20.

Ask your concierge or the tourism office about other performances around town, or check the newspaper.

Fodor's Choice ★ On display at the **Museo del Premio Nacional de la Cerámica Pantaleon Panduro** are prize-winning pieces from the museum's annual June ceramics competition. You can request an English-speaking guide at possibly the best collection of modern Mexican pottery anywhere. ⊠ *Calle Priciliano Sánchez at Calle Flórida, Tlaquepaque* ☎ *33/3562–7036* ⊠ *Free* ⊙ *Mon.–Sat. 10–6, Sun. 10–3.*

In a colonial mansion, the **Museo Regional de la Cerámica** has bilingual displays explaining common processes used by local ceramics artisans; presentation isn't always strong. ⊠ *Calle Independencia 37, Tlaquepaque* ☎ *33/3635–5404* ⊠ *Free* ⊙ *Mon.–Sat. 10–6, Sun. 10–3.*

ZAPOPAN Expanding over the years, Guadalajara's population of almost 4 million now encompasses pre-Hispanic towns, such as Zapopan. The country's former corn-producing capital, Zapopan is now a wealthy enclave of modern hotels and malls. Beyond, some farming communities remain, but the central district is now home to two remarkable museums and one of Mexico's most revered religious icons.

The vast **Basílica de la Virgen de Zapopan,** with an ornate plateresque facade and *mudéjar* (Moorish) tile dome is home to Our Lady of Zapopan: a 10-inch-high, corn-paste statue venerated for miraculous healings and answered prayers. Every October 12, more than a million people pack the streets around the basilica for an all-night fiesta capped by an early-morning procession. Don't miss the adjoining Huichol Museum (⇨ *below*), which has Huichol art for sale.

★ Better known by its initials, MAZ, the **Museo de Arte de Zapopan** is Guadalajara's top contemporary art gallery. It regularly holds expositions of distinguished Latin American painters, photographers, and sculptors. ⊠ *Andador 20 de Noviembre 166, Zapopan* ☎ *33/3818–2200* ⚏ *$2* ⊙ *Tues., Wed., Fri., and weekends 10* AM–6 PM*, Thurs. 10–10* PM.

★ The Huichol Indians are famed for their fierce independence, their use of peyote in religious ceremonies, and their exquisite bead and yarn mosaics (⇨ *"The Art of the Huichol," in Chapter 5*). At the **Museo Huichol Wixarica de Zapopan,** bilingual placards explain tribal history, and the museum exhibits many examples of the Huichols' unique artwork, some for sale. ⊠ *Av. Hidalgo, 152, Zona Zapopan Norte* ☎ *33/3636–4430* ⚏ *50¢* ⊙ *Mon.–Sat. 9:30–1:30 and 3:30–6, Sun. 10–2.*

WHERE TO EAT

Tapatíos love foreign food, but homegrown dishes won't ever lose their flavor. The trademark local dish is *torta ahogada,* literally a "drowned [pork] sandwich" soaked in tomato sauce and topped with onions and hot sauce. Other favorites are *carne en su jugo* (beef stew with bacon bits and beans), *birria* (hearty goat or lamb stew), and *pozole* (hominy and pork in tomato broth). Seafood is popular and is available in trendy restaurants as well as at stands. The best Mexican food is near the main attractions downtown. The most popular non-Mexican restaurants are scattered about western Guadalajara, in Zona Minerva.

CENTRO | ✕ **La Fonda de San Miguel.** Located in a former convent, La Fonda is
HISTÓRICO | perhaps the Centro's most exceptional eatery. Innovative Mexican eats
$–$$ | are presented in a soaring courtyard centered around a stone fountain
★ | and hung with a spectacular array of shining tin stars and folk art from Tlaquepaque and Tonalá. Relish the freshly made tortillas with the *molcajete,* a steaming stew of seafood or beef that comes in a three-legged stone mortar (the molcajete). ⊠ *Donato Guerra 25, Centro Histórico* ☎ *33/3613–0809* ⊟ *AE, MC, V* ⊙ *No dinner in June.*

¢–$ | ✕ **Tacos Providencia del Centro.** This is the place for traditional Guadalajara street-stand fare. Tacos *al pastor* top the clean restaurant's menu, and they come with every possible filling, including *trompa* (pig snout). Quesadillas and *gringas* (tortillas filled with cheese and meat) are also available. ⊠ *Calle Morelos 84-A, at Plaza Tapatía, Centro Histórico* ☎ *33/3613–9914* ⊟ *No credit cards.*

TLAQUEPAQUE | ✕ **Casa Fuerte.** Relax with tasty Mexican dishes at the tables along the
$–$$ | sidewalk or under the palms and by the fountain in the patio. Try
★ | the house specialties: chicken stuffed with *huitlacoche* (a corn fungus that's Mexico's answer to the truffle) and shrimp in tamarind sauce. Live mariachi or trio music accompanies lunch hours every day except Monday. ⊠ *Calle Independencia 224, Tlaquepaque* ☎ *33/3639–6481* ⊟ *AE, MC, V.*

Continued on page 210

MARIACHI: BORN IN JALISCO

By Sean Mattson

It's 4 AM and you're sound asleep somewhere in Mexico. Suddenly you're jolted awake by trumpets blasting in rapid succession. Before you can mutter a groggy protest, ten men with booming voices break into song. Nearby, a woman stirs from her slumber. The man who brought her the serenade peeks toward her window from behind the lead singer's sombrero, hoping his sign of devotion is appreciated—and doesn't launch his girlfriend's father into a shoe-throwing fury.

At the heart of Mexican popular culture, mariachi is the music of love and heartache, of the daily travails of life, and nationalistic pride. This soundtrack of Mexican tradition was born in the same region as tequila, the Mexican hat dance, and *charrería* (Mexican rodeo), whose culture largely defines Mexican chivalry and machismo.

Today, mariachi bands are the life of the party. They perform at weddings, birthdays, public festivals, restaurants, and city plazas. The most famous bands perform across the globe. Guadalajara's annual mariachi festival draws mariachis from around the world.

The origin of the word *mariachi* is a source of some controversy. The legend is that it evolved from the French word *mariage* (marriage), stemming from the French occupation in the mid-1800s. But leading mariachi historians now debunk that myth, citing evidence that the word has its origins in the Nahuatl language of the Coca Indians.

THE RISE OF MARIACHI

Historians trace the roots of mariachi to Cocula, a small agricultural town south of Guadalajara. There, in the 17th century, Franciscan monks trained the local indigenous populations in the use of stringed instruments, teaching them the religious songs to help win their conversion.

The aristocracy, who preferred the more refined contemporary European music, held early mariachi groups in disdain. But by the late 19th century, mariachi had become enormously popular among peasants and indigenous people in Cocula, eventually spreading throughout southern Jalisco and into neighboring states.

MODERN MARIACHI INSTRUMENTS

Traditional mariachi groups consisted of two violins (the melody), and a vihuela and guitarrón (the harmony). Some long-gone groups used a *tambor* or drum, not used in modern mariachi. All members of the group shared singing responsibilities.

TRUMPETS
Added to the traditional mariachi lineup in the 1930s when mariachis hit the big screen, at the insistence of a pioneer in Mexican radio and television

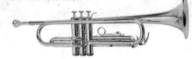

VIOLINS
Essential to any mariachi group

THE FOLK HARP
Longstanding mariachi instrument, used today by large ensembles and by some traditional troupes

THE GUITARRÓN
A large-bellied bass guitar

GUITARS
The round-backed vihuela is smaller and higher-pitched than the standard guitar

5-string Vihuela   6-string guitar

In 1905, Mexican dictator Porfirio Díaz visited Cocula and was received with a performance of a mariachi group. Impressed with the performance, Diaz invited the group to Mexico City where, after a few years and a revolution, mariachi flourished. Over the next two decades, more groups followed to Mexico City. Mariachi groups gained wide popularity by the 1930s, when movie stars as Jorge Negrete and Pedro Infante began portraying mariachi musicians in their films.

MARIACHI STYLE

■ The mariachi *traje* (suit) consists of matching vest, *chaleco* (short jacket), and form-fitting pants, and a complementary *moño* (large bow tie). Simple *trajes* have soutache trim or embroidery; finer versions have suede patterns on the jacket with metal buttons down the pants legs. Trajes come in all colors, but formal costumes are black.

■ Sombreros made from pressed rabbit fur are the highest quality.

■ The modern mariachi's dress is an adaptation of *charro*, or Mexican cowboy, attire, first worn by the members of an early mariachi group led by Cirilo Marmolejo and adopted for Mexican movies of the 1930s–50s. A complete formal outfit can cost as much as US$3,000.

■ *Botonaduras* (decorative buttons on the pants legs) can be simple, or ornate, made of silver or gold. A brooch on the front of the jacket often matches the botonadura.

■ Black leather *botínes* (half-boots) are standard mariachi footwear.

MARIACHI: BORN IN JALISCO

9

WHERE AND HOW TO HEAR MARIACHI

HIRE A MARIACHI GROUP

There may be no better way to thoroughly surprise (or embarrass) your significant other, or a more memorable way to pop the question, than with a mariachi serenade. Hiring a band is easy. Just go to Plaza de los Mariachis, beside Mercado Libertad in downtown Guadalajara. Pablo Garcia, whose Mariachi Atotonilco has been working the plaza for almost 40 years, says a serenade runs about 2,000 pesos, or just under US$200. Normal procedure is to negotiate price and either leave a deposit (ask for a business card and a receipt) and have the band meet you at a determined location, or, as Mexicans usually do, accompany the band to the unexpecting lady.

HIT THE INTERNATIONAL MARIACHI FESTIVAL

The last weekend of every August, some 700 mariachi groups from around the world descend upon Guadalajara for the annual International Mariachi Festival. Mexico's most famous mariachi groups—Mariachi Vargas de Tecalitlán, Mariachi los Camperos, and Mariachi de América—play huge concerts in Guadalajara's Degollado Theater, accompanied by the Jalisco Philharmonic Orchestra. The weeklong annual charro championship is held simultaneously, bringing together the nation's top cowboys and mariachis.

THE WORLD'S BEST MARIACHI BAND

At least, the world's most *famous* mariachi band, Mariachi Vargas de Tecalitlán was founded in 1897, when the norm was four-man groups with simple stringed instruments. Started by Gaspar Vargas in Tecalitlán, Jalisco, the mariachi troupe shot to fame in the 1930s after winning a regional mariachi contest, which earned them the favor of Mexican president Lázaro Cárdenas. The group quickly became an icon of Mexican cinema, performing in and recording music for films. Now in its fifth generation, Mariachi Vargas performs the world over and has recorded more than 50 albums, and music for more than 200 films.

The *gabán* (poncho) was worn traditionally for warmth

CATCH YEAR-ROUND PERFORMANCES

If you miss Guadalajara's mariachi festival you can still get your fill of high-quality mariachi performances on street corners, in city plazas, and at many restaurants. An estimated 150 mariachi groups are currently active in the City of Roses.

Restaurants, most notably Guadalajara's Casa Bariachi chain, hire mariachi groups, whose performance is generally included with your table (though tips won't be refused). On occasion, mariachis perform free nighttime concerts in Guadalajara's Plaza de Armas. Another venue, the Plaza de Mariachi, beside Guadalajara's landmark Mercado Libertad, is a longstanding attraction, albeit during the day—at night it's better known for crime than mariachi.

Tlaquepaque's El Parían, a former market turned series of bars around a tree-filled central patio, is a fantastic intimate setting for mariachi music. Between free performances in the central kiosk, you can request serenades at about $10 per song or negotiate deals for longer performances for your table.

ALL ABOARD THE TEQUILA TRAIN!

To experience the Jalisco quartet of traditions—mariachi, charreria, folkloric dance, and tequila—in one adventure, take the Tequila Express. It includes a train ride from Guadalajara through fields of blue agave to a tequila-making hacienda, live mariachi music, all the food and drink you can handle, and a charro and folkloric dance performance.

WORKING HARD FOR THE MONEY

It is becoming harder for mariachi groups to make a living at the trade. The increasing cost of living has made nighttime serenades, once a staple of a mariachi's diet of work, expensive ($200 and up) and out of the reach of many locals. Performers generally work day jobs to make ends meet.

THE COWBOY CONNECTION

Mariachi and Mexican rodeo, or *charreada* (Mexico's official sport), go together like hot dogs and baseball. Both charreada and mariachi music evolved in the western Mexican countryside, where daily ranching chores like branding bulls eventually took on a competitive edge. The first of Mexico's 800 charro associations was founded in Guadalajara in 1920, and to this day holds a two-hour rodeo every Sunday. Throughout the competition, mariachi music is heard from the stands, but the key mariachi performance is at the end of a competition when female riders perform synchronized moves, riding side-saddle in traditional ribboned and brightly colored western Mexican dresses.

Tlaquepaque

0 ____ 350 meters
0 ____ 350 yards

Bd. Tlaquepaque

Rio Tinto

Av. Niños Héroes

Contreras Medellin

La Villa del Ensueño ◆

Museo Panduro
del Premio Nacional
de la Cerámica **Pantaleón** *Florida*

Av. Cruz Verde

Donato Guerra

Bus to downtown Guadalajara ◆

Francisco Madero

Obregón

Constitución

Priscilliano Sánchez

Prieto

Moctezuma

Moretos

Casa Fuerte ◆

Independencia

Rio Atenguillo

Juárez

Museo Regional de la Cerámica ◆

El Parián

Reforma

Av. Francisco de Miranda

Matamoros

Progreso

Herrera y Cairo

Quinta Don José ◆

Porvenir

Av. Niños Héroes

Camarena

Alfareros

La Casa del Retoño ◆

Santos Degollado

TO
TONALÁ ↘

◆ **Casa de las Flores**

TONALÁ
$
✕**El Rincón del Sol.** A covered patio invites you to sip margaritas while listening to live guitar music (Wednesday to Sunday afternoons). Try one of the steak or chicken dishes or the classic *chiles en nogada* (in walnut sauce) in the colors of the Mexican flag. ⊠*Av. 16 de Septiembre 61, Tonalá* ☎33/3683–1989 *or* 33/3683–1940 ▭*MC, V.*

ZONA
MINERVA
$–$$
★
✕**El Sacromonte.** Come here for creative Mexican food, superior service, and warm ambience. You're surrounded by *artesanías* in the dining area, and there's live music every afternoon and evening. Try a juicy steak or *La Corona de Reina Isabel*—a crown of intertwined shrimp in lobster sauce. ⊠*Pedro Moreno 1398, Zona Minerva* ☎33/3825–5447 ▭*MC, V* ⌕*Reservations essential* ⊙*No dinner Sun.*

$–$$
★
✕**La Trattoria.** Guadalajara's top Italian restaurant is a bustling family place. The menu's highlights include spaghetti *frutti di mare* (with seafood), *scaloppine alla Marsala* (beef medallions with Marsala and mushrooms), and fresh garlic bread. All meals include a trip to the salad bar. Make a reservation if you're eating after 8 PM. ⊠*Av. Niños Héroes 3051, Zona Minerva* ☎33/3122–1817 ▭*AE, MC, V.*

✕**Karne Garibaldi.** Lightning service is made possible by the menu's single item: *carne en su jugo,* a combination of finely diced beef and bacon simmered in rich beef broth and served with grilled onions, tortillas, and refried beans mixed with corn. Don't be put off by the somewhat gritty area surrounding the restaurant. ✉ *Calle Garibaldi 1306, Zona Minerva* ☎ *33/3121–1663* ▭ *AE, MC, V.*

$
★
✕ **La Pianola Avenida México.** Signature piano music and a large, airy courtyard in the back provide a soothing backdrop for you to sample specialties from this restaurant's varied Mexican menu, including pozole and *chiles en nogada* (mild green chilies stuffed with a sweet meat mixture draped in walnut sauce and decorated with pomegranate seeds). ✉ *Av. México 3220, Zona Minerva* ☎ *33/3813–2412* ▭ *AE, MC, V.*

WHERE TO STAY

Choosing a place to stay is a matter of location and price; tourists are often drawn to the Centro Histórico, where colonial-style hotels are convenient to the historical and other sights, or to Tlaquepaque's genial B&Bs. Businesspeople head for the Zona Minerva, specifically around Avenida López Mateos Sur, a 16-km (10-mi) strip extending from the Minerva Fountain to the Plaza del Sol shopping center, where they can take advantage of modern office facilities and four-star comforts.

CENTRO
HISTÓRICO
$$
★
Hotel de Mendoza. This refined hotel with postcolonial architecture and hand-carved furniture is on a relatively calm side street a block from Teatro Degollado. Suites are worth the extra cost: standard rooms are comfortable but small. Balconies overlook the courtyard pool from some rooms. ✉ *Calle Venustiano Carranza 16, Centro Histórico, 44100* ☎ *33/3942–5151, 01800/361–2600 in Mexico* ⊕ *www.demendoza. com.mx* ⇆ *110 rooms, 17 suites* ⌂ *In-hotel: restaurant, pool, gym, parking (fee)* ▭ *AE, MC, V* ⏀ *EP.*

$
Hotel Cervantes. All of the hotel's comfortable, carpeted rooms have sofa beds (as well as standard double beds) and are adorned with old-time photos; suites have terraces. Off the lobby is the hotel's relaxed restaurant with its scrumptious breakfast buffet. Several pastry shops and bookstores are nearby, and the Centro Histórico is a short walk away. ✉ *Calle Priciliano Sánchez 442, Centro Histórico, 44100* ☎ *33/3613–6686 or 33/3613–6816* ⊕ *www.hotelcervantes.com.mx* ⇆ *95 rooms, 5 suites* ⌂ *In-hotel: restaurant, bar, pool, laundry service, parking (no fee)* ▭ *AE, DC, MC, V* ⏀ *EP.*

$–$$
Santiago de Compostela. The more expensive rooms in this 19th-century building face the Parque San Francisco across the street, and have tall, narrow windows with iron balconies. For the most part the hotel has simple, modern accommodations, though the suites have Jacuzzis. From a fifth-floor terrace a pool looks onto Guadalajara's south side. ✉ *Calle Colón 272, Centro Histórico, 44100* ☎ *33/3613–8880, 01800/365–5300 in Mexico* ⇆ *84 rooms, 8 suites* ⌂ *In-hotel: restaurant, bar, pool* ▭ *AE, DC, MC, V* ⏀ *EP.*

TLAQUEPAQUE
$$
Quinta Don José. This B&B is one block from Tlaquepaque's main plaza and shopping area. Natural lighting and room size vary, so look at a few before you choose one. Suites face the pool, and are spacious but a bit dark. There's remarkable tile work in the master suite. Hearty breakfasts are served in an inner courtyard; the inn's hosts are fonts of information, and aim to please. ✉ *Av. Reforma 139, Tlaquepaque, 45500* ☎ *33/3635–7522, 01800/700–2223 in Mexico, 866/629–3753*

9

in U.S. and Canada ⊕*www.quintadonjose.com* ⇄*8 rooms, 7 suites* ☖*In-hotel: bar, pool, laundry service, public Wi-Fi, airport shuttle, massage* ⊟*AE, MC, V* ⦶*BP.*

$ ▦ **La Villa del Ensueño.** Though it's a 10-minute walk from Tlaquepaque's center, this intimate B&B is near the town's shops. The 19th-century hacienda has thick, white adobe walls, exposed-beam ceilings, and plants in huge unglazed pots. Smokers should request a room with private balcony, as smoking isn't allowed inside. ⊠*Florida 305, Tlaquepaque, 45500* ☎*33/3635–8792, 800/220–8689 in U.S.* ⊕*www. villadelensueno.com* ⇄*14 rooms, 4 suites* ☖*In-room: dial-up, Wi-Fi. In-hotel: restaurant, bar, pools, no-smoking rooms, parking (free)* ⊟*AE, MC, V* ⦶*BP.*

$ ▦ **Casa de las Flores.** A favorite with those traveling for business as
★   well as pleasure, this B&B is charismatic and inviting, with lovely art and wonderful food. Owners Stan and José, from the United States and Mexico, respectively, enjoy directing their guests to the best shops and markets for purchasing handicrafts. Guests meet and socialize by the fireplace in the large living room and out in the magical garden. ⊠*Calle Santos Degollado 175, Tlaquepaque, 45500* ☎*33/3659– 3186* ⊕*www.casadelasflores.com* ⇄*7 rooms* ☖*In-room: no a/c (some), no TV (some). In-hotel: laundry service, parking (no fee)* ⊟*MC, V* ⦶*BP.*

$ ▦ **La Casa del Retoño.** On a quiet street several blocks from the shopping district is this newer B&B. Smallish rooms are made of cinder block, but are clean and painted in cheerful hues. Rooms in the back overlook a large garden, while the ones upstairs have terraces. There's a small open-air reading area, and breakfast is served in the small courtyard. ⊠*Matamoros 182, Tlaquepaque, 45500* ☎*33/3587–3989* ⊕*www. lacasadelretono.com.mx* ⇄*8 rooms, 1 suite* ☖*In-room: kitchen (some), public Wi-Fi* ⊟*AE, MC, V* ⦶*CP.*

ZONA   ▦ **Quinta Real.** Stone-and-brick walls, colonial arches, and objets
MINERVA   d'art fill this luxury hotel's public areas. Suites are plush, though on
$$$$ the small side, with neocolonial-style furnishings, glass-top writing
★   tables, and faux fireplaces. The hotel provides discount passes to a nearby Gold's Gym. ⊠*Av. México 2727, at Av. López Mateos Norte, Zona Minerva, 44680* ☎*33/3669– 0600, 01800/500–4000 in Mexico* ⊕*www.quintareal.com* ⇄*76 suites* ☖*In-room: dial-up. In-hotel: restaurant, bar, pool, concierge, no-smoking rooms* ⊟*AE, D, DC, MC, V* ⦶*EP.*

$$$–$$$$ ▦ **Crowne Plaza Guadalajara.** Gardens encircle the pool add a bit of nature to this family-friendly hotel. A mix of antiques and reproductions fills the public spaces. Rooms have marble baths and natural lighting; those in the tower have city views. (Ask for a

---

JALISCO'S HOLY WAR

When ultra right-wing president Plutarco Elías Calles effectively criminalized Catholicism in 1926, Jalisco-area Catholics launched an armed rebellion against the government. During the bitter *La Cristiada* war, many priests were executed. In recent years dozens of *Cristero* martyrs have been canonized by the Vatican, a great source of pride for Guadalajara's Catholics.

room near the back; those near the playground can be noisy.) Plaza Club room rates include a buffet breakfast. The top-floor restaurant is the only one in Guadalajara with a panoramic view. It's just down the street from the Plaza del Sol shopping center. ⊠ *Av. López Mateos Sur 2500, Zona Plaza del Sol, 45050* ☎ *33/3634–1034, 01800/009–9900* ⊕ *www.cpguadalajara.com.mx* ↩ *297 rooms, 4 suites* ⌂ *In-hotel: 2 restaurants, bar, room service, pool, gym, executive floor, public Wi-Fi, laundry service, parking (no fee), no-smoking rooms* ⊟ *AE, DC, MC, V* ꙱ *EP.*

$$–$$$ ⭐ 🏨 **Fiesta Americana.** The dramatic glass facade of this high-rise faces the Minerva Fountain and Los Arcos monument. Four glass-enclosed elevators ascend dizzyingly above a 14-story atrium lobby to the enormous guest rooms, which have modern furnishings, marble bathrooms, and arresting views. The lobby bar has live music every night but Sunday. On the *piso ejecutivo* (executive floor), rooms come with breakfast, and there's a business center. Guests get discount passes to the neighboring gym. ⊠ *Av. Aurelio Aceves 225, Zona Minerva, 44100* ☎ *33/3818–1400, 01800/504–5000 in Mexico* ⊕ *www.fiestamericana.com* ↩ *387 rooms, 4 suites* ⌂ *In-room: dial-up. In-hotel: restaurant, bar, gym, concierge, no-smoking rooms* ⊟ *AE, DC, MC, V* ꙱ *EP.*

$$ 🏨 **Hotel Plaza Diana.** At this modest hotel two blocks from the Minerva Fountain the standard-size rooms have white walls and bright, patterned fabrics. One suite even has a sauna. Stay on the upper floors in the rear for the quietest rooms. ⊠ *Circunvalación Agustín Yáñez 2760, Zona Minerva, 44100* ☎ *33/3540–9700, 01800/024–1001 in Mexico* ⊕ *www.hoteldiana.com.mx* ↩ *127 rooms, 24 suites* ⌂ *In-hotel: restaurant, bar, airport shuttle* ⊟ *AE, DC, MC, V* ꙱ *EP.*

NIGHTLIFE

With the exception of a few well-established night spots like La Maestranza, downtown Guadalajara is mostly asleep by 11 PM. The existing nightlife centers around Avenida Vallarta (Zona Minerva), favored by the well-to-do and under-thirty sets, or the somewhat seedy Plaza del Sol. Bars in these spots open into the wee hours, usually closing by 3 AM. Dance clubs may charge a $15–$20 cover, which includes an open bar, on Wednesday and Saturday nights. Dress up for nightclubs; highly subjective admission policies hinge on who you know or how you look. The local music scene centers around Peña Cuicacalli and the Hard Rock Cafe.

Guadalajara has a decent arts and culture scene. You can catch the University of Guadalajara's Ballet Folclórico on Sunday morning at Teatro Degollado. International exhibitions are sometimes shown at the Instituto Cultural Cabañas or the Arts Museum of Zapopan.

⭐ Open since 1921, **La Fuente** (⊠ *Calle Pino Suarez, Centro Histórico* ☎ *No phone*) draws business types, intellectuals, and blue-collar work-

TIP

For the latest listings, grab a *Público* newspaper on Friday and pull out the weekly Ocio cultural guide.

9

ers, all seeking cheap drinks, animated conversation, and live music. Arrive early to avoid crowds, a din, and a thick carpet of cigarette smoke over the tables. Restaurant by day, Guadalajara hotspot by night, **I Latina** (⊠*Av. Inglaterra at López Mateos* ☎*33/3647–7774*) is where a cool international crowd has cocktails.

For some local color, stop at **La Maestranza** (⊠*Calle Maestranza 179, Centro Histórico* ☎*33/3613–5878*), a renovated 1940s cantina full of bullfighting memorabilia. After 9 PM Tuesday through Sunday, patrons cluster around the small stage at **La Peña Cuicacalli** (⊠*Av. Niños Héroes 1988, at Suarez traffic circle, Centro Histórico* ☎*No*

> **ROOT FOR THE HOME TEAM**
>
> *Futbol* (soccer) is a national obsession. Guadalajara's two main teams nurse a healthy rivalry—as do their fans. Atlas appeals more to the middle and upper classes; working-class Tapatíos and students prefer Las Chivas. In fact the Chivas seem to be the working-class heroes of much of Mexico. Both teams play at Guadalajara's **Estadio Jalisco** (☎*33/3637–0301*) on weekends or Wednesday night January–May and July–December. Tickets are $5–$45.

phone). There's *rock en español* on Tuesday and folk music from Mexico, Latin America, and Spain other nights.

DANCE CLUBS   Well-dressed professionals over 25 go to **El Mito** (⊠*Centro Magno mall, Av. Vallarta 2425, 2nd fl., Zona Minerva* ☎*33/3615–7246*); there's '70s and '80s music Wednesday, Friday, and Saturday 10 PM–4 AM. Wednesday is ladies night, with free entry for women, a $17 entry for men, and an open bar.

Salón Veracruz (⊠*Calle Manzano 486, behind Hotel Misión Carlton, Centro Histórico* ☎*33/3613–4422*) is a spartan, old-style dance hall where a 15-piece band keeps hoofers moving to *cumbia*, merengue, and the waltzlike *danzón*. It's closed Monday and Tuesday. Dance to popular Latin and European music at **Tropigala** (⊠*Av. López Mateos Sur 2188, Zona Minerva* ☎*33/3122–5553 or 33/3122–7903*), across from the Plaza del Sol mall.

SPORTS & THE OUTDOORS

BULLFIGHTS   *Corridas* (bullfights) are held Sunday at 4:30 from October to December at **Plaza Nuevo Progreso** (⊠*Calle M. Pirineos 1930 and Calz. Independencia Norte, Zona Huentitán* ☎*33/3637–9982 or 33/3651–8506*). Tickets are $8–$70; bleacher seats far from the action on the *sol* (sunny) side are much cheaper than more-comfortable up-close seats on the *sombra* (shady) side.

CHARREADAS   These "rodeos" of elegant equestrian maneuvers and rope tricks are
          ↻   the epitome of upper-class rural Mexican culture. Men in tight, elegant suits with wide-brimmed felt hats perform *suertes* in which they subdue young bulls or jump from one galloping horse to another in *el paso de la muerte* (the pass of death). Teams of women in flowing dresses perform audacious (yet less dangerous) synchronized movements on horseback. Mariachi or brass bands play between acts. Charreadas

run year-round at the **Lienzo Charros de Jalisco** (⊠*Av. Dr. R. Michel 577, Centro Histórico* ☎*33/3619–3232*), next to Parque Agua Azul, usually Sunday at noon. Admission is $3–$5.

SHOPPING

Guadalajara is shopping central for people from all over Nayarit, Jalisco, and surrounding states. The labyrinthine Mercado Libertad is one of Latin America's largest markets; modern malls are gathering spots with restaurants and theaters. Tlaquepaque and Tonalá have the best Mexican art and handicrafts. In Tlaquepaque, stroll along Independencia and Juárez streets for dozens of artsy shops. In less touristy Tonalá most shops and factories are spread out, with the exception of a concentration of shops on Avenida de los Tonaltecas, the main drag into town. On Thursday and Sunday, bargain-price merchandise is sold at a terrific street market there packed with vendors from 8 to 4.

CRAFTS & FOLK ARTS

★ **La Casa de los Artesanos** (⊠*Av. de los Tonaltecas Sur 140, Tonalá* ☎*33/3284–3066* ⊕*www.casadeartesanos.com*) has pieces by Tonalá's most talented artisans. Prices are reasonable, and the staff will direct you to nearby studios. It's open weekdays 9–8 and Saturday 9–2. Better known as Mercado San Juan de Dios, **Mercado Libertad** (⊠*Calz. Independencia Sur; use pedestrian bridge from Plaza Tapatía's south side, Centro Histórico*) has shops that are organized thematically on three expansive floors. Be wary of fakes in the jewelry stores. Most shops are open Monday–Saturday 10–8, and 10–3 on Sunday.

★ Cramped **Tonalá crafts market** (⊠*Av. Tonaltecas, north of Av. Tonalá, Tonalá*) is *the* place for Mexican arts and crafts. Vendors set up ceramics, carved wood, candles, glassware, furniture, metal crafts, and more each Thursday and Sunday (roughly 9–5). Look for *vajilla* (ceramic dining sets), but note that the more high-end ceramic offerings are at government-sponsored Casa de los Artesanos down the street. Antiquers come out of the woodwork every Sunday 10–5 to sell their antique European flatware and Mexican pottery at **El Trocadero** (⊠*Av. Mexico at Av. Chapultepec, Zona Minerva*) market in the antiques district.

MALLS

Sprawling, tri-level **La Gran Plaza** (⊠*Av. Vallarta 3959, Zona Minerva* ☎*33/3122–3004*) has nearly 330 shops and a big cinema. The food court is Guadalajara's best. Among the most memorable stores, Eréndira Contis (☎*33/3123–1254*), on the top floor, has exceptional jewelry and modern Mexican art and

---

WHEELING & DEALING

To bargain effectively at markets and other informal venues, react skeptically (yet politely) or with mild disinterest to the first quoted price and see if you can get a lower offering. If not, offer as low as your conscience and intellect will allow and trade offers back and forth from there.

CAUTION

Mercado Libertad has silver at great prices, but not everything that glitters there is certifiably silver. A safer, albeit pricier, bet are the shops along Avenida República in downtown Guadalajara, where there are more than 400 jewelers.

9

crafts. Guadalajara's first mall, **Plaza del Sol** (✉*Av. López Mateos Sur 2375, at Mariano Otero, Zona Minerva* ☎*33/3121–5950*) has 270 commercial spaces scattered around an outdoor atrium and wacky sculpture-fountains by Alejandro Colunga. It's got everything the more modern malls have in a more low-key environment.

TEQUILA

56 km (35 mi) northwest of Guadalajara.

For an in-depth look at how Mexico's most famous liquor is derived from the spiny blue agave plant that grows in fields alongside the highway, stop by this tidy village. Head west from Guadalajara along Avenida Vallarta for about 25 minutes until you reach the toll road junction (Puerto Vallarta Cuota). Choose the toll road (faster, safer, and about $10) or the free road (*libre*) toward Puerto Vallarta. Or catch a bus to Tequila from the Antigua Central Camionera (Old Central Bus Station), northeast of the Parque Agua Azul on Avenida Dr. R. Michel, between Calle Los Angeles and Calle 5 de Febrero. Buses marked Amatitán–Tequila are easy to spot from the entrance on Calle Los Angeles.

■TIP→ **For more information about Jalisco's famous liquor,** *see* "**¡Tequila!**" *in* **Chapter 6.**

WHAT TO SEE

The **Sauza Museum** (✉*Calle Albino Rojas 22* ☎*374/742–0247*) has memorabilia from the Sauza family, a tequila-making dynasty second only to the Cuervos. The museum is open weekdays 10–2, and admission is $1.

Opened in 1795, the **José Cuervo Distillery** (✉*Calle José Cuervo 73* ☎*374/742–2442*) is the world's oldest tequila distillery. Every day, 150 tons of agave hearts are processed into 74,000 liters of tequila here. Hard-hat tours are given daily every hour from 10 to 4. The tours at noon are normally in English, but English-speakers can be accommodated at other times. Admission is $6.50.

TEUCHITLÁN

50 km (28 mi) west of Guadalajara.

For decades, residents in this sleepy village of sugarcane farmers had a name for the funny-looking mounds in the hills above town, but they never considered the Guachimontones to be more than a convenient source of rocks for local construction. Then in the early 1970s an American archaeologist asserted that the mounds were the remnants of a long-vanished, 2,000-year-old state. It took Phil Weigand nearly three decades to convince authorities in far-off Mexico City that he wasn't crazy. Before he was allowed to start excavating and restoring this monumental site in the late 1990s, plenty more houses and roads were produced with Guachimonton rock—and countless tombs were looted of priceless art.

The spot is most distinctive for its sophisticated concentric architecture—a circular pyramid surrounded by a ring of flat ground, surrounded by a series of smaller platforms arranged in a circle. The "Teuchitlán Tradition," as the concentric circle structures are called, is unique in world architecture. Weigand believes the formations suggest the existence of a pre-Hispanic state in the region, whereas it was previously held that only socially disorganized nomads inhabited the region at the time. Similar ruins are spread throughout the foothills of the extinct Tequila Volcano, but this is the biggest site yet detected.

To get to Teuchitlán from Guadalajara, drive west out along Avenida Vallarta for 25 minutes to the toll road junction to Puerto Vallarta: choose the free road 70 (*libre*) toward Vallarta. Head west along Route 15 for a couple of miles, then turn left onto Route 70 and continue until you reach the town of Tala. One-and-a-half kilometers (1 mi) past the sugar mill, turn right onto Route 27. Teuchitlán is 15 minutes from the last junction. The ruins are up a dirt road from town—just ask for directions when you arrive. There's a small museum off the main square. Plans to build greater infrastructure around the site continue. If you visit during the dry season, you may score a look at a dig or restoration project.

> ## DEDICATED TO ITS CRAFT
>
> Like Tlaquepaque, neighboring **Tonalá** was in the crafts business long before the Spanish conquistadors arrived. Independent and industrious, less-touristy Tonalá remains dedicated to traditional pursuits: brilliant blown glass, gold jewelry, and goofy piñatas. But it's the exquisitely stylized *petatillo*-style ceramics that's the town's best-known handcraft. The distinctively Mexican earthenware is decorated with placid-looking birds and beasts and glazed in subtle tans and blues. Thursday and Sunday markets are the source of terrific bargains.

9

LAKE CHAPALA

Lake Chapala is Mexico's largest natural lake and just an hour's drive south of Guadalajara. Surrounded by jagged hills and serene towns, it is a favorite Tapatío getaway and a haven for thousands of North American retirees.

The area's main town, Chapala, is flooded with weekend visitors and the pier is packed shoulder-to-shoulder most Sundays. Neighboring Ajijic, 8 km (5 mi) west, has narrow cobblestone streets and vibrantly colored buildings. Its mild climate and gentle pace has attracted a large colony of English-speaking expats, including many artists.

CHAPALA
45 km (28 mi) south of Guadalajara.

When elitist president Porfirio Díaz bought a retreat in lakeside Chapala in 1904, his aristocratic pals followed suit. Today, some of these residences on the shore of Mexico's largest natural lake have been converted to cozy lodges, many geared to families. About an hour south of downtown Guadalajara, the diminutive but prosperous town is a retreat for the middle and upper classes, with restaurants, shops, and cafés.

Three blocks north of the promenade, the plaza at the corner of López Cotilla is a relaxing spot to read a paper or succumb to sweets from surrounding shops. The Iglesia de San Francisco (built in 1528), easily recognized by its blue neon crosses on twin steeples, is two blocks south of the plaza.

On weekends the town is paralyzed by Mexican families who flock to the shores of the (for now, at least) rejuvenated lake. Vendors sell refreshments and souvenirs, while lakeside watering holes fill to capacity.

WHERE TO STAY & EAT

$$ ✕ **Cozumel.** Ajijic residents regularly drive to Chapala on Wednesday and Friday for live mariachi music and well-prepared specials, which include a free cocktail and appetizers. Wednesday is chicken cordon bleu night; on other days, choose from seafood and international dishes. (You still get the free drink.) Reservations are essential for Friday and sometimes for Wednesday night. ✉*Paseo Corona 22–A* ☎*376/765–4606* ▭*MC, V* ☉*Closed Mon.*

$$ ✕ **Mariscos Guicho's.** Bright orange walls and checkerboard tablecloths lend the best of the waterfront seafood joints an authentic Mexican flair. Dig into savory caviar tostadas, frogs' legs, garlic shrimp, and spicy seafood soup. ✉*Paseo Ramón Corona 20* ☎*376/765–3232* ▭*No credit cards* ☉*Closed Tues.*

¢–$ ✕ **El Arbol del Café.** Expatriates cherish this modest café for its roasted-on-the-premises coffee, imported teas, and homemade cakes. Sip a decaffeinated cappuccino (rare in Mexico) and peruse the English-language papers. The café closes at 3 PM on weekdays and at 2 PM on Saturday. ✉*Av. Hidalgo 236* ☎*376/765–3908* ▭*No credit cards* ☉*Closed Sun.*

$ ▦ **Hotel Villa Montecarlo.** The hotel's simple, clean rooms are in three-story contiguous units, all with patios or terraces. The grounds are enormous and well maintained, with several eating and play areas. One of the two swimming pools (the biggest in the area) is filled with natural thermal water. Popular with Mexican families, the hotel has frequent discounts and packages. ✉*Av. Hidalgo 296, about 1 km (½ mi) west of Av. Madero, 45900* ☎*376/765–2216 or 376/765–2120* ◞*46 rooms, 2 suites* ⌂*In-hotel: restaurant, bar, tennis courts, pools, laundry service, parking (no fee)* ▭*AE, MC, V.*

HEALING WATERS

San Juan Cosalá, 2 km (1 mi) west of Ajijic, is known for its natural thermal-water spas along Lago de Chapala. The **Hotel Balneario San Juan Cosalá** (✉*Calle La Paz Oriente 420, at Carretera Chapala-Jocotepec, Km 13* ☎*387/761–0222 or 387/761–0302* ⊕*www.hotelspacosala.com*) has four large swimming pools and two wading pools; admission is $10. Weekends are crowded and loud.

$
★ ⊞**Lake Chapala Inn.** Now that the lake is back to its original size (the 1990s saw it shrink to an unattractive shadow of its former self due to lack of rainfall and overuse of supplying rivers), this European-style inn is an especially appealing place to stay. Three of the four rooms in this restored mansion face the shore; all have high ceilings and white-washed oak furniture. Rates include an English-style breakfast (with a Continental breakfast on Sunday). ⊠*Paseo Ramón Corona 23, 45900* ☎*376/765–4786* ⊕*www.mexonline.com/chapalainn.htm* ↝*4 rooms* ⏷*In-hotel: restaurant, pool, laundry service* ▤*No credit cards* ❗*BP.*

AJIJIC
8 km (5 mi) west of Chapala.

Ajijic has narrow cobblestone streets, vibrantly colored buildings, and a gentle pace—with the exception of the very trafficky main highway through the town's southern end. The foreign influence is unmistakable: English is widely (though not exclusively) spoken and license plates come from far-flung places like British Columbia and Texas.

The Plaza Principal (aka El Jardín) is a tree- and flower-filled central square at the corner of Avenidas Colón and Hidalgo. In late November the plaza and its surrounding streets fill for the saint's nine-day fiesta of the town's patron, St. Andrew. From the plaza, walk down Calle Morelos (the continuation of Avenida Colón) toward the lake and peruse the boutiques on Ajijic's main shopping strip. (There are also many galleries and shops east of Morelos, on Avenida 16 de Septiembre and Calle Constitución.) Turn left onto Avenida 16 de Septiembre or Avenida Constitución for art galleries and studios. Northeast of the plaza, along the highway, activity centers around the soccer field, which doubles as a venue for bullfights and concerts.

WHERE TO
STAY & EAT
$–$$ ✕**La Bodega de Ajijic.** Eat in a covered patio overlooking a grassy lawn and a small pool at this low-key restaurant. The menu has Italian and Mexican dishes, which are a bit small and overpriced. Still, service is friendly, and there's live music—ranging from Mexican pop and rock to jazz, guitar, and harp—most nights. ⊠*Av. 16 de Septiembre 124* ☎*376/766–1002* ▤*MC, V.*

$–$$ ✕**Johanna's.** Come to this intimate bit of Bavaria on the lake for German cuisine like sausages and goose or duck pâté. Main dishes come with soup or salad, applesauce, and cooked red cabbage. For dessert indulge in plum strudel or blackberry-topped torte. ⊠*Carretera Chapala-Jocotepec, Km 6.5* ☎*376/766–0437* ▤*No credit cards* ⊘*Closed Mon.*

¢–$ ✕**Salvador's.** An old mainstay that's showing its years, this cafeteria-like eatery is a popular expat hangout. There's a well-kept salad bar and specialties from both sides of the border. On Friday people flock here for the fish-and-chips lunch special. ⊠*Carretera Chapala-Jocotepec Oriente 58* ☎*376/766–2301* ▤*No credit cards.*

$
★ ✕⊞**La Nueva Posada.** The well-kept gardens framed in bougainvillea define this inviting inn. Rooms are large, with carpets, high ceilings, and local crafts. Villas share a private courtyard and have tile

9

kitchenettes. The bar has jazz or Caribbean music most evenings. Out in the garden restaurant ($–$$), strands of tiny white lights set the mood for an evening meal. ✉ *Calle Donato Guerra 9, 45920* ☎ *376/766–1344* ⊕ *www.mexconnect.com/MEX/rest/nueva/posada. html* ⬧ *19 rooms, 4 villas* ♿ *In-hotel: restaurant, bar, pool, laundry service* ▤ *MC, V* ⑩ *BP.*

$–$$ ▣ **Los Artistas.** Surrounded by an acre of splendid gardens, this spacious yet intimate inn has rooms with brightly painted walls and red-tile floors. Each has colorful handwoven Mexican bedspreads, wrought-iron or carved-wood bed frames, and fresh-cut flowers. Most rooms have patios shaded by bowers of blooming plants. There are no televisions or radios to spoil the tranquillity. ✉ *Calle Constitución 105, 45920* ☎ *376/766–1027* ⊕ *www.losartistas.com* ⬧ *6 rooms* ♿ *In-room: no a/c. In-hotel: pool* ▤ *No credit cards* ⑩ *BP.*

SPORTS & THE   The **Rojas family** (✉ *Paseo Del Lago and Camino Real, 4 blocks east of*
OUTDOORS   *Los Artistas B&B* ☎ *376/766–4261*) has been leading horseback trips for more than 30 years. A ride along the lakeshore or in the surrounding hills costs around $7 an hour.

GUADALAJARA ESSENTIALS

TRANSPORTATION

BY AIR   Many major airlines fly nonstop from the U.S. to Guadalajara.

Aeropuerto Internacional Libertador Miguel Hidalgo is 16½ km (10 mi) south of Guadalajara, en route to Chapala. Autotransportaciones Aeropuerto operates a 24-hour taxi stand with service to any place in the Guadalajara area; buy tickets at the counters at the national and international exits. Some hotels also offer airport pickup shuttles; these need to be arranged in advance.

Although flying from your hometown to Guadalajara, then back home from PV can be a good deal, flying round-trip to Guadalajara from PV is not. The bus is much cheaper, scenic, and efficient.

Airports Aeropuerto Internacional Don Miguel Hidalgo y Costilla (*Aeropuerto Internacional de Guadalajara* ✉ *Carretera Guadalajara-Chapala* ☎ *33/3688–5504*).

Airport Transfers Autotransportaciones Aeropuerto (☎ *33/3812–4278*).

Carriers Aeroméxico (✉ *Av. Vallarta 2440* ☎ *01800/021-4000 or 01800/021–4010* ⊕ *www.aeromexico.com*). **American Airlines** (✉ *Av. Vallarta 2440* ☎ *33/3688–5394 or 01800/904–6000* ⊕ *www.aa.com*). **Continental** (✉ *Hotel Presidente Intercontinental, Av. López Mateos Sur 3515* ☎ *33/3647–4251 or 01800/900–5000* ⊕ *www.continental.com*). **Delta Air Lines** (✉ *Av. López Cotilla 1701* ☎ *33/3630–3530 or 01800/902–2100 toll-free in Mexico* ⊕ *www.delta.com*). **Mexicana** (✉ *Av. Vallarta 2440* ☎ *33/3615-3227 or 01800/502-2000* ⊕ *www. mexicana.com*).

BY BUS   **Greyhound** (☎ *33/3647–5070 in Guadalajara, 01800/710–8819 toll-free in Mexico, 800/231–2222 in U.S., 800/661–8747 in Canada* ⊕ *www. greyhound.com*).

Luxury buses between Puerto Vallarta and Guadalajara take 4½ hours and cost $33–$37 on ETN or Estrella Blanca buses. With one wide seat on one side of the aisle and only two on the other, ETN is the most upscale line, and has about nine trips a day to and from Puerto Vallarta, except Sunday, with only one. Within Mexico, they accept advance reservations with a credit card. Estrella Blanca is an umbrella of different bus lines; many head straight for Guadalajara. ■TIP➔ **Many bus lines do not accept credit cards.**

Guadalajara's Nueva Central Camionera (New Central Bus Station) is 10 km (6 mi) southeast of downtown.

Most city buses (40¢) run from every few minutes to every half hour between 6 AM and 9 PM; some run until 11 PM. ⚠ **The city's public transit buses are infamously fatal; drivers killed more than 100 pedestrians annually in the late 1990s before the government intervened. These poorly designed, noisy, noxious buses are still driven ruthlessly and cause at least a dozen deaths per year.**

Large mint-green Tur and red Cardinal buses are the safest, quickest, and least crowded and go to Zapopan, Tlaquepaque, and Tonalá for around 80¢. Wait for these along Avenida 16 de Septiembre.

Autotransportes Guadalajara–Chapala serves the lakeside towns from Guadalajara's new bus station (Central Camionera Nueva) and from the old bus station (Antigua Central Camionera); cost is around $4. It's 45 minutes to Chapala and another 15 minutes to Ajijic; there are departures every half hour from 6 AM to 9:30 PM. Make sure you ask for the *directo* (direct) as opposed to *clase segunda* (second-class) bus, which stops at every little pueblo en route.

Bus Lines Autotransportes Guadalajara Chapala (☏ *33/3619–5675*). **ETN** (☏ *33/3600–0477 or 01800/360–4200* ⊕ *www.etn.com.mx*). **Estrella Blanca** (☏ *33/3679–0404*).

Bus Stations Antigua Central Camionera (✉ *Av. Dr. R. Michel, between Calles Los Angeles and 5 de Febrero, northeast of Parque Agua Azul, Guadalajara*). **Central Camionera Nueva** (✉ *Entronque Carretera Libre a Zapotlanejo Tlaquepaque*).

BY CAR Metropolitan Guadalajara's traffic gets intense, especially at rush hour; parking can be scarce. Streets shoot off at diagonals from roundabouts (called *glorietas*), and on main arteries, turns (including U-turns and left turns) are usually made from right-side lateral roads (called *laterales*)—which can be confusing for drivers unfamiliar with big city traffic. ■TIP➔ **Ubiquitous and inexpensive, taxis are the best way to go in Guadalajara.**

From Guadalajara, it's most practical to get to Tlaquepaque by taxi *(⇨below)*; alternatively, take a bilingual, guided tour to focus on shopping and sightseeing.

BY SUBWAY Guadalajara's underground *tren ligero* (light train) system is clean, safe, and efficient. Trains run every 10 minutes from 5 AM to midnight; a token for one trip costs about 35¢.

BY TAXI Taxis are easily hailed on the street in the Centro Histórico, Zapopan, Tlaquepaque, and most other areas of Guadalajara. All cabs are supposed to use meters (in Spanish, *taximetro*)—you can insist the driver use it or else agree on a fixed price at the outset. Many hotels have rate sheets showing the fare to major destinations and parts of town.

Taxi is the best way to get to Tonalá or Tlaquepaque (about $7). To continue from Tlaquepaque to Tonalá, take a taxi from Avenida Río Nilo southeast directly into town and the intersection of Avenida de los Tonaltecas ($4; 5 minutes).

Contacts Taxi Aguirre (✉ *Calle Etopia 660, Centro Histórico, Guadalajara* 📠 *33/3644–4818*). **Taxi Express** (📠 *33/3637–4525*). **Taxi Sitio Miverva no. 22** (📠 *33/3630–0050*).

CAR RENTAL Although renting a car in Mexico is on the expensive side, deals are available because there are lots of international companies. Note that deals found on Internet sites often have hidden charges.

Contacts Alamo (✉ *Av. Niños Héroes 982, south of Centro Histórico, Guadalajara* 📠 *33/3613–5560, 33/3688–6630 at airport*). **Avis** (✉ *Hilton, Av. de las Rosas 2933, Zona Cruz del Sur, Guadalajara* 📠 *33/3671–3422, 33/3688–5784 at airport*). **Budget** (✉ *Av. Niños Héroes 934, at Av. 16 de Septiembre, Centro Histórico, Guadalajara* 📠 *33/3613–0027, 33/3613–0287, 33/3688–5216 at airport*). **Dollar** (✉ *Av. Federalismo Sur 540–A, at Av. de la Paz, Centro Histórico, Guadalajara* 📠 *33/3825–5080*). **Hertz** (✉ *At the airport only* 📠 *33/3688–5633*).

CONTACTS & RESOURCES

EMERGENCIES Like any large Mexican city, Guadalajara has countless police troops with overlapping municipal, state, and federal jurisdictions. In an emergency, don't bother calling any one of them—it would only increase the possibility that no one will show up. Instead, call 066, a 911-type service that channels emergency situations to the correct agency. On the off chance that a call doesn't go through, stay calm and dial again. You can call the Red Cross at 065 for medical emergencies, especially automobile accidents. Call a police agency only if you need information on detainees or have a specific issue to address with a specific agency. Expect to get the runaround regardless.

Guadalajara has a number of expensive, private hospitals. In general, all have top-notch service and staff English-speaking doctors.

Emergency Services Cruz Verde (*Green Cross municipal emergency medical service* 📠 *33/3614–5252 central dispatch, 33/3812–5143, 33/3812–5143*). **Federal Highway Patrol** (📠 *33/3629–5082 or 33/3629–5085*). **General Emergencies** (📠 *066, 065 for Red Cross ambulance*). **Guadalajara City Police** (📠 *33/3668–0800, 33/3617–0770 for detainees*). **Red Cross** (📠 *33/3345–7777*). **Jalisco State Police and Civil Protection** (📠 *33/3675–3060 for natural disaster response unit*).

Hospitals Hospital del Carmen (✉ *Calle Tarascos 3435, Zona Minerva, Guadalajara* 📠 *33/3813–0042 or 33/3648–6200*). **Hospital México-Americano** (✉ *Calle Colomos 2110, Centro Histórico, Guadalajara* 📠 *33/3641–3141*). **Hospital San**

Javier (✉ *Av. Pablo Casals 640, Col. Providencia, Zona Minerva, Guadalajara* ☎ *33/3669–0222*).

Pharmacies Benavides (✉ *Calle Morelos 468, near el Palacio Municipal, Centro Histórico, Guadalajara* ☎ *33/3613–6500* ⊕ *www.benavides.com.mx* ✉ *Av. Hidalgo 307–A, Centro Histórico, Guadalajara* ☎ *33/3637–7280*). **Farmacias Guadalajara** (✉ *Av. Javier Mina 221, between Calle Cabañas and Vicente Guerrero, Centro Histórico, Guadalajara* ☎ *33/3669–3333*).

EXCHANGE SERVICES ATMs are the most convenient way to get cash, and offer the best exchange rates. There are several ATMs at the Guadalajara airport and at banks throughout metropolitan Guadalajara, Chapala, and elsewhere. You can also change U.S. dollars and traveler's checks at a *casa de cambio* in Guadalajara; there are dozens on Calle López Cotilla, east of Avenida 16 de Septiembre. They generally open weekdays 9–7 and Saturday 9–1.

INTERNET, MAIL & SHIPPING There are several decent Internet cafés in the heart of the Centro Histórico. The cost is usually $1.20 to $1.50 per hour, and most places charge in 15-minute increments. Compu-Flash, one block east of the Hotel Cervántes, opens weekdays 9:30 AM–10 PM and Saturday 9–8.

Note that the Mexican postal system is notoriously slow and unreliable; for important letters or packages, use an overnight service.

Internet Café Compu-Flash (✉ *Calle Priciliano Sánchez 402, Centro Histórico, Guadalajara* ☎ *33/3614–7165*).

Overnight Shipping Services Federal Express (✉ *Av. Washington 1129, Centro Histórico, Guadalajara* ☎ *01800/900–1100 toll-free in Mexico*). **DHL** (✉ *Plaza del Sol, Local 20, in front of Banamex, Plaza del Sol, Guadalajara* ☎ *33/3669–0214*).

Post Offices Correos (✉ *Av. Alcalde 500, Centro Histórico, Guadalajara* ☎ *33/3614–4770*).

VISITOR INFORMATION The Guadalajara branches of the Jalisco State Tourist Office are open weekdays 9–8 and weekends 10–2.

Guadalajara Municipal Tourist Office has an outlet in front of the Palacio Municipal and kiosks at several spots: downtown in the Plaza Guadalajara, near Los Arcos monument on Avenida Vallarta east of the Minerva Fountain, in Parque San Francisco, in front of the Instituto Cultural Cabañas, in front of Mercado Libertad, at Calle Vicente Guerrero 233 (closed weekends), and at the airport. Hours are generally Monday–Saturday 9–7.

The Tourist Board of Zapopan opens weekdays 9–7:30. They also have information on Tonalá and Tlaquepaque. The Tlaquepaque Municipal Tourist Office is open weekdays 9–3. The Tonalá Municipal Tourist Office is open weekdays 9–3. In Ajijic, the nonprofit Lake Chapala Society is open daily 10–2.

Contacts Guadalajara Municipal Tourist Office (✉ *Monumento Los Arcos, Pedro Morelos 1596, 1 block east of Minerva Fountain, Zona Minerva, Guadalajara* ☎ *33/3668–1600*). **Jalisco State Tourist Office** (✉ *Calle Morelos 102, in Plaza*

9

Tapatía, Centro Histórico ☎ *33/3668–1600, 01800/363–2200 toll-free in Mexico* ⊕ *http://visita.jalisco.gob.mx [Spanish only])* ✉ *Palacio de Gobierno, Centro Histórico* ☎ *No phone* ✉ *Calle Madero 407-A, 2nd fl., Chapala* ☎ *376/765–3141).* **Lake Chapala Society** (✉ *Av. 16 de Septiembre 16, Ajijic* ☎ *376/766–1582).* **Tlaquepaque Municipal Tourist Office** (✉ *Calle Morelos 288, Tlaquepaque* ☎ *33/3562–7050 Ext. 2319 or 2320).* **Tonalá Municipal Tourist Office** (✉ *Av. de los Tonaltecas Sur 140, in La Casa de los Artesanos, Tonalá* ☎ *33/3284–3092 or 33/3284–3093).* **Tourist Board of Zapopan** (✉ *Av. Vallarta 6503, Ciudad Granja, Zona Zapopan, Guadalajara* ☎ *33/3110–0754 or 33/3110–0755* ⊕ *www. zapopan.gob.mx).*

Gay Puerto Vallarta

WORD OF MOUTH

"Puerto Vallarta is *the* gay destination in Mexico, sort of like a Mexican Ft. Lauderdale or Miami."

—MikeT

"[PV is] as quiet or as happening as you want it to be. You could stay close to town at a big resort hotel like the Westin (*very* nice), or you could stay at a hotel in town, near or even right on the gay beach."

—robertino

PUERTO VALLARTA IS A GAY old town. Men check each other out over drinks and suntan oil at Blue Chairs, dangle from parachutes above Los Muertos beach, buff themselves out at South Side gyms. Rainbow boys (and girls) spend a day sailing on vessels flying the multicolored flag of love and then dance 'til morning in one of the city's oversexed discos. Mexico's most popular gay destination draws crowds of "Dorothy's friends" from both sides of the Río Grande, and from the Old World as well.

GET THE SCOOP

Gay Guide Vallarta (⊕ *www. gayguidevallarta.com*) is an excellent and occasionally opinionated source of info about gay-friendly and gay-owned hotels, restaurants, and nightlife. Equally informative is ⊕ *www.vallartaundiscovered.com.*

The Romantic Zone is the hub for rainbow bars and sophisticated, gay-friendly restaurants. Here, many foreigners have—after falling in love with Puerto Vallarta's beaches, jungly green mountains, and friendly people—relocated to PV to fulfill their ultimate fantasy in the form of bistro, bar, or B&B. International savvy (and backing) teamed up with Mexican sensibilities have produced a number of successful gay businesses.

Clubbing may be the favorite pastime in the Romantic Zone, but there's more than one way to cruise Vallarta. Gay boat tours keep the libations flowing throughout the day, horses head for the hills for bird's-eye views of the beach, and Paco's private beach club encourages a head-to-toe tan.

DAYTIME ACTIVITIES

PV has something for every energy level. You can chill on the beach, get active by joining gay-oriented horse-riding tours or sailing expeditions, or spend the day at a secluded beach.

BEACHES & RESORTS

The undisputed yet unassuming king of daytime beach action is **Blue Chairs** (⊠ *South end of Los Muertos Beach, Col. E. Zapata* ☎ *322/222–5040 or 866/514–7969 toll-free in U.S.* ⊕ *www.bluechairs.com*). Shaded by the bright azure umbrellas that distinguish the restaurant/bar/hotel, local boys from the 'hood mingle with asphalt cowboys from the Midwest. Waiters range from snarky queens to cherubic heteros. This is PV's most popular gay beach scene, a magnet for first-timers as well as those sneaking away from social obligations in Guadalajara.

CRUISES

Boana Tours (⊠ *Torre Malibú, Carretera a Mismaloya* ☎ *322/222–0999* ⊕ *www.boana.net*) offers a gay cruise for up to 20 passengers aboard a private chartered yacht. The tour runs 9 to 5 and leaves from Los

Muertos pier. Guests can swim and snorkel and hang out on the beach at Las Animas. Food and drink on the boat are included, but drinks or eats on the beach are not.

Affiliated with Blue Chairs, **Diana's Tours** (☎ *322/222–5040, 866/514–7969 in U.S.* ⊕ *www.bluechairs. com*) is a Thursday booze cruise popular with lesbians and gays. Go for the swimming, snorkeling, and lunch on the beach at Las Animas, or for the unlimited national brands of beer and mixed drinks. Most of the time is spent on the boat. It's easiest to reserve tickets ($75) online using PayPal; there's a $10 discount for booking more than two weeks in advance.

> **TOTAL RELAXATION**
>
> If you must break a sweat on your vacation, the best way is while experiencing a *temazcal*, an ancient Indian sweat lodge ceremony at **Terra Noble** (✉ *Av. Tulipanes 595, Fracc. Lomas de Terra Noble* ☎ *322/222–5400 or 322/223–3530* ⊕ *www.terranoble. com*). The spa also has therapeutic massage, body treatments, facials, and healing therapies such as Reiki.

SPORTS & OUTDOORS

HORSEBACK RIDING

Four-hour, $40 tours with **Boana Tours** (✉ *Torre Malibú, Carretera a Mismaloya* ☎ *322/222–0999* ⊕ *www.boana.net*) include round-trip transportation to its ranch outside the city, several hours on the horse, a snack, and drinks.

AFTER DARK

Puerto Vallarta's club scene may seem tame compared to that of San Francisco or New York, but it's Mexico's most notorious. Guys and dolls begin their nocturnal perambulations at martini and piano bars and chummy pubs before heading to late-night drag shows, dance clubs, and strip joints.

10

BARS

Lesbian-owned, lovingly run **Apaches** (✉ *Olas Altas 439, Col. E. Zapata* ☎ *322/222–4004*) is Vallarta's original martini bar. The single row of sidewalk tables fills up soon after the 5 PM opening, as that's the start of the two-hour happy hour. Popular with straights, lesbians, and gay men warming up for later-evening activities, the narrow bar has added an equally slender adjoining bistro serving bar food and snacks.

In addition to its famous beach scene, **Blue Chairs** (✉ *South end of Los Muertos Beach, Col. E. Zapata* ☎ *322/222–5040* ⊕ *www.blue-*

> **KEEP 'EM COMING**
>
> Not that we're encouraging massive alcohol consumption, but you can spend all night at "happy hour." Hit the first at 2 in the afternoon and rotate throughout gay bars and clubs until 4 AM the next day.

chairs.com) has a popular rooftop bar, **The Blue Moon**, which is the perfect place to watch the sun set. Nightly late-afternoon and evening entertainment ranges from "Blue Balls" Bingo to the biweekly drag show and the Saturday night "Blue Hombre Review." The place has good snacks, and a small swimming pool. Friday is karaoke night, beginning at 7 PM.

We've heard **Frida** (⊠ *Lázaro Cárdenas, between Insurgentes and Aguacate Col. E. Zapata* ☏ *No phone*) described as "the gay Cheers of Mexico." It's a friendly neighborhood bar where you meet young and old, many Mexicans, fewer foreigners, and maybe even some straights. Show up a few times and everyone is sure to know your name.

As popular with straights as it is with PV's rainbow crowd, **Kit Kat** (⊠ *Calle Púlpito 120, Col. E. Zapata* ☏ *322/223–0093*) has a huge list of fun martinis and other classy cocktails. The small space combines South Beach retro with a Zen-like simplicity. The food's not bad either, and they have drag shows at least two weekends a month in high season, at which times reservations are de rigueur.

The air is sometimes smoky in tightly sealed **Garbo** (⊠ *Púlpito 142, Col. E. Zapata* ☏ *322/223–5753*), open daily 6 PM to 2 AM. The small, highly refrigerated piano and jazz bar has a nice varied menu of sophisticated drinks, good canned or live tunes, and waiters that regularly check on your welfare. On the downside, the beer is pricey, and mixed drinks even more so.

Charming **La Noche** (⊠ *Lázaro Cárdenas 257, Col. E. Zapata* ☏ *322/222–3364*) has red walls and a huge, eye-catching chandelier. Gringo-owned, it attracts a crowd of 20- to 40-year-olds (a mix of foreigners and Mexicans), who bring their CDs to play: electronica and house are the favorites. Speaking of which, the house makes excellent cocktails, and not too expensive, either.

DANCE & STRIP CLUBS

Vallarta's first gay disco, Balcones, has emerged from a remodeling as **After Mix** (⊠ *Av. Juárez 182 Altos, Centro* ☏ *322/140–1797*). Touted as an after-hours bar, things are liveliest on weekends after 3 AM, although you'll find a few eager individuals around midnight.

Billing itself as "The Study of Man," **Anthropology** (⊠ *Calle Morelos 101, near Calle Encino below Ignacio L. Vallarta street bridge, Centro* ☏ *322/221–5013*) has nightly strip shows beginning around 11 PM and yup, they take it all off. The management has no rules about customers, shall we say, "interacting" with the strippers during their nearly nonstop parades. There's a cover of about $5, and the club is open nightly. There's a late-night happy hour between 1 and 4 in the morning.

Club Paco Paco/The Ranch (✉ *Lázaro Cárdenas 257, Col. E. Zapata* ☎ *322/222–1899*) are the most popular dance clubs in town with both gays and lesbians. One cover charge gets you into both. The main draw isn't the high-school-auditorium decor but the crowd

HOTEL ALTERNATIVES

Gayguide Vallarta (⊕ *www. gayguidevallarta.com*) has lots of listings for long- and short-term condo rentals.

(nearly everyone ends up here); the female impersonators miming pop songs aren't too bad either. Back at the Ranch, strippers are the draw: policemen, firefighters, construction-worker types baring ... almost all. Paco Paco's biggest selling point is that it outlasts the other gay clubs: it opens at 1 in the afternoon and doesn't close until 6 in the morning. Admission is $5 and gets you one national-label well drink.

Another club that focuses on the after-hours crowd is **Mañana** (✉ *Venustiano Carranza 290* ☎ *322/222–7772* ⊕ *www.clubmanana.com*). Come for the nightly strip show at 11:30, the theme parties (full-moon party, wear-only-white party)—which usually run about $10 per person including a few drinks—or the many other whacky activities. Things don't wind down until 6 AM or so, unless the authorities are on one of their occasional crack-down moods, enforcing the 4 AM curfew.

WHERE TO STAY

Gay hotels offer entertainment that allows you to party on-site without having to worry about getting "home." In addition to the hotels listed here, which are the crème de la crème of Vallarta, hotels like Emperador, overlooking Los Muertos beach, and Quinta María Cortez above Playa Conchas Chinas (⇨ *Chapter 2*) are gay-friendly.

$$$–$$$$ **Casa Cupula.** This multistory, up-to-date B&B has a variety of rooms and prices. It's just a 15-minute walk down to the beach and the Romantic Zone (but the return trip is uphill). Some of the guest rooms have wonderful views of the sea and of layers of houses up and down the surrounding hills—most have balconies. The suites have kitchenettes, washers, dryers, and a separate bedroom upstairs. All are classy, restrained, and distinctly masculine. The airy shared dining room–lounge is comfortable and welcoming; the rooftop terrace with seating and BBQ is lovely. Gays, lesbians, their dogs, and straight friends are welcome. ✉ *Callejon de la Igualdad 129, Col. Amapas, 48399* ☎ *322/223–2484, 866/261–3516 in U.S. and Canada* ⊕ *www. casacupula.com* 💬 *10 rooms, 2 suites* △*In-room: safe, kitchen (some), refrigerator (some), DVD (some), dial-up, Wi-Fi. In-hotel: restaurant, room service, bar, pools, no elevator, laundry service, concierge, parking (no fee), no kids under 18, some pets allowed* 🖃*AE, MC, V* ✪*Closed Aug. and Sept.* ⦿|*CP.*

$$–$$$ **Blue Chairs.** Guys stay here not for the plain rooms but for all that Blue Chairs offers. Horseback riding, drag and strip shows, theme nights, events, parties, booze cruises, and beach cruising all begin—and often end—right here. ✉ *Los Muertos Beach, Col. E. Zapata, 48380*

10

WORK UP A SWEAT

There's more to a gay Vallarta vacation than drinking and dancing. Before baring your bod at the beach, burn off those extra calories at one of PV's many gyms.

On the South Side, **Acqua Day Spa and Gym** (⊠ *Constitución 450* 🕾 *322/223–5270*) has a sauna and steam room in addition to free weights and machines, massage, body treatments, and more. Closed Sunday.

Serious muscle men and women head for **Gold's Gym** (⊠ *Calle Pablo Picasso s/n, Plaza Las Glorias, Zona Hotelera* 🕾 *322/225-6671 or 322/293–3673*) with aerobics, tai chi, yoga, and Pilates as well as a sauna, hot tub, and chiropractic center. For women only, **Total Fitness Gym** (⊠ *Calle Timón 1, at marina, Marina Vallarta* 🕾 *322/221–0770*) is a sparkly clean gym with yoga, spinning, meditation, aerobics classes, and Pilates.

🕾 *322/222–5040, 866/514–7969 from Canada and U.S.* ⊕ *www. bluechairs.com* 🖙 *24 rooms, 16 suites* ♿ *In-room: kitchen (some). In-hotel: 2 restaurants, bars, pool, concierge* ▤ *AE, MC, V* ⍿*EP.*

$$ ⛶ **Villa David.** The public spaces and rooms here are showpieces, melding traditional Mexican architecture with more modern elements and lots of tile. The owners take good care of their gay (male) guests, and don't allow straights or lesbians to book rooms. A trio of little pomeranians have the run of the place, but they're friendly. The clothing-optional guesthouse is securely tucked behind old walls in Gringo Gulch, a straight neighborhood made famous by Liz and Richard. Views of the town and bay are outstanding from the rooftop aerie, and some of the rooms have great views, too. ⊠ *Calle Galeana 348, Centro, 48300* 🕾 *322/223–0315* ⊕ *www.villadavidpv.com* 🖙 *10 rooms* ♿ *In-room: CD, DVD, Wi-Fi. In-hotel: pool, no elevator, public Internet* ▤ *MC, V* ⍿*CP.*

$ ⛶ **Mercurio.** The rooms here are plain, but there's nonetheless much to be said for this small, motel-like place surrounding a swimming pool. First, it has a fabulous location—although not on the beach—in the heart of the Zona Romántica, PV's gay headquarters. The reasonable price leaves money left over for shopping and cruising. ⊠ *Calle Francisco Rodriguez 168, Col. E. Zapata, 48380* 🕾 *322/222–4793* ⊕ *www. hotel-mercurio.com* 🖙 *28 rooms* ♿ *In-room: no phone, safe, kitchen (some), Wi-Fi. In-hotel: bar, pool, no elevator, laundry service, concierge, public Internet, public Wi-Fi* ▤ *AE, D, DC, MC, V* ⍿*CP.*

UNDERSTANDING PUERTO VALLARTA

PUERTO VALLARTA AT A GLANCE

FAST FACTS

Nickname: Foreigners call it PV, or Vallarta, but it has no real nickname. A *vallartense* (person from Puerto Vallarta), however, is known as a *pata salada* (salty foot).
State: PV is in the state of Jalisco, whose capital is Guadalajara.
Population: 220,368
Population density: 142.03 people per square km
Population growth rate 1990–2000: 65.74%
Literacy rate: 95.78%
Religion: Catholic 90%; Protestant/Evangelical 8.5%; other/no religion 1.5%
Type of government: Federal republic; municipality has a democratically elected city council and mayor
Language: Spanish is the official language and spoken by nearly everyone. Many people speak intermediate to fluent-level English; the few people who speak indigenous languages are Cora- and Huichol-speaking people from remote areas of Jalisco and Nayarit.

I was taken in by the bravado and the sounds of Mexico ... not so much the music, but the spirit.

–Herb Alpert (musician)

In its male, in its public, its city aspect, Mexico is an arch-transvestite, a tragic buffoon. Dogs bark and babies cry when Mother Mexico walks abroad in the light of day. The policeman, the Marxist mayor— Mother Mexico doesn't even bother to shave her mustachios. Swords and rifles and spurs and bags of money chink and clatter beneath her skirts. A chain of martyred priests dangles from her waist, for she is an austere, pious lady. Ay, how much—clutching her jangling bosoms; spilling cigars— how much she has suffered.

–Richard Rodriguez

GEOGRAPHY & ENVIRONMENT

Latitude: 20°N (same as Cancún, Mexico; Port-au-Prince, Haiti; Khartoum, Sudan; Hanoi, Vietnam; Calcutta, India)
Longitude: 105° W (same as Regina, Saskatchewan; Denver, Colorado; El Paso, Texas)
Elevation: 40 meters (131 feet) above sea level
Land area: 1,972,550 square km (761,605 square mi)

Terrain: River basin backed by Sierra Madre foothills
Natural hazards: Hurricanes, tidal surges causing inundation of beachfront properties
Environmental issues: Destruction of natural areas due to migration and tourism

---

ECONOMY

Currency: Mexican Peso
Exchange rate: 11.16 pesos = $1
GDP per capita: $9,000 (for comparison, Mexico national average is $10,000, and U.S. national average is $41,800)
Workers receiving minimum wage or less: 9.5%
Major industries: Tourism, commerce, construction, agriculture

I believe Mexico should dedicate 100% of its oil revenues to developing human capital and technological development. None of us politicians should be able to touch that money.

–Vicente Fox

DID YOU KNOW?

■ Two of the four quadrants in Puerto Vallarta's official seal symbolize the tourism industry: a sailfish represents sportfishing; the hands welcome tourists.

■ International law limits the production of tequila to specific regions of Mexico; most are in Jalisco (with specific regions also in Michoacán, Nayarit, Guanajuato, and Tamaulipas states).

HISTORY

Pre-Columbian Mexico

The first nomadic hunters crossed the Bering Straight during the Late Pleistocene Era, some 30,000 or 40,000 years ago, fanning out and finding niches in the varied landscape of North America. In the hot and arid "Great Chichimeca," as the vast area that included the Sonora and Chihuahua deserts and the Great Plains of the United States was known, lived far-flung tribes whose circumstances favored a nomadic lifestyle. Even the unassailable Aztecs were unable to dominate this harsh wilderness and its resilient people.

Mesoamerica, the name given posthumously to the great civilizations of mainland Mexico, spanned as far south of the Great Chichimeca as Honduras and El Salvador. Here, trade routes were established, strategic alliances were formed through warfare or marriage, and enormous temples and palaces were erected on the backs of men, without the aid of beasts of burden or the wheel. Some cultures mysteriously disappeared, others were conquered but not absorbed.

It was in northern Mesoamerica that the continent's first major metropolis, Teotihuacán—which predated the Aztec capital of Tenochtitlán by more than half a century—was built. The gleaming city with beautifully decorated pyramids, palaces, homes, and administrative buildings covered miles and administered to some 175,000 souls; it was abandoned for unknown reasons around AD 700. On the Yucatán Peninsula, great and powerful Maya cities rose up, but like Teotihuacán were abandoned one by one, seemingly at the height of civilization.

During the rise and fall of these great cities, small, loosely organized bands of individuals occupied Mesoamerica's western Pacific coast. By 1200 BC, the culture that archaeologists call Capacha occupied river valleys north and south of what would later be named Bahía de Banderas. From well-positioned settlements, they planted gardens and took advantage of animal and mineral resources from the sea and the surrounding foothills.

These cultures—centered primarily in the present-day states of Nayarit, Jalisco, and Colima—built no large, permanent structures and left few clues about their society. Some of the most compelling evidence comes from artifacts found in tombs. Unlike their more advanced neighbors, the Pacific coast people housed these burial chambers not in magnificent pyramids but in the bottom of vertical shafts deep within the earth. Lifelike dog sculptures were sometimes left to help their deceased owners cross to the other side; servants, too, were buried with their masters for the same purpose. Realistically depicted figures involved in myriad rituals of daily and ceremonial life, most of them excavated only since the 1970s, have given more clues about pre-Hispanic civilizations of Western Mexico.

Only so much information can be gleaned, however, especially since the majority of tombs were looted before archaeological research began. North and south of Banderas Bay, the Aztatlán people seem to have established themselves primarily in river valleys between Tomatlán, in southern Jalisco, and northern Nayarit. In addition to creating utilitarian and ceremonial pottery, they appear to have been skilled in at least rudimentary metallurgy. Aside from the Purépecha of Michoacán, to whom the Aztatlán (or Aztlán) are related, no other Mesoamerican societies were skilled in making or using metal of any kind.

The Colonial Period

History favors those who write it, and the soldier-priest-scribe who documented the discovery of Banderas Bay in 1525 gave it a decidedly European spin. According to Padre Tello, four years after the Spanish demolished the Aztec capital at Tenochtit-lán, about 100 Spanish troops met 10,000 to 20,000 Aztatlán at Punta de Mita, the bay's northernmost point. Then, by Tello's fantastic account, the sun's sudden illumi-nation of a Spanish battle standard (a large pennant) bearing the image of the Virgin of the Immaculate Conception caused the armed indigenous peoples to give up with-out a fight. When they lay their colorful battle flags at the feet of Francisco Cortés de Buenaventura, the Spanish commander named the site Bahía de Banderas, or Bay of Flags.

Subsequent adventurers and explorers rediscovered and used the region around the bay, but it wasn't colonized until three centuries later. The name Bahía de Banderas is seen on maps from the 1600s, although whalers in the 1800s called it Humpback Bay, after their prin-cipal prey. Boats were built on the beach in today's Mismaloya for a missionary expedition to Baja California, and the long, deep bay was used as a pit stop on other long sailing voyages.

To a lesser extent, Banderas Bay was a place of refuge and refueling for pirates. Around the end of the 16th century, Sir Francis Drake laid in wait here for the Manila galleon—sailing south along the coast laden with wares from the Orient. He sent the booty to his patron, Queen Elizabeth of England.

The Formative Years

Although adventurers made use of the area's magnificent bay, Puerto Vallarta's story started inland and made its way to the coast. Mining in this part of the Sierra Madre wasn't as profitable as in Zacate-cas and Guanajuato, but there was plenty of gold and silver to draw the Spaniards' attention. At the vanguard of Span-ish exploration in 1530, the infamous conquistador Nuño Beltrán de Guzmán arrived in the region with a contingent of Spanish soldiers and indigenous allies.

During his tenure in Nueva Galicia (which included today's Jalisco, Zacatecas, and Durango states), de Guzmán siezed land that was settled by native peoples and parceled out *encomiendas* (huge grants of land) to lucky *encomendados* (land-holders) in return for loyalty and favors to the Crown. The landholders were enti-tled to the land and everything on it: the birds of the trees; beasts of the forest; and the unlucky indigenous people who lived there, who were consequently enslaved. De Guzmán's behavior was so outra-geous that by 1536 he had been stripped of authority and sent to prison.

In exchange for their forced labor, the native population received the "protec-tion" of the encomendado, meaning food and shelter, which they had previ-ously without any help from the Spanish. Abuse was inevitable, and many over-worked natives died of famine. Epidem-ics of smallpox, diphtheria, scarlet fever, influenza, measles, and other imported diseases had a disastrous effect. The region's native population was reduced by about 90% within the first 100 years of Spanish occupation.

By the early 17th century, gold and silver were being mined throughout the region; there were bases of operation at San Sebas-tián del Oeste, Cuale, and Talpa. After the War for Independence (1810–21), Mexican entrepreneurs began to extract gold, silver, and zinc previously claimed by the Spanish. In the mid-1800s, the coast around today's Vallarta was under the jurisdiction of the mountain municipalities.

Independence from Spain brought little contentment to average people, who were as disenfranchised and poor as ever. A prime topic of the day among the moneyed elite was the growing conflict between Lib-erals and Conservatives. Liberals, like the lawyer Benito Juárez, favored curtailing the Church's vast power. When the Liber-als prevailed and Juárez became Mexico's first indigenous president (he was a Zapo-tec from Oaxaca), a host of controversial reforms were enacted. Those regarding separation of church and state had immediate and lasting effects.

Settlers on the Bay

The power struggles of the first half of the 19th century had little real impact on relatively unpopulated coastal areas like Banderas Bay. In 1849, a few men from the fishing hamlet of Yelapa camped out at the mouth of the Cuale River, in present-day Puerto Vallarta. A few years later, young Guadalupe Sánchez, his wife, and a few friends were the first official settlers. This entrepreneur made his money by importing salt, vital for extracting mineral from rock. From this business grew the tiny town Las Peñas de Santa María de Guadalupe.

When silver prices dipped between the two World Wars, some of the mountain-based miners returned to their farming roots, relocating to the productive lands of the Ameca River basin (today, Nuevo Vallarta) at the southern border of Nayarit. The fecund land between the mountains and the bay produced ample corn crops, and the growing town of Las Peñas—renamed Puerto Vallarta in honor of a former Jalisco governor—became the seat of its own municipality in 1918.

Development came slowly. By the 1930s there was limited electricity; a small airstrip was built in the 1950s, when Mexicana Airlines initiated the first flights and electricity was finally available around the clock. Retaining the close-knit society and values brought down from the mining towns, each family seemed to know the others' joys and failures. They sat outside their adobe homes to discuss the latest gossip and the international news of the day.

The Modern Era

Honoring a promise made to the Mexican government by John F. Kennedy, President Richard Nixon flew into an improved PV airport in 1970 to sign a treaty settling boundary disputes surrounding the Rio Grande, meeting with his Mexican counterpart, Gustavo Díaz Ordaz. Upon asking for an armored car, he was cheerfully told that the convertible that had been arranged would do just fine. After riding parade-style along the roadway lined with cheering citizens and burros garlanded in flowers, the American leader is said to have asked why, if he was a Republican, the road was lined with donkeys. To which his host sensibly responded, "Well, where in the world would we get all those elephants?"

It took about 500 years for Puerto Vallarta to transition from discovery to major destination, but the city is making up for lost time. "When I was a child here, in the 1950s, Puerto Vallarta was like a big family," the town's official chronicler, the late don Carlos Munguía, said. "When I married, in 1964, there were about 12,000 people." By the early '70s the population had jumped to 35,000 and continued to grow steadily.

Today the greater Puerto Vallarta area has some 220,368, a significant number of them expat Americans and Canadians who vacationed here and never left. The metropolitan area has three universities and a vast marina harboring yachts, tour boats, and the Mexican navy. In 2005 the harbor was expanded to accommodate three cruise ships; the overflow has to anchor offshore. While many folks lament the loss of the good old days before tourism took off, some things haven't changed: Most *vallartenses* (Puerto Vallarta natives) are still intimately acquainted with their neighbors and the man or woman who owns the corner taco stand, which is likely to have been there for years, maybe even generations.

CHRONOLOGY

ca. 350 BC   Oldest evidence of civilization—a ceramic piece from Ixtapa (northwest of Puerto Vallarta)—dates to this time

ca. 1100   Indigenous Aztatlán people dominate region from present-day Sinaloa to Colima states; create first-known settlement in area

1525   First Spanish–Indian confrontation in the region, at Punta de Mita. By Spanish accounts, 100 Spanish soldiers prevailed over tens of thousands armed native peoples. Bahía de Banderas (Bay of Flags) was named for the battle flags of the indigenous army that were (or so claimed the Spanish) thrown down in defeat

1587   Pirate Thomas Cavendish attacks Punta de Mita, looting pearls gathered from Mismaloya and the Marietas Islands

1664   Mismaloya serves as a shipyard for vessels bound for exploration and conquest of Baja California

1849   Yelapa fishermen are said to have found excellent fishing at the mouth of the Cuale River, making them the first unofficial settlers

1851   Puerto Vallarta founded, under the name Las Peñas de Santa María de Guadalupe, by the salt merchant Guadalupe Sánchez

1918   The small but growing seaside town becomes county seat and is renamed Puerto Vallarta in honor of former Jalisco State governor Ignacio Luis Vallarta (1871–75)

1922   Yellow fever kills some 150 people

1925   Flood and landslides during a great storm form narrow Cuale Island in the middle of the Cuale River in downtown PV

1931   Puerto Vallarta gets electricity (7–10 PM only)

1951   Reporters covering centennial celebrations—marked with a 21-gun naval salute and a wealthy wedding—capture the small town charm, exposing this isolated coastal gem to their countrymen

1963   Hollywood film *Night of the Iguana*, directed by John Huston and starring Richard Burton and Ava Gardner, puts PV on the world map, due to the much-publicized affair between Burton and Elizabeth Taylor (who was not in the movie) during the filming here

1970   Vallarta builds a new airport, and improves the electrical and highway systems for Richard Nixon's official visit with President Díaz Ordaz

2000   Census reports the city's population as 159,080

2005   Population rapidly increases to 220,368 in greater metropolitan area

2006   Ground is broken for the 385-slip luxury-yacht marina at La Cruz de Huanacaxtle, north of Bucerías, continuing the trend of converting quiet fishing villages into big-bucks vacation destinations

GOVERNMENT & ECONOMY

Government & Politics

Mexico is a federal republic with three branches of government—executive, judiciary, and legislative; the latter comprised by a senate and house of deputies (house of representatives). The basis for today's government is the 1917 Constitution, which, when ratified and implemented several years after that date, signaled the end of the Mexican Revolution.

The Revolution, at the dawn of the 20th century, was the combined, if disjointed, effort of various groups with almost polar opposite ideals and reasons for revolt. Campaigning under the slogan "No reelection!" the wealthy and influential northerner Francisco I. Madero's driving desire was to end the 33-year presidency/dictatorship of General Porfirio Diaz. Madero's goals were mainly ideological and intellectual. In the south, the poor, disenfranchised, and mainly indigenous population rallied around the charismatic Emiliano Zapata, who crusaded relentlessly for land reform in his native state of Morelos. Lack of cohesive leadership and goals made the revolt drag on for a decade, resulting in some 2 million deaths—including many civilians.

From the ashes of postwar chaos rose the political party known by its acronym, PRI (Partido Revolucionario Institucional). Adopting the green, red, and white of the Mexican flag, the Institutional Revolutionary Party quickly became the national party of Mexico.

As the decades rolled by, opposition parties were allowed in the legislature in small numbers, mainly to provide an illusion of legitimacy. Outgoing PRI presidents hand-selected their successors and left office with piles of the nation's cash and magnificent properties. And why not, as federal law protects ex-presidents from prosecution?

Modern presidents have been no exception to the pattern of corruption. Well-respected during his term, president (and Harvard-educated economist) Carlos Salinas de Gortari (term: 1988–94) increased his personal fortune while leaving Mexico in financial ruin. Mexico's economy had been on a downward spiral for decades, and Salinas's imprudent fiscal policies pushed the country to the breaking point (⇨ Economy).

Other issues, too, forced the normally fatalistic Mexicans to become increasingly unhappy with the status quo. Mexico City mayor Cuauhtémoc Cárdenas lost the 1988 election due to obvious election fraud. Fighting for social justice, the Zapatista Liberation Army (EZLN) staged a sudden and dramatic uprising in Chiapas State, while lesser rebellions threatened in Guerrero and Oaxaca. Popular presidential candidate Luis Donaldo Colosio was murdered in 1994. It was increasingly difficult to ignore the nation's financial, political, and social crises.

Salinas's successor, Ernesto Zedillo Ponce de León (term: 1994–2000), was left to deal with a massive devaluation of the country's currency and the resulting across-the-board financial hardship for the Mexican people. Middle-class people awoke just weeks after the president's inauguration to find their salaries cut by 40% and their mortgages and car payments increased by roughly the same amount.

Although generally following the mandate of his political party, Zedillo did institute important changes. Instead of hand-selecting his successor in the time-honored tradition, the former banker and education minister established the first presidential primary election. This departure from the norm inspired cautious optimism in previously apathetic voters. Blatantly illegal election maneuvers like voter intimidation and ballot-box stuffing in the countryside were monitored and curtailed.

The election in 2000 of opposition-party candidate Vicente Fox Quesada, and the peaceful transition to power that followed, left the country in a state of shock: more than 70 years of one-party rule was over. Even the winning party, PAN (Partido de Acción Nacional, or National Action Party), could scarcely believe the results.

By his own account, President Vicente Fox (term: 2000–2006) fell far short of such election promises as 7% economic growth per year; however, his historic tenure of office has changed the country. He enjoyed an approval rating averaging nearly 60% during his six-year term, and earned the admiration of his countrymen for his sincere interest in the working poor.

Mexico's 2006 presidential election was nothing if not controversial. The front runner was Andrés Manuel López Obrador, a huge hit with the poor. Representing the left-of-center PRD (Partido de la Revolución Democrática, or Party of Democratic Revolution), the former mayor of Mexico City lost the election by less than 1% to PAN's candidate, Felipe Calderón. Charges of fraud and even meddling by the United States were rampant, and López Obrador initially refused to concede defeat, setting up a "parallel government" and holding massive rallies in downtown Mexico City.

President Calderón got off to a rocky start, amid mass confusion and resentment and a weak mandate from the Mexican people. Still, he's started out with a show of force, especially tackling the twin demons of drug trafficking and corruption. His other most important challenges will be expanding trade-creating jobs, and improving living conditions for millions of underprivileged children and adults.

Following the national template, Puerto Vallarta and Jalisco State have traditionally voted PRI, and the majority of legislators still represent the tri-color party,

as does the mayor of Puerto Vallarta. The last two governors (since 1994) have belonged to the business-oriented PAN, including the incumbent, Francisco Javier Ramírez Acuña. Mirroring the national trend, greater transparency is seen in local and state politics.

Economy

January 2006 figures indicated the country's biggest trade surplus in nine years: $398 million. Record oil exports were reported in 2005 as well as increased auto exports, the latter mainly to the United States. The U.S. is far and away Mexico's largest trading partner, representing 87.6% of its trade as opposed to its second-most-important partner, Canada, with just 1.8%.

Trade statistics in the past had been significantly smaller. Traditionally inward-looking, the government party, PRI, was forced to expand Mexico's static and tightly controlled economy under President Miguel de la Madrid (1982–88) after a necessary but painful devaluation of the peso in 1982. Successor Carlos Salinas de Gortari continued to open the Mexican market, signing the North American Free Trade Agreement (NAFTA) with the United States and Canada in 1994.

However, Salinas and the PRI ignored the country's obvious signs of economic distress. Salinas's blatant corruption and failed economic programs left his successor, Ernesto Zedillo, with a 40% currency devaluation just weeks after taking office, followed by a bank bailout of more than $90 billion.

Zedillo's prudent economic policies slowly got the country back on track. And his handling of the opposition party's triumph in the 2000 presidential election—after 71 years of uninterrupted PRI rule—kept Mexico from erupting into political and economic chaos.

Today Mexico fluctuates between the largest and second-largest economy—and consistently has the highest per-capita income—in Latin America. Conversely, the unemployment rate, 3.6% (April 2006), is the lowest in Latin America. In January 2007 Mexico's inflation rate was 3.981%, one of the lowest rates in 37 years.

It's not all highs and glory, however. The 490,000 new jobs created during President Fox's administration is about one-tenth of what's needed to keep the country employed. Millions of Mexicans—including a significant number from Jalisco State—work illegally in the United States, where they might easily earn 10 times or more the minimum wage of their own country, which is less than US$5 a day. According to a July 2005 article in *The San Diego-Union Tribune,* remittances from these workers are Mexico's second-largest source of income, after oil. More than $23 million is estimated to have been wired south of the border in 2005.

Another of Mexico's leading industries is tourism. Nearly 22 million international visitors came to Mexico in 2005, a 6.5% increase over the previous year. According to Sectur, Mexico's Tourism Secretariat, these visitors left behind $11.8 billion in revenue, compared to $10.84 billion in 2004 and $9.46 billion in 2003. Hotel occupancy and the number of cruise-ship passengers continue to rise as well.

Tourism is far and away the largest sector of Vallarta's economy, and the tourism stats continue to climb. The cruise-ship terminal is being expanded, and the number of hotel rooms in Puerto Vallarta and Nayarit is rapidly increasing.

PEOPLE & SOCIETY

Ethnic Groups

The population of Puerto Vallarta is overwhelmingly of mextizo (mixed native American and Spanish descent). According to the 2000 census, fewer than 1% of Jalisco residents speak an indigenous language. Compare that to nearby states: Michoacán with 3.6%, Guerrero with about 14% and Oaxaca, where more than a third of the inhabitants converse in a native language. Those indigenous people who do live in Jalisco State are small groups of Purépecha (also called Tarascans), in the south. The Purépecha were among the very few groups not conquered by the powerful Aztec nation that controlled much of Mesoamerica at the time of the Spanish conquest.

Although not large in number, the indigenous groups most associated with Nayarit and Jalisco states are the Cora and their relatives, the Huichol. Isolated in mountain and valley hamlets and individual *rancherías* (tiny farms) deep in the Sierra Madre, both have maintained to a large extent their own customs and culture. According to the CDI (Comisión Nacional Para el Desarrollo de los Pueblos Indígenas, or National Commission for the Development of Native Peoples), there are about 24,390 Cora in Durango, Zacatecas, and Nayarit states, and some 43,929 Huichol, mainly in Jalisco and Nayarit. Nearly 70% of the culturally related groups speak their native language and about half of the households have electricity.

In 1947 a group of prominent vallartenses was returning along twisty mountain roads from an excursion to Mexico City. When the driver lost control and the open-sided bus plunged toward the abyss, death seemed certain. But a large rock halted the bus's progress, and "*Los Favorecidos*" ("The Lucky Ones"), as they came to be known, returned to Puerto Vallarta virtually unharmed. Their untrammeled gestures of thanks to the town's patron saint, the Virgin of Guadalupe, set the precedent for this animated religious procession. Today, all Puerto Vallartans consider themselves to be Los Favorecidos, and thus universally blessed. This optimism and good cheer are two vital components of the local persona. For those of us fortunate enough to visit—for a short vacation or half a year—that angelic magnetism is a big part of the pull.

Religion

Mexico is about 89% Catholic; Puerto Vallarta is 90% Catholic. The Catholic population is overwhelmingly dedicated to the Virgin of Guadalupe, the patron saint of Puerto Vallarta, and of Mexico. Most of the non-Catholic 10% of the population have been converted in the last 50 years to Protestant and Evangelical Christianity.

Despite its strong religious character, Mexico has strict anticlerical laws inaugurated by president Benito Juárez and codified in the 1917 Constitution, which still governs the country. Dozens of laws limit religious participation in civil life. A church wedding is not recognized, churches and church land are public property, and Mass may not be held in public. Ministers, priests, and nuns may not vote or wear their vestments in public.

It's no surprise that these and other strict laws outraged the Church and devout Catholics when the Constitution was ratified. The ensuing Cristero Revolt (1926–29) led to tens of thousands of deaths and the assassination of then-President Alvaro Obregón by a religious fanatic. The headquarters for the revolt was staunchly Catholic and traditionalist Guadalajara, the capital of Jalisco State.

Many of the religious laws are not strictly enforced, however. No one dared to deny charismatic John Paul II the right to hold open-air Masses when the hugely popular pope visited in the 1980s and '90s.

And because of the need, foreign priests are permitted to work in Mexico despite a law that bans this.

Family, friends, and having a good time are central to Mexican life, and the Catholic liturgical calendar obliges with many excuses to party. In Puerto Vallarta the biggest fiesta of the year honors the Virgin of Guadalupe. Consecutive visions of *la virgen morena* (the dark-skinned virgin), as she is affectionately called, are said to have appeared to Juan Diego, a Chichimec peasant, soon after the Spanish conquest of Mexico. Asked by a bishop to provide proof of the Lady's visit (on Tepeyac Hill, north of present-day Mexico City), Juan Diego is said to have collected in his cloak a shower of roses that the apparition provided. During transport, however, the bundle of roses disappeared to be replaced by an image of the saint herself. Report of the supposed miracle greatly helped the invaders to convert the pantheistic native population.

The bishop, the Pope, and soon the majority of Mexicans were convinced of the miracle. The cloak, with the image still clearly visible, hangs above the altar in one of several important churches built at Tepeyac Hill, now called La Villa de Guadalupe. The site of the Virgin's reported 1531 visit was near a temple to the Aztec earth goddess Tonantzín.

The Feast Day of the Virgin of Guadalupe is Puerto Vallarta's most important religious holiday. During the weeks leading to the Mass held in her honor on December 12, area congregations, civic leaders, and businesses—including restaurants and hotels—join in colorful processions from their place of business to the downtown cathedral.

Dress

In deference to the tropical heat, vallartenses dress comfortably and casually, yet not indifferently. Young girls wear the latest fashions, with bellies—of all shapes and sizes—bared, while matrons favor comfortable, cool shifts and skirts. Men wear suits (with or without ties) or slacks and guayaberas. Businesswomen wear suits or classy outfits, panty hose, and high heels with elegant aplomb, always managing to look cool and crisp, while their north-of-the-border counterparts sport red faces, swollen ankles ... and swoon at the mere mention of pantyhose.

Mexican men don't walk around shirtless except at the beach or pool, and women don a cover-up at least. While increasingly stylish and modern, Mexicans tend to dress modestly. It's only in the last generation or two that women have felt comfortablewearingbathingsuits,andmany—especially older women from smaller towns—still swim in shorts and T-shirts.

In downtown PV, cobblestone streets make walking in heels difficult, although Mexican women seem to pull it off. The addition of potholes and uneven sidewalks make sensible walking shoes or sandals preferable for most occasions. Popular on PV streets is the comfortable women's "San Miguel shoe," which comes in many styles and colors.

Etiquette

Mexicans are extremely polite people. The proverb "You catch more flies with honey than with vinegar" might have been invented here. Mexicans wait to be invited into a home, even by relatives. Business meetings begin with small talk and inquiries about family and mutual friends. Even phone conversations take a while to get to the point.

Ask a business acquaintance the name of the person who will be leading a meeting, and he might respond "*Su servidor*" (Your servant), referring to himself. Business letters often conclude "I remain your faithful servant."

Some of these formulaic phrases should be taken with a big grain of sea salt. When talking about his home, a Puerto Vallartan might say "*Your* home (meaning *his* home) is at 333 Juárez Street." This form of *"mi casa es su casa"* can be used equally with a great friend or a first-time acquaintance.

Resist the impulse to pay an unsolicited visit. Unspecific invitations to "come visit some time," which are, in most cases, made just to be polite, should be ignored unless a summons to a specific event is made.

Even when extremely annoyed or angry, Mexicans tend to maintain calm and decorum, using hyperbole or veiled sarcasm to display their displeasure. Foreign travelers throwing tantrums because of late tour buses or poor service must seem like creatures from another planet to Mexicans, who would usually endure most any inconvenience rather than create a scene.

This tendency of Mexicans to keep their thoughts to themselves can lead to frustration and confusion for foreigners. "When will the bus come?" a traveler might inquire regarding a bus that is 15 minutes late. *"Ahorita viene"* is the tour leader's inevitable answer. While the literal translation of this phrase is "It will be right here," the meaning in its cultural context is something like: "It will get here when it gets here. I have no control over the matter, but certainly cannot tell you that." Mexicans are experts at reading—and speaking—between the lines.

Language

The Mexican lexicon is full of examples of exceeding reticence and politeness. Some of these phrases leave other Spanish speakers rolling their eyes or rolling in the aisles with mirth. For example, instead of saying *"¿Cómo?"* ("What?") when something is not heard or understood, Mexicans say *"¿Mande?"*, an extremely old-fashioned, formal command meaning "Order me."

Most Mexicans use the terms *"Me da vergüenza"* and *"Me da pena"* interchangeably. To a Spaniard, the former means "I am embarrassed" or "I am ashamed"; the latter, "I'm in pain" or "It hurts me."

Another idiosyncrasy of Mexican Spanish is the use of the diminutive suffix *"–ita."* In Spain this word ending is mainly used to indicate a thing's small size or delicate nature. In Mexico this add-on is so common that words without it seem almost brusque, rude, or indicating lack of love or concern. Few people call their grandmother *abuela,* for example: *abuelita* (dear or little grandmother) is almost universal. One might ask for a *cervecita* instead of a *cerveza* to convey the desire not to impose on another person or put them out. A tour guide mentions that *propinitas* (small tips) are accepted when she is actually hoping for a big, fat tip. It's just another example of the national obsession with dancing delicately around life's baser truths and demands.

In his epic examination of the Mexican national character, *The Labyrinth of Solitude,* Nobel prize–winning essayist Octavio Paz describes the Mexican like this: "His language is full of reticences, of metaphors and allusions, of unfinished phrases, while his silence is full of tints, folds, thunderheads, sudden rainbows, indecipherable threats." Which demonstrates that while the national tendency might be toward disguising true meanings, Mexican speech can be brilliant and filled with imagery.

The Magic of Mexico

To say that Mexico is a magical place means more than it's a place of great natural beauty and fabulous experiences. Cities like Catemaco, in Veracruz, have a reputation for their *brujos* and *brujas* (male and female witches, respectively) and herbal healers (*curanderos/curanderas*). But Mexicans use these services even in modern Mexico City and Guadalajara, and tourist towns like Puerto Vallarta, although they don't always advertise it. Some might resort to using a curandera to reverse *mal de ojo,* the evil eye, thought to be responsible for a range of unpleasant symptoms, circumstances, disease, or even death.

A *limpia,* or cleansing, is the traditional cure for the evil eye. The healer usually passes a raw chicken or turkey egg over the sufferer to draw out the bad spirit. Green plants like basil, or branches from certain trees can also be used, drawing the greenery over the head, front, and back to decontaminate the victim. Prayer is an essential ingredient.

Some cures are of a more practical nature. Mexican herbalists, like their colleagues around the world, use tree bark, nuts, berries, roots, and leaves to treat everything from dandruff to cancer. Epazote, or wormseed, is a distinctly flavored plant whose leaves are used in cooking. As its English name implies, its medicinal task is to treat parasites.

Most folk wisdom seems to draw from both fact and, if not fiction, at least superstition. Breezes and winds are thought to produce a host of negative reactions: from colds and cramps to far more drastic ailments like paralysis. Some people prefer sweating in a car or bus to rolling down the window and being hit by the wind, especially since mixing hot and cold is something else to be avoided. Even worldly athletes may refuse a cold drink after a hot run. Sudden shock is thought by some to cause lasting problems.

Although it doesn't take a leap of faith to believe that herbal remedies cure disease and grandma's advice was right on, some of the stuff sold in shops is a bit "harder to swallow." It's difficult to imagine, for example, that the sky-blue potion in a pint-size bottle will bring you good luck, or the lilac-color one can stop people from gossiping about you. Those that double as floor polish seem especially suspect.

Whether magic and prophesy are real or imagined, they sometimes have concrete results. Spanish conquistador Hernán Cortés arrived on the east coast of present-day Mexico in 1519, which cor-

related to the year "One Reed" of the Aztec calendar. A few centuries prior to Cortés's arrival, the benevolent god-king Quetzalcoatl had, according to legend, departed the same coast on a raft of snakes, vowing to return in the year One Reed to reclaim his throne.

News of Cortés—a metal-wearing god-man accompanied by strange creatures (horses and dogs) and carrying lightning (cannons and firearms)—traveled quickly to the Aztec capital. The Emperor Moctezuma was nervous about Quetzalcoatl's return and his reaction to the culture of war and sacrifice the Aztecs had created. In his desire to placate the returning god, Moctezuma ignored the advice of trusted advisers and literally opened the door for the complete destruction of the Aztec empire.

Machismo & La Malinche

Mexican machismo is a complicated concept fit for entire books of study. It's more than *piropos* (flirtatious or suggestive, and sometimes poetic, comments) or drinking beer for days at a time with the boys. According to essayist Octavio Paz (1914–98), the Mexican's machismo is in fact defensive rather than offensive: a kind of immunity to being hurt or humiliated by the outside world. Several great thinkers, including Paz, have suggested that this stoicism dates back to the Spanish conquest. Taking indigenous women as slaves or concubines, Spanish invaders left the girls' and women's husbands, fathers, and brothers outraged, yet powerless to intervene.

According to this psychological scenario, Mexican men take lovers in order to reject their wives before being snubbed themselves. Scorned and humiliated by her husband, a woman may then lavish her love and attention on her sons, who idolize their perfect mothers but grow up to emulate their fathers, perpetuating the cycle.

If the icon of the perfect woman is the Virgin Mary, the faithless woman who epitomizes female perfidy is La Malinche. Born Malinztín and christened Doña Marina by the Spanish, La Malinche was a real woman who played a fascinating role in the conquest of Mexico. As a young woman of possibly noble birth, Malinztín was sold into slavery and later given as a gift to the Spanish. She became a valued interpreter for Hernán Cortés thanks to her ability to speak three languages: her native Mayan tongue; Nahuatl, language of the Aztecs; and (later) Spanish. Her keen mind helped the Spanish strategize; as Cortés's mistress, she bore him a son. Although it was her own people who originally sold her into slavery, La Malinche has become the national symbol for female infidelity and betrayal.

La Vida Loca

Living the good life in Mexico—specifically in and around Banderas Bay—seems to get easier year by year, but it's getting pricey as well. Americans and Canadians are by far the biggest groups of expats. In addition to those who have relocated to make Mexico their home, many more foreigners have part-time retirement or vacation homes here. Those who realized their dreams of moving to Mexico a decade or more ago are sitting pretty, as the cost of land and houses soars. A two-bedroom property in a gated community by the sea begins at around $350,000, and the cost is climbing. You could get more modest digs for several times less; at the upper end of the spectrum, the sky's the limit. Construction prices keep going up, too, as builders realize how deep are the pockets of foreign investors.

The sheer number of foreigners living in Puerto Vallarta facilitates adventures that were much more taxing a decade or two ago, like building a home or finding an English-speaking realtor or lawyer. Contractors and shopkeepers are used to dealing with gringos; most speak good to excellent English. The town is rich with English-language publications and opportunities for foreigners to meet up for events or volunteer work.

THE NATURAL WORLD

Geography

On the same latitude as the Hawaiian Islands, Puerto Vallarta sits at the center point of C-shape Banderas Bay. Spurs from the Sierra Cacoma run down to the sea, forming a landscape of numerous valleys. This highly fractured mountain range is just one of many smaller ranges within the Sierra Madre—which runs south from the Rockies to South America. Sierra Cacoma sits at the juncture of several major systems that head south toward Oaxarta State. Forming a distinct but related system is the volcanic or transversal volcanic axis that runs east to west across the country—and the globe. Comprising part of the so-called Ring of Fire, this transverse chain of mountains includes some of the world's most active volcanoes. Both Volcán de Fuego, southeast of Puerto Vallarta in Colima State, and the giant Popocateptl, near the Gulf of Mexico, are currently active. Visible from Puerto Vallarta are the more intimate Sierra Vallejo and the Sierra Caule ranges, to the north and south respectively.

Heading down to the sea from these highlands are a number of important rivers, including the Ameca and the Mascota, which join forces not far from the coast at a place called Las Juntas (the joining). The Ameca is a large river whose mouth forms the boundary between Jalisco and Nayarit states. The valley floor is naturally boggy in some areas, but suitable for growing corn, sugarcane, and other crops elsewhere. The Cuale River empties into the ocean at Puerto Vallarta, dividing the city center in two. In addition to many rivers the area is blessed with seasonal and permanent streams and springs.

Banderas Bay, or Bahía de Banderas, is Mexico's largest bay, at 42 km (26 mi) tip to tip. The northern point, Punta de Mita, is in Nayarit state. Towns at the southern extreme of the bay, at Cabo Corrientes, are accessible only by boat or dirt roads. Cabo Corrientes (Cape Currents) is named for the frequently strong offshore currents. The mountains backing the Costalegre are part of the Sierra Madre Occidental range. The hilly region of eroded plains has two main river systems: the San Nicolás and Cuitzmala.

Several hundred miles east of Banderas Bay, Guadalajara—capital of Jalisco State—occupies the west end of 5,400-foot Atemajac Valley, which is surrounded by mountains. Just south of Guadalajara, Lake Chapala is Mexico's largest natural lake. It is fed by the Lerma–Santiago system, which, crossing the mountains, feeds other rivers and streams that empty into the Pacific.

Flora

The western flanks of the Sierra Madre and foothills leading down to the sea are characterized by tropical deciduous forest. At the higher levels are expanses of pine-oak forest. Many species of pines thrive in these woods, mixed in with *encinos* and *robles,* two different categories of oak; within each are many separate species. Walnut trees and oyamel, a type of fir, are the mainstays of the lower arroyos, or river basins. Along the coastal fringe magnificent *huanacaxtle,* also called *parota* (in English, monkey pod or elephant ear tree), mingle with equally huge and impressive mango as well as kapok, cedar, tropical almond, tamarind, flamboyant, and willow. The brazilwood tree is resistant to insects and therefore ideal for making furniture. *Matapalo,* or strangler fig, are common in this landscape. As its name hints, these fast-growing trees embrace others in a death grip; once the matopalo is established, the host tree eventually dies.

Colima palms, known locally as *guaycoyul,* produce small round nuts smashed for oil or sometimes fed to domestic animals. Mango, avocado, citrus, and guava are found in the wild; these and a huge number of cultivated crops thrive in the region. Imported trees and bushes often seen surrounding homes and small farms include Indian laurel, bamboo, and bougainvillea.

The coastal fringe north of San Blas (in Nayarit) is surprisingly characterized by savannahs. Guinea grass makes fine animal fodder for horses and cows. Lanky coconut trees line roads and beaches. These have many uses and are sometimes planted in groves. The watery "milk" is a refreshing drink, and the meat of the coconut, although high in saturated fat, can be eaten or used in many types of candy. Another drink, *agua da tuba,* is made from the heart of the palm; the trunk is used in certain types of construction. Mangroves thrive in saltwater estuaries, providing an ecosystem for crabs and crustaceans as well as migratory and local birds.

South of Banderas Bay, thorn forest predominates along the coastal strip, backed by tropical deciduous forest. Leguminous trees like the tabachin, with its bright orange flowers, have long dangling seed pods used by indigenous people as rattles. Other prominent area residents are the acacias, hardy trees with fluffy puff-balls of light yellow blooms. Many species of cactus thrive in the dry forest, which is home to more than 1,100 species of vascular plants. The *nopal,* or prickly pear cactus abounds; local people remove the spines of the cactus pads and grill them, or use them in healthful salads. The fruit of the prickly pear, called *tuna,* is used to make a refreshing drink, *agua de tuna.* In this region, especially around Chamela and Cuixmala, about 16% of the plant species are endemic.

Fauna

Mammals in the area are few. Hunting, deforestation, and the encroachment of humans have diminished many once-abundant species. In the mountains far from humankind, endangered margay, jaguar, and ocelot hunt their prey, which includes spider monkeys, deer, and peccaries. More commonly seen in a wide range of habitats are skunks, raccoons, rabbits, and coyote. The coatimundi is an endearing little animal that lives in family groups, often near streambeds. Inquisitive and alert, they resemble tall, slender prairie dogs. Along with tanklike, slow-moving armadillo, the sandy-brown coatimundi is among the animals you're most likely to spot without venturing too deep within the forest. Local people call the coatimundi both *tejón* and *pisote,* and often keep them as pets.

Poisonous snakes in the area include the Mexican rattlesnake and the fer-de-lance. Locals call the latter *cuatro narices* (four noses) because it appears to have four nostrils. It's also called *nauyaca;* the bite of this viper can be deadly. There are more than a dozen species of coral snakes with bands of black, yellow, and red in different patterns. False corals imitate this color scheme to fool their predators, but unless you're an expert in the subject, it's probably best not to try to figure out which is which.

Of interest to most visitors are the region's birds and sea creatures both resident and migratory. The most famous of the migratory marine species is the humpback whale for which Banderas Bay was once named. Called *ballena jorobada,* or "humpback" whale, these leviathans grow to 17 meters (51 feet) and weigh 40 to 50 tons and travel in pods, feeding on krill and tiny fish. During a given year the females in area waters may be either mating or giving birth. During their amazing annual migration of thousands of miles from the Bering Sea, the hardy creatures may lose some 10,000 pounds. Hunted nearly to extinction in the 1900s, humpbacks remain an endangered species.

A few Bryde whales make their way to Banderas Bay and other protected waters near the end of the humpback season, as do some killer whales (orca) and false killer whales. Bottlenose, spinner, and pantropic spotted dolphins are present pretty much year-round. These acrobats love to bow surf just under the water's surface and to leap into the air. Another spectacular leaper is the velvety-black manta ray, which can grow to 9 meters (30 feet) wide. Shy but lovely spotted eagle rays hover close to the ocean floor, where they feed on crustaceans and mollusks. Nutrient-rich Pacific waters provide sustenance for a wide range of other sea creatures as well. Among the most eye-catching are the graceful king angelfish and the iridescent bumphead parrotfish, striped Indo-Pacific sargeants and Moorish idols, and the funny-looking guinea fowl puffer and its close relative, the equally unusual black-blotched porcupine fish.

The varied landscape of Nayarit and Jalisco states provides a tapestry of habitats—shoreline, rivers, marshes, lagoons, and mangroves—for some 350 species of birds. In the mangroves, standouts are the great blue heron, mangrove cuckoo, and vireo. Ocean and shore birds include red-billed tropic birds as well as various species of heron, egret, gulls, and frigatebirds. Military macaws patrol the thorn forests, and songbirds of all stripes live in the pine-oak forests. About 40% of the birds in the Costalegre region are migratory. Among the residents are the yellow-headed parrot and the Mexican wood nymph, both threatened species.

Environmental Issues

The biggest threat to the region is deforestation of the tropical dry forest. Slash-and-burn techniques are used to prepare virgin forest for agriculture and pasturing of animals. Like tropical forest everywhere, this practice has a very harmful and nonproductive effect, as the thin soil fails to produce after the mulch-producing trees and shrubs have been stripped.

Although the tropical dry forest (also called tropical thorn forest) has only been easily accessible to settlement since a coast highway opened in 1972, they are now being deforested due to the increasing tourism and human population. Controlled ecotourism offers a potential solution, although failed projects in the area have significantly altered or drained salt marshes and mangrove swamps.

Like similar ecosystems along Mexico's Pacific coast from southern Sonora to Chiapas, the dry forest is an extremely important ecosystem. It represents one of the richest in Mexico and also one with the highest level of endemism (plant and animal species found nowhere else). Several species of hardwood trees, including the Pacific coast mahogany and Mexican kingwood, are being over-harvested for use in the building trade. The former is endangered and the latter, threatened.

South of Puerto Vallarta in the Costalegre are two adjacent forest reserves that together form the 32,617-acre **Chamela–Cuixmala Biosphere Reserve**. Co-owned and managed by nonprofit agencies, private companies, and Mexico's National University, UNAM, the reserve protects nine major vegetation types, including the tropical dry forest, tropical deciduous, and semi-deciduous forests. A riparian environment is associated with the north bank of the Cuixmala River. Within the reserve there are approximately 72 species considered at risk for extinction including the American crocodile and several species of sea turtles.

Hojonay Biosphere Reserve was established by the Hojonay nonprofit organization to preserve the jaguar of the Sierra de Vallejo range and its habitat. The 157,060-acre reserve is in the foothills and mountains behind La Cruz de Huanacaxtle and San Francisco, in Nayarit State.

At the present time there are no tours or casual access to either reserve, which serve as a buffer against development and a refuge for wildlife.

BOOKS & MOVIES

Books

Those interested in Mexican culture and society have a wealth of books from which to choose. *The Mexicans: A Personal Portrait of a People*, by Patrick Oster, is a brilliant nonfiction study of Mexican persona and personality. Like Patrick Oster, Alan Riding, author of *Distant Neighbors: A Portrait of the Mexicans*, was a journalist for many years in Mexico City whose insight, investigative journalism skills, and cogent writing skills produced an insightful look into the Mexican mind and culture.

Written by poet, essayist, and statesman Octavio Paz, *The Labyrinth of Solitude*, is classic, required reading for those who love Mexico or want to know it better. *The True Story of the Conquest of Mexico*, by Bernal Diaz de Castillo, is a fascinating account of the conquest by one of Cortés's own soldiers.

There are few recommended books specifically about Puerto Vallarta. These are available mainly in PV.

La Magia de Puerto Vallarta, by Marilú Suárez-Murias, is a bilingual (English and Spanish) coffee-table book discussing beaches, history, people, and places of Puerto Vallarta. The information is interesting, but the photographs are terribly grainy. For a lighthearted look at life in PV through the eyes of an expat, read *Puerto Vallarta on 49 Brain Cells a Day* and *Refried Brains*, both by Gil Gevins. Those interested in Huichol art and culture might read *People of the Peyote: Huichol Indian History, Religion and Survival*, by Stacy Shaefer and

Peter Furst. If you can get past the first couple of chapters, it's smoother sailing. Also by Stacy Shaefer is *To Think With a Good Heart: Wixarica Women, Weavers and Shamans*.

Movies

Night of the Iguana (1964), directed by John Huston, is the movie that alerted the world to Puerto Vallarta's existence. Set on the beach and bluffs of Mismaloya, the haunting movie with the jungle-beat soundtrack combines great directing with an excellent cast: Richard Burton as a cast-out preacher-turned-tour-guide, Sue Lyons and Deborah Kerr as his clients, and Ava Gardner as the sexy but lonely proprietress of the group's idyllic Mexican getaway. There's no better mood-setter for a trip to Vallarta.

Like Water for Chocolate (Como Agua Para Chocolate) (1992) is a magic-realism glance into rural Mexico during the Mexican Revolution. This visual banquet will make your mouth water for the rose-petal quail and other recipes that the female lead, Tita, prepares. It's based on the novel of the same name by Laura Esquivel, which is equally wonderful. Academy Award winner *Treasure of the Sierra Madre* (1948), with Humphrey Bogart, is a classic with great mountain scenery. For more fantastic scenery and a great town fiesta, see *The Magnificent Seven*, (1960) starring Yul Brenner and Eli Wallach. Set in Mexico City with Pierce Brosnan as a failing hit man, *The Matador* (2005) has some good scenes of the Camino Real in Mexico City, a great bullfighting sequence, and is a good drama.

SPANISH VOCABULARY

	English	Spanish	Pronunciation

Basics

	English	Spanish	Pronunciation
Yes/no	Sí/no	see/no
Please	Por favor	pore fah-*vore*
May I?	¿Me permite?	may pair-*mee*-tay
Thank you (very much)	(Muchas) gracias	(*moo*-chas) *grah-see*-as
You're welcome	De nada	day *nah*-dah
Excuse me	Con permiso	con pair-*mee*-so
Pardon me/what did you say?	¿Como?/Mánde?	ko-mo/mahn-dey
Could you tell me?	¿Podría decirme?	po-*dree*-ah deh-*seer*-meh
I'm sorry	Lo siento	lo see-*en*-toe
Hello	Hola	*oh*-lah
Good morning!	¡Buenos días!	*bway*-nohs *dee*-ahs
Good afternoon!	¡Buenas tardes!	*bway*-nahs *tar*-dess
Good evening!	¡Buenas noches!	*bway*-nahs *no*-chess
Goodbye!	¡Adiós!/¡Hasta luego!	ah-dee-*ohss*/ *ah*-stah-*lwe*-go
Mr./Mrs.	Señor/Señora	sen-*yor*/sen-*yore*-ah
Miss	Señorita	sen-yo-*ree*-tah
Pleased to meet you	Mucho gusto	*moo*-cho *goose*-to
How are you?	¿Cómo está usted?	*ko*-mo es-*tah* oo-*sted*
Very well, thank you.	Muy bien, gracias.	*moo*-ee bee-*en*, grah-see-as
And you?	¿Y usted?	ee oos-*ted*
Hello (on the telephone)	Bueno	*bwen*-oh

Numbers

	English	Spanish	Pronunciation
1	un, uno	oon, *oo*-no
2	dos	dos
3	tres	trace
4	cuatro	*kwah*-tro
5	cinco	*sink*-oh
6	seis	sace
7	siete	see-*et*-ey
8	ocho	*o*-cho

9	nueve	new-*ev*-ay
10	diez	dee-*es*
11	once	*own*-sey
12	doce	*doe*-sey
13	trece	*tray*-sey
14	catorce	kah-*tor*-sey
15	quince	*keen*-sey
16	dieciséis	dee-*es*-ee-*sace*
17	diecisiete	dee-*es*-ee-see-*et*-ay
18	dieciocho	dee-*es*-ee-*o*-cho
19	diecinueve	*dee-es*-ee-new-*ev*-ay
20	veinte	*bain*-tay
21	veinte y uno/ veintiuno	*bain*-te-oo-no
30	treinta	*train*-tah
32	treinta y dos	train-tay-*dose*
40	cuarenta	kwah-*ren*-tah
43	cuarenta y tres	kwah-*ren*-tay-*trace*
50	cincuenta	seen-*kwen*-tah
54	cincuenta y cuatro	seen-*kwen*-tay *kwah*-tro
60	sesenta	sess-*en*-tah
65	sesenta y cinco	sess-*en*-tay *seen*-ko
70	setenta	set-*en*-tah
76	setenta y seis	set-*en*-tay *sace*
80	ochenta	oh-*chen*-tah
87	ochenta y siete	oh-*chen*-tay see-*yet*-ay
90	noventa	no-*ven*-tah
98	noventa y ocho	no-*ven*-tah *o*-cho
100	cien	see-*en*
101	ciento uno	see-en-toe *oo*-no
200	doscientos	doe-see-*en*-tohss
500	quinientos	keen-*yen*-tohss
700	setecientos	set-eh-see-*en*-tohss
900	novecientos	no-veh-see-*en*-tohss
1,000	mil	meel
2,000	dos mil	dose meel
1,000,000	un millón	oon meel-*yohn*

Colors

black	negro	*neh*-grow
blue	azul	ah-*sool*
brown	café	kah-*feh*
green	verde	*vair*-day
pink	rosa	*ro*-sah
purple	morado	mo-*rah*-doe
orange	naranja	na-*rahn*-hah
red	rojo	*roe*-hoe
white	blanco	*blahn*-koh
yellow	amarillo	ah-mah-*ree*-yoh

Days of the Week

Sunday	domingo	doe-*meen*-goh
Monday	lunes	*loo*-ness
Tuesday	martes	*mahr*-tess
Wednesday	miércoles	me-*air*-koh-less
Thursday	jueves	who-*ev*-ess
Friday	viernes	vee-*air*-ness
Saturday	sábado	*sah*-bah-doe

Months

January	enero	eh-*neh*-ro
February	febrero	feh-*brair*-oh
March	marzo	*mahr*-so
April	abril	ah-*breel*
May	mayo	*my*-oh
June	junio	*hoo*-nee-oh
July	julio	*who*-lee-yoh
August	agosto	ah-*ghost*-toe
September	septiembre	sep-tee-*em*-breh
October	octubre	oak-*too*-breh
November	noviembre	no-vee-*em*-breh
December	diciembre	dee-see-*em*-breh

Useful Phrases

| Do you speak English? | ¿Habla usted inglés? | *ah*-blah oos-*ted* in-*glehs* |
| I don't speak Spanish | No hablo español | no *ah*-blow es-pahn-*yol* |

I don't understand (you)	No entiendo	no en-tee-*en*-doe
I understand (you)	Entiendo	en-tee-*en*-doe
I don't know	No sé	no *say*
I am from the United States/ British	Soy de los Estados Unidos/ inglés(a)	soy deh lohs ehs-*tah*-dohs oo-*nee*-dohs/ in-*glace*(ah)
What's your name?	¿Cómo se llama usted?	*koh*-mo say *yah*-mah oos-*ted*
My name is . . .	Me llamo . . .	may *yah*-moh
What time is it?	¿Qué hora es?	keh *o*-rah es
It is one, two, three . . . o'clock.	Es la una; son las dos, tres	es la *oo*-nah/sone lahs dose, trace
How?	¿Cómo?	*koh*-mo
When?	¿Cuándo?	*kwahn*-doe
This/Next week	Esta semana/ la semana que entra	*es*-tah seh-*mah*-nah/ lah say-*mah*-nah keh *en*-trah
This/Next month	Este mes/el próximo mes	*es*-tay mehs/el *proke*-see-mo mehs
This/Next year	Este año/el año que viene	*es*-tay *ahn*-yo/el *ahn*-yo keh vee-*yen*-ay
Yesterday/today/ tomorrow	Ayer/hoy/mañana	ah-*yair*/oy/mahn-*yah*-nah
This morning/ afternoon	Esta mañana/tarde	*es*-tah mahn-*yah*-nah/*tar*-day
Tonight	Esta noche	*es*-tah *no*-cheh
What?	¿Qué?	keh
What is this?	¿Qué es esto?	keh es *es*-toe
Why?	¿Por qué?	pore *keh*
Who?	¿Quién?	kee-*yen*
Where is . . . ?	¿Dónde está . . . ?	*dohn*-day es-*tah*
the train station?	la estación del tren?	la es-tah-see-*on* del *train*
the subway station?	la estación del Metro?	la es-ta-see-*on* del *meh*-tro
the bus stop?	la parada del autobús?	la pah-*rah*-dah del oh-toe-*boos*
the bank?	el banco?	el *bahn*-koh
the ATM?	el cajero automática?	el *kah*-hehr-oh oh-toe-*mah*-tee-kah
the . . . hotel?	el hotel . . . ?	el oh-*tel*
the store?	la tienda . . . ?	la tee-*en*-dah
the cashier?	la caja?	la *kah*-hah

the . . . museum?	el museo . . . ?	el moo-*seh*-oh
the hospital?	el hospital?	el ohss-pea-*tal*
the elevator?	el ascensor?	el ah-*sen*-sore
the bathroom?	el baño?	el *bahn*-yoh
Here/there	Aquí/allá	ah-*key*/ah-*yah*
Open/closed	Abierto/cerrado	ah-be-*er*-toe/ ser-*ah*-doe
Left/right	Izquierda/derecha	iss-key-*er*-dah/ dare-*eh*-chah
Straight ahead	Derecho	der-*eh*-choh
Is it near/far?	¿Está cerca/lejos?	es-*tah* sair-kah/ leh-hoss
I'd like . . .	Quisiera . . .	kee-see-air-ah
a room	un cuarto/una habitación	oon *kwahr*-toe/ oo-nah ah-bee-tah-see-*on*
the key	la llave	lah *yah*-vay
a newspaper	un periódico	oon pear-ee-*oh*-dee-koh
I'd like to buy . . .	Quisiera comprar . . .	kee-see-*air*-ah kohm-*prahr*
cigarettes	cigarrillo	ce-gar-*reel*-oh
matches	cerillos	ser-*ee*-ohs
a dictionary	un diccionario	oon deek-see-oh-*nah*-ree-oh
soap	jabón	hah-*bone*
a map	un mapa	oon *mah*-pah
a magazine	una revista	*oon*-ah reh-*veess*-tah
paper	papel	pah-*pel*
envelopes	sobres	*so*-brace
a postcard	una tarjeta postal	*oon*-ah tar-*het*-ah post-*ahl*
How much is it?	¿Cuánto cuesta?	*kwahn*-toe *kwes*-tah
Do you accept credit cards?	¿Aceptan tarjetas de crédito?	ah-*sehp*-than tahr-*heh*-tahs deh *creh*-dee-toh?
A little/a lot	Un poquito/ mucho . . .	oon poh-*kee*-toe/ *moo*-choh
More/less	Más/menos	mahss/*men*-ohss
Enough/too much/too little	Suficiente/de- masiado/muy poco	soo-fee-see-*en*-tay/ day-mah-see-*ah*-doe/*moo*-ee poh-koh
Telephone	Teléfono	tel-*ef*-oh-no
Telegram	Telegrama	teh-leh-*grah*-mah
I am ill/sick	Estoy enfermo(a)	es-*toy* en-*fair*-moh(ah)

Please call a doctor	Por favor llame un médico	pore fa-*vor ya*-may oon *med*-ee-koh
Help!	¡Auxilio! ¡Ayuda!	owk-*see*-lee-oh/ ah-*yoo*-dah
Fire!	¡Encendio!	en-*sen*-dee-oo
Caution!/Look out!	¡Cuidado!	kwee-*dah*-doh

On the Road

Highway	Carretera	car-ray-*ter*-ah
Causeway, paved highway	Calzada	cal-*za*-dah
Speed bump	Tope	*toh*-pay
Toll highway	Carretera de cuota	car-ray-*ter*-ha day dwoh-tah
Toll booth	Caseta	kah-*set*-ah
Route	Ruta	*roo*-tah
Road	Camino	cah-*mee*-no
Street	Calle	*cah*-yeh
Avenue	Avenida	ah-ven-*ee*-dah
Broad, tree-lined boulevard	Paseo	pah-*seh*-oh
Waterfront promenade	Malecón	mal-lay-*cone*
Wharf	Embarcadero	em-bar-cah-*day*-ro

In Town

Church	Templo/Iglesia	*tem*-plo/e-*gles*-se-*ah*
Cathedral	Catedral	cah-tay-*dral*
Neighborhood	Barrio	*bar*-re-o
Foreign exchange shop	Casa de cambio	*cas*-sah day *cam*-be-o
City hall	Ayuntamiento	ah-yoon-tah-mee *en*-toe
Main square	Zócalo	*zo*-cal-o
Traffic circle	Glorieta	glor-e-*ay*-tah
Market	Mercado (Spanish)/ Tianguis (Indian)	mer-*cah*-doe/ tee-*an*-geese
Inn	Posada	pos-*sah*-dah
Group taxi	Colectivo	co-lec-*tee*-vo
Mini-bus along fixed route	Pesero	pi-*seh*-ro

Dining Out

English	Spanish	Pronunciation
I'd like to reserve a table	Quisiera reservar una mesa.	kee-*syeh*-rah rreh-sehr-*vahr* oo-nah *meh*-sah
A bottle of . . .	Una botella de . . .	oo-nah bo-*tay*-yah deh
A cup of . . .	Una taza de . . .	oo-nah *tah*-sah deh
A glass of . . .	Un vaso de . . .	oon *vah*-so deh
Ashtray	Un cenicero	oon sen-ee-*seh*-roh
Bill/check	La cuenta	lah *kwen*-tah
Bread	El pan	el pahn
Breakfast	El desayuno	el day-sigh-*oon*-oh
Butter	La mantequilla	lah mahn-tay-*key*-yah
Cheers!	¡Salud!	sah-*lood*
Cocktail	Un aperitivo	oon ah-pair-ee-*tee*-voh
Mineral water	Agua mineral	*ah*-gwah mee-neh-*rahl*
Beer	Cerveza	sehr-*veh*-sah
Dinner	La cena	lah *seh*-nah
Dish	Un plato	oon *plah*-toe
Dish of the day	El platillo de hoy	el plah-*tee*-yo day oy
Enjoy!	¡Buen provecho!	bwen pro-*veh*-cho
Fixed-price menu	La comida corrida	lah koh-*me*-dah co-*ree*-dah
Is the tip included?	¿Está incluida la propina?	es-*tah* in-clue-ee-dah lah pro-*pea*-nah
Fork	El tenedor	el ten-eh-*door*
Knife	El cuchillo	el koo-*chee*-yo
Spoon	Una cuchara	oo-nah koo-*chah*-rah
Lunch	La comida	lah koh-*me*-dah
Menu	La carta	lah *cart*-ah
Napkin	La servilleta	lah sair-vee-*yet*-uh
Please give me	Por favor déme	pore fah-*vor* *day*-may
Pepper	La pimienta	lah pea-me-*en*-tah
Salt	La sal	lah sahl
Sugar	El azúcar	el ah-*sue*-car
Waiter!/Waitress!	¡Por favor Señor/Señorita!	pore fah-*vor* sen-*yor*/sen-yor-*ee*-tah

Puerto Vallarta Essentials

PLANNING TOOLS, EXPERT INSIGHT, GREAT CONTACTS

There are planners and there are those who, excuse the pun, fly by the seat of their pants. We happily place ourselves among the planners. Our writers and editors try to anticipate all the issues you may face before and during any journey, and then they do their research. This section is the product of their efforts. Use it to get excited about your trip to Puerto Vallarta, to inform your travel planning, or to guide you on the road should the seat of your pants start to feel threadbare.

GETTING STARTED

We're really proud of our Web site: Fodors.com is a great place to begin any journey. Scan Travel Wire for suggested itineraries, travel deals, restaurant and hotel openings, and other up-to-the-minute info. Check out Booking to research prices and book plane tickets, hotel rooms, rental cars, and vacation packages. Head to Talk for on-the-ground pointers from travelers who frequent our message boards. You can also link to loads of other travel-related resources.

▌ RESOURCES

ONLINE TRAVEL TOOLS

All About Mexico The best of the private enterprise Web sites is ⊕ www.virtualvallarta.com, which has tons of good info and short articles about life in PV. For Bucerías information, go to ⊕ www.buceriasmexico.com. Heading to Punta de Mita? Check out ⊕ www.puntamita.com. For some info about the Costalegre, go to ⊕ www.costalegre.ca.

Excellent English-language sites for general history, travel information, facts, and news stories about Mexico are: the United States' Library of Congress well-organized Mexico pages (⊕ http://lcweb2.loc.gov/frd/cs/mxtoc.html and ⊕ www.loc.gov/rr/international/hispanic/mexico/mexico.html); Mexico Online (⊕ www.mexonline.com); Mexico Connect (⊕ www.mexconnect.com); the Mexico Channel (⊕ www.trace-sc.com); and Mexican Wave (⊕ www.mexicanwave.com); and ⊕ www.eluniversal.com.mx, the online version of the newspaper El Universal, has an English-language section, although you have to hunt for it on the home page.

The nonprofit site Ancient Mexico (⊕ www.ancientmexico.com) has information about Western Mexico as well as more comprehensive information about the Maya and Aztecs.

Currency Conversion Google (⊕ www.google.com) does currency conversion. Just type in the amount you want to convert and an explanation of how you want it converted (e.g., "14 Mexican pesos in dollars"), and then voilà. Oanda.com (⊕ www.oanda.com) also allows you to print out a handy table with the current day's conversion rates. XE.com (⊕ www.xe.com) is a good currency conversion Web site.

Safety Transportation Security Administration (TSA; ⊕ www.tsa.gov)

Time Zones Timeanddate.com (⊕ www.timeanddate.com/worldclock) can help you figure out the correct time anywhere.

Weather Accuweather.com (⊕ www.accuweather.com) is an independent weather-forecasting service with good coverage of hurricanes. Weather.com (⊕ www.weather.com) is the Web site for the Weather Channel.

VISITOR INFORMATION

The Mexican Ministry of Tourism has Infotur, a 24-hour toll-free hotline, and a Web site with general info about the tourism industry. The Mexico Tourism Board has branches in New York, Chicago, Los Angeles, Houston, Miami, Montréal, Toronto, and Vancouver; the official page has information about popular destinations (with 360-degree photos), activities, and festivals.

For information before you visit, try the Puerto Vallarta Tourism Board & Convention and Visitors Bureau. You can also stop in for maps and other information once you're in town. Other convenient sources of information are the Municipal Tourist Office, right on the Plaza Principal. It's open weekdays 8–4.

WORD OF MOUTH

After your trip, be sure to rate the places you visited and share your experiences and travel tips with us and other Fodorites in Travel Ratings and Talk on www.fodors.com.

The friendly folks at the Jalisco State Tourism Office, open weekdays 9–5, are helpful with information about PV and destinations throughout the state, including mountain towns like Mascota and Talpán. For information about Nuevo Vallarta and southern Nayarit, contact the Nayarit State Tourism Office.

Contacts Mexican Ministry of Tourism (☎800/446–3942 Infotur in U.S., 01800/903–9200 in Mexico ⊕www.sectur.gob. mx). **Mexican Tourism Board (U.S. & Canada)** (☎800/446–3942 [44-MEXICO] in U.S. and Canada ⊕www.visitmexico.com).

Puerto Vallarta Tourism Board & Convention and Visitors Bureau (✉Local 18 Planta Baja, Zona Comercial Hotel Canto del Sol Zona Hotelera, Las Glorias ☎322/224–1175, 888/384-6822 in U.S., 01800/719–3276 in Mexico ⊕www.visitpuertovallarta.com). **Municipal Tourist Office** (✉Av. Independencia 123, Centro ☎322/223-2500 Ext. 131). **Jalisco State Tourism Office** (✉Plaza Marina shopping center, Local 144 & 146, Marina Vallarta ☎322/221-2676). **Nayarit State Tourism Office** (✉Paseo de los Cocoteros at Blvd. Nuevo Vallarta, between Gran Velas and Maribal hotels ☎322/297-1006 or 322/297-0180).

▌THINGS TO CONSIDER

GOVERNMENT ADVISORIES

As different countries have different world views, look at travel advisories from a range of governments to get more of a sense of what's going on out there. And be sure to parse the language carefully. For example, a warning to "avoid all travel" carries more weight than one urging you to "avoid nonessential travel," and both are much stronger than a plea to "exercise caution." A U.S. government travel warning is more permanent (though not necessarily more serious) than a so-called public announcement, which carries an expiration date.

▌TIP➜ **Consider registering online with the State Department (https://travelregistration.state.gov/ibrs/), so the government will know to look for you should a crisis occur in the country you're visiting.**

The U.S. Department of State's Web site has more than just travel warnings and advisories. The consular information sheets issued for every country have general safety tips, entry requirements (though be sure to verify these with the country's embassy), and other useful details.

General Information & Warnings Australian Department of Foreign Affairs & Trade (⊕www.smartraveller.gov.au). **Consular Affairs Bureau of Canada** (⊕www.voyage. gc.ca). **U.K. Foreign & Commonwealth Office** (⊕www.fco.gov.uk/travel). **U.S. Department of State** (⊕www.travel.state.gov).

GEAR

High-style sportswear, cotton slacks and walking shorts, and plenty of colorful sundresses are the palette of clothing you'll see in PV. Bring lightweight sportswear, bathing suits, and cover-ups for the beach. In addition to shorts, pack at least a pair or two of lightweight long pants.

Men may want to bring a lightweight suit or slacks and blazers for fancier restaurants (although very few have dress codes). For women, dresses of cotton, linen, or other lightweight, breathable fabrics are recommended. Puerto Vallarta restaurants are extremely tolerant of casual dress, but it never hurts to exceed expectations.

The sun can be fierce; bring a sun hat and sunscreen for the beach and for sightseeing. You'll need a sweater or jacket to cope with hotel and restaurant air-conditioning, which can be glacial, and for occasional cool spells. A lightweight jacket is a necessity in winter, and pack an umbrella for summer or unexpected rainstorms.

Bring along tissue packs in case you hit a place where the toilet paper has run out. You'll find familiar toiletries and hygiene products, as well as condoms, in shops in PV and in most rural areas.

⚠ **In luggage to be checked, never pack essential prescription drugs, valuables, or undeveloped film. To avoid customs and security delays, carry medications in their original packaging.**

PASSPORTS & VISAS

U.S. Homeland Security regulations now require U.S. citizens of all ages traveling by air from Mexico to present a valid U.S. passport upon returning to the States. Those returning by land or sea won't be required to present a passport upon returning to the United States until June 1, 2009.

Citizens of the U.S., Canada, U.K., Australia, and New Zealand don't need a tourist visa to enter Mexico. Canadians, New Zealanders, Australians, and citizens of the United Kingdom must have a valid passport (valid for three months beyond your stay in Mexico). Visitors from other countries also require a visa.

All visitors must get a tourist card. If you're arriving by plane from the United States or Canada, the standard tourist card will be given to you on the plane. They're also available through travel agents and Mexican consulates, and at the border if you're entering by land.

⚠ **You're given a portion of the tourist card form upon entering Mexico. Keep track of this documentation throughout your trip: you will need it when you depart. You'll be asked to hand it, your ticket, and your passport to airline representatives at the gate when boarding for departure.**

A tourist card costs about $20. The fee is generally tacked onto the price of your airline ticket; if you enter by land or boat you'll have to pay the fee separately. You're exempt from the fee if you enter by sea and stay less than 72 hours, or by land and do not stray past the 26- to 30-km (16- to 18-mi) checkpoint into the country's interior.

Tourist cards and visas are valid from 30 to 180 days, at the discretion of the immi-gration officer at your point of entry (90 days for Australians). Americans, Canadians, New Zealanders, and the British may request up to 180 days for a tourist card or visa extension; Australians are allowed up to 90 days. The extension fee is about $20, and the process can easily take up an entire day. There's no guarantee that you'll get the extension you're requesting. If you're planning an extended stay, plead with the immigration official for the maximum allowed days at the time of entry. It will save you time and money later.

■TIP➜ Mexico has some of the strictest policies about children entering the country. Minors traveling with one parent need notarized permission from the absent parent. And all children, including infants, must have proof of citizenship (the same as adults; *see above*) for travel to Mexico.

If you're a single parent traveling with children up to age 18, you must have a notarized letter from the other parent stating that the child has his or her permission to leave his or her home country. If the other parent is deceased or the child has only one legal parent, a notarized statement saying so must be obtained as proof. In addition, you must fill out a tourist card for each child over the age of 10 traveling with you.

Info Mexican Embassy (☎202/728–1600 ⊕www.embassyofmexico.org/eng/).

Passports A passport verifies both your identity and nationality—a great reason to have one. Another reason is that you need a passport now more than ever. At this writing, U.S. citizens must have a passport when traveling by air between the United States and several destinations for which other forms of identification (e.g., a driver's license and a birth certificate) were once sufficient. These destinations include not only Mexico, but also Canada, Bermuda, and all countries in Central America and the Caribbean (except the territories of Puerto Rico and the U.S. Virgin Islands). Soon enough

PACKING 101

Why do some people travel with a convoy of huge suitcases yet never have a thing to wear? How do others pack a duffle with a week's worth of outfits *and* supplies for every contingency? We realize that packing is a matter of style, but there's a lot to be said for traveling light. These tips help fight the battle of the bulging bag.

Make a list. In a recent Fodor's survey, 29% of respondents said they make lists (and often pack) a week before a trip. You can use your list to pack and to repack at the end of your trip. It can also serve as record of the contents of your suitcase—in case it disappears in transit.

Think it through. What's the weather like? Is this a business trip? A cruise? Going abroad? In some places dress may be more or less conservative than you're used to. As you create your itinerary, note outfits next to each activity (don't forget accessories).

Edit your wardrobe. Plan to wear everything twice (better yet, thrice) and to do laundry along the way. Stick to one basic look—urban chic, sporty casual, etc. Build around one or two neutrals and an accent (e.g., black, white, and olive green). Women can freshen looks by changing scarves or jewelry. For a week's trip, you can look smashing with three bottoms, four or five tops, a sweater, and a jacket.

Be practical. Put comfortable shoes atop your list. (Did we need to say this?) Pack lightweight, wrinkle-resistent, compact, washable items. (Or this?) Stack and roll clothes, so they'll wrinkle less. Unless you're on a guided tour or a cruise, select luggage you can readily carry. Porters, like good butlers, are hard to find these days.

Check weight and size limitations. In the United States you may be charged extra for checked bags weighing more than 50 pounds. Abroad some airlines don't allow you to check bags over 60 to 70 pounds, or they charge outrageous fees for every excess pound—or bag. Carry-on size limitations can be stringent, too.

Check carry-on restrictions. Research restrictions with the TSA. Rules vary abroad, so check them with your airline if you're traveling overseas on a foreign carrier. Consider packing all but essentials (travel documents, prescription meds, wallet) in checked luggage. This leads to a "pack only what you can afford to lose" approach that might help you streamline.

Rethink valuables. On U.S. flights, airlines are liable for only about $2,800 per person for bags. On international flights, the liability limit is around $635 per bag. But items like computers, cameras, and jewelry aren't covered, and as gadgetry can go on and of the list of carry-on no-no's, you can't count on keeping things safe by keeping them close. Although comprehensive travel policies may cover luggage, the liability limit is often a pittance. Your home-owner's policy may cover you sufficiently when you travel—or not.

Lock it up. If you must pack valuables, use TSA-approved locks (about $10) that can be unlocked by all U.S. security personnel.

Tag it. Always tag your luggage; use your business address if you don't want people to know your home address. Put the same information (and a copy of your itinerary) inside your luggage, too.

Report problems immediately. If your bags—or things in them—are damaged or go astray, file a written claim with your airline *before leaving the airport.* If the airline is at fault, it may give you money for essentials until your luggage arrives. Most lost bags are found within 48 hours, so alert the airline to your whereabouts for two or three days. If your bag was opened for security reasons in the States and something is missing, file a claim with the TSA.

you'll need a passport when traveling between the United States and such destinations by land and sea, too.

U.S. passports are valid for 10 years. You must apply in person if you're getting a passport for the first time; if your previous passport was lost, stolen, or damaged; or if your previous passport has expired and was issued more than 15 years ago or when you were under 16. All children under 18 must appear in person to apply for or renew a passport. Both parents must accompany any child under 14 (or send a notarized statement with their permission) and provide proof of their relationship to the child.

There are 13 regional passport offices, as well as 7,000 passport acceptance facilities in post offices, public libraries, and other governmental offices. If you're renewing a passport, you can do so by mail. Forms are available at passport acceptance facilities and online.

■TIP➡ Before your trip, make two copies of your passport's data page (one for someone at home and another for you to carry separately). Or scan the page and e-mail it to someone at home and/or yourself.

The cost to apply for a new passport is $97 for adults, $82 for children under 16; renewals are $67. Allow six weeks for processing, both for first-time passports and renewals. For an expediting fee of $60 you can reduce this time to about two weeks. If your trip is less than two weeks away, you can get a passport even more rapidly by going to a passport office with the necessary documentation. Private expediters can get things done in as little as 48 hours, but charge hefty fees for their services.

Visas A visa is essentially formal permission to enter a country. Visas allow countries to keep track of you and other visitors—and generate revenue (from application fees). You *always* need a visa to enter a foreign country; however, many countries routinely issue tourist

visas on arrival, particularly to U.S. citizens. When your passport is stamped or scanned in the immigration line, you're actually being issued a visa.

Sometimes you have to stand in a separate line and pay a small fee to get your stamp before going through immigration, but you can still do this at the airport on arrival. Getting a visa isn't always that easy. Some countries require that you arrange for one in advance of your trip. There's usually—but not always—a fee involved, and said fee may be nominal ($10 or less) or substantial ($100 or more).

If you must apply for a visa in advance, you can usually do it in person or by mail. When you apply by mail, you send your passport to a designated consulate, where your passport will be examined and the visa issued. Expediters—usually the same ones who handle expedited passport applications—can do all the work of obtaining your visa for you; however, there's always an additional cost (often more than $50 per visa).

Most visas limit you to a single trip—basically during the actual dates of your planned vacation. Other visas allow you to visit as many times as you wish for a specific period of time. Remember that requirements change, sometimes at the drop of a hat, and the burden is on you to make sure that you have the appropriate visas. Otherwise, you'll be turned away at the airport or, worse, deported after you arrive in the country. No company or travel insurer gives refunds if your travel plans are disrupted because you didn't have the correct visa.

U.S. Passport Information **U.S. Department of State** (☎877/487-2778 ⊕http://travel.state.gov/passport).

U.S. Passport & Visa Expediters **A. Briggs Passport & Visa Expediters** (☎800/806-0581 or 202/338-0111 ⊕www.abriggs.com). **American Passport Express** (☎800/455-5166 or 800/841-6778 ⊕www.americanpassport.com). **Passport Express**

(☎800/362–8196 ⊕www.passportex-press.com). **Travel Document Systems** (☎800/874–5100 or 202/638–3800 ⊕www.traveldocs.com). **Travel the World Visas** (☎866/886–8472 or 301/495–7700 ⊕www.world-visa.com).

SHOTS & MEDICATIONS

Consult your physician or local travel health clinic about inoculations recommended for your journey. Make sure polio and diphtheria–tetanus shots are up to date well before your trip. Hepatitis A and typhoid are transmitted through unclean food or water. Gamma-globulin shots prevent hepatitis; an inoculation is available for typhoid, although it's not 100% effective.

■**TIP**➔ If you travel a lot internationally—particularly to developing nations—refer to the CDC's *Health Information for International Travel* (aka Traveler's Health Yellow Book). Info from it is posted on the CDC Web site (www.cdc.gov/travel/yb), or you can buy a copy from your local bookstore for $24.95.

According to the CDC, there's a limited risk of malaria, dengue fever, and other insect-carried or parasite-caused illnesses in certain rural areas of Mexico (largely but not exclusively rural and tropical coastal areas). In most urban or easily accessible areas you need not worry. If, however, you're traveling to remote areas or simply prefer to err on the side of caution, check with the CDC's International Travelers' Hotline. Malaria and dengue are both carried by mosquitoes; in areas where these illnesses are prevalent, use insect-repellant coiling, clothing, and sprays/lotion. Also consider taking anti-malarial pills if you're doing serious adventure activities in tropical and subtropical areas. *For more information, see Health under On the Ground, below.*

Health Warnings National Centers for Disease Control & Prevention (CDC ☎877/394–8747 international travelers'

health line ⊕www.cdc.gov/travel). **World Health Organization** (WHO ⊕www.who.int).

TRIP INSURANCE

What kind of coverage do you honestly need? Do you even need trip insurance at all? Take a deep breath and read on.

We believe that comprehensive trip insurance is especially valuable if you're booking a very expensive or complicated trip (particularly to an isolated region) or if you're booking far in advance. Who knows what could happen six months down the road? But whether or not you get insurance has more to do with how comfortable you are assuming all that risk yourself.

Comprehensive travel policies typically cover trip-cancellation and interruption, letting you cancel or cut your trip short because of a personal emergency, illness, or, in some cases, acts of terrorism in your destination. Such policies also cover evacuation and medical care. Some also cover you for trip delays because of bad weather or mechanical problems as well as for lost or delayed baggage.

Another type of coverage to look for is financial default—that is, when your trip is disrupted because a tour operator, airline, or cruise line goes out of business. Generally you must buy this when you book your trip or shortly thereafter, and it's only available to you if your operator isn't on a list of excluded companies.

Consider buying medical-only coverage at the very least. Medical-only policies typically reimburse you for medical care (excluding that related to pre-existing conditions) and hospitalization abroad, and provide for evacuation. You still have to pay the bills and await reimbursement from the insurer, though.

Expect comprehensive travel insurance policies to cost about 4% to 7% or 8% of the total price of your trip (it's more like 8%–12% if you're over age 70). A medical-only policy may or may not be cheaper than a comprehensive policy. Always read the fine print of your policy to make sure that you are covered for the risks that are of most concern to you. Compare several policies to make sure you're getting the best price and range of coverage available.

Insurance Comparison Sites **Insure My Trip. com** (☎800/487-4722 ⊕www.insuremytrip. com). **Square Mouth.com** (☎800/240-0369 or 727/490-5803 ⊕www.squaremouth.com).

Comprehensive Travel Insurers **Access America** (☎800/729-6021 ⊕www.acces-samerica.com). **CSA Travel Protection** (☎800/873-9855 ⊕www.csatravelprotection. com). **HTH Worldwide** (☎610/254-8700 or 888/243-2358 ⊕www.hthworldwide. com). **Travelex Insurance** (☎800/228-9792 ⊕www.travelex-insurance.com). **Travel Guard**

International (☎715/345-0505 or 800/826-4919 ⊕www.travelguard.com). **Travel Insured International** (☎800/243-3174 ⊕www. travelinsured.com).

Medical-Only Insurers **International Medical Group** (☎800/628-4664 ⊕www. imglobal.com). **International SOS** (⊕www. internationalsos.com). **Wallach & Company** (☎800/237-6615 or 540/687-3166 ⊕www. wallach.com).

■TIP→ OK. You know you can save a bundle on trips to warm-weather destinations by traveling in rainy season. But there's also a chance that a severe storm will disrupt your plans. The solution? Look for hotels and resorts that offer storm/hurricane guarantees. Although they rarely allow refunds, most guarantees do let you rebook later if a storm strikes.

BOOKING YOUR TRIP

Unless your cousin is a travel agent, you're probably among the millions of people who make most of their travel arrangements online.

But have you ever wondered just what the differences are between an online travel agent (a Web site through which you make reservations instead of going directly to the airline, hotel, or car-rental company), a discounter (a firm that does a high volume of business with a hotel chain or airline and accordingly gets good prices), a wholesaler (one that makes cheap reservations in bulk and then re-sells them to people like you), and an aggregator (one that compares all the offerings so you don't have to)? Is it truly better to book directly on an airline or hotel Web site? And when does a real live travel agent come in handy?

ONLINE

You really have to shop around. A travel wholesaler such as Hotels.com or Hotel-Club.net can be a source of good rates, as can discounters such as Hotwire or Priceline, particularly if you can bid for your hotel room or airfare. Indeed, such sites sometimes have deals that are unavailable elsewhere. They do, however, tend to work only with hotel chains (which makes them just plain useless for getting hotel reservations outside of major cities) or big airlines (so that often leaves out upstarts like jetBlue).

Also, with discounters and wholesalers you must generally prepay, and everything is nonrefundable. And before you fork over the dough, be sure to check the terms and conditions, so you know what a given company will do for you if there's a problem and what you'll have to deal with on your own.

■TIP→ To be absolutely sure everything was processed correctly, confirm reservations made through online travel agents, discounters, and wholesalers directly with your hotel before leaving home.

Booking engines like Expedia, Travelocity, and Orbitz are actually travel agents, albeit high-volume, online ones. And airline travel packagers like American Airlines Vacations—well, they're travel agents, too. But they may still not work with all the world's hotels.

An aggregator site will search many sites and pull the best prices for airfares, hotels, and rental cars from them. Most aggregators compare the major travel-booking sites such as Expedia, Travelocity, and Orbitz; some also look at airline Web sites, though rarely the sites of smaller budget airlines. Some aggregators also compare other travel products, including complex packages—a good thing, as you can sometimes get the best overall deal by booking an air-and-hotel package.

WITH A TRAVEL AGENT

If you use an agent—brick-and-mortar or virtual—you'll pay a fee for the service. And know that the service you get from some online agents isn't comprehensive. For example Expedia and Travelocity don't search for prices on budget airlines like jetBlue or small foreign carriers. That said, some agents (online or not) *do* have access to fares that are difficult to find otherwise, and the savings can more than make up for any surcharge.

A knowledgeable brick-and-mortar travel agent can be a godsend if you're booking a cruise, a package trip that's not available to you directly, an air pass, or a complicated itinerary. What's more, travel agents that specialize in a destination may have exclusive access to certain deals and insider information on things such as charter flights. Agents who specialize in types of travelers (senior citizens, gays and lesbians, naturists) or types of trips (cruises, luxury travel, safaris) can also be invaluable.

Online Booking Resources

AGGREGATORS

Kayak	www.kayak.com	looks at cruises and vacation packages.
Mobissimo	www.mobissimo.com	examines airfare, hotels, cars, and tons of activities.
Qixo	www.qixo.com	compares cruises, vacation packages, and even travel insurance.
Sidestep	www.sidestep.com	compares vacation packages and lists travel deals.
Travelgrove	www.travelgrove.com	also compares cruises and packages.

BOOKING ENGINES

Cheap Tickets	www.cheaptickets.com	a discounter.
Expedia	www.expedia.com	a large online agency that charges a booking fee for airline tickets.
Hotwire	www.hotwire.com	a discounter.
lastminute.com	www.lastminute.com	specializes in last-minute travel; the main site is for the U.K., but it has a link to a U.S. site.
Luxury Link	www.luxurylink.com	has auctions (surprisingly good deals) as well as offers on the high-end side of travel.
Onetravel.com	www.onetravel.com	a discounter for hotels, car rentals, airfares, and packages.
Orbitz	www.orbitz.com	charges a booking fee for airline tickets, but gives a clear breakdown of fees and taxes before you book.
Priceline.com	www.priceline.com	a discounter that also allows bidding.
Travel.com	www.travel.com	allows you to compare its rates with those of other booking engines.
Travelocity	www.travelocity.com	charges a booking fee for airline tickets, but promises good problem resolution.

ONLINE ACCOMMODATIONS

Hotelbook.com	www.hotelbook.com	focuses on independent hotels worldwide.
Hotel Club	www.hotelclub.net	good for major cities worldwide.
Hotels.com	www.hotels.com	a big Expedia-owned wholesaler that offers rooms in hotels all over the world.
Quikbook	www.quikbook.com	offers "pay when you stay" reservations that let you settle your bill at checkout, not when you book.

OTHER RESOURCES

Bidding For Travel	www.biddingfortravel.com	a good place to figure out what you can get and for how much before you start bidding on, say, Priceline.

■TIP➔ Remember that Expedia, Travelocity, and Orbitz are travel agents, not just booking engines. To resolve any problems with a reservation made through these companies, contact them first.

A top-notch agent planning your trip or booking your cruise may get you a room or cabin upgrade or arrange to have bottle of champagne chilling in your cabin when you embark. And complain about the surcharges all you like, but when things don't work out the way you'd hoped, it's nice to have an agent to put things right.

Agent Resources American Society of Travel Agents (☎703/739–2782 ⊕www.travelsense.org).

■ AIRLINE TICKETS

Most domestic airline tickets are electronic; international tickets may be either electronic or paper. With an e-ticket the only thing you receive is an e-mailed receipt citing your itinerary and reservation and ticket numbers. The greatest advantage of an e-ticket is that if you lose your receipt, you can simply print out another copy or ask the airline to do it for you at check-in. You usually pay a surcharge (up to $50) to get a paper ticket, if you can get one at all. The sole advantage of a paper ticket is that it may be easier to endorse over to another airline if your flight is canceled and the airline with which you booked can't accommodate you on another flight.

■TIP➔ Discount air passes that let you travel economically in a country or region must often be purchased before you leave home. In some cases you can only get them through a travel agent.

■ RENTAL CARS

When you reserve a car, ask about cancellation penalties, taxes, drop-off charges (if you're planning to pick up the car in one city and leave it in another), and surcharges (for being under or over a certain

10 WAYS TO SAVE

1. Nonrefundable is best. If saving money is more important than flexibility, then nonrefundable tickets work. Just remember that you'll pay dearly (as much as $200) if you change your plans.

2. Comparison shop. Web sites and travel agents can have different arrangements with the airlines and offer different prices for exactly the same flights.

3. Beware the listed prices. Many airline Web sites—and most ads—show prices *without* taxes and surcharges. Don't buy until you know the full price.

4. Stay loyal. Stick with one or two frequent-flier programs. You'll rack up free trips faster and you'll accumulate more quickly the perks that make trips easier. On some airlines these include a special reservations number, early boarding, access to upgrades, and roomier economy seats.

5. Watch those ticketing fees. Surcharges are usually added when you buy your ticket anywhere but on an airline Web site. (That includes by phone—even if you call the airline directly—and paper tickets regardless of how you book).

6. Check often. Start looking for cheap fares from three months out to about one month.

7. Don't work alone. Some Web sites have tracking features that will e-mail you immediately when good deals are posted.

8. Jump on the good deals. Waiting even a few minutes might mean paying more.

9. Be flexible. Look for departures on Tuesday, Wednesday, and Saturday, typically the cheapest days to travel. Check prices for departures at different times and to and from alternative airports.

10. Weigh your options. A cheaper flight might have a long layover or land at a secondary airport, where your ground transport costs are higher.

age, for additional drivers, or for driving across state or country borders or beyond a specific distance from your point of rental). All these things can add substantially to your costs. Request car seats and extras such as GPS when you book.

Rates are sometimes—but not always—better if you book in advance or reserve through a rental agency's Web site. There are other reasons to book ahead, though: for popular destinations, during busy times of the year, or to ensure that you get certain types of cars (vans, SUVs, exotic sports cars).

■**TIP**→ Make sure that a confirmed reservation guarantees you a car. Agencies sometimes overbook, particularly for busy weekends and holiday periods.

When you think about renting a car, bear in mind that you will be sharing the road with local drivers whose customs and ideas of acceptable behavior are different from your own. Also, be prepared for different rules of the road and for challenging road conditions *(see By Car in Transportation)*. Check on conditions before you rent, and do your best not to drive on lonely roads between cities at night.

Mexico manufactures Chrysler, Ford, General Motors, Honda, Nissan, and Volkswagen vehicles. With the exception of Volkswagen, you can get the same kind of midsize and luxury cars in Mexico that you can rent in the United States and Canada. Economy usually refers to a Volkswagen Beetle or a Chevy Aveo or Joy, which may or may not come with air-conditioning or automatic transmission.

It can really pay to shop around: in Puerto Vallarta, rates for a compact car with air-conditioning, manual transmission, and unlimited mileage range from $18 a day and $120 a week to $50 or even $60 a day and $300–$400 a week. Full-coverage insurance averages $18 a day. As a rule, stick with the major companies because they tend to be more reliable.

You can also hire a car with a driver (who generally doubles as a tour guide) through your hotel. The going rate is about $22–$25 an hour within town. Limousine service runs about $65 an hour and up, with a three- to five-hour minimum. Rates for out-of-town trips are higher. Negotiate a price beforehand if you'll need the service for more than one day. If your hotel can't arrange limousine or car service, ask the concierge to refer you to a reliable *sitio* (cab stand).

In Mexico the minimum driving age is 18, but most rental-car agencies have a surcharge for drivers under 25. Your own country's driver's license is perfectly acceptable.

Surcharges for additional drivers are around $5 per day plus tax. Children's car seats run about the same, but not all companies have them.

Automobile Associations U.S.: **American Automobile Association** (AAA ☎315/797–5000 ⊕www.aaa.com); most contact with the organization is through state and regional members. **National Automobile Club** (☎650/294–7000 ⊕www.thenac.com); membership open to CA residents only.

Major Agencies Alamo (☎800/522–9696 ⊕www.alamo.com). **Avis** (☎800/331–1084 ⊕www.avis.com). **Budget** (☎800/472–3325 ⊕www.budget.com). **Hertz** (☎800/654–3001 ⊕www.hertz.com). **National Car Rental** (☎800/227–7368 ⊕www.nationalcar.com).

CAR-RENTAL INSURANCE

If you own a car, your personal auto insurance may cover a rental to some degree, though not all policies protect you abroad; always read your policy's fine print. Even if you have auto insurance, seriously consider buying the collision- or loss-damage waiver (CDW or LDW) from the car-rental company, which eliminates your liability for damage to the car. Some credit cards offer CDW coverage, but it's usually supplemental to your own insurance and rarely covers SUVs, minivans, luxury models, and the like.

If your coverage is secondary, you may still be liable for loss-of-use costs from the car-rental company. But no credit-card insurance is valid unless you use that card for *all* transactions, from reserving to paying the final bill. All companies exclude car rental in some countries, so be sure to find out about the destination to which you are traveling.

Some rental agencies require you to purchase CDW coverage; many will even include it in quoted rates. All will strongly encourage you to buy CDW—possibly implying that it's required—so be sure to ask about such things before renting. In most cases it's cheaper to add a supplemental CDW plan to your comprehensive travel-insurance policy (⇨ *Trip Insurance under Things to Consider in Getting Started, above*) than to purchase it from a rental company. That said, you don't want to pay for a supplement if you're required to buy insurance from the rental company.

You must carry Mexican auto insurance, at the very least liability as well coverage against physical damage to the vehicle and theft at your discretion, depending on what, if anything, your own auto insurance (or credit card, if you use it to rent a car) includes. For rental cars, all insurance will all be dealt with through the rental company.

■ VACATION PACKAGES

Packages *are not* guided excursions. Packages combine airfare, accommodations, and perhaps a rental car or other extras (theater tickets, guided excursions, boat trips, reserved entry to popular museums, transit passes), but they let you do your own thing. During busy periods packages may be your best option, as flights and rooms may be sold out otherwise. Packages will definitely save you time.

They can also save you money, particularly in peak seasons, but—and this is a really big "but"—you should price each part of the package separately to be sure. And be aware that prices advertised on Web sites and in newspapers rarely include service charges or taxes, which can up your costs by hundreds of dollars.

■TIP➜ Some packages and cruises are sold only through travel agents. Don't always assume that you can get the best deal by booking everything yourself.

Each year consumers are stranded or lose their money when packagers—even large ones with excellent reputations—go out of business. How can you protect yourself? First, always pay with a credit card; if you have a problem, your credit-card company may help you resolve it. Second, buy trip insurance that covers default. Third, choose a company that belongs to the United States Tour Operators Association, whose members must set aside funds to cover defaults.

■TIP➜ Local tourism boards can provide information about lesser-known and small-niche operators that sell packages to only a few destinations.

Finally, choose a company that also participates in the Tour Operator Program of the American Society of Travel Agents (ASTA), which will act as mediator in any disputes. You can also check on the tour operator's reputation among travelers by posting an inquiry on one of the Fodors.com forums.

Organizations **American Society of Travel Agents** (ASTA ☎703/739–2782 or 800/965–2782 ⊕www.astanet.com). **United States Tour Operators Association** (USTOA ☎212/599–6599 ⊕www.ustoa.com).

10 WAYS TO SAVE

1. Beware of cheap rates. Those great rates aren't so great when you add in taxes, surcharges, and insurance. Such extras can double or triple the initial quote.

2. Rent weekly. Weekly rates are usually better than daily ones. Even if you only want to rent for five or six days, ask for the weekly rate; it may very well be cheaper than the daily rate for that period of time.

3. Don't forget the locals. Price local companies as well as the majors.

4. Airport rentals can cost more. Airports often add surcharges, which you can sometimes avoid by renting from an agency whose office is just off airport property.

5. Wholesalers can help. Investigate wholesalers, which rent in bulk from firms that own fleets, and which offer better rates (note that you must usually pay for such rentals before leaving home).

6. Look for rate guarantees. With your rate locked in, you won't pay more, even if the price goes up in the local currency.

7. Fill up farther away. Avoid hefty refueling fees: Fill the tank at a station away from where you turn in the car.

8. Pump it yourself. Don't pre-pay for rental car gas. The savings isn't that great, and unless you coast in on empty upon return, you wind up paying for gas you don't use.

9. Get all your discounts. Find out whether a credit card you carry or organization or frequent-renter program to which you belong has a discount program. And confirm that such discounts really are a deal. You can often do better with special weekend or weekly rates offered by a rental agency.

10. Check out packages. Adding a car rental onto your air/hotel vacation package may be cheaper than renting a car separately.

▌GUIDED TOURS

Guided tours are a good option when you don't want to do it all yourself. You travel along with a group (sometimes large, sometimes small), stay in prebooked hotels, eat with your fellow travelers (the cost of meals sometimes included in the price of your tour, sometimes not), and follow a schedule. But not all guided tours are an if-it's-Tuesday-this-must-be-Belgium experience. A knowledgeable guide can take you places that you might never discover on your own, and you may be pushed to see more than you would have otherwise.

Tours aren't for everyone, but they can be just the thing for trips to places where making travel arrangements is difficult or time-consuming (particularly when you don't speak the language). Whenever you book a guided tour, find out what's included and what isn't. A "land-only" tour includes all your travel (by bus, in most cases) in the destination, but not necessarily your flights to and from or even within it. Also, in most cases prices in tour brochures don't include fees and taxes. And remember that you'll be expected to tip your guide and driver (in local currency) at the end of the tour.

SPECIAL-INTEREST TOURS

Spanish-Language Study Attending a language institute is an ideal way not only to learn Mexican Spanish but also to acquaint yourself with the customs and the people. For total immersion, most schools offer boarding with a family, but there's generally flexibility in terms of the type of lodgings and the length of your stay.

AmeriSpan Unlimited, based in the United States, specializes in medical and business Spanish; see the Web site for student blogs. The Academia Hispano Americana offers a variety of language-study options as well as weekly cooking classes. Many programs offer courses in Latin American studies and culture, as well as language.

Contacts Academia Hispano Americana (☎415/152–0349 ⊕www.ahaspeakspanish.

com). **AmeriSpan Unlimited** (☎800/879–6640, 215/751–1100 in U.S. ⊕www.amerispan.com). **Centro de Estudios para Extranjeros** (☎33/3616–4399 in Guadalajara, 322/223–2082 in PV ⊕www.cepe.udg.mx).

▌CRUISES

Companies with cruises to the Pacific Coast include Carnival, Cunard, Celebrity Cruises, Holland America, Princess, Norwegian, Royal Caribbean, and Royal Olympia. Most depart from Los Angeles, Long Beach, or San Diego and head to Los Cabos or Mazatlán, Puerto Vallarta, Manzanillo, Ixtapa/Zihuatanejo, and/or Acapulco; some trips originate in Vancouver or San Francisco.

Cruise Lines **Carnival Cruise Line** (☎305/599–2600 or 800/227–6482 ⊕www.carnival.com). **Celebrity Cruises** (☎800/647–2251 ⊕www.celebrity.com). **Cunard Line** (☎661/753–1000 or 800/728–6273 ⊕www.cunard.com). **Holland America Line** (☎206/281–3535 or 877/932–4259 ⊕www.hollandamerica.com). **Norwegian Cruise Line** (☎305/436–4000 or 800/327–7030 ⊕www.ncl.com). **Princess Cruises** (☎661/753–0000 or 800/774–6237 ⊕www.princess.com). **Royal Caribbean International** (☎305/539–6000 or 800/327–6700 ⊕www.royalcaribbean.com).

TRANSPORTATION

The Mexican method of numbering streets can be exasperatingly arbitrary. The fact that street numbers do not ascend in a logical fashion (i.e., the 100s on one block, the 200s on the next, and so on) drives even cab drivers crazy, not to mention the rest of us.

Streets in districts outside El Centro generally have a theme to their names: names of planets, writers, musicians, countries, cities, or types of trees, for example. Many addresses have "s/n" for *sin número* (no number) after the street name. In small towns outside PV, references are often used in lieu of street names ("Across from the airport," for example).

Addresses are written with the street name first, followed by the street number (or "s/n"). A five-digit *código postal* (postal code) goes between the name of the city and the state. Below are some words you should know:

avenida (abbr. Av.): avenue

carretera: highway

colonia (abbr. Col.): neighborhood or district

fraccionamiento (abbr. Fracc.): subdivision

▋ BY AIR

There are nonstop and direct flights from a few U.S. cities. Flights with stopovers in Mexico City tend to take the entire day. If you plan to include Guadalajara in your itinerary, consider an open-jaw flight to Puerto Vallarta with the return from Guadalajara (or vice versa). There's almost no difference in price, especially when factoring in bus fare. Things change, but generally there are the greatest number of flights from Denver and Los Angeles, and sometimes San Francisco; www.latindiscountair.com, a subsidiary of cheapflights.com, quotes rates to Puerto Vallarta from different cities and on different airlines.

Nonstop flights are available from Los Angeles (Alaska Air, America West), San Francisco (United), Seattle (Alaska Air), Phoenix (US Airways, America West), Houston (Continental), Chicago (American), Dallas (American), Las Vegas (America West), St. Louis (American [seasonal]), Denver (Frontier Air, United), and Kansas City, MO (Frontier Air).

Avolar is a Tijuana-based airline with reasonable fares. It flies to Tepic in Nayarit and Guadalajara.

Air Canada has nonstop flights from Toronto, and connecting flights (via Toronto) from all major cities. The nonstop flight is 4½ hours. These flights are expensive, however, so you may save significant dollars by either flying to a U.S. city and connecting with a U.S. or Mexican carrier or taking a charter flight with Air Transat or Skyservice.

You can fly to Manzanillo, just south of the Costalegre, via many airlines with a stop in Mexico City. *For more Guadalajara flight information, see Guadalajara Essentials in Chapter 9.* Flying times are about 2 hours 45 minutes from Houston, 3 hours from Los Angeles, 3½ hours from Denver, 4 hours from Chicago, and 8 hours from New York.

Airline & Airport Links Airline and Airport Links.com (⊕www.airlineandairportlinks.com) has links to many of the world's airlines and airports.

Airlines Aeroméxico (☎800/237-6639 in U.S. and Canada, 01800/021-4030 in Mexico, 322/221-1204 in PV ⊕www.aeromexico.com). **Air Canada** (☎800/361-5373 in Canada, 322/221-1823 in PV ⊕www.aircanada. com). **Alaska Airlines** (☎800/252-7522 or 206/433-3100, 01800/426-0333 in Mexico, 322/221-1350 in PV ⊕www.alaskaair.com). **American Airlines** (☎800/433-7300, 01800/433-7300 or 01800/904-6000 in Mexico, 322/221-1799 in PV ⊕www.aa.com).

America West (☎800/235-9292 in U.S., 01800/235-9292 in Mexico, 322/221-1333 in PV ⊕www.americawest.com). **ATA** (☎800/435-9282 or 317/282-8308 ⊕www. ata.com). **Avolar** (☎01800/2128-6527 in Mexico or 888/328-6527 in U.S. ⊕www.avolar. com.mx). **Azteca** (☎888/754-0066 in U.S., 01800/229-8322 in Mexico, 322/221-2584 in PV). **Click Mexicana** (☎800/531-7921 in U.S., 866/281-3049 in Canada, 01800/502-2000 in Mexico ⊕www.mexicana.com). **Continental Airlines** (☎800/523-3273 for U.S. and Mexico reservations, 800/231-0856 for international reservations, 01800/900-5000 in Mexico, 322/221-2212 in PV ⊕www.continental.com). **Frontier** (☎800/432-1359 in U.S. ⊕www. frontierairlines.com). **Mexicana** (☎800/531-7921 in U.S., 866/281-3049 in Canada, 01800/502-2000 in Mexico, 322/221-1823 in PV ⊕www.mexicana.com).

Airline Security Issues Transportation **Security Administration** (⊕www.tsa.gov) has answers for almost every question that might come up.

AIRPORTS
The main gateway to the country, and where many PV-bound travelers change planes, is Mexico City's large, modern Aeropuerto Internacional Benito Juárez (airport code: MEX), infamous for pickpocketing and taxi scams; be careful with your possessions. Use any extra time to exchange money for your ground transportation, or to buy last-minute gifts (although at high prices) on your way out of the country.

Puerto Vallarta's international airport is small by comparison and usually has just a few flights departing at a time. Aeropuerto Internacional Gustavo Díaz Ordáz is (PVR) 7½ km (4½ mi) north of downtown Puerto Vallarta.

Airport Information Aeropuerto Interna-**cional Benito Juárez** (MEX ✉Mexico City ☎55/5571-3600). **Aeropuerto Internacional Gustavo Díaz Ordáz** (PVR ✉Carretera a Tepic, Km 7.5, Zona Aeropuerto ☎322/221-1298). **Aeropuerto Internacional Playa de**

Oro (Aeropuerto Internacional de Manzanillo, ZLO ✉Carretera 200, Km 38, Manzanillo ☎314/333-1119).

Ground Transportation Vans provide transportation from the airport to PV hotels; there's a zone system with different prices for the Zona Hotelera Sur, downtown PV, and so on. Upon leaving the luggage collection area, vendors shout for your attention. It's a confusing scene. Purchase the taxi vouchers sold at these stands inside the terminal, but make sure to avoid the timeshare vendors which trap you in their vans for a high-pressure sales pitch en route to your hotel.

Before you purchase your ticket, look for a taxi-zone map (it should be posted on or by the ticket stand), and make sure your taxi ticket is properly zoned; if you need a ticket only to Zone 3, don't pay for a ticket to Zone 4 or 5. Don't leave your luggage unattended while making transportation arrangements. Taxis or vans to the Costalegre resorts between PV and Manzanillo are generally arranged through the resort. If not, taxis charge about $19 (200 pesos) an hour—more if you're traveling beyond Jalisco State lines.

▌ BY BUS

Mexico's bus network is extensive. PV's Central Camionero, or Central Bus Station, is 1 km (½ mi) north of the airport, halfway between Nuevo Vallarta and downtown Puerto Vallarta. Elite/Futura has first-class service to Acapulco, Mexico City, the U.S. border, and other destinations.

First-class Mexican buses (known as *primera clase*) are generally timely and comfortable, air-conditioned coaches with bathrooms, movies, and reclining seats—sometimes with seat belts. Deluxe (*de lujo* or *ejecutivo*) buses offer the same and usually have refreshments (soft drinks, bottled water, and white-bread sandwiches). Second-class (*segunda clase*) buses are

FLYING 101

Flying may not be as carefree as it once was, but there are some things you can do to make your trip smoother.

Minimize the time spent standing in line. Buy an e-ticket, check in at an electronic kiosk, or—even better—check in on your airline's Web site before leaving home. Pack light and limit carry-on items to only the essentials.

Arrive when you need to. Research your airline's policy. It's usually at least an hour before domestic flights and two to three hours before international flights. But airlines at some busy airports have more stringent requirements. Check the TSA Web site for estimated security waiting times at major airports.

Get to the gate. If you aren't at the gate at least 10 minutes before your flight is scheduled to take off (sometimes earlier), you won't be allowed to board.

Double-check your flight times. Do this especially if you reserved far in advance. Schedules change, and alerts may not reach you.

Don't go hungry. Ask whether your airline offers anything to eat; even when it does, be prepared to pay.

Get the seat you want. Often, you can pick a seat when you buy your ticket on an airline Web site. But it's not guaranteed; the airline could change the plane after you book, so double-check. You can also select a seat if you check in electronically. Avoid seats on the aisle directly across from the lavatories. Frequent fliers say those are even worse than back-row seats that don't recline.

Got kids? Get info. Ask the airline about its children's menus, activities, and fares. Sometimes infants and toddlers fly free if they sit on a parent's lap, and older children fly for half price in their own seats. Also inquire about policies involving car seats; having one may limit seating options. Also ask about seat-belt extenders for car seats. And note that you can't count on a flight attendant to produce an extender; you may have to ask for one when you board.

Check your scheduling. Don't buy a ticket if there's less than an hour between connecting flights. Although schedules are padded, if anything goes wrong you might miss your connection. If you're traveling to an important function, depart a day early.

Bring paper. Even when using an e-ticket, always carry a hard copy of your receipt; you may need it to get your boarding pass, which most airports require to get past security.

Complain at the airport. If your baggage goes astray or your flight goes awry, complain before leaving the airport. Most carriers require this.

Beware of overbooked flights. If a flight is oversold, the gate agent will usually ask for volunteers and offer some sort of compensation for taking a different flight. If you're bumped from a flight *involuntarily*, the airline must give you some kind of compensation if an alternate flight can't be found within one hour.

Know your rights. If your flight is delayed because of something within the airline's control (bad weather doesn't count), the airline must get you to your destination on the same day, even if they have to book you on another airline and in an upgraded class. Read the Contract of Carriage, which is usually buried on the airline's Web site.

Be prepared. The Boy Scout motto is especially important if you're traveling during a stormy season. To quickly adjust your plans, program a few numbers into your cell: your airline, an airport hotel or two, your destination hotel, your car service, and/or your travel agent.

used mainly for travel to smaller, secondary routes.

A lower-class bus ride can be interesting if you're not in a hurry and want to experience local culture; these buses make frequent stops and keep less strictly to their timetables. Often they will wait until they fill up to leave, regardless of the scheduled time of departure. Fares are up to 15%–30% cheaper than first-class buses. The days of pigs and chickens among your busmates are largely in the past.

■ **TIP**➜ Unless you're writing a novel or your memoir, there's no reason to ride a second-class bus if a first-class or better is available. Daytime trips are generally safer.

Bring snacks, socks, and a sweater—the air-conditioning on first-class buses is often set on high—and toilet paper, as restrooms might not have any. Smoking is prohibited on all buses.

Estrella Blanca goes from Mexico City to Manzanillo, Mazatlán, Monterrey, Nuevo Laredo, and other central, Pacific coast, and northern-border points. ETN has the most luxurious service to Guadalajara, Mexico City, and many other destinations, with exclusively first-class buses that have roomy, totally reclining seats. Primera Plus connects Mexico City with Manzanillo and Puerto Vallarta along with other central and western cities.

TAP serves Mexico City, Puerto Vallarta, and Tepic before continuing north through Sinaloa and Sonora and to border cities like Tijuana (BCN) and Agua Prieta (Sonora). Basic service, including some buses with marginal or no air-conditioning, is the norm on Transportes Cihuatlán, which connects the Bahía de Banderas and PV with southern Jalisco towns such as Barra de Navidad.

Rates average 45–67 pesos per hour of travel, depending on the level of luxury. For the most part, plan to pay in pesos, although most of the deluxe bus services have started accepting Visa and MasterCard.

Tickets for first-class or better—unlike tickets for the other classes—can be reserved in advance; this is advisable during peak periods, although the most popular routes have buses on the hour. You can make reservations for many, though not all, of the first-class bus lines, through the Ticketbus central reservations agency. To travel by bus from the United States and Canada, visit www.greyhound.com.

City buses (4.5 pesos) serve downtown, the Zona Hotelera Norte, and Marina Vallarta. Bus stops—marked by blue-and-white signs—are every two or three long blocks along the highway (Carretera Aeropuerto) and in downtown Puerto Vallarta. Green buses to Playa Mismaloya and Boca de Tomatlán (5.5 pesos) run about every 15 minutes from the corner of Avenida Insurgentes and Basilio Badillo downtown.

Gray ATM buses serving Nuevo Vallarta and Bucerías (20 pesos), Punta de Mita (30 pesos), and Sayulita (50 pesos) depart from just two places: Plaza las Glorias, in front of the HSBC bank, and Wal-Mart, both of which are along Carretera Aeropuerto between downtown and the Zona Hotelera.

■ **TIP**➜ It's rare for inspectors to check tickets, but just when you've let yours flutter to the floor, a figure of authority is bound to appear. So hang on to your ticket, and hang on to your hat: PV bus drivers race from one stoplight to the next in jarring, jerky bursts of speed.

There's no problem with theft on city buses aside from perhaps an occasional pickpocket that might be at work anywhere in the world.

Bus Information Central Camionero (✉ Puerto Vallarta–Tepic Hwy., Km 9, Las Mojoneras ☎ 322/290–1008). **Estrella Blanca** (☎ 01800/507–5500 toll-free in Mexico, 322/290–1001 in Puerto Vallarta ⊕ www.estrellablanca.com.mx). **ETN** (☎ 01800/800–0386 toll-free in Mexico, 322/290–0996, 322/290–0997 in PV ⊕ www.

etn.com.mx). **Greyhound** (☎33/3679-0404 in Guadalajara, 01800/710-8819 toll-free in Mexico, 800/231-2222 in U.S., 800/661-8747 in Canada ⊕www.greyhound.com). **Primera Plus** (☎322/290-0715 in PV). **Transportes Cihuatlán** (☎322/290-0994 in PV). **Transporte del Pacifico (TAP)** (☎322/290-0119, 322/290-0993 in PV).

▮ BY CAR

Driving in PV can be unpleasant, but the main problem is parking. From December through April—peak season—traffic clogs the narrow streets, and negotiating the steep hills in Old Vallarta (sometimes you have to drive in reverse to let another car pass) can be frightening. Avoid rush hour (7–9 AM and 6–8 PM) and when schools let out (2–3 PM). Travel with a companion and a good road map or atlas. Always lock your car, and never leave valuable items in the body of the car. The trunk is generally safe, although any thief can crack one open if he chooses.

▮TIP➙ **It's absolutely essential that you carry Mexican auto insurance for liability, even if you have full coverage for collision, damages, and theft** *(⇨ Car-Rental Insurance under Rental Cars in Booking Your Trip, above).* **If you injure anyone in an accident, you could well be jailed—whether it was your fault or not—unless you have insurance.**

Taxis and buses are the way to get around downtown; rent a car for days when you'll be sightseeing outside the city center. The trick to getting a good deal on a rental car is to book it before arriving in PV through Hertz and other international companies.

To get to the Costalegre from Puerto Vallarta, simply head south on Highway 200. It's about 2¼ hours to El Careyes Resort, a little more than halfway to Barra de Navidad; the latter is about 3½ to 4 hours to the south.

If you're heading to the Costalegre from Guadalajara, the most direct route is toll route 54D south; 2½ hours from the city you'll reach Colima; coastal Barra de Navidad is an additional hour and 45 minutes from there.

Gasoline Pemex (the government petroleum monopoly) franchises all of Mexico's gas stations, which you'll find at most junctions and in cities and towns. Gas is measured in liters, and stations usually don't accept U.S. or Canadian credit cards or dollars, but this is beginning to change. Fuel prices tend to be about the same as in the United States.

Premium unleaded gas (called *premium,* the red pump) and regular unleaded gas (*magna,* the green pump) are available nationwide, but it's still best to fill up whenever you can and not let your tank get below half full. Fuel quality is generally lower than that in the United States and Europe, but it has improved enough so that your car will run acceptably. *For general opening times, see Hours of Operation, below.*

Gas-station attendants pump the gas for you and may also wash your windshield and check your oil and tire air pressure. A 5- or 10-peso tip is customary, depending on the number of services rendered (including simply pumping the gas). Keep a close eye on the gas meter to make sure the attendant is starting it at "0" and that you're charged the correct price.

Parking A circle with a diagonal line superimposed on the letter *E* (for *estacionamiento*) means "no parking." Illegally parked cars are usually either towed or have wheel blocks placed on the tires, which can require a trip to the traffic-police headquarters for payment of a fine.

When in doubt, park in a lot rather than on the street; your car will probably be safer there anyway. Lots are plentiful, although not always clearly marked; and fees are reasonable—as little as $4 for a whole day up to $1 or more an hour, depending on where you are. Sometimes you park your own car; more often, though, you hand the keys over to an attendant.

Road Conditions Several well-kept toll roads head into and out of major cities like Guadalajara—most of them four lanes wide. However, these *carreteras* (major highways) don't go too far into the countryside. *Cuota* means toll road; *libre* means no toll, and such roads are often two lanes and not as well-maintained.

Some excellent roads have opened in the past decade or so, making car travel safer and faster. Those leading to, or in, Nayarit and Jalisco include highways connecting Nogales and Mazatlán; Guadalajara and Tepic; and Mexico City, Morelia, and Guadalajara. However, tolls as high as $40 one-way can make using these thoroughfares expensive.

In rural areas roads are sometimes poor; other times the two-lane, blacktop roads are perfectly fine and enjoyable to drive. Be extra cautious during the rainy season, when rock slides and potholes are a problem.

Watch out for animals, especially untethered horses, cattle, and dogs, and for dangerous, unrailed curves. *Topes* (speed bumps) are ubiquitous; slow down when approaching any town or village and look for signs saying TOPES or VIBRADORES. Police officers often issue tickets to those speeding through populated areas.

Generally, driving times are longer than for comparable distances in the United States. Allow extra time for unforeseen occurrences as well as for traffic, particularly truck traffic.

Roadside Emergencies To help motorists on major highways, the Mexican Tourism Ministry operates a fleet of more than 250 pickup trucks, known as the Angeles Verdes, or Green Angels, easily reachable by phone throughout Mexico by sim-

ply dialing 078. (If this number doesn't work—occasionally the case—call the Mexico Tourism Hotline at 01800/903–9200 toll-free.) The bilingual drivers provide mechanical help, first aid, radio-telephone communication, basic supplies and small parts, towing, tourist information, and protection.

Services are free, and spare parts, fuel, and lubricants are provided at cost. Tips are always appreciated (figure a minimum of $5–$10 for big jobs and $3–$5 for minor repairs). The Green Angels patrol fixed sections of the major highways twice daily 8–8 (usually later on holiday weekends). If you break down, pull off the road as far as possible, lift the hood of your car, hail a passing vehicle, and ask the driver to notify the patrol. Most drivers will be quite helpful.

Emergency Services Angeles Verdes (☎078, 01800/903–9200 toll-free in Mexico).

Rules of the Road When you sign up for Mexican car insurance, you may receive a booklet on Mexican rules of the road. It really is a good idea to read it to familiarize yourself with not only laws but also customs that differ from those of your home country. For instance: if an oncoming vehicle flicks its lights at you in daytime, slow down: it could mean trouble ahead; when approaching a narrow bridge, the first vehicle to flash its lights has right of way; right on red is not allowed; one-way traffic is indicated by an arrow; two-way, by a double-pointed arrow. (Other road signs follow the widespread system of international symbols.)

On the highway, using your left turn signal to turn left can be extremely dangerous. Mexican drivers—especially truck drivers with big rigs that block the view of the road ahead—use their left turn signal on the highway to signal the car behind that it's safe to pass. Conversely they rarely use their signal to actually make a turn. Foreigners signaling a left turn off the highway into a driveway or onto a side road have been killed by cars or trucks behind that mistook their turn signal for a signal to pass. ⚠ **To turn left from a highway when cars are behind you, it's best to pull over to the right and make the left turn when no cars are approaching, to avoid disaster.**

Mileage and speed limits are given in kilometers: 100 kph and 80 kph (62 mph and 50 mph, respectively) are the most common maximums on the highway. A few of the toll roads allow 110 kph (68 mph). However, speed limits can change from curve to curve, so watch the signs carefully. In cities and small towns, observe the posted speed limits, which can be as low as 20 kph (12 mph).

Seat belts are required by law throughout Mexico. Drunk driving laws are fairly harsh in Mexico, and if you're caught you may go to jail immediately. It's difficult to say what the blood-alcohol limit is since everyone we asked gave a different answer, which means each case is probably handled in a discretionary manner. The best way to avoid any problems is simply to not drink and drive.

If you're stopped for speeding, the officer is supposed to take your license and hold it until you pay the fine at the local police station. But the officer will usually prefer a *mordida* (small bribe). Just take out a couple hundred pesos, hold it out discreetly while asking politely if the officer can "pay the fine for you." Conversely, a few cops might resent the offer of a bribe, but it's still common practice.

If you decide to dispute a charge that seems preposterous, do so with a smile, and tell the officer that you would like to talk to the police captain when you get to the station. The officer usually will let you go rather than go to the station.

Safety on the Road Never drive at night in remote and rural areas. *Bandidos* are one concern, but so are potholes, free-roaming animals, cars with no working lights, road-hogging trucks, and difficulty

in getting assistance. It's best to use toll roads whenever possible; although costly, they're safer, too.

Driving in Mexico can be nerve-wracking for novices, with people sometimes paying little attention to marked lanes. Most drivers pay attention to safety rules, but be vigilant. Drunk driving skyrockets on holiday weekends.

A police officer may pull you over for something you didn't do; unfortunately a common scam. If you're pulled over for any reason, be polite—displays of anger will only make matters worse. Although efforts are being made to fight corruption, it's still a fact of life in Mexico, and for many people, it's worth the $10 to $100 it costs to get their license back to be on their way quickly. (The amount requested varies depending on what the officer assumes you can pay—the year, make, and model of the car you drive being one determining factor.) Others persevere long enough to be let off with a warning only. The key to success, in this case, is a combination of calm and patience.

By Taxi PV taxis area aren't metered, and instead charge by zones. Establish the fare beforehand, and count your change. Most of the larger hotels have rate sheets, and taxi drivers should produce them upon request. Tipping isn't necessary unless the driver helps you with your bags, in which case a few pesos are appropriate.

The minimum fare is 30 pesos (about $3), but if you don't ask, or your Spanish isn't great, you'll probably be overcharged. Negotiate a price in advance for out-of-town and hourly services as well; many drivers will start by asking how much you want to pay or how much others have charged you to get a sense of how street-smart you are. The usual hourly rate at press time is $19 (200 pesos) per hour. In all cases, if you are unsure of what a fare should be, ask your hotel's front-desk personnel or bell captain.

The ride from downtown to the airport or to Marina Vallarta costs $10, it's $19 to Nuevo Vallarta, and $21 to Bucerías. From downtown south to Mismaloya it's about $4 to the hotels of the Zona Hotelera Sur, $8 to Mismaloya, and $13 to Boca de Tomatlán. Cabs are plentiful, and you can easily hail one on the street. They aren't metered; be sure to agree on a fare before embarking. Radio Taxi PV provides 24-hour service.

Taxi Company **Radio Taxi PV** (☎ 322/225–0716).

ON THE GROUND

■ COMMUNICATIONS

INTERNET

Internet cafés have sprung up all over Puerto Vallarta and even small surrounding towns and villages, making e-mail by far the easiest way to get in touch with people back home. At PV Café you can enjoy a sandwich or a salad and coffee while downloading digital photos, sending a fax, or surfing the Web (35 pesos per hour).

At less-comfortable PV Net (computers lower than eye level promote slouching), which is open 24 hours a day, 365 days a year, you obtain an access code and use your minutes each time you visit; the cost for Internet access is 20 pesos per hour, offers monthly and weekly rates, and has a room at the back just for the kids and teens. For laptop connections you can pay by the day, week, or month.

If you're bringing a laptop with you, check with the manufacturer's technical support line to see what service and/or repair affiliates they have in the areas you plan to visit. Carry a spare battery to save yourself the expense and headache of having to hunt down a replacement on the spot. Memory sticks and other accessories are usually more expensive in Mexico than in the U.S. or Europe, but are available in megastores such as Sam's Club and Office Depot.

The younger generation of Mexicans are computer savvy and there are some excellent repair wizards and technicians to help you with problems; many are bilingual.

Contacts Cybercafes (⊕ www.cybercafes. com) lists over 4,000 Internet cafés worldwide. **PV Café** (✉ Calle Olas Altas 250, Olas Altas ☎ 322/222-0092). **PV Net** (✉ Blvd. Francisco M. Ascencio 1692, across from Sheraton Buganvilias, Zona Hotelera Norte ☎ 322/223-1127).

PHONES

The good news is that you can now make a direct-dial telephone call from virtually any point on earth. The bad news? You can't always do so cheaply. Calling from a hotel is almost always the most expensive option; hotels usually add huge surcharges to all calls, particularly international ones. In some countries you can phone from call centers or even the post office.

Calling cards usually keep costs to a minimum, but only if you purchase them locally. And then there are mobile phones (⇨ below), which are sometimes more prevalent—particularly in the developing world—than land lines; as expensive as mobile phone calls can be, they are still usually a much cheaper option than calling from your hotel.

A *caseta de larga distancia* is a long-distance/overseas telephone service usually operated out of a store such as a *papelería* (stationery store), pharmacy, restaurant, or other small business; look for the phone symbol on the door. Casetas may cost more to use than pay phones, but you tend to be shielded from street noise, as you get your own little cabin. They also have the benefit of not forcing you to buy a prepaid phone card with a specific denomination—you pay in cash according to the calls you make. The store employee places the call for you.

Using a prepaid phone card is by far the most convenient way to call long distance within Mexico or abroad. Look for a phone *booth* away from traffic noise; these phones are tucked behind three sides of plexiglass, but street noise can make hearing difficult. If you're calling long distance within Mexico, dial 01 before the area code and number. For local calls, just dial the seven-digit number; no other prefix is necessary. If calling

LOCAL DO'S & TABOOS

CUSTOMS OF THE COUNTRY

In the United States and elsewhere in the world, being direct, efficient, and succinct is highly valued. But Mexican communication tends to be more subtle, and the direct style of Americans, Canadians, and Europeans is often perceived as curt and aggressive. Mexicans are extremely polite, so losing your temper over delays or complaining loudly will get you branded as rude and make people less inclined to help you. Remember that things move slowly here, and that there's no stigma attached to being late; be gracious about this and other local customs and attitudes.

You'll probably notice that local friends, relatives, and significant others show a fair amount of physical affection with each other, but you should be more retiring with people you don't know well.

GREETINGS

Learning basic phrases in Spanish such as "*por favor*" (please) and "*gracias*" (thank you) will make a big difference in how people respond to you. Also, being deferential to those who are older than you will earn you lots of points, as does addressing people as señor, señora, or señorita.

Also, saying "*Desculpe*" before asking a question of someone is a polite way of saying "Excuse me" before launching into a request for information or directions. Similarly, asking "*¿Hable inglé?*" is more polite than assuming every Mexican you meet speaks English.

SIGHTSEEING

In Puerto Vallarta, it is acceptable to wear shorts in houses of worship, but do avoid being blatantly immodest. Bathing suits and immodest clothing are also inappropriate for shopping and sightseeing in general. Except at beach and fishing communities, Mexican men do not generally wear shorts, even in extremely hot weather. This rule is generally ignored by both Mexican and foreign men on vacation here and other beach resorts.

OUT ON THE TOWN

Mexicans call waiters "*joven*" (literally, "young man") no matter how old they are (it's the equivalent of the word "maid" being used for the old woman who cleans rooms). Call a female waitress *señorita* ("miss") or *señora* ("ma'am"). Ask for "*la cuenta, por favor*" ("the check, please") when you want the bill; it's considered rude to bring it before the customer asks for it. Mexicans tend to dress nicely for a night out, but in tourist areas, dress codes are mainly upheld only at the more sophisticated discoteques. Some restaurants have separate smoking sections, but in smaller establishments people usually smoke with abandon anywhere.

DOING BUSINESS

Business etiquette is much more traditional and stylized in Mexico than in the United States and Canada. Personal relationships always come first here, so developing rapport and trust is essential. A handshake and personal greeting is appropriate along with a friendly inquiry about family, especially if you have met the family. In established business relationships, don't be surprised if you're greeted with a kiss on the cheek or a hug. Always be respectful toward colleagues in public and keep confrontations private.

Meetings may or may not start on time, but you should be patient. When invited to dinner at the home of a client or associate, its not necessary to bring a gift; however, sending a thank-you note afterward scores points.

Your offers to pick up the tab at business lunches or dinners will be greatly appreciated but will probably be declined; as a guest in their country, most Mexicans will want to treat you to the meal. Be prepared to exchange business cards, and feel free to offer yours first. Professional attire tends to be on the conservative side. Mexicans are extremely well-groomed, so you'll do well if you follow suit.

abroad, buy the 100-peso card, the largest denomination available.

Sometimes you can make collect calls from casetas, and sometimes you cannot, depending on the individual operator and possibly your degree of visible desperation. Casetas will generally charge 70¢–$1.50 to place a collect call (some charge by the minute); it's usually better to call *por cobrar* (collect) from a pay phone. Casetas charge about $1 a minute to call the U.S. or Canada, slightly less on the weekends.

The area code for PV (and the northern Costalegre) and Nuevo Vallarta is 322; San Francisco has both 311 and 329 area codes, otherwise between Bucerías and San Francisco it's 329. Lo De Marcos and Rincón de Guayabitos: 327. The Costalegre from around Rancho Cuixmala to San Patricio–Melaque and Barra de Navidad has a 315 area code.

The country code for Mexico is 52. When calling a Mexico number from abroad, dial any necessary international access code, then the country code, and then all of the numbers listed for the entry. When calling a cell phone in Mexico dial 01152 (access and country codes) and then 1 and then the number.

Calling Within Mexico Directory assistance is 040 nationwide. For assistance in English, dial 090 first for an international operator; tell the operator in what city, state, and country you require directory assistance, and he or she will connect you.

For local or long-distance calls, you can use either a standard public pay phone or a *caseta de larga distancia*, or long-distance telephone service. To make a direct long-distance or local call from a caseta, tell the person on duty the number you'd like to call, and she or he will give you a rate and dial for you. Rates seem to vary widely, so shop around, but overall they're higher than those of pay phones, and more importantly, infrequently seen in the Vallarta area.

Toll-free numbers in Mexico start with an 800 prefix. These numbers, however, are billed as local calls if you call one from a private phone. To reach them, you need to dial 01 before the number. In this guide, Mexico-only toll-free numbers appear as follows: 01800/123–4567. The toll-free numbers listed simply 800/123–4567 are U.S. or Canadian numbers, and generally work north of the border only (though some calling cards will allow you to dial them from Mexico, charging you minutes as for a toll call). Numbers listed as 001800/123–4567 are toll-free U.S. numbers; if you're calling from Mexico, you'll be charged for an international call.

Calling Outside Mexico To make an international call, dial 00 before the country code, area code, and number. The country code for the United States and Canada is 1. Avoid phones near tourist areas that advertise in English (e.g., "Call the U.S. or Canada here!"). They charge an outrageous fee per minute. If in doubt, dial the operator and ask for rates. AT&T, MCI, and Sprint calling cards are useful, although infrequently hotels block access to their service numbers.

Access Codes AT&T Direct (☏ 01800/112–2020 or 001800/462–4240 toll-free in Mexico). **MCI WorldPhone** (☏ 01800/674–7000 toll-free in Mexico). **Sprint International Access** (☏ 01800/877–8000 toll-free in Mexico).

Calling Cards Most pay phones only accept prepaid cards, called Ladatel cards, sold in 30-, 50-, or 100-peso denominations at newsstands, pharmacies, or grocery stores. These Ladatel phones are all over the place—on street corners, in bus stations, and so on.

Older, coin-only pay phones are rarely encountered, those you do find are often broken or have poor connections. Still other phones have two unmarked slots, one for a Ladatel (a Spanish acronym for "long-distance direct dialing") card and the other for a credit card. These are primarily for Mexican bank cards, but some accept Visa or MasterCard, though *not* U.S. phone credit cards.

To use a Ladatel card, simply insert it in the appropriate slot with the computer chip insignia forward and right-side up, and dial. Credit is deleted from the card as you use it, and your balance is displayed on a small screen on the phone. You'll be charged about 1 peso per minute for local calls, 4 pesos per minute for national long-distance, and 5 pesos for calls to the United States or Canada. Most pay phones display a price list and dialing instructions.

Mobile Phones If you have a multiband phone (some countries use different frequencies from those used in the United States) and your service provider uses the world-standard GSM network (as do T-Mobile, Cingular, and Verizon), you can probably use your phone abroad. Roaming fees can be steep, however: 99¢ a minute is considered reasonable. And you normally pay the toll charges for incoming calls. It's almost always cheaper to send a text message than to make a call, since text messages have a very low set fee (often less than 5¢).

If you just want to make local calls, consider buying a new SIM card (note that your provider may have to unlock your phone for you to use a different SIM card) and a prepaid service plan in the destination. You'll then have a local number and can make local calls at local rates. If your trip is extensive, you could also simply buy a new cell phone in your destination, as the initial cost will be offset over time. Companies like Verizon Wireless allow you to switch to a calling plan that includes Mexico so you don't have to pay roaming charges. Verizon's North America Plan costs $59.99/month and gives you 450 anytime minutes within North America with no long distance, as well as 1,000 night and weekend minutes. Otherwise their roaming charges are $0.69 per minute.

■TIP➜ **If you travel internationally frequently, save one of your old mobile phones or buy a cheap one on the Internet; ask your cell phone company to unlock it for you, and take it with you as a travel phone, buying a new SIM card with pay-as-you-go service in each destination.**

There are now many companies that rent cell phones (with or without SIM cards) for the duration of your trip. You get the phone, charger, and carrying case in the mail and return them in the mailer. Prices with companies like EZ Wireless and Daystar start at about $3.50 per day or $88 per month. Charges vary for incoming and outgoing calls depending on the plan you choose.

Contacts Daystar (☎888/908–4100 ⊕www. daystarwireless.com) rents cell phones at $6 per day, with incoming calls at 22¢ a minute and outgoing at $1.20. **EZ Wireless** (☎866/939–9473 ⊕www.rentawirelessphone. com) charges $22 per week for equipment (phone, charger, adapter) and $1.50/minute for incoming calls, a whopping $2.50 per minute for outgoing.

∎ CUSTOMS & DUTIES

You're always allowed to bring goods of a certain value back home without having to pay any duty or import tax. But there's a limit on the amount of tobacco and liquor you can bring back duty-free, and some countries have separate limits for perfumes; for exact figures, check with your customs department. The values of so-called duty-free goods are included in these amounts.

When you shop abroad, save all your receipts, as customs inspectors may (rarely) ask to see them as well as the items you purchased. If the total value of your goods is more than the duty-free limit, you'll have to pay a tax (most often a flat percentage) on the value of everything beyond that limit.

Upon entering Mexico, you'll be given a baggage declaration form and asked to itemize what you're bringing into the country. You are allowed to bring in 3 liters of spirits or wine for personal use; 400 cigarettes, 25 cigars, or 200 grams of tobacco; a reasonable amount of perfume for personal use; one video camera and one regular camera and 12 rolls of film for each; and gift items not to exceed a total of $300. If driving across the U.S. border, gift items must not exceed $50.

You aren't allowed to bring firearms, ammunition, meat, vegetables, plants, fruit, or flowers into the country. You can bring in one of each of the following items without paying taxes: a cell phone, a beeper, a radio or tape recorder, a musical instrument, a laptop computer, and portable copier or printer. Compact discs and/or audio cassettes are limited to 20 total and DVDs to five.

Mexico also allows you to bring one cat or dog, if you have two things: (1) a pet health certificate signed by a registered veterinarian in the United States and issued not more than 72 hours before the animal enters Mexico; and (2) a pet vaccination certificate showing that the animal has been treated (as applicable) for rabies, hepatitis, distemper, and leptospirosis.

For more information or information on bringing other animals or more than one type of animal, contact the Mexican consulate, which has branches in many major American cities as well as border towns. To find the consulate nearest you, check the Ministry of Foreign Affairs Web site ⊕http://portal.sre.gob.mx/sre; go to the list of embassies, consulates, and delegations and choose the "Consulados de México en el Exterior" option.

Information in Mexico Mexican Embassy (☎202/728–1600 ⊕www. embassyofmexico.org).

U.S. Information U.S. Customs and Border Protection (⊕www.cbp.gov).

▌ ELECTRICITY

For U.S. and Canadian travelers, electrical converters aren't necessary because Mexico operates on the 60-cycle, 120-volt system; however, many Mexican outlets have not been updated to accommodate three-prong and polarized plugs (those with one larger prong), so to be safe bring an adapter.

Blackouts and brownouts—often lasting an hour or so—are fairly common everywhere, particularly during the rainy season, so bring a surge protector.

Consider making a small investment in a universal adapter, which has several types of plugs in one lightweight, compact unit. Most laptops and mobile phone chargers are dual voltage (i.e., they operate equally well on 110 and 220 volts), requiring only an adapter. These days the same is true of small appliances such as hair dryers. Always check labels and manufacturer instructions to be sure. Don't use 110-volt outlets marked FOR SHAVERS ONLY for high-wattage appliances such as hair dryers.

Contacts Steve Kropla's Help for World Traveler's (⊕www.kropla.com) has information on electrical and telephone plugs around the world. **Walkabout Travel Gear** (⊕www. walkabouttravelgear.com) has information about surge protectors and adapters.

▌ EMERGENCIES

In an emergency call ☎060 or ☎066. For roadside assistance contact the Angeles Verdes. If you get into a scrape with the law, you can call your nearest consulate (⇨below); U.S. citizens can also call the Overseas Citizens Services Center in the United States. The Mexican Ministry of Tourism has Infotur, a 24-hour toll-free hotline. Two medical emergency evacuation services are Air Ambulance Network and Global Life Flight.

Cornerstone Hospital accepts various types of foreign health insurance and traveler's insurance and is American owned. The other recommended, privately owned hospital is Hospital San Javier Marina. Although most small towns have at least a clinic, most travelers would be more comfortable traveling to the major hospitals than using these clinics.

Both the Cornerstone and San Javier Marina hospitals have pharmacies that are open to the public.

Consulate & Embassy United States Consul (⌂Local 4, Int. 17, 2nd fl., Centro Comercial Paradise Plaza, Nuevo Vallarta, Puerto Vallarta ☎322/222–0069).**U.S. Embassy** (⌂Paseo de la Reforma 305, Col. Cuauhtémoc, Mexico City ☎55/5080–2000 ⊕www.usembassy-mexico. gov/emenu.html).

General Emergency Contacts Air Ambulance Network (☎800/327–1966 in U.S. and Canada, in Mexico 001800/010–0027 ⊕www. airambulancenetwork.com). **Ambulance/Red Cross** (☎065 or 322/222–1533). **Angeles Verdes** (☎078, 01800/903–9200 toll-free in Mexico). **General Emergency (Police, Transit, Fire)** (☎060). **Global Life Flight** (☎01800/305–9400 toll-free in Mexico, 800/831–9307 in U.S., 877/817–6843 in Canada ⊕www.globallifeflight.com) provides 24/7 emergency medical flights between Canada, the United States, Mexico, and the Caribbean. **Infotur** (☎01800/903–9200 toll-free in Mexico).**U.S. Overseas Citizens Services Center** (☎202/501–4444 ⊕www.travel.state.gov).

Hospitals & Clinics Cornerstone Hospital (⌂Av. Los Tules 136, next to Plaza Caracol, Zona Hotelera ☎322/224–9400 ⊕www. hospitalcornerstone.com). **Hospital San Javier Marina** (⌂Blvd. Francisco M. Ascencio 2760, at María Montessori, Zona Hotelera Norte ☎322/226–1010).

Pharmacy Farmacia CMQ (⌂Calle Basilio Badillo 365 ☎322/222–2941) is open 24 hours.

▌ HEALTH

The most common types of illnesses are caused by contaminated food and water. Especially in developing countries, drink only bottled, boiled, or purified water and drinks; don't drink from public fountains or use ice unless you know it's made from bottle water (as is the case in most tourist-oriented restaurants). You should even use bottled water to brush your teeth. Make sure food has been thoroughly cooked and is served to you fresh and hot; avoid vegetables and fruits that you haven't washed (in bottled or purified water) or peeled yourself. If you have problems, mild cases of traveler's diarrhea may respond to Imodium (known generically as loperamide) or Pepto-Bismol. Be sure to drink plenty of fluids; if you can't keep fluids down, seek medical help immediately.

Infectious diseases can be airborne or passed via mosquitoes and ticks and through direct or indirect physical contact with animals or people. Some, including Norwalk-like viruses that affect your digestive tract, can be passed along through contaminated food. If you are traveling in an area where malaria or dengue fever is prevalent, use a repellant containing DEET and take malaria-prevention medication before, during, and after your trip as directed by your physician. Condoms can help prevent most sexually transmitted diseases, but they aren't absolutely reliable and their quality varies from country to country. Speak with your physician and/ or check the CDC or World Health Organization Web sites for health alerts, particularly if you're pregnant, traveling with children, or have a chronic illness.

For information on travel insurance, shots and medications, and medical-assistance companies, see Shots & Medications under Things to Consider in Getting Started, above.

SPECIFIC ISSUES IN PUERTO VALLARTA

A little *turista*, or traveler's diarrhea, is to be expected when you plop down in a foreign culture, but to minimize risks, avoid questionable-looking street stands; and if you're not sure of a restaurant's standards, pass up *ceviche,* raw fish cured in lemon juice, and don't eat any raw vegetables that haven't been, or can't be, peeled (e.g., lettuce and raw chili peppers).

Drink only bottled water or water that has been boiled for at least 10 minutes, even when you're brushing your teeth. *Agua mineral* or *agua con gas* means mineral or carbonated water, and *agua purificada* means purified water. Hotels with water-purification systems will post signs to that effect in the rooms; even then, be wary.

Despite these warnings, keep in mind that Puerto Vallarta, Nuevo Vallarta, and the Costalegre have virtually no industry beyond tourism and are unlikely to kill the geese that lay their golden egg. Some people choose to bend the rules about eating at street stands and fresh fruits and chopped lettuce or cabbage, as there's no guarantee that you won't get sick at a 5-star resort and have a delicious, healthful meal at a shack by the sea. If fish or seafood smells or tastes bad, send it back and ask for something different.

Don't fret about ice: tourist-oriented hotels and restaurants, and even most of those geared toward the locals, used purified water for ice, drinks, and washing vegetables. Many alleged cases of food poisoning are due instead to hangovers or excessive drinking in the strong sun. But whenever you're in doubt, ask questions about the origins of food and water and if you feel unsure, err on the side of safety.

Mild cases of turista may respond to Imodium (known generically as loperamide), Lomotil, or Pepto-Bismol (not as strong), all of which you can buy over the counter; keep in mind, though, that these drugs can complicate more serious illnesses. You'll need to replace fluids, so drink plenty of purified water or tea; chamomile tea (*te de manzanilla*) is a good folk remedy, and it's readily available in restaurants throughout Mexico.

In severe cases, rehydrate yourself with Gatorade or a salt-sugar solution (½ teaspoon salt and 4 tablespoons sugar per quart of water). If your fever and diarrhea last longer than a day or two, see a doctor—you may have picked up a parasite or disease that requires prescription medication.

Mosquitoes are most prevalent during the rainy season, where it's best to be cautious and use mosquito repellent daily, even in the city; if you're in jungly or wet places and lack strong repellent, consider covering up well or going indoors at dusk (called the "mosquito hour" by locals).

An excellent brand of *repelente de insectos* (insect repellent) called Autan is readily available; do not use it on children under age two. Repellents that are not at least 10% DEET or picaridin are not effective here. If you're hiking in the jungle or boggy areas, wear repellent and long pants and sleeves; if you're camping in the jungle, use a mosquito net and invest in a package of *espirales contra mosquitos,* mosquito coils, which are sold in *ferreterías* or *tlalpalerías* (hardware stores).

Caution is advised when venturing out in the Mexican sun. Sunbathers lulled by a slightly overcast sky or the sea breezes can be burned badly in just 20 minutes. To avoid overexposure, use strong sunscreens, sit under a shade umbrella, and avoid the peak sun hours of noon to 2 PM. Sunscreen, including many American brands, can be found in pharmacies, supermarkets, and resort gift shops.

You can call International SOS Assistance's U.S.-based phone number collect from Mexico.

OVER-THE-COUNTER REMEDIES

Farmacias (pharmacies) are the most convenient place for such common medicines as *aspirina* (aspirin) or *jarabe para la tos* (cough syrup). You'll be able to find many U.S. brands (e.g., Tylenol, Pepto-Bismol, etc.), but don't plan on buying your favorite prescription or nonprescription sleep aid, for example. The same brands and even drugs aren't always available. There are pharmacies in all small towns and on practically every corner in larger cities. The Sanborns chain stores also have pharmacies.

▌HOURS OF OPERATION

Banks are generally open weekdays 9 to 3. In Puerto Vallarta most are open until 4, and some of the larger banks keep a few branches open Saturday from 9 or 10 to 1 or 2:30; however, the extended hours are often for deposits or check cashing only. HSBC is the one chain that stays open for longer hours; on weekdays they are open 8 to 7 and on Saturday from 8 to 3. Government offices are usually open to the public weekdays 9 to 3; along with banks and most private offices, they're closed on national holidays.

Gas stations are normally open 7 AM–10 PM daily. Those near major thoroughfares stay open 24 hours, including most holidays.

Pharmacies are usually open daily 9 AM to 10 PM; on Sunday and in some small towns they may close several hours earlier. Puerto Vallarta has some 24-hour pharmacies: look for the big names such as Farmacias del Ahorro or Farmacia Guadalajara. In neighborhoods or smaller towns where there are no 24-hour drug stores, local pharmacies take turns staying open 24 hours so that there's usually at least one open on any given night—it's called the *farmacia de turno*. Information about late-night pharmacies is published in the daily newspaper, but the staff at your hotel should be able to help you find an all-night place.

Stores are generally open weekdays and Saturday from 9 or 10 AM to 5 or 7 PM; in resort areas, those stores geared to tourists may stay open until 9 or 10 at night, all day on Saturday; some are open on Sunday as well, but it's good to call ahead

before making a special trip. Some more traditional shops close for a two-hour lunch break, roughly 2–4. Airport shops are open seven days a week.

HOLIDAYS

Banks and government offices close on January 1, February 5 (Constitution Day), March 21 (Benito Juárez's birthday), May 1 (Labor Day), September 16 (Independence Day), November 20 (Revolution Day), and December 25. They may also close on unofficial holidays, such as Day of the Dead (November 1–2), Virgin of Guadalupe Day (December 12), and during Holy Week (the days leading to Easter Sunday). Government offices usually have reduced hours and staff from Christmas through New Year's Day.

▌LANGUAGE

English is widely understood by most people employed in tourism, although less so in the less-developed areas. At the very least, shopkeepers in remote places will usually know numbers and basic phrases. Remember that regional accents vary (imagine trying to understand a Brit, French Canadian, Texan, and Aussie all in the same day). The average Mexican in and around Puerto Vallarta speaks good English, but speak slowly and avoid idiomatic expressions and slang.

As in most other foreign countries, knowing the mother tongue has a way of opening doors, so learn some Spanish words and phrases. Mexicans welcome even the most halting attempts to use their language. The exception to this rule are Mexicans who speak fluent English having a conversation with someone who wants to use his or her halting, high-school Spanish. This may work when you're seated at adjacent bar stools, but is less effective when there's a long line waiting for help at the front desk of your hotel.

▌ MAIL

The Mexican postal system is notoriously slow and unreliable; never send packages through the postal service or expect to receive them, as they may be stolen. (For emergencies, use a courier service.) If you're an American Express cardholder, you may be able to receive packages at a branch office, but check beforehand with customer service to find out whether this client mail service is available at your destination.

Post offices (*oficinas de correos*) are found in even the smallest villages. International postal service is all airmail, but even so your letter will take anywhere from 10 days to six weeks to arrive. Service within Mexico can be equally slow.

It costs 10.5 pesos (about 95¢) to send a postcard or letter weighing under 20 grams to the United States or Canada; it's 13 pesos ($1.17) to Europe and 14.5 pesos ($1.30) to Australia and New Zealand.

To receive mail in Mexico, you can have it sent to your hotel or use *poste restante* at the post office. In the latter case, the address must include the words "a/c Lista de Correos" (general delivery), followed by the city, state, postal code, and country. To use this service, you should first register with the post office at which you wish to receive your mail. The post office posts and updates daily a list of names for whom mail has been received. Mail is generally held for 10 days, and a list of recipients is posted daily.

Contacts American Express (⊕www.americanexpress.com/travel).

Correos (⊠Calle Mina 188, El Centro ☎322/222–1888).

SHIPPING PACKAGES

Federal Express, DHL, Estafeta, and United Parcel Service are available in major cities and many resort areas (though PV doesn't have a FedEx office). It's best to send all packages using one of these services. These companies offer office or hotel pickup with 24-hour advance notice (sometimes less, depending on when you call) and are very reliable. FedEx's Web site is especially easy to navigate. From Puerto Vallarta to large U.S. cities, for example, the minimum charge is around $30 for an envelope weighing about ½ pound.

Express Services DHL (⊠Blvd. Federico M. Ascencio 1834, Col. Olímpica ☎322/222–4720 or 322/222–4620 ⊕www.dhl.com). **Estafeta** (⊠Blvd. Federico M. Ascencio 1046, between Calle Sierra Rocosa and Av. De las Américas, Col. Olímpica ☎322/223–1700 or 322/223–2898 ⊕www.estafeta.com). **Mail Boxes Etc.** (⊠Edifício Andrea Mar Local 7, Blvd. Francisco M. Ascencio 2180, Zona Hotelera Norte (Col. Versalles) ⊹Across from Hotel Los Tules ☎322/224–9434).

▌ MONEY

Prices in this book are quoted most often in U.S. dollars. We'd prefer to list costs in pesos, but because the value of the currency fluctuates considerably, what costs 90 pesos today might cost 120 pesos in six months.

A stay in one of Puerto Vallarta's top hotels can cost more than $250, but if you aren't wedded to standard creature comforts, you can spend as little as $50 a day on room, board, and local transportation. Lodgings are less expensive in the less-developed spots north and south of Puerto Vallarta as well as the charming but unsophisticated mountain towns like San Sebastián del Oeste.

You can get away with a tab of $50 for two at a wonderful restaurant (although it's also easy to pay much more). The good news is that there are hotels and eateries for every budget, and inexpensive doesn't necessarily mean bargain basement. This guide will clue you in to some excellent places to stay, eat, and play for extremely reasonable prices.

ITEM	AVERAGE COST
Cup of Coffee	80¢ to $1.50
Glass of Wine	$3.50–$5
Bottle of Beer	$2–$3
Sandwich	$1.50–$2.50
One-Mile Taxi Ride	$3
Museum Admission	free

Prices throughout this guide are given for adults. Substantially reduced fees are almost always available for children, students, and senior citizens.

ATMS & BANKS

Your own bank will probably charge a fee for using ATMs abroad; the foreign bank you use may also charge a fee. Nevertheless, you'll usually get a better rate of exchange at an ATM than you will at a currency-exchange office or even when changing money in a bank. And extracting funds as you need them is a safer option than carrying around a large amount of cash.

ATMs (*cajeros automáticos*) are widely available, with Cirrus and Plus the most frequently found networks. However, the transaction fees charged by your bank can be up to $5 a pop; before you leave home, ask your bank about fees for withdrawing money in Mexico.

Many Mexican ATMs cannot accept PINs with more than four digits. If yours is longer, change your PIN to four digits before you leave home. If your PIN is fine yet your transaction still can't be completed, chances are that the computer lines are busy or that the machine has run out of money or is being serviced. Don't give up.

For cash advances, plan to use Visa or MasterCard, as many Mexican ATMs don't accept American Express. Large banks with reliable ATMs include Banamex, HSBC, BBVA Bancomer, Santander Serfín, and Scotiabank Inverlat. *(For*

information about avoiding ATM robberies, see Safety.)

Banks **Banamex** (✉ Calle Juárez, at Calle Zaragoza, Centro ☎ 322/226–6110 ✉ Plaza Marina, Local 37 ☎ 322/221–0733 ✉ Calle Emiliano Zapata 48, Centro ☎ 322/224–8115 ✉ Paseo de los Cocoteros s/n, Paradise Plaza, Nuevo Vallarta ☎ 322/297–0688). **Banorte** (✉ Paseo Díaz Ordaz 690 at Calle L. Vicario, Centro ☎ 322/222–4040 ✉ Calle Olas Altas 246, at Calle Basilio Badillo, E. Zapata ☎ 322/223–0481 ✉ Blvd. Francisco Medina Ascencio 500, Zona Hotelera Norte ☎ 322/224–9744).

CREDIT CARDS

Throughout this guide, the following abbreviations are used: **AE,** American Express; **D,** Discover; **DC,** Diners Club; **MC,** MasterCard; and **V,** Visa.

It's a good idea to inform your credit-card company before you travel, especially if you don't travel internationally very often. Otherwise, the credit-card company might put a hold on your card owing to unusual activity—not a good thing halfway through your trip. Record all your credit-card numbers—as well as the phone numbers to call if your cards are lost or stolen—in a safe place, so you're prepared should something go wrong.

Both MasterCard and Visa have general numbers you can call (collect if you're abroad) if your card is lost, but you're better off calling the number of your issuing bank, since MasterCard and Visa usually just transfer you to your bank; your bank's number is usually printed on your card.

If you plan to use your credit card for cash advances, you'll need to apply for a PIN at least two weeks before your trip. Although it's usually cheaper (and safer) to use a credit card abroad for large purchases (so you can cancel payments or be reimbursed if there's a problem), note that some credit-card companies *and* the banks that issue them add substantial percentages to all foreign transactions, whether they're in a foreign currency or not. Check on these fees before leaving home, so there won't be any surprises when you get the bill.

■ TIP➜ **Before you charge something, ask the merchant whether or not he or she plans to do a dynamic currency conversion (DCC). In such a transaction the credit-card** *processor* **(shop, restaurant, or hotel, not Visa or MasterCard) converts the currency and charges you in dollars. In most cases you'll pay the merchant a 3% fee for this service in addition to any credit-card company and issuing-bank foreign-transaction surcharges.**

Dynamic currency conversion programs are becoming increasingly widespread. Merchants who participate in them are supposed to ask whether you want to be charged in dollars or the local currency, but they don't always do so. And even if they do offer you a choice, they may well avoid mentioning the additional surcharges. The good news is that you *do* have a choice. And if this practice really gets your goat, you can avoid it entirely thanks to American Express; with its cards, DCC simply isn't an option.

Credit cards are accepted in Puerto Vallarta and major hotels and restaurants in outlying areas. Smaller, less expensive restaurants and shops, however, tend to take only cash. In general, credit cards aren't accepted in small towns and villages, except in some hotels. The most widely accepted cards are MasterCard and Visa.

When shopping, you can often get better prices if you pay with cash, particularly in small shops. But you'll receive wholesale exchange rates when you make purchases with credit cards. These exchange rates are usually better than those that banks give you for changing money. The decision to pay cash or to use a credit card might depend on whether the establishment in which you are making a purchase

finds bargaining for prices acceptable, and whether you want the safety net of your card's purchase protection. To avoid fraud or errors, it's wise to make sure that "pesos" is clearly marked on all credit-card receipts.

Before you leave for Mexico, contact your credit-card company to get lost-card phone numbers that work in Mexico; the standard toll-free numbers often don't work abroad. Carry these numbers separately from your wallet so you'll have them if you need to call to report lost or stolen cards. American Express, MasterCard, and Visa note the international number for card-replacement calls on the back of their cards.

Reporting Lost Cards **American Express** (☎800/528–4800 in U.S. or 336/393–1111 collect from abroad ⊕www.americanexpress. com). **Diners Club** (☎800/234–6377 in U.S. or 303/799–1504 collect from abroad ⊕www. dinersclub.com). **Discover** (☎800/347–2683 in U.S. or 801/902–3100 collect from abroad ⊕www.discovercard.com). **MasterCard** (☎800/627–8372 in U.S. or 636/722–7111 collect from abroad ⊕www.mastercard.com). **Visa** (☎800/847–2911 in U.S. or 01800/847–2911 toll-free in Mexico ⊕www.visa.com).

CURRENCY & EXCHANGE

Mexican currency comes in denominations of 20-, 50-, 100-, 200-, and 500-peso bills. Coins come in denominations of 1, 2, 5, 10, and 20 pesos, and 10, 20, and 50 centavos. (Ten and 20-centavo coins are only rarely seen.) Many of the coins and bills are very similar, so check carefully.

U.S. dollar bills (but not coins) are widely accepted in tourist-oriented shops and restaurants in Puerto Vallarta. Pay in pesos where possible, however, for better prices. Although in larger hotels U.S. dollars are welcome as tips, it's generally better to tip in pesos so that service personnel aren't stuck going to the bank to exchange currency.

■TIP→ Banks never have every foreign currency on hand, and it may take as long as a week to order. If you're planning to exchange funds before leaving home, don't wait until the last minute.

At this writing, the peso was fluctuating between 10.75 and 11.3 pesos to the U.S. dollar. Check with your bank or the financial pages of your local newspaper for current exchange rates. For quick, rough estimates of how much something costs in U.S. terms, divide prices given in pesos by 10. For example, 50 pesos would be $5.

ATM transaction fees may be higher abroad than at home (⇨ *ATMs & Banks, above*), but ATM currency-exchange rates are the best because they're based on wholesale rates offered only by major banks. And if you take out a fair amount of cash per withdrawal, the transaction fee becomes less of a strike against the exchange rate (in percentage terms). However, most ATMs allow only up to $300 per transaction. Banks and *casas de cambio* (money-exchange bureaus) have the second-best exchange rates. The difference from one place to another is usually only a few pesos.

Some banks change money on weekdays only until 1 or 3 PM (though they stay open until 4 or 5 or later). Casas de cambio generally stay open until 6 or later and often operate on weekends; they usually have competitive rates and much shorter lines. Some hotels exchange money, but they help themselves to a bigger commission than banks for providing you this convenience.

You can do well at most airport exchange booths, though not as well as at the ATMs. You'll do even worse at bus stations, in hotels, in restaurants, or in stores.

When changing money, count your bills before leaving the window of the bank or casa de cambio, and don't accept any

WORST-CASE SCENARIO

■ All your money and credit cards have just been stolen. In these days of real-time transactions, this isn't a predicament that should destroy your vacation. First, report the theft of the credit cards. Then get any traveler's checks you were carrying replaced. This can usually be done almost immediately, provided that you kept a record of the serial numbers separate from the checks themselves.

■ If you bank at a large international bank like Citibank or HSBC, go to the closest branch; if you know your account number, chances are you can get a new ATM card and withdraw money right away. **Western Union** (☎800/325-6000 ⊕www.westernunion.com) sends money almost anywhere. Have someone back home order a transfer online, over the phone, or at one of the company's offices, which is the cheapest option.

■ The U.S. State Department's **Overseas Citizens Services** (☎202/501-4444 ⊕*www.travel.state.gov/travel*) can wire money to any U.S. consulate or embassy abroad for a fee of $30. Just have someone back home wire money or send a money order or cashier's check to the state department, which will then disburse the funds as soon as the next working day after it receives them.

partially torn or taped-together notes: you won't be able to use them anywhere. Also, many shop and restaurant owners are unable to make change for large bills. Enough of these encounters may compel you to request *billetes chicos* (small bills) when you exchange money. It's wise to have a cache of smaller bills and coins to use at these more humble establishments to avoid having to wait around while the merchant runs off to seek change.

■ TIP➔ **Even if a currency-exchange booth has a sign promising no commission, rest assured that there's some kind of fee—obviously they're in business to make money. As for rates, you're almost always better off getting foreign currency at an ATM or exchanging money at a bank.**

TRAVELER'S CHECKS & CARDS

Some consider this the currency of the cave man, and it's true that fewer establishments accept traveler's checks these days. Nevertheless, they're a cheap and secure way to carry extra money, particularly on trips to urban areas. Both Citibank (under the Visa brand) and American Express issue traveler's checks in the United States, but Amex is better known and more widely accepted; you can also avoid surcharges by cashing Amex checks at Amex offices. Whatever you do, keep track of all the serial numbers in case the checks are lost or stolen.

American Express now offers a stored-value card called a Travelers Cheque Card, which you can use wherever American Express credit cards are accepted, including ATMs. The card can carry a minimum of $300 and a maximum of $2,700, and it's a very safe way to carry your funds. Although you can get replacement funds in 24 hours if your card is lost or stolen, it doesn't really strike us as a very good deal. In addition to a high initial cost ($14.95 to set up the card, plus $5 each time you "reload"),

you still have to pay a 2% fee for each purchase in a foreign currency (similar to that of any credit card). Further, each time you use the card in an ATM you pay a transaction fee of $2.50 on top of the 2% transaction fee for the conversion—add it all up and it can be considerably more than you would pay when simply using your own ATM card. Regular traveler's checks are just as secure and cost less.

Contacts American Express (☎888/412–6945 in the U.S., 801/945–9450 collect outside of the U.S. to add value or speak to customer service ⊕www.americanexpress.com).

■ RESTROOMS

Expect to find reasonably clean flushing toilets and cold running water at public restrooms in the major tourist destinations and attractions; toilet paper, soap, hot water, and paper towels aren't always available, though. Keep a packet of tissues with you at all times.

At many markets, bus stations, and the like you usually have to pay 5 pesos to use the facilities.

■ TIP➔ **Remember that unless otherwise indicated you should put your used toilet paper in the wastebasket next to the toilet; many plumbing systems in Mexico still can't handle accumulations of toilet paper.**

Gas stations have public bathrooms—some tidy and others not so tidy. You're better off popping into a restaurant, buying a little something, and using its restroom, which will probably be simple but clean and adequately equipped.

Find a Loo The Bathroom Diaries (⊕www.thebathroomdiaries.com) is flush with unsanitized info on restrooms the world over—each one located, reviewed, and rated.

▌ SAFETY

Despite recent growth, PV retains a small-town attitude and crime is not as much of a problem here as in some other areas of Mexico. One of the most serious threats to your safety is local drivers. Although pedestrians have the right of way by law, drivers disregard it. And more often than not, drivers who hit pedestrians drive away as fast as they can without stopping, to avoid jail. Many Mexican drivers don't carry auto insurance, so you'll have to shoulder your own medical expenses. Pedestrians should be extremely cautious of all traffic, especially city bus drivers, who often drive with truly reckless abandon.

Horror stories about highway assaults, pickpocketing, and bus robberies by armed bandits don't really apply to the area around Puerto Vallarta. Pickpocketing can be a problem even in sleepy Vallarta, and precaution is in order here as elsewhere. Store only enough money in your wallet or bag to cover the day's spending. And don't flash big wads of money or leave valuables like cameras unattended. Leave your passport and other valuables you don't need in your hotel's safe.

Bear in mind that reporting a crime to the police is often a frustrating experience unless you speak excellent Spanish and have a great deal of patience. If you're victimized, contact your local consulate or your embassy in Mexico City.

If you're on your own, consider using only your first initial and last name when registering at your hotel. Solo travelers, or women traveling with other women rather than men, may be subjected to *piropos* (flirtatious compliments). Piropos are one thing, but more aggressive harassment is another. If the situation seems to be getting out of hand, don't hesitate to ask someone for help. If you express outrage, you should find no shortage of willing defenders.

If you carry a purse, choose one with a zipper and a thick strap that you can drape across your body; adjust the length so that the purse sits in front of you at or above hip level.

▌ TIP→ **Distribute your cash, credit cards, IDs, and other valuables between a deep front pocket, an inside jacket or vest pocket, and a hidden money pouch. Don't reach for the money pouch once you're in public.**

▌ TAXES

Mexico charges an airport departure tax of US$18 or the peso equivalent for international and domestic flights. This tax is usually included in the price of your ticket, but check to be certain. Traveler's checks and credit cards aren't accepted at the airport as payment for this, but U.S. dollars are. Jalisco and Nayarit charge a 2% tax on accommodations, the funds from which are being used for tourism promotion.

Puerto Vallarta and environs have a value-added tax of 15%, called IVA (*impuesto al valor agregado*). It's often waived for cash purchases, or it's incorporated into the price. When comparing hotel prices, it's important to know if yours includes or excludes IVA and any service charge. Other taxes and charges apply for phone calls made from your hotel room.

▌ TIME

Puerto Vallarta, Guadalajara, and the rest of Jalisco State fall into Central Standard Time (the same as Mexico City). Nayarit and other parts of the northwest coast are on Mountain Standard Time.

The fact that the state of Nayarit (including Nuevo Vallarta and points north) are in a different time zone from Puerto Vallarta and points east and south leads to confusion. And to add to this confusion, Mexico does observe daylight savings time, but not on the same schedule as the United States.

■TIP➔ **Businesses in Nuevo Vallarta and many tourism-related businesses in Bucerías run on Jalisco time.**

Since tourism in these towns has always been linked to that of Puerto Vallarta, hotels in the two areas almost always run on Jalisco time to avoid having their clients miss planes when returning home. When asking the time, checking hours of operation, or making dinner reservations, double check whether the place runs on *hora de Jalisco* (Jalisco time) or *hora de Nayarit.*

▮ TIPPING

When tipping in Mexico, remember that the minimum wage—which is what maids, bellmen, and others in the tourism industry earn—is just under $5 a day. Waiters and bellmen in international chain hotels think in dollars and know, for example, that in the United States porters are tipped about $2 a bag; they tend to expect the equivalent.

TIPPING GUIDELINES FOR PUERTO VALLARTA	
Bartender	10% to 15% of the bill
Bellhop	10 to 50 pesos (roughly $1 to $5) per bag, depending on the level of the hotel
Hotel Concierge	30 pesos or more, if he or she performs a service for you
Hotel Doorman	10 to 20 pesos if he helps you get a cab
Hotel Maid	10 to 30 pesos a day (either daily or at the end of your stay); make sure the maid gets it, and not the guy who checks the mini-bar prior to your departure
Hotel Room-Service Waiter	10 to 20 pesos per delivery, even if a service charge has been added
Porter/Skycap at Airport	10 pesos per bag
Restroom Attendant	5 to 10 pesos
Taxi Driver	cab drivers aren't normally tipped; give them 5 to 10 pesos if they help with your bags
Tour Guide	10% of the cost of the tour
Valet Parking Attendant	10 to 20 pesos but only when you get your car
Waiter	10% to 15%; nothing additional if a service charge is added to the bill

INDEX

PHOTO CREDITS